WORKING WITH SENIORS

HEALTH, FINANCIAL, AND SOCIAL ISSUES

CSA

Society of
Certified Senior Advisors®

E ISBN 0-9762451-0-8

Contents

Part 1
Aging

1. TRENDS IN AGING

2. AGING AND SOCIETY

3. PHYSIOLOGICAL CHANGES OF AGING

Part 2

Aging within the Family and Community

8. HOUSING

9. HOME AND COMMUNITY-BASED SERVICES

Part 3
Health and Mental Health

10. CHRONIC ILLNESS IN SENIORS

11. SENIOR NUTRITION, FITNESS, AND HEALTHY LIFESTYLES

Part 4

Financial Literacy

16. FINANCIAL CHOICES AND CHALLENGES FOR SENIORS

17. LONG-TERM CARE COVERAGE

18. FUNERAL PLANNING

Acknowledgments

Editorial

Edwin J. Pittock, CSA
President
Society of Certified Senior Advisors

Norm Bouchard, MDiv, CSA
Vice-President of Education
Society of Certified Senior Advisors

Elizabeth Vierck, MS
Senior Editor/Writer
Society of Certified Senior Advisors

Production

Mary Janak, MBA, MA
Education Program Manager
Society of Certified Senior Advisors

Jeffrey A. Mlady
Copyeditor

Contributors

Robert C. Atchley, PhD
Chair, Department of Gerontology
Director, Research Office
Naropa University

Sharil L. Baxter, CLTC, LTCP, CSA
LTCI Partners

Janice Blanchard, MSPH, CSA
Senior Writer
Society of Certified Senior Advisors

Karen Brady, JD
Karen Brady & Associates, P.C.
Attorneys and Counselors at Law

William E. Comfort, CSA, CLTC
Comfort Assurance Group, LLC

Andrea Bishman Egbert
Freelance Writer

Erin E. Emery, PhD
Long Island Jewish Medical Center

V. Raymond Ferrara, CFP
President and CEO
ProVise Management Group, LLC

Stephen M. Golant, PhD
Department of Geography & Center for Gerontological Studies
University of Florida

Laura Higgins
Senior Marketing Consultant

Gregory A. Hinrichsen, PhD
Director of Psychology Training
The Zucker Hillside Hospital
Associate Professor of Psychiatry
Albert Einstein College of Medicine

Mary Jean Kindschuh, Esq
Attorney and Counselor at Law

Michael J. Klug, JD
Westport Cooperative Services
Caregiver Training & Support Program

Harry R. Moody, PhD
Director of Academic Affairs
AARP

Lee E. Norrgard
Director
Catholic Relief Services, Kosovo

Janice K. Olson, RN, MS, MEd, CSA
Nursing Consultant, Geriatrics and Long-Term Care

Michael Snowdon, CFP, CMFC
Professor, Financial Planning
The College for Financial Planning

David Wolfe
The Center for Ageless Marketing

President's Message

Dear Colleague:

All of us at Society of Certified Senior Advisors® want you to know how proud we are that you've decided to join us as a Certified Senior Advisor (CSA)®. As you travel the path of thousands who've earned the CSA designation, you'll discover, as they have, the enormous personal and professional satisfaction that comes with understanding and serving the health, financial, and social needs of seniors.

Becoming a CSA begins with the book you now hold in your hands. *Working with Seniors: Health, Financial, and Social Issues* is the product of the brightest minds in the country—experts who are best suited to address these topics. It represents a multidisciplinary approach to the largest single challenge facing professionals today: how to identify and accurately serve the complex and diverse needs of our aging population.

Dozens of professionals, all dedicated to your success, have reviewed *Working with Seniors*. It contains the latest and most insightful information, backed by solid research and illustrated with numerous stories and examples.

Ed Pittock with granddaughter, Lauren

As you read it, you'll notice this is not your ordinary textbook. Most chapters offer a list of resources that you can draw on to better serve seniors and their families, making this book an easy-to-use, on-the-job reference guide that you'll turn to long after you've earned your CSA designation.

With every passing week, our burgeoning senior population makes your CSA education even more valuable to you. Baby boomers, the largest age-based group in the country, are moving quickly into a new stage of life as seniors, and your success will likely depend on your ability to effectively address their needs. We'll be with you along the way, providing you with regular new information about seniors and how to work with them successfully. Our CSA Continuing Education requirements will also enhance your understanding of how to approach the ethical aspects of serving seniors and give you the satisfaction that comes from selfless service as a volunteer for seniors.

Many of our CSAs tell us their experiences in becoming a CSA and applying their CSA education have been life-changing. I'm convinced this is no exaggeration. CSAs see the profound effects of what it means to earn the trust and faith of their senior clients. They also feel the enduring gratification that comes with being able to improve the lives of others—clients, friends, and family.

Congratulations on your decision to become a CSA! You're in for an amazing experience.

Edwin J. Pittock, CSA
President
Society of Certified Senior Advisors®

Foreword

Robert C. Atchley, PhD

It is difficult to think of an aspect of human life that is not affected by the fact that we age. Aging is a complex of physical, psychological, and social forces that play out in intricate and far-reaching ways. The processes of aging significantly influence the physical and psychological experience of being an adult, our capacity to generate financial resources, and the family, community, and societal contexts within which aging people try to meet their needs.

Aging shapes the array of services that are relevant for people of various life stages. Aging is affected by the social policies that govern access to and delivery of such vital resources as health care, social services, and retirement income.

Nevertheless, aging is not a set of irresistible forces to which we must fall victim. Aging is a set of processes that are significantly affected by what we think. Our attitudes, values, and beliefs have great impact on our physical health, psychological well-being, and social involvement during our later years.

Most of us believe that we have some degree of control over our own fate—that our actions have consequences. We believe we can anticipate what our needs will be and plan in advance to meet them. Most of us also recognize that we need professional assistance in many important areas of planning and decision-making, and this recognition creates a demand for the services of Certified Senior Advisors (CSAs).

CSAs are part of the field of aging, a collection of organizations and professionals whose training prepares them for a specific occupation and who also understand how various specialties interrelate to serve seniors. The CSA education provides the specialized learning required to move beyond being a professional who works with seniors to being *qualified* to work with seniors. One goal of this book is to give you a sense of the organizational and professional context within which you will be working. Part of the service expected of you as a CSA is the capability to refer clients to other professionals within the field of aging.

SERVING SENIORS

To serve seniors effectively, we need to begin long before people officially become part of the older population. For example, preventive steps to preserve physical health and mobility are best begun years before physical symptoms appear. And planning for adequate income in later adulthood is

Robert Atchley, wife Shelia, and grandchildren

best begun as early as possible in adulthood. As obviously important as these advance steps are, most people lack the motivation or the know-how to address them.

To serve seniors and prospective seniors, we must understand how to raise their consciousness about the issues of aging and help them to be proactive. In this process it is essential that we focus as much on the promise of freedom and autonomy that healthy and financially secure aging can bring as on the negative results that can occur.

Over the long run, people tend to be motivated more by a positive vision of a hopeful future than by fear of a negative outcome. The good news: research has shown that positive outcomes of aging outnumber negative ones by at least two to one. Planning and prevention work; those who take action to improve the odds of healthy aging and to secure their financial future are likely to be successful. But the fact that there are no guarantees means that denial of aging remains a formidable obstacle to be overcome.

In serving seniors, many people sell their potential clients short by aiming to "help the helpless." They assume that seniors are clueless unfortunates who need to be taken by the hand and led out of the dark woods of confusion. It is more accurate and effective to assume a "counsel the capable" stance, in which you recognize that seniors have a long experience of being able to adapt to change and fend for themselves. They have intelligence and resources at their disposal to help them cope. What they most often want from you as a CSA is help in identifying and evaluating their options. They want someone they can trust to give them straight answers.

THREE TYPES OF POTENTIAL CLIENTS

As a Certified Senior Advisor, who are your potential clients? There are at least three categories: seniors-in-training, seniors, and family members of seniors—most often their adult children.

Seniors-in-Training

Seniors-in-training are mostly middle-aged people who are thinking about how they want their lives to be when they become seniors. Most people who think ahead in this way are action-oriented. They are often financially literate and tend to be well educated, although their education may come from the school of hard knocks rather than through formal channels.

Seniors

The senior population itself is very diverse. If we define seniorhood as starting at age 65, then seniors range in age from 65 to 110 or so. If we consider the life experiences and aspirations of people across this huge age range, what could we expect them to have in common? Any general statement we could make would have as many exceptions as there are seniors. Therefore, if we want to understand how aging plays out—or might play out—for a particular person, we would be better off having a good inventory of questions rather than having a good inventory of answers.

If we follow a birth cohort (people who share the same period of birth) into later life, we see that as the cohort ages, the diversity of physical and mental capabilities within the group increases. Some have no apparent changes well into their 80s, others show marked declines, and most show mostly inconsequential changes. Diversity within the senior population also results from cultural, gender, and social class differences. Although we tend to use chronological or calendar age to define seniors, we are really interested in life stage and how it influences aspirations as well as needs and resources. As you read the following paragraphs, be aware that many of the issues that arise in the various life stages involve elements that can be important service opportunities for you.

Family Members

In later adulthood many people find themselves participating in caregiving for older family members. Families of seniors come into the picture mainly for frail elders who are no longer able to be self-sufficient. Here you are likely to be asked to assist with issues such as managing funds efficiently or arranging services for elders who live at a distance from their families. Often you will be working with people who have been struggling to meet the needs of a family member for a long time and are tired and dispirited. What they most need is a sense that there is someone to whom they can hand off some of the day-to-day responsibilities.

LIFE STAGES

We are interested in how to identify people who are in middle age, later adulthood, and old age because each of these life stages carries with it a set of issues and situations that most people can expect to experience.

Middle Age

In middle age, people become aware that physical aging has noticeably changed them. During middle age, vision and hearing may decline and most people begin to seek less physically demanding activities and experience the onset of minor chronic illness. But psychologically and socially, middle age can seem a time when we "have it all." Careers peak, family satisfactions can increase with the launching of children into adulthood, and marriages often improve due to changes in parenting responsibilities and financial obligations to children. Middle age is also a time when many people begin to look for a deeper meaning in life, beyond the achievement-oriented, materialistic values that dominate our culture's view of adult roles, toward an inner exploration of the intrinsic meaning of life. Midlife is often a time for reevaluating our lifestyles and for charting new directions. It is also a time when many people begin to accompany their parents on their last life stages, and in doing so become especially aware of the issues of old age.

Later Adulthood

Later adulthood begins at about age 65 and continues the gentle slope of physical and mental aging that began in middle age. Peak physical condition is harder to maintain—most people decide it is not worth the time and effort. Although they slow down, most maintain the same activity patterns they enjoyed in middle age. The deaths of older family members and friends heightens sensitivity to one's own mortality.

Retirement usually occurs during this stage, and for most people is a welcome release. Because retirement is not a well-defined role, people have the freedom to structure their lives in ways that genuinely reflect their personalities and values. Although some people are apprehensive about how they will cope with retirement, a large majority find that their preretirement lifestyles, life experiences, and long-standing values provide ample direction.

The new personal freedom that typifies later adulthood creates opportunities to open oneself to a wide range of new experiences. That many people take advantage of these opportunities is illustrated by the growth of Elderhostel, an organization that provides an extraordinarily diverse array of educational offerings aimed primarily at people in later adulthood who want to couple travel and education. Elderhostel grew from 14,000 participants in 1979 to more than 250,000 in 2003.

Later adulthood can also be a time in which creative expression is "shaped by the desire to find larger meaning in the story of our lives" (Cohen, 2000, p. 78) and by the desire to share the wisdom we have earned. This process can involve autobiography writing, personal storytelling, and mentoring of the young, often in the context of continued participation in community organizations. As one senior put it, "We've learned a lot about how to work with people patiently to get things done. We seniors have knowledge that is really needed."

Old Age

Old age is characterized not by chronological age but by extreme physical frailty and sometimes by luminous wisdom. Various types of dementia become more common. Activity is greatly restricted and social networks are thinned by the death of peers. But even in old age, most people have frequent contact with family and friends. Although old age is defined by physical and mental frailty and increased likelihood of living in assisted living or nursing home settings, most people die before they experience extreme disability.

Despite its aura of negativity, old age can also be a stage of summing up, of fruition in grasping the ultimate meaning of life. As one frail elder put it, "It's not so much what I do that's important, but how I am while I'm doing it. I want to be kind and gentle toward others, whatever I do."

Plan of the Book

Working with Seniors provides an in-depth look at the multiple dimensions of aging and how they interface with various areas of service. The book has more than 20 chapters, divided into six parts. Part 1 sets the stage by providing general background. It offers information on general trends in aging, an overview of the societal context within which aging take place, basic facts about physiological and psychological aging, and a discussion of the experience of aging. Together, these chapters cover basic concepts, perspectives, language, and research findings about individual aging.

Part 2 deals with the family and community context of aging. Family relationships are a crucial aspect of adapting to aging for most people. Caregiving for seniors is mostly done by family members, who themselves often are seniors. As seniors encounter the need for assistance with activities of daily living, housing becomes an important issue. Also, the array of services available in the community can have a profound affect on whether community-dwelling seniors can meet their needs for assistance.

Part 3 concerns health and mental health in the broadest sense. It considers the occurrence and implications of various types of chronic illness that increase in prevalence with age. It also discusses the positive side—the dramatic positive effects possible through nutrition, fitness, and healthy lifestyles. Cognitive impairment is the most feared possibility associated with aging, and it is important to understand the difference between normal cognitive changes with aging and various kinds of dementia. On the other hand, spirituality often develops in a positive direction and becomes more important with age, and for most people, spirituality is an important resource for coping with changes associated with aging. Finally, Part 3 considers end-of-life issues, particularly care planning and advance directives.

Part 4 deals with financial literacy, the knowledge that seniors need about estate planning, financial planning, long-term care insurance, and funeral planning. It is important to understand that clients come to you in part to be educated so they can understand issues and make informed decisions. This may involve teaching them new concepts and language.

Part 5 provides details about how various programs and services for seniors work. It has chapters on Medicare, Medicaid, Social Security retirement, survivor and disability pensions, and Supplemental Security Income welfare benefits for seniors. Your career as a CSA will benefit from a thorough understanding of these programs.

Part 6 covers some important areas of knowledge for being a practicing CSA. It discusses ethics in general and the *CSA Code of Professional*

Responsibility in particular. It also addresses special ethical concerns when serving the senior market and provides examples of ethical behavior to guide you in your interactions with seniors.

Rewards and Challenges of Serving Seniors

Serving seniors is a high calling with many rewards and challenges. As a CSA, you will come into contact with extraordinary people. As you get to know them, you will be impressed with their depth, capability, humor, generosity, and vitality. In my career I have interviewed about 450 seniors and surveyed more than 10,000. When I first began this journey more than 40 years ago, I was struck by how comfortable most of them were in their own skins. They accepted themselves as they were.

I have also met many seniors who are suffering. They are dealing with physical pain or disability. They are experiencing a decline in their customary mental capabilities. Some are involved in family disagreements or conflicts with service providers about their care. Suffering comes in countless forms. As a CSA you sometimes will be able to do something about a senior's suffering or discomfort by suggesting a resolution, but often there is nothing you can do—but care. We can just be with our clients so they do not have to suffer alone. We listen. That is a very valuable gift.

References

Cohen, G.D. (2000) *The Creative Age: Awakening Human Potential in the Second Half of Life*. New York: Avon.

Resources

Recommended Reading

Encyclopedia of Aging, 3rd ed. George Maddox, et al. (Eds.). New York: Springer, 2003.

Social Forces and Aging: An Introduction to Social Gerontology, 10th ed. Robert C. Atchley and Amanda S. Barusch. Belmont, CA: Wadsworth, 2004.

Services

Elderhostel, http://www.elderhostel.org

A Note About the Text

Working with Seniors uses the age break of 65-years-and-over to describe the senior, elderly, or elder population.

Throughout the text we have used stories and case examples to illustrate issues important to seniors. Unless otherwise identified, we have protected the privacy of the individuals involved by changing their names and other identifying characteristics.

Part 1

AGING

Age is opportunity no less than youth itself except in another dress.

Henry Wadsworth Longfellow

What does it mean to age? Part 1 will help answer this question. In the first chapter you will learn about current trends in aging, plus new research findings about growing older and the changes it brings. In the following chapters, you will learn about the destructive forces of ageism and age discrimination, along with other important aspects of aging and society. You will explore the basics about the physiological and psychological aspects of aging, and, through the stories and perspectives of seniors, you will learn about the diversity and richness of the aging experience. Finally, chapter 5 introduces you to the experience of aging and four major ways that seniors handle the aging process.

Chapter 1

Trends in Aging

For yesterday is already a dream, and tomorrow is only a vision; But today, well lived, makes every yesterday a dream of happiness and every tomorrow a vision of hope. Look well therefore, to this day.

From the Sanskrit

This is the first time in human history that the prospect of living a long, healthy, and productive life has become reality for the majority of people in most parts of the world. What was once a special advantage of the few has become the destiny of many. And it is likely that this increase in longevity will continue. As important as is liberation by health, as powerful as is liberation by law, older people must be liberated, too, from stereotypes that limit their horizons. We are in the midst of the wonderful new world of longevity. It is in our power to make it a celebration.

Robert Butler, 2001

Introduction

Would you like to know what our senior population will be like in 5, 10, or 20 years? Would it help your business to know their health status, where they will live, or their needs for financial planning? It is a safe bet that this knowledge would benefit you and your clients.

Forecasting trends in aging is a lot like weather prediction. It involves levels of certainty and uncertainty. No one can predict if it will rain or snow next December 15. But there is a very good chance that the weather will be colder on that day than it will be on July 15 of the same year. Therein lies the level of forecasting we can make about trends in aging.

Fortunately, we have a knowledge-base that we can use to make some speculations. For example, we know that the seniors of the year 2020 will come from the current group of people who are about 45 and older. Certain key trends affecting this group are already clearly in view (Francese, 2002). For instance, we know their contingent is large, their incomes as a whole are larger than those of their parents, their acceptance of nontraditional family structures has stretched the American idea of "family," and while they have a greater knowledge of the benefits of health, exercise, and nutrition than probably any American generation in history, they still face medical challenges unknown to previous generations. We can combine these generalized facts with research findings about work, retirement, education, economic development, and other factors to create a range of expectations for the future (Cutler, Whitelaw, & Beattie, 2002). Certainly, some of the next generation's seniors will live lives not unlike what many of us consider "normal" for seniors today and in the past. But each generation has its unique makeup, and anyone who works with seniors now and in the future must be prepared for change.

What challenges lie ahead for seniors, their families, and those who offer their services to seniors? How can seniors and their families best prepare to provide themselves with enjoyable and healthy lifestyles? And how can our society manage the economic, physical, and emotional needs of this cohort as it moves through its middle years and on to the next stage of life?

In this spirit, this chapter covers the following key trends, which will have impact on your future business of working with seniors:

- an aging America
- increase in the oldest-old population
- increased longevity
- population aging
- older women outnumbering older men
- growing ethnic diversity
- the retirement of baby boomers
- longer period of retirement
- the end of early retirement
- shift in the reliability of pension coverage
- a less disabled senior population
- new patterns in family life
- an educated senior population
- changes in how and where seniors live

An Aging America

From 1900 to the end of the last century, the population of people 65 and older grew 11 times larger, compared to the entire United States population, which multiplied to 3 times its size. This unprecedented growth in the senior population will continue in this century, dominating society, economics, and public policy.

Our current contingent of senior Americans were children of the Great Depression and the decade that followed. They were born during the 1930s, when the song "Brother, Can You Spare a Dime?" was on the hit parade, or in the early 1940s, before World War II altered the economic and industrial landscape. As a portion of the population, their numbers were relatively small. As a result, the growth of the elderly population now is actually slower than in the past, and it will remain slow until about 2005 (Census Bureau, 2000).

When the baby boomers begin to turn age 65 in 2011 our society will again experience rapid growth in the senior population. The number of seniors is projected to swell from 39 million in 2010 to 53 million in 2020 and further

4

to 82 million in 2050. Incredibly, 100 years from now America will have 131.2 million persons ages 65 or older. That number is equivalent to the population of the entire country in 1940.

Population aging is a global phenomenon. According to the United Nations Population Division, in 2000 there were about 606 million people ages 60 or older in the world, the equivalent of the entire current populations of the United States, the United Kingdom, and the Netherlands combined (United Nations Population Division, 2001). Globally, the number of 60-year-olds is expected to triple by 2050 to 2 billion.

This overall trend of population aging means enormous opportunities for you as a CSA, if you can apply your skills to meeting the needs of this growing segment of the population.

INCREASE IN THE OLDEST-OLD POPULATION

A major achievement of medical advances and health services in this century is the increase in the population of people ages 85 and older, termed the *oldest-old*. In the next decades, the oldest-old will be the fastest growing age group. Between 1990 and 2000, the number of people ages 85 and older increased from 3 million to 4.2 million. This number is expected to increase five-fold by 2050, when there will be 19.3 million people aged 85 or older (Census, 2000).

INCREASED LONGEVITY

One of the major accomplishments of the 20th century is that 30 years were added to life expectancy in the United States. A baby born in the United States in 1900 could expect to live an average of 47 years (NCHS, 1989). A baby born in 2000 can expect to live 77 years (NCHS, 2001).

Like life expectancy at birth, life expectancy at age 65 improved over the last century. However, those gains were far more modest. From the beginning to the end of the last century, 6 years were added to life expectancy at age 65. Americans who reached their 65th birthday in 2000 could expect, on average, to live another 17.9 years, compared to 11.9 years in 1900 (NCHS, 2002).

Future gains in longevity are expected to continue but slow down, because our society has already experienced the biggest benefits from advances in health care, in such critical areas as decreasing infant mortality and finding cures for infectious disease. Even if science today found the cure for the biggest killers—all forms of cancer, stroke, and heart disease—life expectancy would rise only by about 15 years (Olshansky & Carnes, 2002).

Longevity is an important issue for CSAs because today's seniors have to plan for many more years of life than did older people of the past. Many of the traditional techniques for retirement planning are not appropriate to today's older population.

OLDER WOMEN OUTNUMBER OLDER MEN

Women greatly outnumber men in the senior cohort, and this disparity increases with age. This fact reflects the longevity advantage of women, who on average, live longer than men do. Beyond age 65 women currently outnumber men 3 to 2. After age 85, there are 7 women for every 3 men (Census Bureau, 2000).

The population imbalance between the sexes is expected to decrease over the next several decades because of the improved health of men relative to women. It is projected that in 2050 senior women will outnumber senior men by 5 to 4 (42.8 million senior women, 36 million senior men). Women ages 85 and over will outnumber men of the same age by roughly 5 to 3 (13.1 million women, 7.8 million men) (AoA, 2004).

As long as the mortality of men exceeds that of women, women will outnumber men among the elderly, especially among the oldest-old age group. Even though the trend is changing somewhat, women will still dominate the older age ranges, and the majority of your senior clients will be women.

GROWING ETHNIC DIVERSITY

You will increasingly need to be sensitive to the needs of an ethnically diverse population. Currently, 16 percent of seniors are minorities. In the future, their numbers are expected to increase dramatically. By 2050 more than 1 in 3 (36 percent) seniors will be minorities (Federal Interagency Forum on Aging-Related Statistics, 2000).

THE RETIREMENT OF THE BABY BOOMERS

One of the biggest factors driving population aging is the aging of baby boomers—the cohort of 78 million people born between 1946 and 1964. The oldest boomers are nearing early retirement age. By 2011, the oldest boomer will reach age 65 and, after that point, 10,000 boomers will turn 65 every day. This is the biggest and quickest aging of America's population in history, and it will create a huge market for you as a CSA, who will be in a position to offer skillful guidance on the choices people will make as they age.

Much thinking and analysis are now directed at trying to forecast the retirement prospects of aging baby boomers. For example, the Congressional Budget Office (CBO) reports that, compared with their parents at the same age, baby boomers typically have higher current incomes, are preparing for retirement at largely the same pace, and have accumulated more private wealth (CBO, 2003). On the whole, boomers are on track to have higher incomes in retirement than their parents did, and they appear much less likely to live in poverty after they retire. The CBO also reports that:

- about a quarter of baby-boomer households have failed to accumulate significant savings and are likely to have to depend entirely on government benefits in retirement;
- at least half of boomer households are expected to maintain their working-age standard of living during retirement (under the assumption that current laws governing federal benefit programs do not change);
- for the remaining quarter of boomer households, the evidence is mixed, but they may have moderate declines in their standard of living during retirement, which could be offset by modestly increasing saving and by working for a few more years.

The CBO points out that many boomers could be greatly affected by—and should plan for—future changes in federal retirement benefits.

LONGER YEARS IN RETIREMENT

With more years added to life, people are spending a longer period of time in retirement than ever before. Consequently, there is a greater need to plan and prepare for later life. Despite gains in longevity, our society does very little formal planning or preparation for retirement.

According to gerontologist Harry Moody, retirement in the future will not be like it was in the past. Longer years in retirement will be combined with new opportunities—for second careers, for volunteer roles, and for continuing education. It is likely that tomorrow's seniors will invent new roles and patterns of life for aging in the 21st century and may change the meaning of retirement itself (Moody, 2004).

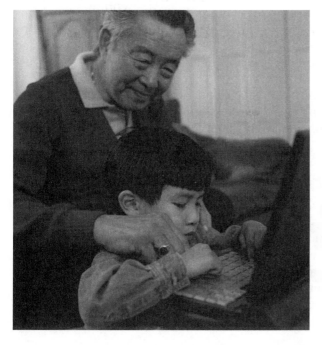

THE END OF EARLY RETIREMENT

The average age of retirement has been declining since public pensions were first introduced in the early 20th century. In the United States, the Social Security system provided a powerful incentive for workers to leave the labor force at earlier and earlier ages. Reduced Social Security benefits at age 62 were made available to women in 1956 and to men in 1961. Since that time, the age of retirement has moved downward. In 1940, the average age at which men started collecting their Social Security retirement benefit was 68 years (Vierck & Hodges, in press). In 1965 it was 66 years. In 2001 it was 64 years. Women have experienced a similar pattern, but with more complexities arising from new work opportunities that have opened up for women in recent decades.

In the past few years the trend to earlier retirement has stopped and appears to be heading in the opposite direction (Clark, Burkhauser, Moon, Quinn, & Smeeding, 2004). In fact, retirement may be becoming more of a process than an event (Bruce, Holtz-Eakin, & Quinn, 2000). A recent analysis found that at least one-third of older men and nearly one-half of older women worked in transitional *bridge jobs* before completely leaving the job market (Quinn, 2002). (Bridge jobs are positions that usually take a worker from full-time work to part-time work before full retirement.) Further evidence of this trend is the fact that 12 percent of elderly men and 7 percent of senior women currently work while receiving pension income (Purcell, 2000).

Some futurists project that people will extend their working years in ways unknown to previous generations (Burtless & Quinn, 2002). There are several reasons for this prediction: the end of mandatory retirement; the rise in the age of eligibility for Social Security; the increase in the average number of years that people live after age 65; and the current change in the type and availability of pension coverage. No one can be sure what the future will bring, but the recent trend is reinforced by the fact that 80 percent of baby boomers now tell survey researchers that they expect to work during years that those in previous decades spent in retirement (Roper Starch Worldwide, 1998).

SHIFTS IN THE RELIABILITY OF PENSION COVERAGE

In the past, half of the American labor force was eligible to receive a pension upon retirement, usually in the form of *defined benefit pension plans*, which pay a pension amount at a specific level depending upon years of service (Purcell, 2002). Over the past decade many employers dropped defined benefit plans in favor of *defined contribution plans*. Defined contribution plans set aside a certain amount or percentage of income for the benefit of the employee. There are restrictions as to when and how individuals can withdraw the funds without penalties. Defined contribution plans do not fix in advance the amount of pension income. This shift in pension coverage means that clients face more unpredictability about their income after they leave the work force (GAO, 2002).

Greater individual responsibility for finances is already creating a new need for more complex planning and professional advice, and you will want to be ready to respond to this new environment, especially if you specialize in a financial field.

A LESS DISABLED OLDER POPULATION

Demographer Kenneth Manton has found a remarkable bit of good news that has become recognized as a significant trend: Today's seniors as a whole have far fewer disabilities than did those in the past (Manton & Gu, 2001). If the rate of senior disability were the same as last century's rate, nursing homes would need to make room for a million or more disabled residents. Today's older population is healthier than in the past and likely to remain so for a longer period of time (Cutler, 2001). This trend underscores the point that you cannot look at the senior population of yesterday in order to predict what tomorrow's older people will be like. The client base of the future, at least among the young-old (ages 65 to 74) is likely to be more active than in the past.

However, we need to be cautious about taking attributes of only one part of the senior population and creating from that a generalization about all seniors. Because of increasing longevity, the likelihood of frailty and limitations still increases for older seniors. This means that, with advancing years, seniors spend more time and money on health care. Seniors are today and will continue to be the heaviest users of health services. In addition, health care costs continue to increase as new technologies become available. Both businesses and the government have responded to the situation by attempting to curtail health care costs. The result is a health service delivery system that has become increasingly more complicated—a patchwork of private insurance and government programs, including Medicare and Medicaid.

All these trends make health care decision-making a major challenge for an aging population. Seniors need a lot of help navigating the complex health care delivery system. In addition, you will need to be skilled in responding to seniors' health problems and diminished mental capacity if they occur, as well as issues surrounding end-of-life care.

NEW PATTERNS IN FAMILY LIFE

With greater longevity, we are seeing new patterns of family life. The increased chance of survival into old age means that the four-generation family is no longer rare. In addition, the family system itself is changing (Bengtson, 2001). Patterns of divorce and remarriage raise new questions for multigenerational families. For example, an ex-daughter-in-law might wonder what responsibility she has for caring for her ex-mother-in-law, who as grandmother to her children has played an important role in her family's life. Or, great-grandparents might want assurance that they will be able to visit their great-grandchildren in the event of their parents' divorce.

Family caregiving will also continue to be an enormous challenge. Today families provide the vast majority of the informal care received by older people. Geographic mobility often demands caregiving at a distance, and families struggle to reconcile their own needs with the imperative to care for elderly relatives (Montgomery, 1999).

Inheritance is often an important family issue that can make planning for the future complicated. There has been much attention paid to the "trillion-dollar bonanza" of inheritance for aging baby boomers. However, the reality is that big legacies will be limited to small numbers of heirs. Baby boomers shouldn't count on financing their retirement from money passed down by their elders (Gokhale & Kotlikoff, 2000). Be aware of this fact when counseling seniors and baby boomers.

AN EDUCATED SENIOR POPULATION

When we compare the education levels of today's seniors with those of the aging baby boomers behind them, we see a clear trend: rising education levels for each successive cohort of older people (Besl & Kale, 1996). A majority of tomorrow's seniors will have had at least some period of college education, and larger proportions will be college graduates or have professional training. That trend means that senior clients in years to come will be more sophisticated and more demanding. They will be less likely to accept advice without questions, and they may challenge expert opinions with ideas of their own. On the other hand, they may also be more open to discussions and planning in complex ways that might not be so feasible with clients lacking substantial educational experience. Your role will become less a matter of giving answers and more one of suggesting resources to help people find their own answers.

CHANGES IN HOW AND WHERE SENIORS LIVE

The image of seniors living out the end of their lives in nursing homes is a thing of the past. Use of nursing homes is declining. This trend is being fueled by the increasing availability of home and community-based services, in-home products and technology that make it easier for disabled people to live independently, and society's preference that we remain in our own homes as we age. Public- and private-sector programs that provide incentives for seniors to stay in their own homes for as long as possible are increasing. On the rise: reverse mortgages, insurance for home and community-based services, businesses (such as home health care) that cater to older adults at home, adult day care and geriatric care management, and state and federal governments intent on lowering long-term care costs associated with residential care. In addition, alternative housing developments that offer independent living for seniors are springing up all over the country.

Nursing homes are also attempting to change their appearance and philosophy of care. The most publicized effort is the Eden Alternative, developed by Dr. William Thomas. It aims to eliminate residents' feelings of loneliness, helplessness, and boredom through providing a stimulating and homelike environment. Eden Alternative nursing homes also promote a flexible management style with greater staff empowerment and advocate less rigid scheduling of activities and care plans, which encourages a stronger atmosphere of spontaneity. Many experts see the Eden Alternative as the wave of the future in care for the disabled of all ages.

Trends in Aging: Summary

Knowing the key trends that will shape the next decades is a first step to helping your clients create optimal futures. As a navigational consultant, you can provide tools—facts, resources, and experience—that help your clients and their loved ones chart their paths in life.

References

AoA (Administration on Aging). (2004). *A profile of older Americans: 2003.* Retrieved July 13, 2004, from http://www.aoa.gov/prof/statistics/profile/2003/profiles2003.asp

Besl, J. R., & Kale, B. D. (1996, June). Older workers in the 21st century: Active and educated, a case study. *Monthly Labor Review, 119*(6), 18–28.

Bengtson, V. L. (2001 February). Beyond the nuclear family: The increasing importance of multigenerational bonds. *Journal of Marriage and Family, 63*(1), 1–16.

Bruce, D., Holtz-Eakin, D., & Quinn, J. (2000, December). Self-employment and labor market transitions at older ages. Working paper #2000-13. Retrieved July 13, 2004, from http://www.bc.edu/centers/crr/wp_2000-13.shtml

Burtless, G. T., & Quinn, J. F. (2002, December). *Is working longer the answer for an aging workforce?* Chestnut Hill, MA: Center for Retirement Research at Boston College.

Butler, R. N. (2001, October 1). The wonderful world of longevity. Augusta, ME: The State of Maine Conference on Aging.

Census Bureau. (2000). Projections of the resident population by age, sex, race, and Hispanic origin, 1999 to 2100. Retrieved July 13, 2004, from http://www.census.gov/population/www/projections/natsum.html

CBO (United States Congressional Budget Office). (2003). *Baby boomers' retirement prospects: An overview.* Retrieved July 13, 2004, from http://www.cbo.gov/showdoc.cfm?index=4863&sequence=0

Clark, R. L., Burkhauser, R. V., Moon, M., Quinn, J. F., & Smeeding, T. M. (2004). *Economics of an aging society.* Malden, MA: Blackwell Publishing.

Cutler, N. E., Whitelaw, N. A., & Beattie, B. I. (2002). *American perceptions of aging in the 21st century: A myths and realities of aging chartbook.* Washington, DC: National Council on the Aging.

Cutler, D. M. (2001, June 5). Reduction in disability among the elderly. *Proceedings of the National Academy of Sciences, 8*(12), 6546–6547.

Federal Interagency Forum on Aging-Related Statistics. (2000). Older Americans 2000: Key indicators of well-being. Washington, DC: U.S. Government Printing Office. Retrieved July 13, 2004, from http://www.agingstats.gov/chartbook2000/default.htm

Francese, P. (2002, December). Top trends for 2003. *American Demographics,* Vol. 24, No. 11, 48–51.

GAO (United States General Accounting Office). (2002). *Private pensions: Improving worker coverage and benefits.* Report GAO-02-225. Retrieved July 13, 2004, from http://www.gao.gov/new.items/d02225.pdf

Gokhale, J., & Kotlikoff, L. J. (2000, October 1). Baby boomers' mega-inheritance— Myth or reality? *Federal Reserve Bank of Cleveland—Economic Commentary,* 1–4.

Manton, K. G., & Gu, X. (2001, May 22) Changes in the prevalence of chronic disability in the United States black and nonblack population above age 65 from 1982 to 1999. *Proceedings of the National Academy of Sciences,* Vol. 98, No. 11, 6354–6359.

Montgomery, R. J. V. (1999, August). Family role in the context of long-term care. *Journal of Aging and Health,* Vol. 11, No. 3, 383–416.

Moody, H. (2004). Trends in aging (unpublished written analysis presented to SCSA).

NCHS. (National Center for Health Statistics). (1989, March). *Health, United States, 1988.* Hyattsville, MD: National Center for Health Statistics.

NCHS. (2001, October) *National Vital Statistics Report 49.* Hyattsville, MD: National Center for Health Statistics.

NCHS. (2002, December) *National Vital Statistics Reports, 51*(3). Hyattsville, MD: National Center for Health Statistics.

Olshansky, J., & Carnes, B. (2002). *The quest for immortality: Science at the frontiers of aging.* New York: Norton.

Purcell, P. J. (2000, October). Older workers: Employment and retirement trends. *Monthly Labor Review Online,* Vol. 123, No. 10, 19–30. Retrieved July 13, 2004, from http://www.bls.gov/opub/mlr/2000/10/contents.htm

Purcell, P. J. (2002, September). Pension sponsorship and participation: Trends and policy issues. *Social Security Bulletin,* Vol. 64, No. 2. Retrieved July 13, 2004, from http://www.ssa.gov/policy/docs/ssb/v64n2/v64n2p92.pdf

Quinn, J. F. (2002). Changing retirement trends and their impact on elderly entitlement programs. In S. H. Altman & D. I. Shactman (Eds.), *Policies for an aging society.* Baltimore: The Johns Hopkins University Press.

Roper Starch Worldwide, Inc. (1998). *Polarized retirement: Optimism divides the baby boomers.* Washington, DC: AARP.

United Nations Population Division. (2001). World population prospects: The 2000 revision. Retrieved July 13, 2004, from http://www.un.org/esa/population/publications/wpp2000/highlights.pdf

Vierck, E., & Hodges, K. (2005). *Aging: Lifestyles, work, and money.* Westport, CT: Greenwood.

Chapter 2

Aging and Society

The life of Colin Powell is a classic American success story. Powell's parents were Jamaican immigrants. He was born into poverty in Harlem in 1937, the same year that African-American singer Bessie Smith died as a result of an auto accident in Mississippi—a hospital where she had been taken refused to treat her.

Powell attended New York public schools and the City College of New York. He also received a master of business administration degree from George Washington University. Powell served two tours of duty in Vietnam. He rose through the ranks of the United States military and served as the 12th chairman of the joint chiefs of staff under both President George H. W. Bush and President Bill Clinton. As of this writing he is secretary of state under President George W. Bush.

General Powell has been the recipient of numerous military decorations, including the Defense Distinguished Service Medal, Bronze Star, and the Purple Heart. His civilian awards include the Presidential Medal of Freedom, the Congressional Gold Medal, and an honorary knighthood (Knight Commander of the Bath) from the Queen of England.

Powell describes his climb up the ladder this way: "I was born in Harlem, raised in the South Bronx, went to public school, got out of public college, went into the Army, and then I just stuck with it."

. . .

The life of Jane Fonda is also an American success story. Fonda's parents were screen legend Henry Fonda and Frances Seymour Fonda, a New York socialite. Like Colin Powell, Fonda was born in 1937 in New York City. Unlike Powell, she was born into wealth and privilege. Fonda was educated at exclusive girls' schools, Vassar College, and the Actors Studio in New York, where she studied with Lee Strasberg. The movie Cat Ballou *made her a top star.*

Fonda has won two Oscars, six Golden Globes, an Emmy, and numerous other awards. While she was winning awards she suffered from bulimia—living on cigarettes, coffee, speed, and strawberry yogurt.

Fonda also went to Vietnam, but as a war protester. She was given the derisive nickname Hanoi Jane when she was photographed sitting at a North Vietnamese anti-

aircraft gun, the same kind used to shoot down American planes. Many Americans have never forgiven her for this period in her life.

Fonda sums up her activist years this way: "You can do one of two things: Just shut up, which is something I don't find easy, or learn an awful lot very fast, which is what I tried to do."

> *. . . Against the backdrop of history, changes in people's lives influence and are influenced by changes in social structures and institutions. These reciprocal changes are linked to the meanings of age, which vary over time.*
>
> Mathilda White Riley, Annee Foner, John W. Riley, "The Aging and Society Paradigm," in *Handbook of Theories of Aging*, p. 327.

Introduction

The interaction of aging and society is a complex two-way exchange. Society influences the individual and the individual influences society in never-ending circles. For example, we might ask: What impact did being born in 1937 in New York have on Colin Powell? On Jane Fonda? Or we might ask: What impact did Powell, a loyal soldier, have on the Vietnam war? What impact did Fonda, the movie star protestor, have? We might also ask: What impact did Vietnam have on the life of Colin Powell? Of Jane Fonda?

In turn, what are their lives like as seniors? Most of us would agree that neither one is representative of most seniors today. For that matter, are the lives of Mary, Ben, and Lois, described below, any more typical?

Mary: "I was 5 years old on D-Day. I had two older brothers who died in the war. I became an only child. My mother never recovered from the loss of her sons. I went to college in Iowa and wanted to be a mathematician, but my parents insisted that I major in one of the liberal arts. They wanted grandchildren; I wanted to leave our town and see the world. Eventually I married Stan, a graduate student in Chicago. I thought it was the right thing to do. We had three children—none of whom have children of their own. I wasn't a very good mother. I wasn't really cut out for it. I should have gotten that mathematics degree.

"Today I am divorced. I live in California, and all of my children live on the East Coast. I own and run a string of medical supply shops, and I plan to keep on running them until I absolutely can't anymore, and then I have no idea what I will do with myself. I am not cut out for retirement."

Ben: "I was 9 when the stock market crashed. My parents had a general store, and the Great Depression hit us hard. I was also very aware of fascism and what was happening in Europe. That made a big impression on me."

Like many men in his age group, Ben worked hard to be a model member of the community and a successful businessman. He was head of the city council in his town outside Denver and top sales manager for a major clothing company. And like many women of that generation, Ben's wife, Lois, worked in the home raising their two children. Lois says, "Even though we had a nice home, those were hard years emotionally. The kids and I played second fiddle to Ben's job and his political ambitions."

Everything changed. Ben says, "I was lucky to have a triple bypass in time. I woke up in the hospital surrounded by Lois and our kids, who still loved me even though I barely ever saw them. It changed my life."

Ben retired early. He and Lois have been on a second honeymoon for 20 years. After the bypass, Ben quit his job and took up biking. Lois learned how to cook healthy food. Chicken-fried steak became a thing of the past. Ben says, "I have had two decades of good fortune. My pride and joy are my two grandchildren. I missed their parents' childhoods. I am not missing theirs."

For the 37 million seniors in the United States, there are 37 million styles of aging. Each senior has a personal story, as we all do. At the same time, there are general patterns that can be observed in aging and adult development. This chapter discusses some of the most identifiable patterns as described by gerontologists and others who have studied them. In addition, it covers other major topics that are important for you to understand about aging and society. The topics are:

- ageism
- age discrimination in employment
- retirement as a major role in later life
- widowhood as a major role in later life
- activities during later life
- community involvement during later life
- crime and fear of crime
- elder abuse
- social policy and aging

Introduction to the Studies of Gerontology and Social Gerontology

In order to study aging and society it is important to know some definitions and concepts.

Gerontology is the study of aging. It includes analysis of information from many disciplines ranging from science to the humanities.

Geriatrics is the medical study of aging.

Society is a human group that shares the same territory and culture, has a sense of unity and a feeling of belonging, and engages in activities that satisfy its needs and interests.

Social gerontology is the study of the social lives of older people. According to Jay Gubrium and James Holstein,

This covers a large territory, ranging from interpersonal relationships, living arrangements, and retirement, to social inequality, the politics of age, health, caregiving, death, and bereavement. (Gubrium & Holstein, 2000, p. 1)

These definitions are important to students embarking on the study of age and aging. Learning how society influences the individual and the individual influences society is key to understanding the lives of your senior clients.

Systems for Defining and Describing Aging and Later Life

Gerontologists use various measures to describe people's aging process in a social context. The measures include *chronological age, social roles, functional age, subjective age, cohorts and generations,* and *life stages.* In addition, Erikson's stages of psychosocial development are frequently used to describe tasks of later life. You should be familiar with these concepts and attitudes and know how they affect seniors today.

CHRONOLOGICAL AGE

Chronological age is used by many public programs to define age groups. However, it is not an accurate measure to describe the characteristics of a group of people, whether they are teenagers, 30-somethings, or seniors. Such chronological age breaks often differ. For example:

- Until recently in the United States eligibility for full Social Security benefits came at age 65.
- The age for eligibility for Medicare remains at age 65, even though the age of eligibility for full retirement benefits from Social Security is increasing.
- The Age Discrimination in Employment Act of 1967 (ADEA) protects workers who are 40 years of age or older from employment discrimination based on age.
- To be eligible for Older Americans Act programs, individuals must be at least 60 years old or be married to someone 60 or older.

These chronologically determined qualifications or restrictions have far-reaching impacts on the lives of seniors. For example, some older people put off important surgeries until age 65, when Medicare will cover much of the bill. And some employers avoid hiring people over age 40 because they are afraid that if it the arrangement does not work out and they have to let the employee go, they will be sued for age discrimination.

Some gerontologists also use chronological age to make a distinction between the young-old (ages 65 to 74), the old-old (ages 75 to 84), and the oldest-old (ages 85 and older).

It is also important to remember that the senior population spans from age 65 to 105 or thereabouts, and the needs and resources of the youngest seniors are very different from those of the oldest seniors. It is also important for you to encourage your clients to think about how their needs and resources might change as they move through these age categories.

SOCIAL ROLES AND AGING

Some social positions create images of seniors in people's minds. For example, the word *retiree* often elicits an image of an older man shopping at Home Depot between 9:00 a.m. and 5:00 p.m. on a workday, and the word *widow* sometimes conjures up the image of an older wrinkled woman with white hair and a sad smile.

However, today some people can retire with a pension after a couple of decades. For example, members of the military can retire after 20 years, so that a recruit who entered the military at age 18 could be a retiree at age 38. Lisa Beamer was age 32 when she became a widow. (Lisa was the wife of Todd Beamer, a software executive, whose last words, "Let's roll," were heard on September 11, 2001, by an airphone operator on United Flight 93 before the plane crashed in a field outside Shanksville, Pennsylvania. Many of the "widows of 9-11" are in her age group.)

FUNCTIONAL AGE

Functional age is determined by what people can do. According to Jill Quadagno (2002),

> In functional terms, people become older when they can no longer perform the major roles of adulthood. Among the Inuit Eskimos, for example, a man becomes old around 50 when he can no longer hunt during the winter. Women become old about a decade later because the roles they perform are less physically strenuous. (p. 7)

Functional age may also be measured by such normal physical changes as stiffness of joints or decreased skin elasticity (Schneider, 1983).

We all age differently, and while one person may have a chronological age of 65 and functional age of 45, another with a chronological age of 65 may have a functional age of 85. In addition, different parts of the body may age at different rates. You may have great hearing and poor eyesight at age 65, while your neighbor of the same age has poor hearing and great eyesight.

One common measure of functional age involves activities of daily living (ADLs), which measure the low end of functionality (see chapter 7).

Neither of the definitions of older age we have discussed so far takes into account what people in our society think of as "old." The next section covers this topic.

To me, old age is always 15 years older than I am.

Bernard M. Baruch

SUBJECTIVE AGE

Subjective age is how old people feel. One person may be 75 and feel young; a 55-year old may feel old (Vierck & Hodges, 2003). But the perception of when people become old shifts by age group. For example, people ages 60 and over think of others as old at age 77, while those ages 18 to 29 think old age starts 10 years earlier, at age 67 (see Table 2.1).

Table 2.1 What Is "Old"?

AGE OF RESPONDENT (YEARS)	AGE AT WHICH OTHERS ARE "OLD"
18+ years	72
18–29	67
30–44	72
45–59	74
60+	77

Source: Vierck & Hodges, 2003.

Another study by Harris Interactive for the National Council on Aging found that nearly half of people ages 65 and older consider themselves to be middle-aged or young (The National Council on Aging, 2000). There were no noticeable gender or education group differences in these findings. And only 15 percent of people ages 75 and over consider themselves "very old."

How old would you be if you didn't know how old you are?

Satchel Paige

COHORTS AND GENERATIONS

Cohorts are groups who have experienced the same significant life event within a specified time period. Colin Powell and Jane Fonda are in the same cohort. The process of *cohort aging* is the advancement of one cohort from one age category to another.

Sociologists do not equate cohorts and generations. Even though the word *generation* is sometimes used loosely to define a cohort, it does not serve the same purpose when speaking scientifically. Sociologists reserve the term *generations* to describe families, such as the generations of grandparents, children, and grandchildren.

Birth cohorts of today's seniors are:

- Great Depression, born 1901 to 1920
- The 1930s, born 1931 to 1940
- The World War II years, born 1939 to 1945.

Cohorts differ in composition by such factors as racial makeup, gender, ethnic composition, and size. They also differ in terms of their interaction with social institutions such as educational systems, the availability of pensions, and trends in access to social services. For example, today's seniors have many more options for receiving long-term care in their homes than seniors had in the past. Therefore, members of future cohorts who become frail in older age may have very different experiences than those of previous cohorts who, if they became frail, moved to nursing homes.

LIFE STAGES

Life stages are another way of describing life's transitions. Robert Atchley describes *life stages* as a combination of physical and social attributes such as adolescence, young adulthood, adulthood, middle age, later maturity, and old age (Atchley & Barusch, 2004). In this chapter we look at middle age, later adulthood, and old age.

Middle Age

Middle age is when physical changes become noticeable. It is also the age at which people are thought of as part of the "aging population" (but not the elderly population).

Examples of changes during middle age:

- People seek less physically demanding activities.
- Recovery from exercise takes longer.
- Minor chronic illness becomes more prevalent.
- Vision and hearing begin to decline.

Chronologically, middle age begins sometime near the 40s. During this stage, a number of social changes may occur:

- Children leave home and become independent.
- Married couples often grow closer.
- People sometimes make midlife job changes.
- Community involvement may increase.
- Stay-at-home mothers enter the workforce.
- Most women experience menopause.
- Some middle-aged people retire with no continuation of employment.

Atchley and Barusch (2004) comment that this is a time marked by social transitions—at home, on the job, and in the family. Physical transitions come later.

For many, midlife is a time of reflection and "the beginning of an inner process of developing personal life meaning" (Atchley & Barusch, 2004, p. 8). In addition, middle-aged people often experience the deaths of those close to them, such as parents.

Later Adulthood

Later adulthood generally occurs sometime in the 60s. Declines in physical functioning and energy continue during this period, and chronic illness becomes more common. Most people are active, but the prevalence of activity limitations is more common. Middle-aged people experience more frequent deaths among family and friends. The changes that occur during this time are primarily social, as is the case with middle age.

Retirement usually occurs during this period. For most people this is welcome, although income is often reduced. During this period many are caring for aging parents.

Atchley and Barusch (2004) sum up later adulthood with this positive note: "Most people retain a fair amount of physical vigor in later adulthood that, coupled with freedom from responsibilities, makes this life stage one of the most open and free for those who are prepared to take advantage of it" (p. 9).

Old Age

The onset of *old age* typically occurs in the late 70s to early 80s (although many people in their 80s and 90s show few signs of it). Old age is characterized by extreme physical frailty. In addition:

- Disabling chronic conditions are more common.
- Mental processes slow down.
- Chronic brain conditions become more common.
- People feel that death is near.
- Activity is decreased.
- Social groups change due to deaths of family and friends (but, even in old age, most people have frequent contact with family and friends).
- Physical dependency and institutionalization are common.

Old age is defined more by physical and mental changes rather than the social changes that accompany middle age and late adulthood. However, Atchley points out, "most people die before they reach extreme disability" (Atchley, 2000a, p. 9).

These stages are important for you to be aware of because many of your clients will travel through all three of them and your work with them will differ accordingly.

AGING: THE CULTURAL LIFE COURSE

The *cultural life course perspective* emphasizes the interaction of historical events, individual decisions and opportunities, and the effect of early life experiences in determining later life outcomes. During a life course, people move through different social roles (transitions) such as child, student, spouse, parent, and grandparent. During older age most Americans follow the life course through the steps of the children leaving home, one or both spouses retiring, and playing the role of grandparent. During this time, participation in activities such as church attendance and volunteering tends to decrease. Other far less desirable roles that people can assume during this time are widowhood, dependency, and institutional resident.

When you hear people express some of the following thoughts, they are expressing changes in social roles and the impact such changes have on their feelings about their aging:

- "When my mother died, I suddenly thought, 'I'm no one's daughter anymore.'"
- "When my last child graduated from school, I thought, 'That's it—the next step is the retirement village.'"
- "I won't let my grandchildren call me 'Grandma.' It makes me feel really old. They call me by first name, Louise."

And at the other end of the spectrum:

- "Now that we're retired, we can make love in the morning."
- "I like being able to decide for myself what work is significant and meaningful for me to do."
- "Even though my best friend has been dead for 15 years, I think of her often. I can imagine her take on things, and it still gives me perspective."
- "I looked forward to not having the heavy weight of day-to-day responsibility for the children. I love them completely, but it was a major relief when they left the nest and took responsibility for their own lives."

STAGES OF LIFE

Erik Erikson's psychosocial theory on development is a unique theory because it emphasizes society's influence on the development of the psyche. Erikson said that humans develop in psychosocial stages throughout the life span (Erikson, 1963).

In Erikson's theory, eight stages of development occur during our lives. In addition, just before his death he was beginning to theorize about a ninth stage called gerotranscendance. Each stage consists of an *identity crisis* that must be faced. According to Erikson, this crisis is a turning point of increased vulnerability and enhanced potential. Successful completion of each stage results in a healthy personality and successful interactions with others. The stages can be resolved successfully at any time during an individual's life.

In this chapter we focus only on the three stages of later life: generativity versus stagnation, integrity versus despair, and gerotranscendance.

Generativity Versus Stagnation

During middle adulthood, we give back to society through raising our children, being productive at work, and becoming involved in community activities and organizations. If we fail to achieve these tasks, we feel stagnant and unproductive.

Integrity Versus Despair

During late adulthood we look back and evaluate what we have done with our lives. If we have developed a positive outlook in most of all of the previous stages of development, we will feel a sense of satisfaction and integrity. If we have not resolved the earlier stages, we will feel despair.

Gerotranscendance

With his wife, Joan, Erikson theorized about a ninth stage called gerotranscendance, in which healthy resolution of the earlier stages leads to a deepening appreciation of the past while living within the constrained, care-receiving present. During this stage there is an expansion of self that embraces others and a sense of communion with all things, including death itself.

If we don't listen carefully to older people or fail to encourage them to speak for themselves, our own stereotypical views can easily color their lives so that they appear to be "different." Their lives can be seen much more negatively or positively than they actually are.

Jaber F. Gubrium and James A. Holstein, Aging and Everyday Life, 2000, p. 1.

Now that we have covered some basic concepts about systems for defining and describing aging and later life, the remainder of the chapter covers key topics regarding aging and society. The first of these is ageism.

Ageism

Ageism is prejudice or discrimination against older persons because of their age (Palmore, 1998). (Ageism has also been discussed in chapters 1 and 5 in this text.) The following is Elizabeth Vierck's description of ageism (Vierck, 1988):

Ageism is manifested in our society's worship of youth and its anxiety over wrinkles, in the contradictions of our desire for longevity and reluctance to grow old, and in the media's use of phrases like "geritol jock" (an aging athlete) and "blue hair" concerts (those attended by older women).

Ageism can occur at any age. When Eddie Mannix, an old-time executive at Warner Brothers, saw a screen test of 34-year-old Fred Astaire, he said: "He's too old and too bald." (For those of you who are too young to remember Fred Astaire, he was a big star from the 1930s through 1981, when he made his last film. He received an honorary Academy Award in 1950, many Emmy Awards for television, a Kennedy Center Honors award in 1978, the first year they were awarded, and numerous other honors.)

Many people fall victim to ageism by, in older age, becoming prejudiced against themselves. A rerun of the "Mary Tyler Moore Show" reminds us of this when a delightful, white-haired older man explains to perky, youthful Mary that part of his daily routine is going to the park and sitting on a bench. He finds it rather boring, he says, but ever since he was little he has seen old men sitting on benches and feels it his obligation to the younger generation to do the same.

The moral of the story is clear: Ageism can be a self-fulfilling prophecy. A child learns to expect old men to take to benches and, faithfully, in older age, sits out the expectation.

THE INSTITUTIONALIZATION OF AGEISM

Recent results of a groundbreaking study conducted at Yale University Medical School demonstrate the effect that the negative stereotypes of aging have on older people (Levy, Wei, & Hausdorff, 2000).

The study included 54 participants between the ages of 62 and 82, who performed tasks such as recalling the most stressful event in the last five years. Participants were divided into two groups, one that was exposed to positive stereotypes of aging (words such as *wisdom* and *creative*) and one that was exposed to negative stereotypes (words like *senile* and *dying*).

After such exposure, the positive-stereotype group showed a significant decrease in two cardiovascular measures: systolic and diastolic blood pressure. In contrast, participants in the negative-stereotype group showed a significant increase in these measures, even before they performed the stressful tasks.

Negative stereotypes of aging are found in many aspects of our culture," Levy writes. "From casual conversations to television advertisements that often present the elderly either as close to childhood or close to death. . . . The study suggests that negative stereotypes of aging may contribute to health problems in the elderly without their awareness. This, in turn, could lead to older individuals mistakenly attributing decline in their health to the inevitability of aging, which might then reinforce the negative stereotypes and prevent successful aging.

The study also found that the elderly participants who were exposed to positive aging stereotypes demonstrated significantly higher self-confidence and higher mathematical performance than those exposed to the negative aging self-stereotypes.

This is how Thomas R. Cole described this century's lack of progress against ageism in his history of aging, the *Journey of Life* (1992): "In our century vastly improved medical and economic conditions for older people have been accompanied by cultural disenfranchisement—a loss of meaning and vital social roles."

Cole was describing the institutionalization or establishment of retirement policies. According to Robert Atchley (2004), "The enormous prosperity of the 1950s and 1960s was used to fund retirement, but underlying this policy decision was a belief that older workers couldn't cut it. The institutionalization of retirement let us have the illusion that retirement did no harm."

Atchley continues, "Although most retirees see retirement as a positive change, it is still an action based in ageism and the needs of a wage economy to control the number of people seeking employment. To our credit, we have created networks of volunteer opportunities. But do those opportunities take full advantage of the wisdom and skill that elders bring? Not usually. Why not? Ageism" (Atchley, 2004).

Sadly, evidence of ageism exists today in the media and the workplace. For example, today many older people who desire to work hit a "gray ceiling."

PREJUDICE AND DISCRIMINATION

There are two types of ageism: prejudice and discrimination.

Prejudice involves beliefs, specifically negative beliefs and attitudes about seniors. When people act on the basis of their prejudices they are discriminating against seniors.

Discrimination involves behaviors, specifically those behaviors that restrict, impair, exploit, humiliate, or otherwise hurt seniors (Palmore, 1998).

The most common type of ageism is the stereotype that most old people are sick, senile, sexually impotent, ugly, isolated, poor, and miserable (Palmore, 1998). Erman Palmore writes, "In fact, research has shown that none of these stereotypes applies to the vast majority of people over 65. The most common types of discrimination are in employment, training, some government agencies, some families, housing, and health care."

Ageism today is sometimes expressed as "intergenerational warfare," with objections to the proportion of the federal budget that goes to pay for programs benefiting seniors, such as Social Security and Medicare. Some critics believe that these programs are funded at the expense of programs for younger people.

THE NEW AGEISM

The *new ageism* is a tendency to patronize seniors and be overly solicitous toward them (Quadagno, 2002). These excerpts of dialogue from the novel *Family Matters* by Rohinton Mistry (2002) typifies an extreme of this attitude.

Ageism's Self-Sabotage Checklist

Often people behave, think and feel, according to the feedback they get from society. Columnist Ellen Goodman puts it this way: "At age 2 we are required to be terrible, at 6 to go to school, and by 65 or 70 at the latest to be old" (as reported in Vierck, 1988).

You can use the following checklist to examine whether you are ageist toward yourself. When appropriate, you can also use it with your clients to examine their ageist attitudes.

- *Do you avoid doing things you'd like to do because you are afraid your age might make you feel out of place?*

- *Do you find yourself thinking things like, "I can't do that (start a new career, go dancing, take a vacation) because I'm too old"?*

- *Do you feel that it is inevitable that negative and extreme age-related changes will happen to you? Do you feel that there is nothing that you can do about these changes?*

- *Do you equate looking old with looking bad?*

- *Do you pretend to others or yourself that you are younger than you are?*

- *Do you find yourself feeling ashamed of physical signs of aging such as age spots and wrinkles?*

- *Do you find yourself avoiding the elderly or frail people in your life?*

- *Do you find yourself not wanting to think about older people because of your own fears (particularly if they are in places that make you uncomfortable, such as nursing homes or hopitals)?*

- *Do you feel that on issues such as employment or leadership you have few choices because of your age?*

- *When you hear that someone you are about to meet is over 75 do you assume that they're "over the hill"?*

Source: Checklist from Vierck, 1988.

The protagonist, Nariman, has Parkinson's disease and lives in Bombay with his stepchildren, who worry about him. He is in the bathroom getting ready to take an evening walk, which is his custom. His stepdaughter beseeches:

> "How many times have I told you, Papa? Don't lock the door! If you fall or faint inside, how will we get you out? Follow the rules!"
>
> "Now, Papa, is it too much to ask? Please stay home, for your own good."
>
> "A stubborn child, that's what you are. Should be punished like a child. No dinner for disobedience, hanh?"

This latter passage borders on verbal abuse. But the new ageism is usually more subtle. For example, the medical professional who does not talk directly to a senior patient who is perfectly able to hear and cognitively intact, but

Charles

instead talks to a caregiver who accompanies her, is being patronizing. The family who moves their mother to a new location without checking with her first is being patronizing. The financial planner who does not listen to the desires of the senior client—but assumes that they know what the senior needs—is being patronizing.

As a society we make policies that serve the most people. Basing policy decisions on any of the ageist stereotypes does not serve this need. In addition, when, as a society, we either overstate or understate the magnitude of policy issues, we may create unduly positive or negative stereotypes. What this means for you as a CSA is that you should strip your attitudes of any preconceived ideas about your senior clients, including those that are ageist or patronizing. What this means on a societal level is that we should work to establish social policies that are grounded in reality, not prejudice.

Age Discrimination in Employment

As mentioned above, one of the most frequently recognized forms of age discrimination is in employment. Workers should be hired for jobs, and maintain them, because of their job performance and not their age. AARP suggests the following types of events are indicative of age discrimination (AARP, n.d.):

- An employer wants a younger-looking person to do a job, so the older worker is not hired.
- A boss won't let an older worker take a training course. Then he or she gets a poor job evaluation because of lack of flexibility in taking on new assignments.
- Money is tight, so a boss fires the older worker and keeps the younger worker, who is paid less.
- An employer gives the older worker undeserved poor performance evaluations and then uses his record of poor performance to justify firing or demoting him.
- A boss turns down an older worker for promotion. Instead, he hires someone younger from the outside because the company says it needs new blood.

Age discrimination is illegal under the Age Discrimination in Employment Act (ADEA, see sidebar). With some exceptions, the law covers job applicants and workers who are 40 and older. The law is overseen by the Equal Employment Opportunity Commission (EEOC).

However, the truth is that the EEOC pursues only a tiny percentage of cases brought to them. In addition, employers have the resources to bury private suits against them. The result is that, at this time, the ADEA, under EEOC's enforcement, does not give as much protection as its mandate suggests. However, it is sometimes used effectively by employees older than 40 to settle age discrimination cases out of court.

The Age Discrimination in Employment Act of 1967 protects individuals who are 40 years of age or older from employment discrimination based on age. The ADEA's protections apply to both employees and job applicants. Under the ADEA, it is unlawful to discriminate against a person because of his or her age with respect to any term, condition, or privilege of employment— including, but not limited to, hiring, firing, promotion, layoff, compensation, benefits, job assignments, and training.

It is also unlawful to retaliate against an individual for opposing employment practices that discriminate based on age or for filing an age discrimination charge, testifying, or participating in any way in an investigation, proceeding, or litigation under the ADEA.

The ADEA applies to employers with 20 or more employees, including state and local governments. It also applies to employment agencies and to labor organizations, as well as to the federal government.

The Older Worker Benefit Protection Act (OWBPA) amended the Age Discrimination in Employment Act in 1990. It prohibits discrimination with respect to employee benefits on the basis of age and regulates early-retirement incentive programs.

In 2003 the EEOC won the biggest age discrimination settlement in American history (EEOC and Arnett et al. v. CalPERS). They recovered $250 million in back pay for 1,700 public safety officers in California. It is the biggest settlement of a single lawsuit in the history of the Equal Employment Opportunity Commission. The case focused attention on the growing problem of discrimination of older workers.

One of the officers who brought the complaint was Ron Arnett, who in 1992 fractured a vertebra while on duty. The city told Arnett he would have to retire. He appealed and lost. Arnett applied for disability retirement pay from the California Public Employees Retirement System (CalPERS). (CalPERS is the nation's largest public pension fund. At that time it had assets of $133 billion [Harris, 2003].) CalPERS typically paid members who were injured on the job half of their former salary. But Arnett got only 32 percent of his former pay.

CalPERS' rationale for paying Arnett less than half his salary was based on the California Government Code Section 21417. According to the code, CalPERS was allowed to adjust the amount of a disability pension below the 50 percent of compensation standard using a formula based on the worker's age at the time of hiring. Arnett joined the police at age 43. As it turned out, one of Arnett's classmates became disabled about the same time as Arnett. That officer, who was 30 at the time he was hired, got half his regular pay.

Source: EEOC, 2004

Retirement as a Major Role in Later Life

As mentioned earlier, the institutionalization of retirement perpetuates the ageist myth that older workers can't cut it. Retirement as an expected part of the lifecycle, came into being in the 20th century (see Table 2.2). In 1900, 63 percent of elderly men were in the labor force (Fischer, 1978). By 1998, less than 17 percent were in the labor force.

Table 2.2 Labor Force Participation, Senior Males

Years	Percent Labor Force Participation Rates, Males 65 and Over
1900	63.1
1920	55.6
1930	54
1940	44.2
1950	45.8
1960	33.1
1970	26.8
1978	20.4
1988	16.5
1998	16.9

Source: Howard N. Fullerton Jr., "Labor Force Projections to 2008: Steady Growth and Changing Composition," *Monthly Labor Review*, November, 1999, p. 22.
Note: These century-spanning figures cloud a recent increase in the working patterns of older men. Since 1985, labor force participation rates for men 65 and older have increased slightly. For example, the rates for men ages 65 to 74 increased by 1.3 percentage points from 1988 to 1998 (Fullerton, 1999).

PHASES OF RETIREMENT

According to Robert Atchley (1999), ageism aside, seniors generally feel favorable toward retirement, regardless of age or gender. Most adults expect to retire, and to retire before age 65. Atchley and Barusch (2004) have sketched out the phases of retirement, which can help you understand the changes that your senior clients go through as they adjust to this period in their lives.

Preretirement

According to Atchley (1999), preretirement has two phases: remote and near. In the *remote phase*, the individual sees retirement as far off, but as an expected part of the work cycle. However, few people see retirement as something to plan for. (The exceptions are workers whose companies offer retirement planning.) This lack of planning is important to you because many of your clients will reach retirement without a plan or with a plan that was gathered a day late and a dollar short.

During this period there are important prerequisites to retirement that individuals should be building. According to Atchley, "The most important of these is a retirement income adequate for the style of life one wants to adopt in retirement" (Atchley, 2000b, p. 119). In retirement the outlay is larger and the time to accumulate resources is longer than during the younger years. Atchley writes, "Most people require a supplement to whatever retirement pensions they receive in order to sustain their desired lifestyle. But in order to provide for this supplement, the individual must be aware of the need during the remote phase of preretirement" (Atchley, 2000b, p. 119).

Developing leisure skills is another important prerequisite that individuals should develop during the remote stage. Developing a wide array of leisure skills is easier to accomplish in the early years than later. The same is true for developing a network within the community.

The *near phase* of preretirement begins when retirement is looming. Although many people remain positive, attitudes toward retirement usually become more negative during this phase. The public definition of this phase includes preretirement planning programs, retirement ceremonies, on-the-job-training for a replacement, and possibly promotion into a less essential job.

Two important things can happen during this period. First, older workers may get ready for separation from their jobs and prepare for the accompanying social situation. They may notice subtle differences in how people view them. They may see their jobs as more burdensome than they did previously. Second, they may fantasize about what their retirement will be like. According to Atchley and Barusch,

> These fantasies may turn out to be quite accurate pictures of the future, or they may be totally unrealistic. If realistic, they can serve as a 'dry run' that smoothes the transition into retirement by identifying issues that require advanced decision making. But if the fantasies are unrealistic, they thwart a smooth transition into retirement by setting up detailed but unrealistic expectations (Atchley & Barusch, 2004, p. 259).

The Honeymoon Phase

The retirement event is followed by a euphoric phase in which retirees do all the things they did not have time for before. This period may be short or last years, depending largely on financial resources. According to Atchley, this phase is critical: "If the individual is able to settle into a routine that provides a satisfying life, then that routine will probably stabilize" (Atchley & Barusch, 2004, p. 259).

Extended travel is common during this phase.

Immediate Retirement Routine

If the retirement routine provides a satisfying life, then that routine will stabilize. People who had full off-the-job lives are often able to establish such a routine easily.

Rest and Relaxation

After retirement many people go through a period of low activity, which differs greatly from the activity in the honeymoon period. Atchley calls this period the *R & R phase*. However, this low activity is usually temporary. Atchley followed a cohort of 168 people for four years. Activity levels went down after retirement but returned to preretirement levels three years after retirement. Atchley and Barusch hypothesize that, "after a long period of having been employed, many people apparently welcome a period of taking it easy. But after sufficient rest and relaxation, and perhaps a lengthy life assessment, they become restless and at that point begin to pursue their planned retirement activities" (Atchley & Barusch, 2004, p. 259).

The Disenchantment Phase

Some people have a very hard time adjusting to retirement. After the honeymoon is over, some retirees feel a letdown. Atchley relates this letdown to a number of factors (Atchley, 2000a, p. 121). People who are more likely to have difficulty:

- have few alternatives;
- have little money;
- have poor health;
- were over-involved in their jobs;
- are unaccustomed to running their own lives;
- experience other role losses in addition to retirement;
- leave communities where they have lived for many years.

The Reorientation Phase

During this phase individuals who have experienced the letdown pull themselves together and develop new avenues of involvement.

Retirement Routine

In this phase of retirement, the individual has a well-developed set of criteria for making choices, and they allow him to deal with life in a reasonably comfortable, orderly fashion. Life during this period is predictable and satisfying. The individual has mastered the retirement role.

The Termination Phase

Many people die during the previous phase of retirement. Some others may develop illness or disability, which transfers them from the retirement role to a "sick and disabled role" (Atchley, 2000a, p. 123). Increasing dependence usually occurs gradually, so loss of the retirement role also happens gradually. Other ways of losing the retirement role are returning to work or losing finances to the point that the individual becomes dependent on someone else.

Widowhood as a Major Role in Later Life

Like retirement, widowhood and widowerhood are other societal roles associated with later life. The death of a spouse results in an involuntary change in social roles. (For more information on loss of a spouse, see chapter 6.)

As stated in chapter 6, while the death of any family member is tragic, the death of a longtime spouse is particularly devastating. Along with grieving the loss of the individual, the spouse is dealing with the loss of the role and identity of being a spouse and part of a couple.

WIDOWS

Deborah Kestin Van Den Hoonaard analyzed 10 autobiographical accounts of widowhood, including the well-known *Widow* by Lynne Caine (Van Den Hoonaard, 2000). Hoonaard writes, "the ten authors focus on their experience as transformation, rather than one of recovery or adjustment. Their stories give us a sense of how their changing relationships and circumstances have effected that transformation by stripping them of their identity and forcing them to see themselves differently." Van Den Hoonaard calls this *identity fore-closure*, meaning that the widows no longer have the social resources to hang on to their identity. Some of the widows' comments are:

- "After Martin died, I learned that my identity had been derived from him. I did not know who I was."
- "My life was focused to his and without him, the focus flickered out like a burnt match."
- "Darling, I'm half living without you; half of me is dead."

While adjustment to the loss of a husband creates identity problems for many widows, Robert Atchley points out that "some women are glad their husbands have passed away. For example, a large percentage of elder abuse consists of long-standing spouse abuse. Not all marriages are idyllic. Not all wives love their husbands. For some wives the wife role is not central to identity. In addition, some women carry their spouse identity into widowhood. I've interviewed many women who still get satisfaction from being able to look back over their married life and see that they were good wives" (Atchley, 2004).

WIDOWERS

While many older women gain their identity from their husbands and the family that they have created together, many men also experience difficulty when they lose a wife. As mentioned in chapter 6, many men assume that they will die first and have not prepared themselves to be the survivor. Again, the loss of identity as a couple can result in identity foreclosure. Perhaps this is why men tend to remarry more often than women. Not only are there more potential spouses available for men than for women, but men also look to remarriage as a way to reframe their identities rather than adjust to being single.

At the same time, the proportion of widowers who don't remarry increases with age, so men who are widowed at advanced age are often bereft of their major caregiver as well as their main confidant and companion. For many men, their wife was their closest friend, and their social networks greatly diminish after her death.

Activities during Later Life

Role changes such as retirement and widowhood, which often occur for seniors, result in changes of activities. Some other factors that lead to change in roles:

- disability or illness
- reduced finances
- age discrimination
- a change of housing
- a move to a new location

The following story demonstrates the adjustment that is called for by the inability to maintain previous activities:

"You can't swim fourteeners," says Dr. Roger White, a retired surgeon in his 80s. Dr. White was one of the best thoracic surgeons in the country. But the arthritis in his hands forced his retirement in his mid-70s. An avid mountaineer, White decided to spend his retirement climbing Colorado's 54 peaks over 14,000 feet, or fourteeners, as they are affectionately referred to by climbers.

After climbing his 10th peak, the arthritis in White's spine put a quick and dramatic halt to this activity. White returned from his last climb in severe pain and, soon after, had surgery to fuse part of his spine. His doctors advised him to stop climbing, and, in fact, to cut back way back on all activities except for swimming.

These two events took a toll on White's sense of self, and, relegated to his home and his health club's swimming pool, he became depressed. Bored and frustrated, White started "noodling around with my computer." Soon he learned how to write software programs. He developed an automated management system for surgeons. Commercially it was very successful and started him on a new career. White's depression gradually lifted. But he still looks back longingly at his years as a surgeon and an active outdoorsman.

In contrast, the following story demonstrates the excitement that can come from experiencing new roles:

Nan is a tall, slender, and soft-spoken woman who retired from her job as a laboratory technician at age 64. She relishes being able to pace her life according to her own values and sensibilities. She spends eight hours a week in structured volunteering at a local hospice program. Her favorite activity is flower gardening, and her greenhouse room allows her to do it most of the year. She enjoys flower arranging, and weekly she takes arrangements to several seniors who live in nursing homes in her community. She genuinely enjoys their company and likes seeing them light up when they see her coming. She reports that her retirement lifestyle gives her just the right combination of solitary activity, contact with people, and sense of being of service. She is very satisfied with her retirement lifestyle.

Community Involvement during Later Life

Seniors often play major social roles in their communities. They volunteer, vote, and join clubs and other groups in large numbers. In fact, club or organizational membership is highest among seniors of all age groups (Vierck & Hodges, 2005). In addition:

- While the rate of volunteering decreases with age, seniors, among all age groups, devote the most time to volunteering.
- Seniors respond generously when asked to give money to charity.
- Religious organizations are the top membership category for seniors.
- Seniors have the highest rate of voter participation of all age groups.
- Virtually all (95 percent) retired people give money to charity when asked.

The following stories are from the Family Friends project (senior volunteers working with children who have special needs) and Senior Counselors Against Medicare Swindlers (volunteers working in their communities to help

identify deceptive health care practices, such as overbilling, overcharging, or providing unnecessary or inappropriate services). They illustrate the tremendous contribution of senior volunteers:

Dorothy, Family Friends Program:

Dorothy adds a unique perspective as a Family Friends volunteer in Dallas, Texas (Family Friends, n.d.). She is a retired military nurse who, with her husband, a military officer, has lived all over the world. Back in the '70s they were stationed in Beirut, Lebanon, where she lost both her legs as a result of a terrorist bombing attack. Once able-bodied, Dorothy understands the physical and mental challenges of learning how to become mobile again. Her hard-earned patience and understanding are what she brings to her new friend, Thomas. She coaxes him to speak— over and over, they blow bubbles and play games that help Thomas form the sounds essential to speech.

Michael T. Carroll, Operation Restore Trust of Iowa:

Michael Carroll had barely retired from his job as a machinist with Bodine Electric Company in 1999 when he became involved with Operation Restore Trust of Iowa as a community education volunteer (Senior Medicare Patrols, 2000). His eight years of military service and his long work history in construction equipped him with a kind of worldly wisdom that has allowed him to easily engage audiences eager to learn about Medicare and Medicaid waste, fraud, and abuse. What many members of his audience remember best is being scammed by Mr. Carroll. He subtly asks his all-too-trusting audiences to take out their Medicare cards for him, and most of them do so without a second thought.

He points out how easily he could take advantage of anyone who gives his or her card to him. He continues by teaching people what they can do to protect themselves and their numbers. Mr. Carroll comments, "Until I give a presentation and not one person gives me their Medicare card, my job isn't finished."

In 2003 AARP published results of their survey, *Time and Money: An In-Depth Look at 45+ Volunteers and Donors* (AARP, 2003). The study over-sampled African Americans, Asian Americans, and Hispanics and used a new definition of volunteering and giving based on adding behaviors not usually captured by traditional research. These behaviors include activities such as neighborhood cleanup projects, mowing the lawn for an elderly neighbor, a letter-writing campaign to troops in Iraq, or any other positive social behaviors that result in the betterment of one's community.

AARP's innovative approach resulted in a higher percentage of seniors as volunteers or donors than found by other research organizations that commonly gather statistics on volunteering. Eighty-six percent of people ages 58 to 69 said they had volunteered in the last 12 months, and 80 percent of those ages 70 and over said they had volunteered.

Crime and Fear of Crime

Fear of being a victim of crime is one of the greatest concerns seniors have about society. The National Council on Aging's 2000 survey of the aging experience in the United States found that 36 percent of seniors feel that fear of crime is a personal problem for them. Fear of crime equaled fear of not having enough money to live on (36 percent of respondents) and was greater than loneliness (21 percent of respondents).

When seniors are victims of crime, they usually suffer greater physical, mental, and financial injuries than other age groups. According to the Department of Justice (2000), seniors are twice as likely to suffer serious physical injury and to require hospitalization than any other age group. Furthermore, the physiological process of aging brings with it a decreasing ability to heal after injury—both physically and mentally. Thus, seniors may never fully recover from the trauma of their victimization.

Seniors who are victims of crime often know the perpetrator of the crime. In 2001, for example, 44 percent of the time that seniors were victims of violent crimes they knew the perpetrator (Vierck & Hodges, 2005). This figure is 65 percent for assault, but only 13 percent for robbery. And half of senior women who were victims of rape said they knew the rapist.

Fear of crime can result in isolation from the community. However, the reality is that crime is actually less of a threat for seniors than for younger age groups. Seniors are crime victims less often than younger people, and the rate of violence against this group is decreasing (Vierck & Hodges, 2005). For example:

- In 2001 the personal crime rate for seniors was 4 per 1,000 persons, compared to a high of more than 59 per 1,000 persons for victims ages 16 to 19. In fact, the rate for seniors was the lowest of all age groups for most major types of crime. The exception was robbery, for which the rate for people ages 50 to 64 was similar to that for the elderly.

- Following a pattern affecting all age groups, the rate of violent crime against seniors has been decreasing since the early 1990s.

- Seniors have the lowest rate (6 percent) of all age groups of injury resulting from an assault.

- In 2001 the rate (66 per 1,000) for property crimes, such as household burglary and motor vehicle theft, for senior households was less than half that for people age 50 to 64 (133 per 1,000) and one-sixth of the rate for victims age 12 to 19 (393 per 1,000).

Helping seniors overcome their fear of crime presents opportunities for you to work effectively with and build trust with senior clients. Consider sponsoring a seminar on safety for seniors in your community. Do not use this as a sales tool. This is a trust-building function. Bring in experts such as representatives from local police and fire departments or state consumer protection offices.

You can also arrange for seniors who are fearful of going out in the community to receive help from escort services (see chapter 9). Escort services are also excellent volunteer activities for you.

ELDER ABUSE

An all-too-frequent crime against seniors is elder abuse. Elder abuse is a widespread and serious problem, affecting hundreds of thousands of seniors in the United States. According to the best available estimates, between 1 million and 2 million seniors have been injured, exploited, or otherwise mistreated by someone on whom they depended for care or protection (National Research Council, 2002). For more facts on elder abuse see the sidebar below.

As reported by the National Center on Elder Abuse (NCEA), "Because it is still largely hidden under the shroud of family secrecy, elder abuse is grossly under-reported. Some experts estimate that only 1 out of 14 domestic elder abuse incidents (*excluding* incidents of self-neglect) comes to the attention of authorities" (NCEA, n.d.).

Neglect is the most common form of elder abuse (NCEA, n.d.). Other forms include physical abuse, financial exploitation, emotional abuse, sexual abuse, and abandonment. Most elder abuse victims are female, and most perpetrators are males. Adult children are the most frequent abusers of seniors. Other family members and spouses are the second most likely abusers of seniors.

The 1998 National Elder Abuse Incidence Study

- *551,011 persons, aged 60 and over, experienced abuse, neglect, or self-neglect in a one-year period.*

- *Almost four times as many new incidents of abuse, neglect, or self-neglect were not reported as those that were reported to and substantiated by adult protective services agencies.*

- *Persons ages 80 and older suffered abuse and neglect two to three times their proportion of the older population.*

- *Among known perpetrators of abuse and neglect, the perpetrator was a family member in 90 percent of cases. Two-thirds of the perpetrators were adult children or spouses.*

Here are two recent cases of elder abuse reported to the Kentucky Cabinet for Health and Family Services (n.d.):

A local bank alerted county police of possible exploitation of an elderly client, whom we will call Roy. His savings account had gone from a balance of $96,000 to zero in *six months. Roy insisted to police that he had willingly given the money to a young man who lived with him. He denied that the young man had committed any wrong-doing and refused to press charges. Further investigation by police revealed that the young man had forged checks for $24,000.*

Police asked the Cabinet to assess Roy's physical and mental state. Police accompanied a state social worker and nurse consultant to the home, since the alleged perpetrator still lived there. Roy was found to be mentally alert, fully oriented, and free of acute mental or physical distress. He was more worried about keeping the alleged perpetrator out of jail than about losing his money. Roy said he had helped raise the young man and would go to any length to protect him from going to jail. He acknowledged that the young man had stolen some checks and forged his name, but he said he had freely given the young man most of his savings.

With no money left from his life savings, Roy was forced to live on his Social Security check. For at least two months, he did not take his prescribed medications because he could no longer afford to buy them. Although Roy refused to press charges, police arrested the alleged perpetrator and charged him with check forgery.

. . .

An elderly woman, whom we will call Lynn, lived alone and was essentially bedridden. Her son, who lived next door, was her designated caregiver. He and his wife worked outside the home during the day. A social worker visited the home and found Lynn home alone, in a hospital bed, totally dependent on others for care. In an emergency, she could not have left the house unaided. Lynn was basically alert, but somewhat confused. Her son had left water and food at her bedside within her reach. Home health nurses visited three times weekly, but Lynn was alone in the home for extended intervals. During the evenings, family members were in and out of the house to meet Lynn's needs. At night, a grandson slept in the house and was available to provide care until he left for an 11 a.m. class.

Lynn was incontinent and had a bedsore on her buttocks. She could feed herself but needed much encouragement to eat or drink. She had suffered dehydration in the past and was underweight. The family thought they were doing the right thing.

Risk factors for elder abuse include:

- social isolation
- dementia in the victim
- mental illness of the abuser
- alcohol or drug abuse
- depression on the part of the abuser
- mutual dependence between the abuser and the victim

As a CSA it is important to consider your practices and obligations toward seniors if you notice signs of elder abuse or criminal intent. All 50 states have elder abuse prevention laws, and you should be familiar with the regulations in your state.

You should never infringe on the privacy of clients. At the same time it is important to try to protect seniors if you notice anything amiss. One key option is to report signs of abuse to local authorities. You can do this anonymously.

Until the great mass of the people shall be filled with the sense of responsibility for each other's welfare, social justice can never be attained.

Helen Keller

Social Policy and Aging

Social policy refers to the actions of governments in making decisions and allocations for social programs such as Social Security, Medicare, and Older Americans Act programs. Elections are often won and lost on social policy issues.

You should be aware of social policies that affect your senior clients. For example, as of this writing, there is controversy over Medicare's drug discount program—a social policy that directly affects seniors. Research by the Kaiser Family Foundation found that the drug discount card can save seniors money, but similar discounts can be found outside the program (Kaiser Family Foundation, 2004). (Studies have also concluded that drug companies raised prices in anticipation of the Medicare changes, which neutralized potential savings to consumers.) In addition, the policy offers "excessive choice," making a decision about whether to purchase a card a time-consuming research activity, which is daunting for most seniors.

Early in the twentieth century, Americans learned to think of old age in a new way. That stage of life began to be seen as a problem to be solved by the intervention of society.

Fischer, 1978 (p. 157)

SOCIAL POLICIES BENEFITING SENIORS SINCE 1900

Beginning early in the last century social policies regarding seniors concentrated on their economic situation. This resulted in a burgeoning of organizations and government programs whose sole purpose was to pull seniors out of poverty, advocate for them, and assist in passing a number of government programs to protect them.

The sidebar on the facing page provides some of the highlights of the social policy and aging movement from the turn of the century to 1965. These events reflect a momentum in which programs, services, and advocacy for the elderly became dominant forces in American life.

Highlights of the social policy and aging movement from the turn of the century to 1965—the landmark year in which Medicare, Medicaid, and the Older Americans Act were passed:

- *The first public commission on aging in the United States was established in Massachusetts in 1909.*

- *The science of geriatrics was born in 1909, and the first textbook in the field was published in 1914.*

- *The first old age pension system was created by Arizona in 1915.*

- *Beginning early in the 1920s, senior interest groups were formed to provide platforms for lobbying.*

- *Social Security was established in 1935. (In fact, the United States created its federal retirement system late in the game; most European countries had enacted old age insurance decades before America did.)*

- *The first senior center was established in 1943.*

- *The Gerontological Society was established in 1945.*

- *The Friendly Visitors Program was founded in 1946.*

- *The National Retired Teacher's Association was founded in 1947.*

- *The National Council on the Aging was founded in 1950.*

- *The American Association of Retired Persons was founded in 1958, growing out of the National Retired Teacher's Organization.*

- *In 1961, the first White House Conference on Aging was convened, the Senate Special Committee on Aging was formed, and the National Council of Senior Citizens was founded.*

- *The political force behind the events listed above resulted in passage of Medicare, Medicaid, the Older Americans Act, Foster Grandparent Program, Service Corps of Retired Engineers, and Green Thumb, all in 1965.*

Now, in the 2000s in the United States, there is a vast network of agencies on aging that advocate on behalf of and coordinate programs for the elderly. Funded through the Older Americans Act, the network includes 57 state agencies on aging, 660 area agencies on aging, and more than 27,000 service providers. In addition, hundreds of national and local interest groups advocate for the elderly. AARP alone has a membership of more than 33 million people. Perhaps most important, Medicare and Social Security touch the lives of nearly every American, and the politics behind the two programs are at the forefront of every politician's mind.

Social Policy and Seniors: The Future

The Congressional Budget Office estimates that in 2000 spending on the elderly accounted for more than one-third of the federal budget, up from about 22 percent in 1971 and 29 percent in 1990 (Congressional Budget Office, 2000).

The portion of the federal budget spent on the elderly is projected to climb to nearly 43 percent by 2010. Under the laws in place in 2000, that share is expected to grow even faster after 2010 as the baby boomers retire and the population aged 65 and older expands by nearly three-quarters over the 2010–2030 period. Spending for Social Security and Medicare consistently accounts for about four-fifths of that total. Given these fiscal problems, social policies affecting seniors in the future are likely to focus on how to provide such benefits for the aging baby boomers and at the same time balance the federal budget.

Aging and Society: Summary

Now that you have a greater understanding of the interaction between society and the individual, it is important that you apply this insight to your work with seniors. For example, you should not impose on your clients your ideas of what activities are appropriate for them; nor should you assume that, if a senior is slower at a task than a younger person would be, it is not an appropriate task.

As a CSA, it is important that you examine your attitudes toward seniors. And you should understand what your clients' attitudes are toward their own aging and that of others. What are their views on their life course? What is their preferred lifestyle? What values do they wish to pursue? Has their experience taught them to be frugal? Are they so afraid of being a victim of crime that they don't leave the house? Do you see any hints of elder abuse? Have any of your clients been victims of age discrimination? If so, what recourse do they have?

The answers to questions such as these will tell you a great deal about the experience of your senior clients.

References

AARP. (n.d.). *Age discrimination at work*. Retrieved May 6, 2004, from http://www.aarp.org/money/careers/jobloss/Articles/a2004-04-28-agediscrimination.html

AARP. (2003). *Time and Money: An In-Depth Look at 45+ Volunteers and Donors*. Retrieved May 6, 2004, from: http://research.aarp.org/general/multic_2003.pdf.

Atchley, R. C. (1999). *Continuity and adaptation in aging*. Baltimore, MD: John Hopkins University Press.

Atchley, R. C (2000a). *Social forces and aging: An introduction to social gerontology* (9th ed.). Stamford, CT: Wadsworth Publishing.

Atchley, R. C. (2000b). Continuity therapy in daily living. In J. F. Gubrium, & J. A. Holstein, (Eds.), *Aging and everyday life*. Malden, MA: Blackwell.

Atchley, R. C. (2004, August 8). Personal communication.

Atchley, R. C., & Barusch, A. S. (2004). *Social forces and aging: An introduction to social gerontology* (10th ed.). Stamford, CT: Wadsworth Publishing.

Cole, T. R. (1992). *The journey of life*. New York: Cambridge University Press.

Congressional Budget Office. (2000). *Federal spending on the elderly and children*. Retrieved July 30, 2004, from http://www.cbo.gov/ftpdocs/23xx/doc2300/fsec.pdf

Department of Justice. (2000, May). *First response to victims of crime, chap. II*. Retrieved July 6, 2004, from http://www.ojp.usdoj.gov/ovc/publications/infores/firstrep/eldvic.html

Equal Employment Opportunity Commission (EEOC). (2004, January 6). *Age discrimination*. Retrieved May 6, 2004, from http://www.eeoc.gov/types/age.html

Erickson, E. H. (1963). Childhood and Society. New York: Macmillan.

Family Friends. (n.d.). *Who we are*. Retrieved July 30, 2004, from http://www.family-friends.org/who.htm

Fischer, D. H. (1978). *Growing old in America*. New York: Oxford University Press.

Fullerton, H. N. (1999, November). Labor force projections to 2008: Steady growth and changing composition. *Monthly Labor Review, 22*.

Gubrium, J. F., & Holstein, J. A. (2000). *Aging and everyday life*. Malden, MA: Blackwell.

Harris, D. (2003, July–August). Simple justice. *AARP: The Magazine*. Retrieved August 22, 2004, from http://www.aarpmagazine.org/Articles/a2003-05-21-mag-justice age.html

Kaiser Family Foundation. (2004, July). *Medicare drug discount cards: A work in progress*. Retrieved July 30, 2004 from http://www.kff.org/medicare/7136.cfm

Kentucky Cabinet for Health and Family Services. (n.d.). *Case histories of elder abuse and neglect*. Retrieved May 6, 2004, from http://cfc.ky.gov/elderabuse/docs/case_histories_all.pdf

Levy, B., Wei, J. Y., & Hausdorff, J. M. (2000). Reducing cardiovascular stress with positive self-stereotypes of aging. *Journal of Gerontology: Psychological Sciences: 55*, 205–213.

Mistry. R. (2002). *Family matters*. New York: Random House.

NCEA (National Center on Elder Abuse). (n.d.). Trends in elder abuse in domestic settings. *Elder abuse information series no. 2*. Retrieved May 6, 2004, from http://www.elderabusecenter.org/pdf/basics/fact2.pdf

The National Council on Aging. (2000). National survey on myths and realities of aging. Retrieved August 22, 2004, from http://www.ncoa.org/content.cfm?sectionID=93

National Research Council. (2002). *Elder mistreatment: Abuse, neglect, and exploitation in an aging America*. Washington, DC: The National Academies Press.

Palmore, E. B. (1998). Ageism. In D. E. Redburn & R. P. McNamera (Eds.) *Social gerontology*. Westport, CT: Auburn House.

Quadagno, J. (2002). *Aging and the life course: An introduction to social gerontology* (2nd ed.). New York: McGraw-Hill.

Schneider, E. L. (1983). Natural death and the compression of morbidity: Another view. *New England Journal of Medicine, 309,* 854–856.

Senior Medicare Patrols. (2000, September 21). Outstanding senior volunteer awards ceremony, National Health Care Fraud and Abuse Control Program conference. Retrieved July 30, 2004, from http://www.aoa.gov/smp/media/aoa_awards _print.asp

Van Den Hoonaard, D. K. (2000). Identity foreclosure: Women's experience of widowhood as expressed in autobiographical accounts. In J. F. Gubrium & J. A. Holstein (Eds.), *Aging and everyday life.* Malden, MA: Blackwell.

Vierck, E. (1988). *Older is better.* Washington, DC: Acropolis Books.

Vierck, E., & Hodges, K. (2003). *Aging: Demographics, health, and health services.* Westport, CT: Greenwood.

Vierck, E., & Hodges, K. (2005). *Aging: Lifestyles, work, and money.* Westport, CT: Greenwood.

Resources

Suggested Reading

Aging and the Life Course, by J. Quadagno. McGraw-Hill, 2002.

Social Forces and Aging: An Introduction to Social Gerontology, 10th ed., by R. C. Atchley & A. S. Barusch. Wadsworth Publishing, 2003.

Services

The National Center on Elder Abuse (NCEA), http://www.elderabusecenter.org, email ncea@nasua.org, 1201 15th St. NW, Ste. 350, Washington, DC 20005, 202-898-2586, fax 202-898-2583. Funded by the United States Administration on Aging, NCEA is a gateway to resources on elder abuse, neglect, and exploitation. Anyone who suspects elder abuse or is concerned about the well-being or safety of an older person should call their state's abuse hotline (listed on NCEA's Web site).

Equal Employment Opportunity Commission (EEOC), http://www.eeoc.gov, 1801 L St. NW, Washington, DC 20507, 800-669-4000, TTY 800-669-6820. Age discrimination charges may be filed with the EEOC by mail or in person at the nearest EEOC office.

Chapter 3

Physiological Changes of Aging

Richard, formerly a research and development officer with a large manufacturing company, is approaching his 74th birthday. Retired for nine years, he enjoys working in his large yard and caring for his flowers. However, some changes in the vertebrae of his lower back have made this increasingly difficult the past three years. Because gardening is such an enjoyable part of his life, he has designed a way to continue with this activity despite the back pain that accompanies it. He works in small time segments, uses equipment that reduces the amount of kneeling and bending he must do, keeps his back straight, and takes frequent breaks. These strategies, combined with carefully planned medication regimens and regular exercise routines, allow him to continue with the hobby that is so important to him.

. . .

Gretchen is a 63-year-old widow with two grown children. She lives alone in a northeastern city, where she is a secretary at a large university. Although Gretchen has osteoporosis, she still keeps very active. She rides her bike daily, climbs rocks, and takes frequent walks along the beach. She is aware that osteoporosis places her at greater risk of a fracture if she should be injured during any of these activities. But that is a risk she is prepared to take rather than give up the outdoor exercise she cherishes.

Introduction

As Richard and Gretchen can testify, our bodies change as we grow older. Mention the word *aging*, and listeners will likely develop images of gray hair, wrinkled skin, stooped posture, and frailty. They may even think of diseases commonly associated with aging, such as stroke, heart attack, and cancer. Further, they may identify a point in life—such as at 60 years of age—when they think this occurs.

But aging is much more complex than that. The outward appearances frequently associated with aging are just that—the manifestations or consequences of much more complex processes going on inside the body. Researchers have developed a number of theories about why the body ages, but there are many unanswered questions.

Just as researchers don't agree about *why* we age, they are not in agreement about *when* we age. Some theorize that aging begins when we are born; others believe that the process doesn't begin until the body has reached maturity. There is also disagreement about whether aging and disease are synonymous or not.

These differing viewpoints illustrate one thing—that while there have been great strides in developing knowledge about the whole aging process in recent years, there is much more to be learned. Research continues on why we age, when it begins, what affects aging, and what, if anything, we can do to slow down or even reverse the process.

In this chapter, you will be introduced to the current theories of physiological aging and what is believed to affect the aging process. Consequences of physiological aging will be discussed along with lifestyle practices that effectively reduce or overcome those consequences.

It is important for you to have awareness of the physiological aspects of aging so as to better understand what your elderly clients are experiencing. However, you must also recognize that most persons age so gradually that many of the physiological manifestations are noticeable only over a period of time. This gradual change gives your clients opportunity to adapt to and assimilate these changes into daily living. Knowledge of this process allows you to offer the necessary support and encouragement to clients, and to individualize services as necessary.

DEFINITION OF TERMS

In order to understand the information in this chapter, it is important to be familiar with several concepts.

Life Expectancy

Life expectancy refers to the length of time that one can expect to live. It is calculated by tracking the number of births and deaths that occur each year, along with how old each person was at death. By combining this data with census data on how many people are alive at each age, scientists can determine for people of every age the risk of dying and the probability of living another year (Olshansky & Carnes, 2001).

Life expectancy figures have shown dramatic changes over the past century. As mentioned in chapter 1, a person born in 1900 could expect to live to age 47, but by 1999 a male's life expectancy was 73 years compared to 79 years for a female. These dramatic changes are attributed to environmental factors such as better sanitation, discovery of antibiotics, and improved medical care. As research uncovers new and improved treatments for the chronic diseases, cancer and heart disease for example, some scientists believe that life expectancy may increase to 100 years or more in this century.

Life Span

Life span is the maximum length of life biologically possible for a given species, assuming an event such as disease or accident doesn't occur. In humans this is believed to be about 100 to 122 years and is based on comparisons made across species. The observations of species—ranging from fruit flies to turtles—shows that the oldest age of any species is approximately six times the length of time from birth to maturity, which in humans is between 18 and 20 years. Whether the life span can increase much beyond 120 years is a subject of much debate among scientists. Life span increases when there is a slowed rate of aging, delayed onset of age changes, or survival to sexual maturity of physiologically capable individuals able to sustain good health. However since these increases occur so slowly it may take thousands of years to recognize that any change in life span has happened (Hayflick, 1996).

The longest documented life on record is that of Jeanne Calmet of France, who died in August 1997 at the age of 122 years, 5 months, and 14 days. Although there are reports of persons in Ecuador, Kashmir, and the Caucasus Mountains living longer than that, it has not been possible to verify those reports due to lack of records.

Calmet outlived her husband, her daughter, her grandson, and even her lawyer, who made an unusual agreement with her. Believing that Calmet, who was 90 years old at the time, probably had few years left, the lawyer, age 47, offered to buy her apartment in exchange for giving her a lifetime monthly pension. Soon after her 120th birthday the lawyer himself died at age 77, but not until the pension payments he'd made to her equaled more than three times the worth of her apartment.

Senescence

Senescence is a term used to more precisely describe the process of aging and refers to the progressive deterioration of many bodily functions over a period of time. The word *aging* generally refers to changes that occur over time. But not all of those changes, gray hair and wrinkles for example, are harmful, so scientists prefer to use the word *senescence* instead because it better describes the loss of function, decreased fertility, and increased risk of mortality that accompanies aging changes in the body.

There is great variability in how senescence presents itself from person to person in terms of both rate and progression; the reasons for this variability are unknown. But what is known is that it eventually affects every major organ of the body. How it affects some of the major systems will be discussed later in this chapter.

Why We Age

The question of why we physiologically age has intrigued scientists for many years. A number of theories have been developed and advanced over time—some have been discarded and others have survived to varying degrees. Current research supports several theories. It is quite likely that there is not just one theory that explains why we biologically age, but rather that our aging is due to a complex interweaving of many processes.

The theories explaining our physiological changes as we get older fall generally into two groups. (Information about these theories is summarized from a National Institutes of Health publication, *Aging Under the Microscope* [NIH, 2002]). One group is that of the *programmed* ideas, namely that aging follows a biological timetable, possibly a continuation of the same timetable that controls childhood growth and development. The other group comprises *error* theories—those ideas that say physiological aging is due to damage to our body systems causing things to go wrong.

PROGRAMMED THEORIES

The major programmed theories are programmed longevity, the endocrine theory, Hayflick's Limit, and the immunological theories.

Programmed Longevity

According to this theory, aging is the result of certain genes switching on and off in a sequential manner throughout a person's lifetime. Programmed longevity theory presumes that there is a biological clock controlled by a person's genes. Therefore one's longevity and senescence follow a pattern determined by the genetic structure.

Much of the research studying genes has been done with roundworms, fruit flies, and mice, easy to study because their life spans are shorter than those of humans. It is believed, based on these studies, that some genes manufacture proteins that limit life span. But when these genes are tampered with or mutated, they produce either defective proteins or no proteins at all, which actually results in greater longevity. For example, the mutation of one gene, affectionately named the I'm Not Dead Yet gene, doubled the life span of the fruit fly so that by the time 80 to 90 percent of normal flies were dead, those with the mutated genes were still vigorous and reproducing.

The genes that scientists have isolated so far are likely to be only a small percentage of those having an impact on longevity and aging. Further research is needed to determine whether the discoveries about genes of the fruit fly and other species can be applied to humans. Other questions must answer what exactly the genes do, and how and when they are activated.

Endocrine Theory

The endocrine theory is based on the idea that there is a biological clock that acts through hormones to control the rate of aging. Hormones are chemical messengers in the body that move throughout the bloodstream, and attach themselves to and unlock receptors located on the cells in order to carry out their particular action.

Individually and collectively these hormones fulfill numerous functions. While each has a primary action, it appears that the hormones support each other in carrying out their roles. The production and circulating levels of many hormones decline with age, and this has led many to assume that restoring the level of these circulating hormones to levels in young people would be an anti-aging strategy. However, it may be beneficial to the older organism to have these levels decline. Examples of hormones include estrogens, growth hormone, melatonin, testosterone, and DHEA.

- *Estrogens* are sex hormones primarily found in women, but also in small amounts in men. These hormones have many roles, one of which is to slow thinning of bone as one ages, but they also may help prevent frailty and disability.
- *Growth hormone* is a hormone that promotes growth. Growth is the result of the complex interaction of several hormones and growth factors.
- *Melatonin* appears to play a part in regulating seasonal changes in the body and assists with sleep. Some believe it can slow or reverse aging, but many questions remain.
- *Testosterone* is a hormone primarily found in men, but women also have small amounts. Although production peaks in early adulthood, most men even into older age still produce amounts within normal limits. Studies are now under way to determine whether supplementation can prevent frailty, sharpen memory, or help maintain strong muscles and bones.
- *DHEA* is produced in the adrenal glands. Like testosterone, DHEA production peaks in the mid-20s and then gradually declines. It influences other hormones, including testosterone and estrogen, but how it affects the aging process is still not understood. Research is currently under way to study its effects on aging, muscles, and the immune system.

Hayflick's Limit

Leonard Hayflick, a prominent researcher in the 1960s, discovered that fibroblast cells isolated from human skin can reproduce themselves only about 50 times, at which point they stop dividing and enter a state referred to as *cell senescence*. This *Hayflick Limit* thus implies that the human body may actually be designed to wear out.

In the early 1990s, this discovery led to yet another important finding. At the ends of each chromosome are structures called *telomeres* (from the Greek words meaning *end body*). Telomeres protect the ends of the chromosome, but each time the DNA in the chromosome is replicated, the telomeres at each end get a little shorter. Eventually, after about 50 doublings, the telomeres become so short that the DNA is no longer able to be replicated, so cell division stops.

Thus, one of the most interesting areas of research in gerontology today is how to retain or restore the length of telomeres so that cells will continue to reproduce beyond the Hayflick Limit. However, this does not explain why nondividing cells, such as brain cells, age.

Interestingly, certain cells in the human body, such as germ cells, stem cells, and cancer cells, have telomeres that do not shorten as they reproduce. For instance, cancer cells produce an enzyme called telomerase. This enzyme allows the telomeres on cancerous cells to regrow sufficiently to enable the cancer cell to thrive for as long as the host, or body, is alive. Telomere research could potentially yield numerous advances, such as possible cures for both cancer and HIV/AIDS, as well as slowing the human aging process (Fossel,

1996). The biggest hurdle to overcome in this research is how to selectively maintain telomere lengths in some, but not all, tissue.

Immunological Theories

The immune system is the elaborate defense system that protects our bodies from infection, fungi, parasites and viruses, and other toxins. It is comprised of organs, substances, and cells stationed throughout the body that are designed to recognize intruders not normally a part of the body. It then mobilizes the body's defenses—antibodies—to fight against these intruders.

The system is able to distinguish "non-self" tissue from "self" tissue—those elements normally present in the body—because the molecules of "self" carry markers that the system recognizes. This ability to distinguish "self" from "non-self" prevents the immune system from attacking normal tissue.

As one ages, it is believed there is a programmed decline in the system's ability to function. As a result the body is less able to fight off threats from the "non-self" intruders, resulting in disease and death. Additionally, in a process referred to as *autoimmune*, the system may produce antibodies that destroy normal "self" tissue. The autoimmune action is believed to be a factor in development of some aging-related diseases.

ERROR THEORIES

Theories that are part of the error system of biological aging include that of wear and tear, rate of living, crosslinking, free radicals, and somatic DNA damage. These theories presume that aging is not due to programming, but to random events that cause damage.

Wear and Tear Theory

In this early theory of aging, the belief is that years of damage to cells, tissues, and organs from toxins, radiation, ultraviolet light, and other stressors repeatedly harm DNA in the genes. Although the body has a remarkable ability to repair itself, many repairs are incomplete or inaccurate, leading to progressive accumulation of damage. This results in eventually killing tissues and organs—and finally the entire body.

Rate of Living Theory

"Live fast, die young" is sometimes used to describe this theory. It is based on an ancient belief that the body has a finite amount of some substance that, when used up, causes us to age and die. For example, we might be allocated a certain number of breaths or even a definite number of heartbeats. The argument against this is that it is too simplistic and doesn't explain why some people live much longer than others.

Many scientists believe that rate of living involves the rate of oxygen metabolism, not finite numbers of other factors, and that perhaps some species die sooner because they have a faster rate of metabolism. Other studies are researching the relationship of total weight of body organs to increased oxygen metabolism. This has led to testing how caloric restriction and reduction of total organ weight could slow metabolism and aging and lead to longer life.

Investigators have found that rats and mice fed a nutritionally balanced diet with 30 percent fewer calories live up to 40 percent longer, appear to be more resistant to age-related diseases, and demonstrate a delay of usual age-related degeneration of almost all their physiological systems. These researchers are unclear about why this happens but speculate that there is reduced oxidative damage to the cells, the immune system functions at a more youthful level, and the cells more effectively retain their capacity to proliferate (NIH, 2002).

Crosslinking Theory

As we age, proteins, DNA, and other structural molecules develop inappropriate and excessive attachments between each other, similar to the rungs of a ladder. These excessive attachments, or *crosslinks*, lead to decreased mobility and elasticity of these structures. Effects are more easily seen in the skin where protein crosslinks lead to skin wrinkling and less pliability. Crosslinked proteins in the eye lens lead to cataracts, in artery walls cause arteriosclerosis, in rib cartilage create less flexibility, and in kidneys are responsible for decreased kidney function.

While the protein crosslinks in organs such as the skin can be identified based on experimental evidence, the crosslinks occurring in the DNA are not as easily observed or substantiated, and instead are more speculative. Consequently it is believed that crosslinking as a biochemical reason for aging is one of many explanations for aging, but not the most important one. (Hayflick, 1996).

Free Radical Theory

Oxygen is metabolized in our cells to provide energy for the body. During the metabolism process toxic byproducts, called *free radicals*, are released. Natural substances—for example, antioxidants—absorb and neutralize the toxic radicals so they can't harm the body. However, some radicals manage to escape capture by the antioxidants and harm the cells anyway. According to the free radical theory, accumulated damage caused by oxygen free radicals causes the cells and, eventually, the organs to stop functioning.

Scientists who support this theory believe that the free radicals cause DNA damage, protein crosslinking, and formation of age pigments. They point to studies showing the effects of antioxidants in slowing the aging process in animals. Other scientists argue that slowed aging happens because antioxidants suppress the animals' appetites and lead to calorie restriction.

Somatic DNA Damage Theory

This theory is based on the belief that changes or mutations of our gene structure occurring in egg or germ cells will be passed on to future generations, but the mutations that occur in other cells of the body will affect only that particular individual instead. While most of those mutations will be either corrected or eliminated, others will not and will go on to cause malfunction and death of the cells.

Those who argue against this theory say that shorter life spans should result from inbreeding of animals with mutations and longer life spans of inbred animals without the mutations. But in reality, any inbreeding results in shorter life spans.

How Do Aging and Disease Differ?

From the discussion of the theories of biological aging presented above, we learn that there are changes occurring in our bodies as we get older. Some "normal" changes—such as decreased muscle strength or stamina, hearing loss, or lessened immune response, to name a few—may be visible and apparent, while others are not so noticeable. But the changes that accompany the aging process are not the same as disease or sickness. Aging is a predictable process that occurs in all of us over time, while a disease is an abnormal process not present in everyone. One theorist argues that to distinguish it from disease, a normal aging change must meet three criteria: it is universal, it comes gradually from within the body, and it has a negative effect on body functioning (Atchley & Barusch, 2004).

However, the presence of these changes in organs and cells from the normal aging process makes us more vulnerable to becoming ill and suffering age-related diseases. We may suffer a stroke because of changes in blood vessels as we age. Fractures occur more easily because of loss of bone mass following menopause. With declines in our immune system, we may not fight off an infection as quickly or easily. Our immune system may even malfunction, mistake our own cells as the invaders, and lead a fight against them, resulting in an autoimmune disorder.

Hayflick argues that while it is important to distinguish between normal aging changes and disease, it is not always easy. Sometimes, in fact, it is impossible to do for several reasons. For example, protein changes in the lens of the eye result in cataract formation, while the same protein changes elsewhere in the body cause no discomfort.

Although scientists can detect the differences between aging and disease in the higher levels of cells, tissues, and organs, they really don't know the differences between an aging cell and a diseased cell at the molecular level. But they do believe that the physiological losses characterizing aging are universal in all older members of a species, while changes attributable to disease are found only in some of the species (Hayflick, 1996).

What Factors Affect Aging and Longevity?

Scientists don't agree on the degree of influence that genetics, environment, and lifestyle each have on our aging and, ultimately, our life spans. However, most believe that all three factors likely play roles in determining whether someone will lead a long and healthy life.

Research on theories of biological aging appears to demonstrate that genetics plays a strong role. Madame Calmet of France could give some credit for her longevity to her genes. She had numerous ancestors who had lived long lives and had several descendents who did the same. Studies of twins have found that the life spans of fraternal (nonidentical) twins vary more than that of identical ones.

Dr. Thomas Perls and his colleagues at Boston University Medical School have been studying centenarians since 1994 to determine why they live to an old age, much of it in excellent health. Approximately 1,000 subjects are enrolled in their New England Centenarian Study, the largest genetic study of centenarians in the world. The study looks not only at the centenarians, but also their siblings, children, and some control subjects. Knowledge gained from the study will help others understand how to age well for a long life span.

Although the centenarians differ from each other in such characteristics as education, socioeconomic status, religion, ethnicity, dietary habits, and exercise, they do share a number of other characteristics. It has been found that at least 50 percent of the centenarians have first-degree relatives or grandparents that also lived to an old age. Many of the subjects have siblings achieving advanced years. Other common characteristics include:

- a rarity of significant obesity
- rare history of smoking
- low score of neuroticism in personality testing
- high functioning (90 percent of the centenarians retained high functioning to an average of 92 years; 75 percent had high functioning until age 95)
- bearing children after age 35, and even after age 40—a woman bearing a child beyond age 40 had four times the chances of living to age 100 compared to one who gave birth before age 40, a finding that likely indicates that the reproductive system is aging well
- centenarians' children aged 65 to 82 years showed significantly lower rates of age-related diseases, including such conditions as high blood pressure, diabetes, and heart disease, as well as lowered susceptibility to stress (Boston University, 2002).

Researchers stress the difficulty of separating the purely genetic influence on aging and health from environmental and lifestyle influences. Heredity plays a strong role in the development of some diseases—Huntington's disease, certain forms of cancer, or familial high cholesterol syndromes, for example. Other families show strong histories of hypertension, diabetes, hypothyroidism, heart disease, or arthritis. Some researchers say genetics plays a part in promoting a disease, but this is probably only half the story. Just because family members share similar characteristics may not mean that genetics is responsible for the characteristics. Rather the habits they share— diet, exercise, stress management, where they live—can make a difference, and, in fact, may be more important than heredity (Rowe & Kahn, 1998).

The MacArthur Research Program on Successful Aging studied both identical and fraternal twins raised apart to determine the importance of heredity and environment on their mental and physiological changes as they aged. They found that only about 30 percent of physiological aging was attributable to genetics. Furthermore, when they studied Swedish twins who were older than 80, they found that only about half the changes in mental functioning were related to genetics.

Researchers with the MacArthur Program believe that the role of genetics becomes less important as we get older. They found that the likelihood of being fat, having hypertension, having high cholesterol and triglyceride levels, and having decreased lung function was largely not inherited but instead was due to lifestyle and environmental factors. They concluded that greater importance should be attached to where and how we live in determining age-related changes in organ function throughout the body (Rowe & Kahn, 1998).

The role of regular physiological activity in promoting healthy aging is supported by numerous studies. The NIA stresses that it may be the most important factor, and that the more one exercises in later life, the better off one will be. Not only can regular, sustained exercise help prevent or delay disease and disability, but it may actually improve these conditions once they have developed. One study showed that subjects ages 80 and older discarded their walkers and adopted canes instead after 10 weeks of simple muscle-building exercises (NIH, 2002).

Endurance, strength, balance, and stretching exercises all can improve overall health. Brisk walking has an effect on the heart, lungs, and circulatory system by enhancing stamina. Muscles are improved by doing strength exercises. Balance exercises help prevent falls. Stretching keeps the body limber (NIH, 2002).

The MacArthur Study looked beyond exercise as a factor in maintaining physiological functioning. They utilized a variety of tests and measurements with a group of more than 4,000 older persons from Massachusetts and North Carolina to identify "successful agers" in terms of their mental and physiological functions. Some of the factors that contributed to the subjects' successful aging were predictable—younger age group, higher income, high lung function, male, normal weight, and moderate activity—but other findings were quite surprising. They found that those who had higher mental function were more likely to retain more physiological function than others. Most surprising was that the frequency of emotional support strongly predicted enhanced physiological functioning over a period of time. Based on these findings, they believe that having someone around who can provide cheering up and "talk therapy" can actually promote better physiological status (Rowe & Kahn, 1998).

The National Institute on Aging continues to study the effects of caloric restriction on longevity in monkeys. Both rhesus and squirrel monkeys in their study consume nutritionally sound diets, but are fed 30 percent less food. (A control group gets as much food as desired.) As expected, the restricted monkeys' maturation as measured by onset of puberty and skeletal development has been delayed by approximately one year. Now the monkeys, moving into midlife and smaller in size, are just as active as the controls. Early findings point to the possibility of less heart disease and cancer in the restricted monkeys, although more years of observation are needed (NIH, 2002).

We can't ignore the environmental factors affecting longevity and aging. In earlier decades, individuals with shorter life expectancies faced epidemics of influenza, polio, diphtheria, and other infectious diseases for which there were no antibiotics. Overcrowding, poor water supply, hazardous working conditions, malnutrition, and contaminants in the environment took their toll. But many of these environmental hazards have been overcome for a substantial segment of the population. So while some may still assume that genes play the dominant role, new research suggests that environment and lifestyle may in fact be more important in terms of risk factors associated with aging and longevity (Rowe & Kahn, 1998).

Calculating Your Expected Longevity

Tools are available for those who wish to estimate their longevity based on genetics, lifestyle, and environment. One tool, developed by researchers at the New England Centenarian Study, is built on the assumption that we are born with a set of genes that allow us to live to age 85 or more. However, positive behaviors can add as much as 10 more quality years, while a lack of preventive behaviors will subtract a substantial number of years. Questions in the longevity calculator address issues of personal data, lifestyle and environmental factors, nutrition and exercise, medical check-ups, and family history. The calculator has been published by the Alliance for Aging Research and is available online at http://www.agingresearch.org.

What Is Your True Age?

Researchers have posed this interesting question as they attempt to find a correlation between our physiological aging and our chronological age. So far, scientists know that age in years and physiological aging aren't necessarily the same. It is obvious in looking at a group of persons of roughly the same chronological age that their physiological characteristics may be very different.

By collecting data on various organ functions, researchers hope to establish markers of physiological aging. They believe these markers would be more precise indicators of aging than chronological age and would make it easier to study normal aging, diseases, and interventions. So far their efforts to identify markers have been unsuccessful (NIH, 2002).

In pondering the question of how old we are, researcher Hayflick raises some interesting thoughts. One's exact age is difficult to determine if we base it on the age of our body cells, he theorizes. Since some cells turn over at short intervals but others live longer, our exact age is elusive. For example, many of the cells of the skin and the digestive tract, as well as red and white blood cells, divide constantly. That makes these parts of our bodies potentially different each day and perpetually newborn. Other cells are replaced in 7- to 10-year cycles, so those parts of our bodies are always less than 10 years old.

Our molecules, whether they have turned over or not, at their very basic level, are composed of atoms. Most of these atoms have been around since our planet was formed, and since we are simply unique rearrangements of this immortal material, parts of our bodies may be many years old (Hayflick, 1996).

mal Aging

Important to the understanding of normal aging is the concept of *homeostasis*. Homeostasis means that the body is able physiologically to maintain a static, or constant, state in its internal environment. All organs of the body perform functions that help to maintain constancy. For example, the lungs provide oxygen needed by the cells, while the nervous system and hormones regulate the tissues in response to changes in the body's internal environment.

The ability of the body systems to maintain constancy decreases over time. Consequently, dysfunction of various systems is more likely and the potential for death increases. Homeostasis changes can affect body temperature, immune system efficiency, energy levels, metabolism, and sleep patterns. As we age, adaptation—rather than maladaptation—is necessary to have satisfaction in life.

Even so, determining what constitutes normal aging in humans is especially challenging for several reasons. Humans live longer than other species that have been studied so it takes longer to make the observations. Ideally a study should follow the same group of subjects over a long period of time.

One ambitious project is doing just that. The Baltimore Longitudinal Study of Aging (BLSA), begun in 1958 and still continuing, is the oldest continuing scientific study of human aging in America (NIH, 2004). The project attempts to define which changes are parts of normal aging and which are parts of disease process.

More than 1,000 persons from throughout the country are participating in the study. The group includes both men and women, ranging across the age spectrum from people in their 20s to people in their 90s. Every two years the subjects are tested and measured to determine what may have changed in their vital organs, immune system, metabolism, hormone levels, mental skills, and other areas.

To date two conclusions have been reached—that it is possible to differentiate normal aging from disease and that there is no single chronological timetable of human aging. Different rates of aging have been observed—one rate among individuals and another within organs in the same individual. These findings support the belief that not only genetics, but also lifestyle and disease processes affect the rate at which one ages.

Other interesting findings, although not conclusive, have surfaced as well. For example, there appears to be a difference in the immune systems between men and women. The response to bacteria and other antigens is better in older women than it is in older men. However, a woman's immune system doesn't "remember" antigens as well and has a limited number of tetanus antibodies. These observations suggest that prevailing immunization guidelines for women need reevaluation.

Carrying out a study over the long term allows scientists an opportunity to see if there are changes that are precursors to disease. An example is that of the relationship of an elevated prostate-specific antigen (PSA) to the presence of prostate cancer. Elevated PSA levels have been used to make the diagnosis of prostate cancer, but in many individuals with high levels of PSA, there is no malignancy. The BLSA has found that there is a sharp rise in PSA levels when cancerous cells are present. Consequently, an early indicator of prostate cancer may be the presence of the sharp rise.

1975

75

55 4MD

12/19/19

Aug 2013 -
Ellie older
than
mom

UNIVERSAL CHANGES

In spite of the differing rates of aging from person to person, there are some universal changes noted in organ systems. This summary, based on data collected by the Baltimore Longitudinal Study of Aging, comes from Aging Under the Microscope (NIH, 2002). More specific changes to selected systems will follow in this chapter.

Heart

As we age, the heart muscle thickens. The maximum oxygen consumption in men during exercise decreases by about 10 percent with each passing decade. In women the decrease is approximately 7.5 percent. The reason for the decrease in oxygen consumption is that there is diminution of the heart's maximum pumping rate and the body has less ability to extract oxygen from the blood.

Arteries

As we age, arteries become stiff and more resistant to blood being pushed through blood vessels by the heart. In turn, the heart must work harder to propel the blood. This results in higher systolic blood pressure, increased load on the heart, and enlargement of the left ventricle.

Lungs

About 40 percent of lung function is lost between the ages of 20 and 80. This function may be decreased even more if smoking or disease is present. The decreased function can be attributed to more rigidity in the chest wall, decreased respiratory muscle strength, loss of elasticity in the lung tissue, and loss of gas exchange surface area.

Brain

Some of the axons, the connecting links between nerve cells, are lost with age. The function and amount of nerve cells themselves may also decrease with age. It is believed that the system is capable of producing new neurons, but the conditions under which this may happen is unknown.

Kidneys

During the aging process, the kidneys become less proficient in removing wastes from the circulating blood. This is especially significant in the excretion of byproducts of medication breakdown. If these byproducts aren't satisfactorily removed, they build up in the body, leading to accentuated actions and adverse reactions or possible kidney damage.

Bladder

The capacity of the bladder declines with age. Urinary incontinence may occur with atrophy of tissues. This is problematic in women, but exercise and behavioral techniques may be helpful in managing it.

Body Fat

The typical pattern is for body fat to increase gradually until middle age, stabilize, then decline in old age as weight decreases. Muscle loss accompanies this weight and fat decrease. As we age, the fat distribution in our bodies changes by migrating from just under the skin to deposits around deeper organs. Men usually have a lower percentage of body fat than women, with distribution in the abdomen as opposed to fat on the hips and thighs of women. This distribution may be a factor in women being less susceptible to heart disease and other conditions.

Muscles

There is a 22 percent decline in muscle mass in non-exercising women and a 23 percent decline in non-exercising men between the ages of 30 and 70. Exercise can slow the rate of muscle mass loss.

Bones

Throughout early life, bone mineral is lost and replaced in balanced amounts, but beginning at around age 35 there is more loss than replacement of bone cells. This loss is accelerated in women at the time of menopause, leading to the possibility of osteoporosis and fractures. Bone loss can be decreased by regular weight-bearing exercise such as walking, running, and strength training.

Vision

There is noticeable change in close-up vision in the mid-40s. Increased susceptibility to glare becomes apparent in the 50s, including decreased vision with low light levels, and more difficulty detecting moving objects. By the 70s there may be decline in the ability to distinguish fine details.

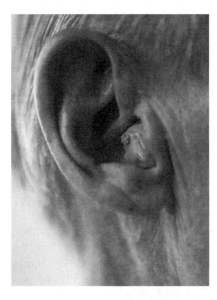

Hearing

The ability to hear high frequencies decreases with age. There may be some difficulty understanding speech, especially when background noise is present. Men notice a decline in hearing more than women.

CONSEQUENCES OF PHYSIOLOGICAL AGING IN SYSTEMS

As a CSA, it is important for you to remember that your clients are aging at different rates. So while you may have several clients who are about the same age, they may be very different from each other in external appearance and behavior. In fact, a client who is 80 may act and appear as young as, or younger than, another client who is in his 60s. Internally the changes may be less obvious, except according to the client's subjective report.

The key to a successful relationship with your client is to recognize that while similarities exist, there will be individual differences that must be respected and treated accordingly. Knowledge of normal aging changes and how they may manifest and be exhibited in your client is crucial to the client's satisfaction and your success as a professional in the relationship.

Aging changes and the physiological manifestations in systems particularly relevant to your practice with seniors follows. The discussion will focus on the aging changes, how they can be treated or compensated for, and what actions you should follow to maximize functioning with the client.

Sensory Changes

Our senses of hearing, vision, taste, smell, and touch are the means with which we connect with our world. When there is a decrement in one of the senses, we attempt whenever possible to compensate for the loss through one of the other senses.

Hearing

Hearing loss is a common impairment, especially in older adults. It affects more than 28 million Americans, but one in three persons over age 60 and half of those 85 and older have significant loss. Untreated hearing loss results in misunderstood communication. It can also lead to depression, isolation, irritability, and a decreased quality of life (National Academy on an Aging Society, 1999). A review of the ear's anatomy and function will help you better understand hearing loss and its impact on the senior client.

The ear has three main parts:

- The outer ear includes the pinna and the ear canal.
- The middle ear includes the eardrum and three bones (ossicles) commonly referred to as the hammer, anvil, and stirrup. These bones are suspended in an air-filled cavity.

59

- The inner ear is called the cochlea and includes nerve endings that allow us to hear. It also is the organ that helps us control our physical balance.

Sound is gathered by the pinna, then travels through the ear canal, striking the eardrum and causing it to vibrate. This in turn causes the ossicles to vibrate and mechanically conduct sound through the middle ear to the inner ear. The sound moves fluid over nerve endings (hair cells) in the inner ear and then travels as electrical impulses to the brain. Although any senior is susceptible to hearing loss, men are most often affected, as well as farmers, construction workers, musicians, and others exposed to long-term noise.

The most common age-related hearing loss is called *presbycusis*. This is a sensorineural disturbance caused by death of the hair cells in the inner ear. Sounds in the high frequency range are lost first, followed by those in the middle frequencies. Since most speech sounds are in the middle range, presbycusis results in speech sounding distorted and occasionally unintelligible. Words sound fuzzy and the listener frequently accuses speakers of mumbling. The sounds of *c, ch, f, s, z,* and *th* are most easily misunderstood; vowels are usually heard better because they occur in the lower frequencies (Olson, 2004).

Presbycusis is especially troubling because the senior may hear a part of the conversation, but not enough of it to understand the meaning. The senior, either out of pride or self-consciousness, may hesitate to ask for the words to be repeated. So the speaker may assume that all was heard and not realize the communication was incomplete. Some seniors may compensate by lip-reading but others do not.

Conductive hearing loss is a result of sound waves not passing satisfactorily to the inner ear. Common causes of this are wax buildup in the ear canal, perforated eardrum, fluid in the middle ear, or damage to the ossicles. Other hearing losses may be a combination of both conductive and sensorineural.

Tinnitus is a condition frequently referred to as "ringing in the ears," but it actually may sound like buzzing, chirping crickets, blowing, roaring, or popping. The noise level of the tinnitus may be quite variable, and tinnitus frequently is accompanied by some hearing loss. Causes of tinnitus may be infections, injuries, allergies, tumors, or unknown reasons. It is estimated that 50 million Americans have the condition, 2 million so severely that it interferes with day-to-day functioning. Treatment options include amplification products, biofeedback, medications, masking techniques, and retraining exercises that desensitize the brain to the noise (NIA, 2002e).

Seniors may occasionally complain of *dizziness* or *vertigo*. This may be associated with high blood pressure, inflammation in the inner ear, or unknown causes. A major concern, in addition to the extreme discomfort felt by the client, is its contribution to falling and potential injury.

As a CSA you should encourage your client to seek the services of an otologist or audiologist so that the hearing condition may be appropriately assessed and treated. Medical treatments, hearing aids, cochlear implants, and a variety of amplifying devices may help to reduce the hearing loss.

Much of your role will be that of facilitating communication and understanding. These simple rules will help you to communicate more effectively with the hearing-impaired client (Olson, 2004):

- Face your client directly when speaking. Avoid chewing gum or food while talking.

- Use appropriate facial expressions and gestures while communicating, but don't overdo it. Avoid covering your mouth while talking because it will garble your words and prevent the client from lip-reading.

- Speak slowly and with a lowered voice. Slow down your rate of speech, as fast speech makes it difficult for the client to understand and also gives the impression that you are hurried.

- Don't shout. Many persons automatically raise their voices several decibels when speaking with elderly clients thinking that it's necessary. It usually isn't. Clarity is what's more important.

- Instead of repeating a misunderstood sentence, rephrase it. If the words weren't understood the first time, they may not be the second time around either. By rephrasing you can select a different set of words that may be understood better.

- When in a restaurant or at a social gathering with a hearing-impaired client, select a place away from noisy areas such as kitchens, entries, and passage areas. Ask to be seated on the side of the room instead of in the middle.

- Avoid using patronizing behavior with a client with hearing limitations. Include the person in the conversations rather than speaking *over* him or *about* him to others in your party.

Vision

Our eyes are remarkable organs and usually serve us well over the years. The aging changes taking place in the eye frequently are so subtle and slow that we are able to adapt to the changes that occur and make the modifications necessary. To better understand these changes one must know the structures of the eye.

These structures constitute the basic anatomy of the eye:

- The *cornea* takes light rays from varying angles and bends them toward the pupil.

- The *pupil* is a dark round opening in the center of the iris, through which light enters the eye. The pupil adjusts in size according to the amount of light present.

- The *lens*, located behind the pupil, bends light rays as they enter, so that they are focused on the retina.

- The *retina* is a membrane on the back wall of the eye that contains photoreceptor nerve cells. These cells change the light rays into electrical impulses and send them to the brain via the optic nerve. The impulses are then assembled into an image by the brain.

The majority of normal vision changes result from alterations in the structures of the eye. This includes the lens becoming yellowed, opaque, and less flexible; pupils shrinking; and decreased response of the pupils to dim light.

A readily noticed change, and a common one involving almost everyone over the age of 40, is that of *presbyopia*, or farsightedness. This is a condition in which the lens loses flexibility and is less able to focus on objects that are close. One of the first indicators is moving objects farther away from the eyes when reading in an attempt to see images better. The treatment for presbyopia is to use reading glasses or bifocals, but some seniors may also use large print books or magnifying glasses (NIA, 2002d).

Yellowing of the lens results in *distorted color vision*, usually so subtle that it may not be readily apparent. As we age it becomes more difficult to discern the color intensities, particularly the cool colors of blue, green, and violet, which are filtered out. As a result, a person may not be able to discriminate between the various shades of these colors. An item similar in color to its backdrop may blend into it and not be readily distinguishable. Yellow, red, and orange are seen more readily. Sharper color contrasts must be used to make the colors stand out from each other.

Opaqueness of the lens means that less of the light entering the eye reaches the photoreceptors. By age 60 this amount is only a third of what it was at age 20, and by age 70 it decreases to 12 percent. Most seniors compensate for this by increasing illumination. Seniors may also complain of glare, a result of increased scattering of light by the lens.

Diminished diameter of the pupils, accompanied by decreased ability of the pupils to change size quickly and chemical changes in retinal structure, results in difficulty adjusting quickly between areas of dim and bright light. This results in more problems with night driving. After confronting the bright lights of an oncoming car, the structures don't adapt quickly enough to the decreased amount of light after the car has passed. The difficulties in distinguishing roadside features in dim light adds to the concern with night driving (Olson, 2004).

Many seniors notice a diminishing of peripheral vision as they get older and don't see objects off to the side as readily. This is especially an issue in driving, when the decreased peripheral vision combined with the normal blind spot impairs seeing cars in an adjacent lane. The senior must compensate by turning the head completely to the side instead of just looking out the corners of the eye.

A common complaint of seniors is that they see *floaters*, or specks, in the field of vision. Floaters are small, dark shapes resembling spots, threads, or squiggly lines. The floaters seem to dart around like small flies when the eyes move. Floaters are common as we age and are due to shrinkage of the vitreous, the gel-like substance that fills 80 percent of the eye. With shrinkage, the vitreous becomes stringy, and these stringy strands cast shadows on the retina. These shadows are the floaters.

Mostly the floaters are distracting and a nuisance. Fortunately, they eventually tend to settle down below the sight line and become less noticeable. However, it is important to distinguish between the nuisance floater and the more serious condition of a retinal detachment, the lifting or pulling of any part of the retina from its normal position at the back of the eye. Frequently accompanied by sudden increase in floaters, flashes of light, and loss of peripheral vision, immediate treatment is indicated to avoid permanent visual impairment or even blindness (NEI, 2004b).

A *cataract* is a condition of the lens becoming opaque or cloudy. By age 80, more than half of Americans have had a cataract or cataract surgery. Symptoms associated with a cataract include blurred and dimmed vision, glare from lights, and color fading. Cataract surgery is one of the most common, safest, and most effective types of surgery and involves removal of the lens, which is usually replaced with an artificial one. In about 90 percent of cases, the result is better vision (NIA, 2002d; Prevent Blindness America, n.d.).

Glaucoma is a serious condition in which there is elevated pressure within the eye that can ultimately damage the retina. The result is vision loss and even blindness. Because the symptoms—loss of peripheral vision, headaches, and halos around images—may develop slowly, the senior may not be aware of it until some damage has already been done. However, there is a test easily and quickly performed by an optometrist or ophthalmologist that should be done annually. There is no cure for glaucoma, and vision lost cannot be restored. Treatment, which includes medications, laser, or surgery, may save the remaining vision (NIA, 2002d).

An increasing threat to vision in seniors is that of *age-related macular degeneration* (AMD). It can occur in middle age, but risk increases with age. AMD is the leading cause of vision loss in Americans 60 years of age and older. Degeneration of the macula, the light-sensitive tissue at the back of the eye, is responsible for blurring of central vision, so important for reading or other fine detail work.

There are two forms of the disease—dry AMD, which is the most common, and wet, which is responsible for most of the vision loss. Dry AMD occurs when the light-sensitive cells in the macula slowly break down. Wet AMD occurs when abnormal fragile blood vessels behind the retina grow under the macula and leak both blood and fluid. Elevation of the macula results and damage happens quickly. Currently treatment is high doses of antioxidants and surgery, but neither is a cure (NEI, 2004a).

As a CSA, you should recognize the importance of vision to your clients' everyday functioning. Encourage regular eye exams so that identified problems can be treated promptly. There are other actions you can take as you work with them to maximize their visual acuity (Olson, 2004):

- Provide adequate lighting in your office setting. Lighting must be bright but not glaring. Watch for glare from floors, walls, lights, and windows.

- Have gradual luminance changes in your office suite to give eyes time to adjust to light variations. Lighting should be lower in the entry than in the office area at night; reverse it in the daytime.

- Use contrasting colors in decorating. Especially take note of color contrasts between walls and floors, walls and switch plates, and steps and their edges.

- Ensure printed materials are easily readable by using larger fonts, black lettering against white background, and plenty of white space. Avoid all-capital letters, pastel colors or fonts, and cluttered background designs.

- Arrange activities during the day instead of at night.

Taste and Smell

Numbers of taste buds, found on the tongue, pharynx, and lining of the mouth, begin to decline after age 20 and drop off dramatically after age 70. There are four different taste sensations—sweet, sour, bitter, and salty. Greatest decline is noted in the sweet and salty buds, resulting in older persons frequently using heavier amounts of sugar on cereal or in coffee and generously salting other foods.

Smell is more sensitive than taste and also shows a decrease in acuity as we age. By age 80 four of five persons demonstrate major dysfunction in smell, resulting in not only a loss of the sense, but difficulty in discriminating between smells. Medications that alter taste and smell sensations complicate the issue. The close relationship between smell and taste—smell is responsible for 75 percent of our sense of taste—has implications for creating appetite and an enjoyment of food. But there are more serious implications as well in that ability to detect noxious odors, such as natural gas, plays a large role in our being safe in our environment.

If you are providing food at activities for senior clients, make an effort to provide an assortment of herbs and spices to enhance flavors in place of the less healthy sweet and salty items. Aromas of freshly baked bread and freshly brewed coffee are also appealing to the sense of smell.

Skin Changes

As a society we are frequently overly concerned about how our skin looks. Society attaches great value to skin that is soft and unwrinkled, so many seniors tend to be self-conscious about the appearance of their skin and what it says about their age.

While not a major health issue, aging skin does cause inconvenience and sometimes discomfort. Two-thirds of persons over age 70 consult a physician about problems related to skin—dryness, itching, calluses, corns, and changes in nails.

As we age there are changes in the elastin and collagen, the connective tissue that gives skin its firmness and elasticity. The changes in the elastin and collagen result in less elastic and drier skin. Then the fat padding underneath the skin begins to disappear, leaving a sagging appearance in the skin. This leads to wrinkles, dryness, and slower healing of cuts. Sun exposure and a history of cigarette smoking contribute further to the skin changes.

Other changes in the skin explain common concerns among seniors. The fat layer acts as a shock absorber and controls loss of body heat. Loss of the fat on the face and hands leads to increased susceptibility to bruising, while in the feet, fat loss may be a reason for increased trauma in walking and complaints of foot problems. Reduction in density of small blood vessels under the skin may be responsible for older people needing higher room temperatures to be comfortable. Nerve cells in the skin lose efficiency with age and may lead to seniors being less sensitive to skin pain and having a reduced sense of touch. Reduced sensitivity to both pain and heat increases the withdrawal reaction time. Seriousness of burns in seniors may be a result.

Sleep Changes

Mary Margaret is a 73-year-old professional, retired for only three years. Single, she lives with her brother and sister-in-law, also retired, in their home in a large Midwestern city. All during her career Mary Margaret was accustomed to arising at 4 a.m., napping at intervals during the day, and retiring by 9 p.m. Her usual schedule even in retirement is to continue getting up at 4 o'clock. Feeling mentally and physically alert in the early morning, she spends the next three to four hours typing the draft of a book she is writing about her lifelong work with disadvantaged children in the inner city. About 8 a.m., she gets sleepy, so she has a light breakfast and naps until 9:30. Upon waking from her nap, she continues working on her book until she stops for lunch at noon. Then it's time for an hour's nap. Finding that her alertness is diminished by afternoon, she spends the time until supper on lighter activities—working crossword puzzles, watching TV, or playing solitaire. After supper she watches more TV. Bedtime for her is around 9 p.m., though she may have already fallen asleep on the couch in front of the TV set. She prepares herself for bed and the next day starts her routine all over again. Although this pattern of sleeping and waking may seem unorthodox to some, it is a pattern that has worked well for Mary Margaret for many years and continues to work for her now.

Although many seniors have minimal problems with sleep, many others feel they are not getting the sleep they would like. According to the National Institute on Aging, sleep patterns change as we age, but disturbed sleep and waking up tired every day is not a normal part of aging (NIA, 2002a), Disturbed sleep may be an indication of either physical or emotional problems and should be discussed with a physician.

The quality of sleep may decrease slightly as we age for several reasons. Our bodies secrete lesser amounts of the chemicals that regulate the sleep-wake cycles. Melatonin, which promotes sleep, and growth hormone, also a factor in sleep, decrease. In addition, changes in the body temperature cycle, daytime inactivity or lack of exercise, daytime napping, and decreased mental stimulation may have some responsibility. During the night an aging bladder or pain may awaken a person.

There are two kinds of sleep in a normal sleep cycle—rapid eye movement (REM), or dreaming sleep, and quiet (non-REM) sleep. Everyone has about four or five cycles of REM and non-REM sleep a night. For older people, the amount of time spent in the deepest stages of non-REM sleep decreases and may explain why older people are thought of as light sleepers. Although the amount of sleep each person needs varies widely, the average range is between seven and eight hours a night. As we age, the amount of sleep we can expect to get at any one time drops off. By age 75, for many reasons, some people may find they are waking up several times each night (NIA, 2002a).

At any age, insomnia is the most common sleep complaint. Insomnia includes such manifestations as:

- taking a long time to fall asleep (more than 30 to 45 minutes);
- waking up many times each night;
- waking up early and being unable to go back to sleep;
- waking up feeling tired.

Insomnia is usually a symptom of a problem and not the problem itself. It can be linked with other sleep disorders such as sleep apnea, a common problem that causes breathing to stop for periods of up to two minutes many times each night.

There are two kinds of sleep apnea:

- *Obstructive sleep apnea* is an involuntary pause in breathing—air cannot flow in or out of the person's mouth or nose.
- *Central sleep apnea* is less common and occurs when the brain doesn't send the right signals to start the breathing muscles.

In either case, the sleeper is totally unaware of his or her difficulties breathing. Daytime sleepiness combined with loud snoring at night are clues that there may be sleep apnea. A doctor specializing in sleep disorders can make a diagnosis and recommend appropriate treatment that may include devices that keep the airway open, surgery, or medication.

Here are some suggestions seniors can follow to get a good night's sleep:

- Follow a regular sleep schedule and avoid napping if possible.
- Exercise at a regular time each day.
- Try to get some natural light in the afternoon.
- Avoid caffeine, heavy snacks, alcohol, or nicotine before bedtime.
- Create a safe and comfortable sleep area with an accessible lamp and phone, a dark but well-ventilated and quiet room, smoke alarms, and locks on all doors.
- Follow a bedtime routine to communicate to your body that it's bedtime— bath, reading, or TV.
- Use your bedroom only for sleeping—not for office work or TV. If you're not drowsy after 15 minutes in bed, get up. When sleepy, go back to bed.
- Excess worry about sleep may keep you awake. Use mental exercises to help you fall asleep.

Energy, Bone, and Muscle Changes

Age-related changes in bones, muscles, and joints have an impact on our activity level. While some seniors are able to maintain many of their previous activities, others are hampered by the effects of muscle wasting, joint restriction, and porous bones. Regardless of the changes present, exercise and diet play a large role in keeping a senior functioning at a high level in spite of the aging changes.

As we age, muscles begin to shrink and lose mass because of decreases in number and size of fibers. This leads to several noticeable results—it takes our muscles longer to respond, our handgrip decreases in strength, and we tire more quickly since the heart muscle isn't as effective.

Additionally, our tendons, the cord-like tissues attaching muscles to bones, lose water content. This makes us stiffer and less able to tolerate stress. Cartilage in joints is also affected by this water loss, so joints become inflamed as bone rubs against bone. Concurrently our metabolic rate slows, leading to increased obesity and cholesterol levels (American Academy of Orthopaedic Surgeons, n.d.)

Loss of bone tissue is a formidable issue for aging women, although men can be affected to a lesser degree. Throughout life a constant process of absorption and formation takes place in the bone. This process, called *remodeling*, keeps bones strong until the mid-30s, when the balance changes and more bone is lost than is formed new. Gradually this can lead to osteopenia (low bone mass) or osteoporosis (porous bones). According to the NIA (2002b), 10 million Americans (8 million of them women) have osteoporosis. Thirty-four million more have osteopenia. One of the effects of osteoporosis is a dowager hump, caused by collapse of vertebrae. This results in decreased height of the individual.

But the unfortunate consequence of osteoporosis is that of fracture. Half of women and one in four men over 50 will experience some type of fracture—hips, vertebrae, and wrists are most common—attributable to osteoporosis. A hip fracture has a particularly negative outcome. About a fourth of those sustaining a hip fracture will require long-term care, and worse, the person's risk of dying within a year of the fracture increases substantially.

Fortunately there are ways to head off some of this damage. A healthy diet with balanced nutrients, especially the minerals, is important. Medications are available to slow down the process of bone loss. Hormones are known to have a positive impact on bone structure and to reduce fracture rates, but many postmenopausal women have discontinued taking them amid fears of heart attack, stroke, and breast cancer. Exercise is the one variable that seems to have greater effect in slowing the impact of the bone loss and promoting bone strength.

There are simple tests that measure bone density in various sites of the body. A bone density test can detect osteoporosis before a fracture occurs and predict one's chances of a fracture in the future. Requiring only a few minutes, it can be done annually to determine rate of bone loss and monitor effectiveness of treatment.

Falls

Falls are a major concern for seniors because of the life change a fracture and disability may bring. Falls are due to numerous factors—decreased coordination, reflexes, and muscle strength, and poor vision or hearing. Medications, high blood pressure, or other disease processes may impair a person's balance and ability to right oneself quickly.

However many falls can be prevented by making some changes in the home or in behaviors:

- Have medications evaluated regularly for side effects, interactions, and reduction of dosage to the lowest possible that will control symptoms.
- Rise slowly from a lying or sitting position. *Orthostatic hypotension* is a condition in which blood pressure drops dramatically when getting up. Go from lying to sitting to standing over a longer period of time.
- Use sturdy shoes for walking. Avoid going barefoot or in stocking feet. Use a cane or walker to aid in balance.
- Have a regular exercise program. Tai chi and yoga can be helpful in maintaining balance and improving muscle tone.
- Keep floors free of clutter. Remove throw rugs. Avoid having electrical or phone cords in walking areas.
- Install handrails in stairwells and have light switches at both top and bottom of stairs.
- Install grab bars above tubs, in showers, and beside toilets.
- Place a nonskid mat in the shower or use a shower chair.
- Use nightlights throughout the house.

Numerous types of technology are available to use in one's home. Sensors can detect movement around rooms, video cameras can follow activity, and alarm systems can be activated to alert emergency personnel. Before deciding to implement technology, the expense of the equipment and the intrusion of it into one's daily activities must be weighed against the benefits.

You should make your office arrangements as user-friendly as possible for clients with mobility challenges. Power doors, wide hallways and doorways to accommodate walkers or wheelchairs, nonskid flooring, wall-mounted rocker switches, and lever hardware instead of round doorknobs are all methods to make the office more navigable. Chairs should have armrests and have seats high enough to make rising easier. You should encourage clients to assess their homes for safety hazards and make appropriate changes. Encourage seniors to have medications assessed regularly, practice weight-bearing exercises, and take advantage of bone testing.

Cognition and Perception Changes

Although some changes in cognition occur as we age, there are so many areas of variability that generalizations are not appropriate. For example, in the Baltimore Longitudinal Study of Aging, performance on tests of logic decreased for most participants after age 70, but in some participants there was no change. Individuals with no decline in mental task performance were found in every age group, including the oldest. Ability to learn oral material decreased only in those over age 70. Vocabulary scores did not change with age.

Some consistencies have been found, however. Short-term memory appears to shorten with age. Visual memory, measured by ability to reproduce geometric designs from memory, declines slightly between ages 50 and 60 but rapidly after age 70.

Many seniors are very capable of not only maintaining cognitive skills but learning new ones as well. Strategies used to do so include reading, crossword puzzles, card playing, and taking classes. Recent research is suggesting that exercise, especially walking, does play a role in increasing cognitive ability.

Perception is the process of assigning meaning to information collected by our senses. As we age it appears there is a decrease in the speed of evaluating the information and reacting to it. A reason may be that aging affects the speed with which the nervous system processes one stimulus before acting on another. Older persons also become less capable of making a decision regarding a stimulus, thereby appearing less decisive. However, neither of these slowed functions has a serious impact until later years (Atchley & Barusch, 2004).

Do not assume that perception and cognition are declining in your senior clients. Seniors react negatively if they sense they are being treated as being in decline. However, be aware that there may be some change in memory, processing information, and making decisions. Avoid speaking too rapidly or asking multiple questions without allowing time for mental processing. Provide proposals or information in writing instead of having the client depend on remembering what you said. Encourage clients to engage in intellectually stimulating activities and support new learning efforts.

Sexual Changes

Normal aging brings sexual changes in both men and women. These changes may affect one's ability to have and enjoy sex with another person.

Menopause usually begins for women sometime in their 40s. Menopause is a mixed blessing for many women, as decline in hormone production signals the end of both fertility and fears of an unwanted pregnancy. This may actually increase a woman's enjoyment of sexual activity (NIA, 2002c). But there are some physical changes that may be uncomfortable, although not untreatable. The vagina shortens and narrows, vaginal walls become thinner and stiffer, and there is less vaginal lubrication. These changes may reduce sexual pleasure if pain is present. Gels and lubricants can help.

Hot flashes and night sweats often accompany menopause, but do not affect all women equally. Women may note other changes at the time of menopause—more fat around the waist and hips, stiffening of joints, and occasional mood changes. Consultation with a physician is appropriate to address these issues. Both prescription medications and some alternative therapies may be effective in reducing symptoms.

A man may find it takes longer to achieve an erection, amount of ejaculate may be smaller, and there may be a greater interval before another erection is possible. Men, also, should be encouraged to consult their physicians for advice.

In both men and women, illness, disability, or medications taken for other health problems can affect the ability to have and enjoy sex. But even the most serious health problems don't need to deter one from a satisfying sex life. Factors that may require modification of sexual activity include arthritis, chronic pain, diabetes, heart disease, incontinence, and stroke.

Most seniors desire and maintain a satisfying sex life throughout the aging process in spite of the above changes. Important to persons as they age is the intimacy, affection, and closeness that a relationship with a partner provides. How that relationship is expressed depends on the ability to communicate desires and make accommodations necessary so that both persons in the partnership feel their needs are met.

Aging and Health Perceptions

The good news about aging is that most people age relatively well. Aging changes happen so gradually that most are unnoticeable except over the long term. Adaptations necessary to maximize functioning are made regularly, and it's usually not until later that one will note aspects of their physical functioning decreased as compared to 10 or 20 years before.

Successful aging is not necessarily dependent on the absence of physiological disabilities, but embraces the realm of the psychosocial as well. So we recognize that seniors may demonstrate varying attitudes about their health status. It is not unusual for persons with relatively similar health problems to label themselves differently. For example, one may have numerous observable aging changes but consider himself to be in good health, while another person with the same or fewer problems and observable changes considers himself as ill or disabled. As a CSA you may recognize these differences readily, but refrain from making judgments about your clients' subjective evaluations of health status. Instead offer support and encourage them to practice positive health behaviors within the limitations of their health status.

Researchers find that older people generally have a positive view of their own health. In one study, older persons were asked to rate their health as excellent, very good, good, fair, or poor. Thirty-nine percent of those over the age of 65 viewed their health as very good or excellent. Only 29 percent considered they were in fair or poor health. Even those over 85 years showed positive findings—31 percent considered themselves in very good or excellent health, with 36 percent viewing their health as poor.

In the study, men and women generally showed similar degrees of positiveness in their attitudes. Most notable were the differences among racial groups. Older African Americans were more likely than Caucasians to view their health as poor.

How do the researchers explain the differences between these positive perceptions of health and the reality of aging changes? They believe that it reflects a remarkably successful adaptation to disability. Society may view older persons as being frail and in poor health, but the seniors themselves don't agree with that viewpoint in spite of physical evidence to the contrary (Rowe & Kahn, 1998).

Physiological Changes of Aging: Summary

While several theories exist to explain physiological aging, there is no one theory with which scientists can completely agree. The body and its various systems are extremely complex and intricate, so theories presented still leave many unanswered questions. It is probable that current and future theories will interact with each other in ways that we may never understand.

Some theories promote the role of genetics in determining longevity and aging changes, while others give stronger credence to environment and lifestyle. Evidence appears to exist that would support all of them.

Regardless of the research findings, we can make our own observations of similarities and differences in persons as they age. We may notice changes in appearance, stamina, and stature in some persons but not in others. We may guess one person as being age 60 and another age 80 and we could be right—but we could also be wrong.

We may be surprised by a person's perception of their health status. We may judge based on a conversation that one person is very unhealthy while another is healthy, but realize later that our conclusion was wrong also.

What this tells us is although we can generalize about aging changes, aging is still a process occurring within each individual. Seniors may share common characteristics in theory, but our interactions with each person must reflect a respectful, individualized approach if we are to work successfully with them.

References

American Academy of Orthopaedic Surgeons. (n.d.). Effects of aging. Retrieved July 10, 2004, from http://orthoinfo.aaos.org/fact/thr_report.cfm?Thread_ID=224&topcategory=General%20Information

Atchley, R., & Barusch, A. (2004). *Social forces and aging*. Belmont, CA: Wadsworth.

Boston University. (2002, February). The New England centenarian study: A brief history. *The New England Centenarian Study Newsletter*, Vol. 1, 1–2. Available from http://www.bumc.bu.edu/departments/homemain.asp?departmentid=361

Fossel, M. (1996). *Reversing human aging*. New York: William Morrow and Company.

Hayflick, L. (1996). *How and why we age*. New York: Random House.

National Academy on an Aging Society. (1999, December). *Hearing loss: A growing problem that affects quality of life*. Washington, DC: National Academy on an Aging Society.

NEI (National Eye Institute). (2004a, April 13). Vision loss from eye diseases will increase as Americans age (press release). Retrieved July 10, 2004, from http://www.nei.nih.gov/news/pressreleases/041204.asp

NEI. (2004b, June). Facts about floaters. Retrieved July 10, 2004, from http://www.nei.nih.gov/health/floaters/index.asp

NIA (National Institute on Aging). (2002a, May). A good night's sleep. *Age Page*. Gaithersburg, MD: National Institute on Aging. Retrieved July 10, 2004, from http://www.niapublications.org/engagepages/sleep.asp

NIA. (2002b, August). Osteoporosis: The bone thief. *Age Page.* Gaithersburg, MD: National Institute on Aging. Retrieved July 10, 2004, from http://www.niapublications.org/engagepages/osteo.asp

NIA. (2002c, August). Sexuality in later life. *Age Page.* Gaithersburg, MD: National Institute on Aging. Retrieved July 10, 2004, from http://www.niapublications. org/engagepages/sexuality.asp

NIA. (2002d, September). Aging and your eyes. *Age Page.* Gaithersburg, MD: National Institute on Aging. Retrieved July 10, 2004, from http://www.niapublications.org/engagepages/eyes.asp

NIA. (2002e, September). Hearing loss. *Age Page.* Gaithersburg, MD: National Institute on Aging. Retrieved July 10, 2004, from http://www.niapublications. org/engagepages/hearing.asp

NIA. (2002f, September). Life extension: Science fact or science fiction? *Age Page.* Gaithersburg, MD: National Institute on Aging. Retrieved July 10, 2004, from http://www.niapublications.org/engagepages/lifeext.asp

NIH. (National Institutes of Health) (2002, September). Aging under the microscope: A biological quest. NIH Publication No. 02-2756. Bethesda, MD: National Institute on Aging. Retrieved July 10, 2004, from http://www.niapublications. org/pubs/microscope/index.asp

NIH. (2004). Research for a new age. NIH Publication No. 93-1129. Bethesda, MD: National Institute on Aging. Retrieved July 14, 2004, from http://www.healthand age.com/html/min/nih/content/booklets/research_new_age/page3.htm

Olshansky, S., & Carnes, B. (2001). *The quest for immortality.* New York: Norton.

Olson, J. (2004, March). Putting your best foot forward. *CSA Journal.* Denver, CO: Society of Certified Senior Advisors.

Prevent Blindness America (n.d.). Frequently asked questions about cataracts. Retrieved June 3, 2004, from http://www.preventblindness.org/eye_problems/ cataractFAQ.html

Rowe, J., & Kahn, R. (1998). *Successful aging.* New York: Random House.

Resources

Services

AARP World Aging Map, http://www.aarp.org/international/map/. This site contains aging-related information on specific nations around the world. It includes demographic data, research reports, and other information about dozens of nations.

Administration on Aging (AOA), http://www.aoa.dhhs.gov, U.S. Administration on Aging, Washington, DC 20201, 202-619-0724. This comprehensive site addresses topics involving aging.

Alliance for Aging Research, http://www.agingresearch.org. This Web site includes a calculator to estimate one's life expectancy.

American Federation of Aging Research (AFAR), http://www.afar.org, 70 West 40th Street, 11th Floor, New York, NY 10018, 212-703-9977, 888-582-2327. Biomedical research articles that promote healthier aging appear here.

American Sleep Apnea Association, http://www.sleepapnea.org, 1424 K Street NW, Suite 302, Washington, DC 20005, 202-293-3650. This site offers information about sleep apnea disorder, evaluation, and treatment.

American Society on Aging (ASA), http://www.asaging.org, 833 Market Street, Suite 511, San Francisco, CA 94103-1824, 415-974-9600. An association site for professionals in the field of aging, ASA publishes *Aging Today* and *Generations*, which are valuable resources for aging professionals.

American Tinnitus Association, http://www.ata.org, P.O. Box 5, Portland, OR 97207-0005, 800-634-8978. This nonprofit organization is dedicated to finding a cure for tinnitus. The site offers research, education, and publications.

Gerontological Society of America (GSA), http://www.geron.org, 1030 15th Street NW, Suite 250, Washington, DC 20005, 202-842-1275. GSA is a nonprofit professional organization with more than 5,000 members in the field of aging.

International Longevity Center—USA (ILC), http://www.ilcusa.org, 60 East 86th Street, New York, NY 10028, 212-288-1468. International Longevity Center—USA is a nonprofit and nonpartisan research, policy, and education organization dedicated to addressing issues of the population of aging and longevity in positive and constructive ways. An affiliate of Mount Sinai School of Medicine, it publishes the ILC Policy Report to highlight longevity news and trends in the United States and abroad.

Macular Degeneration Foundation, http://www.eyesight.org, P.O. Box 531313, Henderson, NV 89053, 888-633-3937. The Macular Degeneration Foundation's Web site features articles, newsletters, and additional links to other Web sites.

National Council on Aging (NCOA), http://www.ncoa.org, 300 D Street, SW, Suite 801, Washington, DC 20024, 202-470-1200. NCOA is an association of organizations and professionals dedicated to promoting the dignity, self-determination, well-being, and contributions of older persons.

National Institute on Aging (NIA), http://www.nia.nih.gov, Building 31, Room 5C27, 31 Center Drive, MSC 2292, Bethesda, MD 20892, 301-496-1752. NIA is one of the institutes of the National Institutes of Health (NIH). Its Web site follows the efforts of the government in researching aging. It also provides extensive consumer information, such as *The Resource Directory for Older People*, a database of information that includes federal and state agencies, resource centers, professional societies, private groups, and volunteer programs. NIA's *Age Page* provides up-to-date information for seniors on issues such as hearing and vision loss.

National Institute on Deafness and Other Communication Disorders (NIDCD), http://www.nidcd.nih.gov, 31 Center Drive, MSC 2320, Bethesda, MD 20892-2320, 800-241-1044, TTY 800-241-1055. NIDCD is one of the institutes of the National Institutes of Health (NIH). NIDCD conducts and supports research and training on the disordered processes of hearing and related problems.

National Osteoporosis Foundation (NOF), http://www.nof.org, 1232 22nd Street NW, Washington, DC 20037-1292, 202-223-2226. NOF is a nonprofit, voluntary health organization focusing on osteoporosis research, education, and advocacy. The Web site includes information on prevention, patient information, and locating a doctor.

The Rose Resnick LightHouse, http://lighthouse-sf.org, 214 Van Ness Avenue, San Francisco, CA 94102, 415-431-1481, TTY 415-431-4572. The Rose Resnick

LightHouse offers comprehensive services and serves as an advocacy agency for the blind and visually impaired.

United Nations—International Institute on Aging, http://www.inia.org, 117 St. Paul Street, Valletta VLT 07, Malta, (356+) 21 24 30 44/5/6. This United Nations institute researches aging and longevity and associated issues, particularly for less developed countries.

Chapter 4

Mental Health, Grief, and Loss in Later life

For many years Mr. Nyang joked with his daughters, Mia and Amy, about his poor memory. However, they recently started to worry that something was seriously wrong. Their father stopped going out, which he attributed to his arthritis pain; he lost all interest in food; and he acted dazed a lot of the time. He also stopped joking about his memory problem, which seemed to be getting worse. "I'm 84 years old— I'm just slowing down," he snapped at his daughters.

Mia and Amy went to a seminar on dementia held at a local hospital, and they came away certain that their father was suffering from Alzheimer's disease. Mia made an appointment for Mr. Nyang with a geriatric psychiatrist. During the appointment the psychiatrist asked a number of questions about Mr. Nyang's history and mood, when the symptoms began, and whether he had a history of depression. She also gave him a mental status examination. The doctor recommended that Mr. Nyang have further tests and try taking a low dose of an antidepressant medication for four weeks.

A month later Mia and Amy escorted their father to the psychiatrist for a follow-up visit. Mr. Nyang told the doctor that he was feeling a little better after a month of medication, and the doctor reported that the results of Mr. Nyang's tests did not indicate dementia. Mr. Nyang did not have Alzheimer's disease. These facts confirmed what the psychiatrist had suspected: Mr. Nyang was suffering from a major depressive episode. The psychiatrist continued to treat Mr. Nyang's depression, and he slowly felt better. The daughters felt tremendous relief when their father started joking about his memory again.

. . .

Mr. Bernstein, 76 years old, spent the early years of his retirement playing handball in his neighborhood park with neighbors half his age. He enjoyed the respect and admiration his younger friends had for him for the agility and skill he maintained at his age. He also enjoyed mentoring these friends as they shared stories between games.

Then Mr. Bernstein hurt his back while lifting a box. The injury kept him off the court for six weeks. When he returned to the game, he found that he was out of shape and could not play as well as he had played prior to the injury. Despite attempts to rebuild his strength, Mr. Bernstein struggled with the game and eventually stopped playing due to fears of having another injury. He was embarrassed that he could not keep up with others. Believing that he had lost not only his ability to play, but also the respect of his neighbors, Mr. Bernstein stopped going to the park. He felt discouraged at the loss of roles as athlete, community member, and mentor. Mr. Bernstein is now at a crossroads, facing the challenge of finding other roles that will utilize other strengths, or continuing on the path toward feeling bad about himself.

Introduction

As the stories here demonstrate, later life presents seniors with a number of challenges. Such challenges include adapting to changes in physical, functional, recreational, and social status as well as transitions to new roles. In addition, many seniors have the challenge of giving or receiving care. They must also confront the realities of physical limitations and death. Despite these challenges, most seniors have the personal and social resources to understand and deal with them.

Many seniors also develop wisdom, or expertise in the pragmatics of life, which research demonstrates is more prevalent among older adults than younger adults (Baltes, Smith, & Staudinger, 1992). Wisdom comes through experience and provides many older adults with tools for coping with challenges in later life.

Despite late-life problems, many older adults report feeling more self-confident, better adjusted, and more accepting than when they were younger. Further, the experience and expression of both positive and negative emotions tends to be less intense for older adults, which may account for their improved emotional control in later life (Fillip, 1996). In short, the vast majority of older adults function very well in their later years.

At the same time, some older adults develop mental disorders. This chapter will review the major mental health problems that older adults may face, and what can be done to address these problems. This chapter will also review the many losses of later life and associated bereavement and grief.

Depression

Many people, including older adults, assume that it is reasonable to become depressed in later life. Since depression and emotional suffering are considered part and parcel of later life, remediable mental health problems may be overlooked and not treated. Depression, though, is not a normal part of aging. Results of a major epidemiological study (Weissman, Bruce, Leaf, Florio, & Holzer, 1991) indicate that fewer older adults (1 to 2 percent) meet the diagnostic criteria for a major depressive episode (MDE) than younger adults (3 to

4 percent). However, a larger proportion of older adults do report clinically significant symptoms of depression that do not meet diagnostic criteria for an MDE. Rates of depressive symptoms range from 10 to 15 percent among community dwelling elders to 25 to 30 percent among older adults in inpatient medical centers and long-term care facilities. Clinically significant symptoms that are not as severe as MDE are sometimes called minor depression. Recent research shows that treatment for depression can be effective in returning individuals to normal levels of functioning.

Professionals diagnose depression using criteria in the *Diagnostic and Statistical Manual of Mental Disorders* (DSM-IV; American Psychiatric Association, 1994), the official listing and definition of psychiatric disorders by the American Psychiatric Association. The following symptoms, which must be present for *at least two weeks* and *impair the individual's normal daily functioning*, are included in the diagnosis of a major depressive episode:

- feeling sad, blue, or depressed or experiencing a loss of interest or enjoyment in life
- at least four of the following symptoms:
  —changes in appetite (may be accompanied by weight loss or gain)
  —changes in sleep (too much or not enough)
  —agitation or retardation of movement
  —fatigue or decreased energy
  —feeling worthless or guilty
  —problems with attention and concentration or difficulty making decisions
  —thoughts of suicide

To be considered part of depression, these symptoms cannot be the direct result of an organic factor (i.e., medication, medical illness, or an abused drug). The symptoms also cannot be part of usual bereavement after the loss of a loved one (see the Bereavement and Grief section of this chapter for more information).

DEPRESSION IN LATER LIFE

Depression in later life is much like that of younger adults, but there are some differences. First, some depressed older adults deny feeling sad, reporting instead a loss of interest or pleasure in life.

Second, rates of completed suicide are higher among older adults, particularly Caucasian men over the age of 74. Younger adults attempt suicide more often than older adults, but older adults are twice as likely to complete the suicide. Women attempt suicide more than men across the life span, but men are more likely to complete the suicide, often because they use more lethal means (e.g., men more frequently use guns, while women are more likely to overdose on pills).

Third, older adults have more medical illnesses than younger adults do. Depression is more prevalent among the medically ill elderly (an average of 12

percent) than healthy older adults (Koenig et al., 1992). Rates of depression increase among those with more severe illnesses. Later-life illnesses and the medications used to treat them may also cause problems with energy, attention and concentration, appetite, and sleep. The overlap between these symptoms and those of depression may cause an older adult to appear depressed when they are not. Conversely, depression may be overlooked if symptoms are attributed to medical problems or side effects of medication. Further, many in the current cohort of older adults are reluctant to report feeling depressed to their medical providers but will report physical symptoms.

Some medical problems have been associated with distinct patterns of depressive symptoms. For example, older adults with vascular disease or cardiovascular symptoms (e.g., congestive heart failure, multiple strokes, hypertension, high cholesterol) often experience what is sometimes called *vascular depression* (Alexopolous et al., 1997). Individuals with this depressive syndrome often experience relatively little guilt or sadness but have poor motivation or initiative, move very slowly, and do not recognize that what they are experiencing is related to a mental disorder.

Depression vs. Dementia

While both older and younger adults may experience deficits in attention and concentration, older adults tend to have more significant cognitive problems in the context of depression. This is sometimes called *pseudodementia*. Below is a summary of symptoms of depression and symptoms of dementia.

DEPRESSION	DEMENTIA
▪ sleep disturbance	▪ sleep disturbance
▪ loss of interest in pleasurable activities	▪ loss of interest in pleasurable activities
▪ poor attention/concentration	▪ poor attention/concentration
▪ loss of appetite/unexpected weight loss	▪ loss of appetite/unexpected weight loss
▪ agitation/retardation of movement	▪ agitation/retardation of movement
▪ irritability	▪ irritability
▪ memory impairment	▪ memory impairment
▪ loss of energy	▪ difficulty organizing; losing things
▪ feelings of guilt or regret	▪ language deficits
▪ thoughts of suicide	▪ incontinence in later stages

Notice the overlap of more than two-thirds of the symptoms. The overlap challenges mental health professionals to determine whether an older adult is experiencing depression, dementia, or both. Often neuropsychological testing is required to make a definitive diagnosis. (See chapter 12 for more about dementia.) Another issue is that many older adults experience depressive symptoms in the early stages of dementia in reaction to losses associated with cognitive decline. Diagnosis and treatment by a mental health professional specializing in geriatrics or with extensive experience with depression and dementia are optimal.

Dysthymia

Dysthymia is a chronic, less severe form of depression. People with dysthymia experience depressed moods most of the time for at least two years, causing significant distress or impairment in daily functioning. Some older adults have dysthymia their whole lives, while for others it begins in later life. Dysthymia also includes changes in appetite and sleep, low energy, low self-esteem, difficulty concentrating or making decisions, and feeling hopeless. Dysthymia is *not* a normal part of aging.

Adjustment Disorders

People often experience distress following an upsetting event. When the distress is beyond what most people experience or is getting in the way of an individual's daily functioning, he or she may be experiencing an *adjustment disorder*. Adjustment disorders occur within three months following a specific event and do not last longer than six months after the stressful event has ended. Note that some stressors common in later life are longstanding (e.g., caregiving for an elderly family member, multiple medical problems), thus adjustment disorders may persist much longer than six months if not appropriately treated. If symptoms persist beyond six months, other disorders may be considered. Bereavement is not included as a stressor for this disorder.

TREATMENT OF DEPRESSION

The effective treatment of depression in later life comes through three basic types of intervention: psychotherapy, antidepressant medication, and—for severe depression—electroconvulsive therapy (ECT). It is notable that psychotherapy and medication each have been found to be effective alone or in combination in the treatment of depression.

Psychotherapy

Psychotherapy is an effective treatment for later-life depression among older adults. Psychotherapy includes cognitive behavior therapy, interpersonal psychotherapy, and psychodynamic psychotherapy. Cognitive behavior therapy and interpersonal psychotherapy, both time-limited therapies, have been studied and shown to be effective treatments for depression (Reynolds et al., 1999; Thase et al., 1997). Cognitive behavior therapy helps patients to understand the link between their thoughts, behaviors, and emotions and to modify unhelpful thoughts and behaviors. Interpersonal psychotherapy for depression focuses on depression's associated interpersonal factors, including grief, role transitions (e.g., retirement, care for an infirm relative), interpersonal conflict, and interpersonal skills deficits.

Medications

Tricyclic antidepressants (TCAs, such as imipramine [Tofranil] and nortriptyline [Pamelor]) and selective serotonin reuptake inhibitors (SSRIs, such as citalopram [Celexa], fluoxetine [Prozac], sertraline [Zoloft], paroxetine [Paxil], venlafaxine [Effexor], mirtazapine [Remeron], escitalopram oxalate [Lexapro]), and buproprion [Wellbutrin]) have all been found to be very effective in the treatment of depression among older adults. TCAs tend to have more side effects that can be very dangerous for older adults. Thus clinicians rarely prescribe TCAs, instead prescribing SSRIs, which have fewer side effects. Because older adults tend to metabolize medications more slowly than younger adults, these medications are started at lower doses and increased more gradually than for younger people.

Electroconvulsive Therapy

Electroconvulsive therapy involves inducing a brain seizure by passing an electrical current through the brain for a few seconds via small electrodes attached to the head. Although the notion of passing electricity through the brain to treat depression is unsettling to some, ECT is a very effective treatment for severe depression. It is not used for mild depression. During the procedure, patients are kept quite comfortable with the use of anesthesia. Most people experience confusion for about an hour following the procedure, and they experience mild memory loss for a few weeks. Most return to their previous level of cognitive functioning. ECT appears to be a more effective treatment for later-life depression with hallucinations and delusions (read further for a description of these symptoms) than medications (Parker, Roy, Hadzi-Pavolvik, & Pedic, 1992).

Bipolar Disorder

Bipolar disorder, formerly known as manic depression, was named for the two emotional poles of the syndrome. People with bipolar disorder cycle back and forth between periods of mania (see the following description), normal functioning, and depression. Some people with bipolar disorder return to their regular level of functioning following a manic episode, while others fall into a major depressive episode. The latter is more common, particularly among older adults. Some older adults also experience psychiatric episodes with both depressive and manic symptoms (a *mixed episode*). Onset of the disorder usually comes when people are between 18 and 22 years of age, although the disorder may appear later in life (Almeida & Fenner, 2002). Treatment for bipolar disorder includes mood-stabilizing medications (e.g., lithium, valproate [Depakote], or carbemazepine [Tegretol]). Psychotherapy may also be beneficial in helping people cope with the interpersonal and practical consequences of bipolar disorder.

Mania

It is estimated that 5 to 19 percent of older adults who are treated for a mood disorder experience an episode of mania (van Gerpen, Johnson, & Wistead, 1999). Manic symptoms are relatively rare among older adults who do not have a history of this syndrome, however (Weissman et al., 1991). For most older adults, manic symptoms are the result of a medication (such as toxic levels of a steroid like prednisone), medical illness, or drug abuse. Periods of mania are characterized by the following symptoms (not already accounted for by another illness):

- extremely elevated mood (feeling overly joyful for no particular reason) or very irritable mood for a distinct period of time
- at least three of the following symptoms:
  —inflated self-esteem—feelings of invincibility, to the point being out of touch with reality
  —decreased need for sleep
  —extreme talkativeness
  —racing thoughts or shifting ideas
  —high distractibility
  —increased level of activity
  —engaging in behaviors with potentially serious consequences, such as being in dangerous places, spending a great deal of money, or increasing sexual activity
- impairment in daily functioning or interpersonal relationships

Anxiety Disorders

Anxiety is a normal response to stressful situations. Generally healthy community-dwelling older adults have developed excellent skills for coping with it. But anxiety becomes a problem when it prevents an individual from engaging in normal activity or diminishes ability to enjoy activities. Among adults over 65 years of age, 5.5 percent experience anxiety disorders, compared to 7.3 percent among younger adults (Stanley & Beck, 2000). Anxiety symptoms are more common in persons with other psychiatric or medical disorders. The rate of anxiety is approximately 11.7 percent among nursing home residents (Stanley & Beck) and as high as 38 percent among people with medical disorders such as Parkinson's disease and early dementia (Sadavoy & LeClair, 1997). It is very common for anxiety to accompany other psychiatric disorders, most notably depression.

PANIC ATTACKS AND PANIC DISORDER

Panic attacks are limited periods (usually several minutes) of intense fear that come on unexpectedly. These periods are accompanied by multiple symptoms, such as heart palpitations, sweating, shortness of breath, nausea, chest pain, dizziness, shakiness, or fear of losing control, going crazy, or dying. Some people experience panic attacks in response to certain situations, and some people experience them without any apparent trigger. Panic attacks may be part of the anxiety disorders described below. If an individual experiences recurrent, unexpected panic attacks in the absence of another anxiety disorder, they may have a panic disorder. Panic disorder is rare among older adults, however (Stanley & Beck, 2000). Treatment often includes a short-acting sedating medication called a benzodiazepine, such as lorazepam (Ativan) or alprazolam (Xanax), and cognitive behavioral psychotherapy.

GENERALIZED ANXIETY DISORDER

Generalized anxiety disorder (GAD) is commonly seen in clinical practice with older adults. The prevalence among community-residing older adults has been documented at 4.6 percent, although some speculate that rates are much higher (Stanley & Beck, 2000). As its name implies, people with GAD experience excessive worry or anxiety about multiple things, and it impairs their daily functioning, creating difficulty in controlling their worry. People with GAD experience at least three of the following symptoms: restlessness, problems concentrating, irritability, muscle tension, sleep problems, or premature fatigue. Sometimes the symptoms of GAD are directly due to a medical condition such as thyroid, cardiovascular, respiratory, metabolic, or neurological disorders. In such a case, an individual may be diagnosed with an anxiety disorder due to a general medical condition. Generalized anxiety treatment often includes a long-acting benzodiazepine, such as buspirone (Buspar), and cognitive behavioral psychotherapy.

PHOBIAS

Phobias are extreme fears of specific situations or objects. The most common phobia is agoraphobia, which is the fear of being in places from which it is not easy to escape. This phobia, which can develop later in life (Sadavoy & LeClair, 1997), makes it less likely that people will venture from their homes—some find it very difficult to leave home at all. Many people with agoraphobia also have panic disorder. Another phobia is social phobia, which is extreme fear of social or performance situations in which the individual may feel embarrassed. Social phobia is often experienced as public speaking anxiety but may be as broad as fears of any social situation. Older adults tend to experience less social anxiety than do younger adults (Gretarsdottir, Woodruff-Borden, Meeks, & Depp, 2003). Other phobias are of animals, natural environments (e.g., heights, water), blood or needles, and certain situations (e.g., airplanes, enclosed spaces). Researchers estimate that 4.8 percent of older adults have a phobia (Stanley & Beck, 2000). Cognitive behavioral therapy has been found to be helpful in the treatment of phobias. Treatment focuses primarily on teaching relaxation techniques, and then exposing the individual to the feared object or situation while relaxed.

OBSESSIVE-COMPULSIVE DISORDER

People with obsessive-compulsive disorder (OCD) have recurrent obsessions or compulsions that are severe enough to impair their daily functioning. Obsessions are persistent thoughts, ideas, or images that are anxiety-provoking and, at least initially, absurd to the individual experiencing them. Common examples of obsessions are contamination (e.g., being infected with germs), doubts (e.g., questioning if one left the stove on or locked the door), or a need to have things in a certain order. Compulsions are repeated behaviors (e.g., hand washing, repeating a word to prevent someone from getting hurt, checking locks, cleaning) that are intended to reduce anxiety, often about an obsession. One compulsion that may be a problem in later life is hoarding (e.g., saving newspapers, clothes, or other objects).

Mrs. Kane had been collecting things for years. She loved thrift stores and yard sales and never came home with less than two bags of new treasures. She also saved newspapers and magazines because there might be an article she was sure she'd need to refer to in the future or a coupon she wanted to clip. The problem was that Mrs. Kane lived in a small, one-bedroom apartment with her husband, and there was very little space for her collections. Newspapers were piled on counters and the stovetop, preventing her from doing any cooking. Magazines, old lamps, and bags of clothes were piled in every room and on the balcony. Mrs. Kane did not have guests because she was embarrassed about the mess, but she couldn't bear to part with her things. After a complaint, the landlord came to the apartment and demanded that the apartment be cleaned out because it was a fire hazard. He was also very concerned about Mrs. Kane, and called a state agency, the Adult Protective Services (APS). The mobile crisis team came to see Mrs. Kane and referred her for treatment in a geriatric clinic for treatment of obsessive-compulsive disorder. Mrs. Kane's psychologist worked with her and with APS to clean her apartment—a traumatic experience for her. The psychologist also educated Mrs. Kane's husband about OCD, as he couldn't understand why his wife couldn't just throw things away. After months of treatment and working with cleaning crews, Mrs. Kane's apartment was cleaned and painted. She continued to work with her psychologist to avoid thrift stores and find ways to manage anxiety.

POSTTRAUMATIC STRESS DISORDER

Posttraumatic stress disorder (PTSD) may develop after exposure to an extraordinarily stressful event, such as being threatened with death or personal harm, or witnessing the death or severe injury of someone else. This disorder was first recognized in the United States after the Vietnam War, and since that time, many military veterans and other trauma victims have been treated for it. Lifetime prevalence of PTSD in the general population of the United States ranges from 1 to 9.2 percent (Hidalgo & Davidson, 2000). Determining the prevalence of PTSD among older adults is difficult, however. Most studies have been done with war veterans, Holocaust survivors, and disaster victims and do not include other types of trauma survivors. Current estimates of prevalence of

PTSD among older adults range from 3 percent to 56 percent, depending on the group studied, with highest rates for former prisoners of war.

PTSD involves recurrent thoughts about or images of the traumatic event, recurrent nightmares, feelings of reliving the event, or intense distress when reminded of the event. People with PTSD avoid thoughts about or people who were involved in the event, feel distant from others, have difficulty experiencing emotions, are very irritable, have trouble sleeping or concentrating, or are hyperaware of their surroundings (fearing the event might sneak up on them again). These symptoms often get worse during stress, and some sufferers attempt to medicate themselves with alcohol or drugs. Older adults who have had traumatic events earlier in life tend to experience periods of symptoms intermittently over the course of their lives (Hyer, Summers, Braswell, & Boyd, 1995). Some older adults experience increased symptoms in later life (McLeod, 1994).

Treatment for PTSD often includes anti-anxiety medications, antidepressant medications, and psychotherapy to minimize the impact of the traumatic event on the individual's current life.

TREATMENT OF ANXIETY DISORDERS

Psychotherapy is effective in reducing symptoms of anxiety. Research has shown that helping an individual with anxiety to change thoughts in specific situations and thought patterns across situations (as in cognitive behavioral therapy) decreases the frequency and intensity of symptoms. Medications have also been found to be very helpful. Short-acting anti-anxiety medications, such as benzodiazepines (e.g., lorazepam [Ativan] and alprazolam [Xanax]) relieve symptoms of anxiety quickly, but do not last long and can be addictive. These medications can produce dangerous side effects in older adults, including cardiac and pulmonary problems, increased fall risk, and confusion. Long-acting medications, such as buspirone (Buspar) or diazepam (Valium), take longer to take effect but minimize symptoms for a longer period of time. These are not used as often due to potential side effects for older adults. Beta-blockers (such as propranolol [Inderal] or metoprolol [Lopressor]), which are typically used for cardiovascular problems, are often prescribed to treat severe physical symptoms of anxiety, such as tremors, pounding heart, muscle tension, and sweating. Beta-blockers are often given for use in a single situation that causes anxiety, such as public speaking or flying. Antidepressant medications are also prescribed for some people with anxiety disorders, particularly panic disorder and obsessive-compulsive disorder.

Substance Use Disorders

Many people think that alcohol and drug abuse and dependence are a problem of the young. However, there are as many older adults hospitalized for alcohol-related problems as for heart attacks (Weintraub et al., 2002), and older adults who abuse substances are 2.5 times more likely than nonabusers to die prematurely (Moos, Mertens, & Brennan, 1994). Estimates of alcohol and drug abuse among older adults range from 13 percent to 17 percent

(Weintraub et al.; Rigler, 2000), and fewer than half of these people are referred for treatment (Weintraub et al.). After alcohol, the most common substances to be abused are benzodiazepines (Finlayson, 1995). Recent studies have also shown surprisingly high usage rates of cocaine (10 percent), marijuana (2 percent), and even heroin (8 percent) (Weintraub et al.). Rates of drug use among future generations of older Americans will likely increase as baby boomers reach old age.

Although symptoms of physiological dependence on or withdrawal from specific substances vary somewhat, criteria for substance dependence include the following:

- development of a tolerance for the substance (need for increasing amounts to achieve the desired effect or diminished effect with the same amount over time)
- substance withdrawal symptoms, such as trembling, sweating, heart palpitations, nausea, headache, and insomnia
- considerable time spent obtaining, consuming, and recovering from using the substance
- desire or unsuccessful efforts to reduce the amount of the substance or stop taking it
- use of larger amounts of the substance over a longer period of time than was intended
- giving up or decreasing involvement in important social, occupational, or recreational activities because of the substance use
- continuation of substance use despite problems that it may be causing

Like younger adults, some older adults may need to be initially detoxified from an abused substance. This may involve hospitalization, particularly if the older adult has other medical problems that require observation during withdrawal. Once the individual has been detoxified, psychotherapeutic treatment focuses on building coping skills and changing activity patterns so that the individual does not return to substance use. This treatment often enlists family members and friends to assist in preventing relapse. There is little evidence for the effectiveness of medications for older adult substance abusers (Bartels et al., 2002).

Psychotic Symptoms and Psychotic Disorders

The term *psychotic* generally refers to symptoms in which the individual is not in touch with reality. Psychotic symptoms are primarily hallucinations (perceptions of things that are not really there, such as hearing voices or feeling as though bugs are crawling all over one's body) and delusions (false beliefs that are maintained in the face of evidence that they are false, such as believing that one's children are trying to poison or steal from the individual). Approximately 10 percent of older adults admitted to psychiatric hospitals report psychotic symptoms that began after the age of 65 (Webster &

Grossberg, 1998). The most common causes for these symptoms are dementia, severe depression, and various medical problems, such as infections or metabolic imbalances. Early in life, more men than women are admitted to hospitals with psychotic symptoms. However, more women than men are admitted with psychotic symptoms later in life, perhaps due to the protective effect of estrogen in the brain that declines after menopause. Following is a description of the two most common types of psychotic disorders among older adults.

Schizophrenia

Schizophrenia is the most chronic and severely disabling disorder, affecting every aspect of its victims' lives. It is very rare, occurring in only 1 percent of the general population. Onset of the disorder typically comes in the early 20s for men and in the late 20s for women. Schizophrenia can also begin later in life, though it is less common. Among patients hospitalized for schizophrenia, approximately 13 percent of them experienced the onset of the illness in their 40s, 7 percent in their 50s, and 3 percent after the age of 60 (Harris & Jeste, 1988). Women are 2 to 10 times more likely than men to develop late-onset schizophrenia (McClure, Gladsjo, & Jeste, 1999).

Contrary to popular belief, schizophrenia does not mean *split personality*. Symptoms of schizophrenia include:

- psychotic symptoms (hallucinations and delusions)
- disorganized speech (such as absurd associations, nonsense words, illogical sentences)
- disorganized behavior (such as wild gestures, aggressiveness)
- negative (inactive) symptoms: deficiency of motivation, emotional expression, or speech

These symptoms often come in phases, with periods of active psychotic symptoms often preceded and then followed by periods of impaired daily functioning and strange ideas or behavior. Most people with schizophrenia do not return to their previous level of functioning and have increasing difficulty relating to people and managing life independently. People who develop schizophrenia in later life are more likely to be paranoid, but they generally function better than older adults with early-onset schizophrenia (McClure et al., 1999).

Treatment for schizophrenia largely involves managing psychotic symptoms through the use of medications (e.g., clozapine [Clozaril], risperidone [Risperdal], zyprazadone [Zyprexa], quetiapine [Seroquel]) and building social skills. Some therapeutic programs focus on empowering individuals with schizophrenia to utilize their strengths and maximize productivity in the community. The latter programs are in their infancy for older adults. Most people with schizophrenia need a great deal of support to live in the community. Earlier in life, that support often comes from families, group homes, or psychiatric institutions. As adults age and families or group homes may no longer be able to care for complex psychiatric and medical needs, many with serious mental illness move to nursing homes. While staff are trained to treat a variety of medical illnesses, the vast majority lack training in treating and managing the behavioral symptoms of psychiatric problems, particularly with severe illnesses like schizophrenia.

Delusional Disorder

People with delusional disorder experience delusions in the absence of other symptoms. Among older adults, the most common delusion is that family or friends are trying to steal from or harm them (Webster & Grossberg, 1998). Since these delusions are often plausible at first, the beliefs are often not seen as a disorder or treated until long after onset of the illness (Thorpe, 1997). Delusional disorder is very rare, occurring in approximately 0.02 percent of the general population (Andreason & Black, 2001). The prevalence of delusional disorder increases in middle and late adulthood, however, with rates as high as 4 percent (Christenson & Blazer, 1994). Treatment of delusional disorder is very difficult. Antipsychotic medications and psychotherapy are often unsuccessful in resolving the delusions, although psychotherapy can help the older adult cope with the distress caused by the delusions.

Loss in Later Life

Most literature on grief and loss focuses on bereavement after the death of a loved one. While this focus is extremely important, there are many other losses that occur in later life. Although most people look to later life as a time of leisure and enjoyment of family and friends, many also contend with an increasing number of losses. These losses include social roles, relationships, health, cognition, and functional ability. In some sense, the elderly experience the loss of pieces of themselves.

PHYSICAL HEALTH

Two-thirds of older adults report having good to excellent health. Three-quarters report minimal limitations in carrying out activities of daily living (Jette, 1996). Aging involves the decline of many physiological processes, however, and half of people over the age of 85 report various disabilities in their daily activities (Jette). Normal aging includes the following:

- hearing loss
- vision loss
- loss of muscle and bone mass
- decreased sensitivity to touch, smell, and taste
- decreased ability to heal from injuries and illnesses
- slowed metabolism
- loss of muscle and skin elasticity

Later life is also accompanied by chronic illness and disease for many older adults. Common illnesses of later life include:

- cardiovascular problems (high blood pressure, high cholesterol, heart disease, congestive heart failure)
- diabetes
- osteoporosis, brittle bones, significant ramifications of falling
- arthritis
- cancer
- chronic pain
- kidney disease

These illnesses and resulting disabilities lead some older adults to stop participation in previously enjoyed physical activities, including sports, gardening, housekeeping, cooking, and even attendance at social or community events and religious services.

COGNITIVE FUNCTIONING

As discussed in chapter 12, later life is accompanied by small declines in short-term memory, memory for nonverbal information, speed of information retrieval, and speed of reaction time. Most older adults' daily functioning is not affected by these normal changes. However, a minority will experience dementia, which results in the loss of most cognitive functions.

INDEPENDENCE

Physical and cognitive declines leave many older adults dependent on others for household maintenance, activities of daily living, transportation, and (for some) total personal care. Loss of independence is difficult for many and seen by some as tantamount to the end of life as they knew it. The loss of ability to drive a car, in particular, is a major loss of independence that can lead to isolation and depression (Marottoli et al., 1993). Dependence on others can be humiliating and infantilizing and, for some, can have a significant negative impact on an individual's sense of self and self-esteem.

VALUED SOCIAL ROLES

A *role* is an individual's pattern of activity that occurs within a specific type of social situation. For example, the role of employee is enacted in the work setting, and includes the tasks that one was hired to do, as well as the formal and informal social rules that govern behavior at work. *Valued social roles* are those roles that society has deemed worthy of value, such as employee, parent, teacher, volunteer, student, or friend. These valued roles are in contrast to *devalued roles* that many older adults view themselves as taking on later in life, such as medical patient or care recipient.

The general consensus among early American theorists was that old age is a time for reviewing past experiences and accepting one's life course while shifting away from the larger community (Erikson, Erikson, & Kivnick, 1986; Jung, 1958; Neugarten, 1977). This position assumed that it was a normal, acceptable part of later life to relinquish valued social roles and allow younger generations to step into them. However, roles largely define identity. For example, a woman may think of herself as a mother, a wife, a lawyer, a community advocate, or a friend. These roles provide meaning to her life and shape her sense of self and self-esteem (Wells & Stryker, 1988). Generally, the greater the number of valued roles people view themselves as having, the better they feel and function. Similarly, the greater the number of devalued roles people view themselves as having, the worse they feel and function. It follows, then, that loss of valued roles would have negative consequences for some elders, a phenomenon that has been supported by research. In a study of elderly assisted living facility residents, older adults reported having lost an average of 40 percent of the valued roles they had as younger adults (Emery & Pargament, 2002). This loss was subjectively reported as distressing and was associated with higher levels of depressive symptoms.

As the case of Mr. Bernstein at the beginning of this chapter illustrates, a physical loss can create a social loss and result in loss of self-esteem and the esteem of others. Without replacement of valued roles, Mr. Bernstein was at risk for social isolation, depression, and further decline.

WHAT CAN YOU DO?

- *Remember that every person has inherent worth and something to offer.* Don't be blinded to an individual's strengths in the face of a loss. Consider, for example, a nursing home resident with multiple sclerosis who had become quadriplegic. Despite her physical losses, she was able to make audio recordings of her life story and favorite recipes to share with her children and grandchildren, thus leaving a legacy to her family.

- *Explore individuals' remaining strengths.* What can they do? What are they good at? What do they enjoy doing that they are able to do? Mr. Bernstein, for example, was still generally physically healthy, just not agile enough to play handball. He could utilize his training as a carpenter and experience as a handyman to help friends and neighbors with needed tasks around the house. He could also fulfill his wish to spend time outside by helping his wife in the garden.

- *Identify ways they can get involved in the community.* Mrs. Kim, a Christian minister, had been in the hospital for weeks with end-stage stomach cancer. She had little strength left and knew that her life was coming to an end. Mrs. Kim remained connected to her congregation by saying prayers and giving blessings to those who wrote and visited her in the hospital. This activity gave her last days meaning.

Bereavement and Grief

Bereavement is the experience of the death of a loved one. *Grief* is the emotional response to a loss. Note that grief can also include the emotional response to the losses discussed above that don't include death. Although

mourning is often used interchangeably with *grief,* some loss experts consider mourning to include the social and cultural response to loss. The distinction is important because there are often cultural expectations for how people behave after a loss, and they may or may not be related to how an individual is actually feeling. For example, Jewish tradition dictates an official period of mourning, called *shivah,* following a death, during which family and friends congregate to grieve together and offer support to the family. For those closest to the deceased, there is an ongoing period of mourning for one year. The end of this period is marked by a ceremony in which a headstone is placed on the grave. It is expected that grieving will largely have come to a close by the end of that year. For most, this ritual period provides an acceptable period to return to normal functioning. Others who continue to grieve beyond this period may feel abnormal. Conversely, those whose grief resolves more quickly than the prescribed period of mourning may feel guilty. It is important for you to be aware of cultural beliefs and traditions that may affect the grief experiences of your clients.

LOSS OF FAMILY AND FRIENDS

Later life is accompanied by the loss of an increasing number of friends and family members. As people age, social networks shrink, leaving some older adults with few or no friends or family members. Some researchers suggest that most older adults learn to adapt after experiencing multiple losses (Moss, Moss & Hansson, 2002). However, multiple losses can have a cumulative harmful effect (Norris & Murrell, 1990). In either case, the effect of multiple losses in later life may be overlooked by those around older adults and therefore go untreated. For example, when the sibling of an older adult dies, most attention is focused on the spouse and children of the deceased, regardless of the number of siblings the individual may have lost. Bereaved siblings have been shown to have the same decreased functional level as a bereaved spouse, however, and even lower self-rated health (Hays, Gold, & Pieper, 1997). Perhaps an even more tragic loss is the death of a child, experienced by 10 to 25 percent of older adults after the age of 60 (Moss, Lesher, & Moss, 1986).

SPOUSAL LOSS

The loss of a spouse is tragic at any point in life, but the secondary losses (losses that occur as a result of the death) can be traumatic after 50 or 60 years of marriage. Not only does the individual lose a spouse, but also daily routine, companionship, valued social roles (husband, wife, caretaker, etc.), and what some subjectively describe as "a large piece" of themselves. In short, some bereaved spouses feel as though they've lost their lives and their world as they knew it.

> *Mr. and Mrs. Morely were married for 62 years and went everywhere together. When his wife died following a long battle with pneumonia, Mr. Morely was devastated. Prior to her death, he had been at her bedside most of every day. When the funeral was over and family and friends had gone, Mr. Morely was left alone with the palpable absence of his wife and no one to take care of. As a young man, he moved from his parents' home into a home with his wife. He had therefore never lived alone before and was frightened about what that would mean for him. He had to face the cooking, upkeep of the house, and paying bills, all of which had been his wife's tasks. His wife had also been the social butterfly, and without her he feared that he would have no friends. She was the one who stayed in touch with their social circle. Even if he did see them, as they'd encouraged him to do at the funeral, he felt like a third wheel in the company of couples. His children had encouraged him to go to the senior center to be with other people, but he feared meeting other older adults who might also die. He didn't think he could bear another loss.*

Mr. Morely and other seniors who have lost a spouse are at great risk for social isolation and depression if they do not maintain their activity level and social interaction. As described above, you can help older adults identify their individual strengths and the activities they enjoy and help them find ways to engage in those activities to facilitate the grieving process and prevent emotional and physical decline.

WHAT IS NORMAL GRIEF?

This is a question that researchers, theorists, and clinicians have puzzled over for decades. Some people recover and move on right after the loss, others grieve intensely for a short period of time then move on, while others experience profound grief for years. With such variability between individual reactions to loss, determining a normal disruption of daily functioning, its extent, and its length of time becomes a very difficult task. Review of the research on grief in the general American population suggests that 50 to 80 percent of people experience moderate disruption of cognitive, emotional, physical, or interpersonal functioning for the first few months after the loss of a loved one, returning to normal functioning within one year (Bonnano & Kaltman, 2001, p. 709). This common pattern of disruption in functioning during grief includes:

- disorganization of thinking
- sadness, feeling empty
- health problems
- problems in social and occupational functioning
- some positive experiences, including thoughts about the deceased

Approximately 15 to 50 percent of people experience minimal grief and return to normal functioning quickly, and another 15 percent go on to develop more severe, chronic problems with grief that persist beyond one to two years (Bonnano & Kaltman, 2001). Studies of grief among older adults suggest that older adults who lose a spouse may grieve longer than many others. Plus, older adults who have lost a spouse have shown significantly more symptoms of grief than adults who lost a family member other than a spouse (Lehman, Wortman, & Williams, 1987; Thompson, Gallagher-Thompson, Futterman, Gilewski, & Peterson, 1998). This difference has been found up to seven years after the death, which led the researchers to suggest that some later-life widows and widowers may never entirely resolve their grief.

Experts have developed models of the process of grieving. These models are frameworks from which to understand what might be happening with an individual who is grieving. They do not necessarily outline what each individual should expect to experience after a loss, or define what an individual must experience in order to resolve the grief.

Stage Model of Grieving

In perhaps the best-known model, Elisabeth Kübler-Ross (1969) suggested that people go through a process of grieving that involves five stages: denial, anger, bargaining, depression, and acceptance. She described these stages in relation to getting a diagnosis of serious illness, and the stages were later used more generally in relation to grieving. Years after her original publication about these stages, we now know that most people do not progress linearly through any set stages. The concepts she described are useful in thinking about what some people may experience, however, particularly with regard to anticipatory grief. Anticipatory grief is experienced in advance of a loss, such as by people who learn about a life-limiting illness for themselves or a loved one. People begin to grieve as they think ahead about what will be lost. Anticipatory grief is common among family members caring for relatives with dementia or other chronic, life-limiting illnesses (see chapter 7).

Denial

Denial can be an adaptive response that buffers unexpected shocking news. Reacting with disbelief helps to prepare for impending loss. It allows time to collect oneself until other coping responses can be used. Denial can be detrimental if maintained too long. Working with people who refuse to accept the reality of a situation can be very frustrating. It is futile, insensitive, and most often counterproductive to force people to deal with something before they are ready to do so. This is especially true after the loss of a loved one.

Anger

Anger is the second stage of grief in this model. Anger may be directed at the disease, at doctors for failing to prevent the illness or death, or at the deceased for having the disease and dying. Anger may be directed at oneself for not doing more before the onset of the disease, or for remaining healthy.

Experience of loss can make people feel very out of control. Anger may be a way to try to exercise some control over a situation. If someone or something is to blame, that implies that something could have been done differently and that future situations can be controlled.

Bargaining

When the angry response doesn't work to change the situation, Kübler-Ross suggests that people try to bargain, like a child might after a temper tantrum doesn't work. People may plead with God or powerful others to return to them that which they have lost, promising to do more or be a better person in return.

Depression

Some symptoms of depression may be expected after getting news about a life-limiting illness or the loss of a loved one. It is important to note, however, that clinical depression (described earlier in the chapter) is not part of normal grief. If symptoms of depression interfere with an individual's ability to function and persist beyond two months, the individual may be experiencing traumatic grief (described later) or a major depressive episode (described earlier), and should be referred to a mental health professional.

Acceptance

Acceptance of an illness, disability, or death can feel like giving up, so many people avoid it as long as possible. Acceptance can invoke a great deal of fear of living with a disability or without a deceased loved one, as well as apprehension about building a new life in that world. Acceptance can also bring a sense of peace. Fighting an uphill or futile battle is exhausting. Once a person is able to stop the fight, they can focus energy on moving forward, into the stage of hope.

Task Model of Grieving

Another way of looking at grief is through a task model, in which the bereaved individual has a number of tasks to complete in the grieving process. This is different from the stage model in that people may be working on all of the tasks at the same time, but the effort associated with them may increase or decrease in importance over the course of the grief. One does not need to complete one stage before moving on to the next, and some tasks may apply more to some people than to others. In contrast to the stage model, in which it is expected that people passively pass through each stage in due time, the task model may be more empowering to some. Believing that there are tasks that they can actively work on to manage their grief may be comforting. At the same time, it may not be the case that checking each of these tasks off a list will relieve all suffering.

Experts have developed multiple task models, each of which has a slightly different focus. One example of a task model is presented here (Vickio, 1999). Completion of these tasks is expected to facilitate not only a return to normal functioning but to facilitate growth through the creation of new meaning in life.

Accepting the Reality of the Loss

This task can involve not only the belief that the individual is gone, but coming to terms with all of the associated losses described above (transportation, cleaning, cooking, paying bills, income, etc.). Many people, particularly older adults who have lost a spouse, have described seeing, hearing, or feeling the deceased after they have passed. These sensations may be misunderstood as psychiatric symptoms (i.e., hallucinations) and evidence that the individual has not accepted the loss. This experience is actually not unusual and may not be a psychosis. Some experts have also questioned whether sensing the deceased may be sensory recall (remembering and reexperiencing a visual, auditory, or touch perception). In the absence of other psychotic symptoms, it is possible that these visions may be comforting and not require intervention.

Some theorists suggest that the process of grieving facilitates the breaking of bonds with the deceased. For many people, particularly those who have had a lifelong relationship with the deceased, it may be helpful to think of the grieving process as changing the relationship from a physical or interpersonal connection to a spiritual connection.

An 87-year-old woman whose husband had died created somewhat of a shrine to him on her dresser with pictures and medals he had won. She spoke to him daily and told people that he responded to her. When her children became distressed about this behavior, they brought her to a psychologist. Exploration of the relationship with her deceased husband revealed that she was comforted by being able to talk to her husband daily, believing that he was in heaven listening to her. She didn't physically hear him respond to her (i.e., she was not hallucinating); she just knew him so well that she knew what he would say. Continuing to have conversations with him allowed her to feel connected to him, prevented her from feeling lonely, and allowed her to maintain regular activities without getting depressed about the loss. The psychologist suggested to her children that they think of her mother's behavior like talking to God or an angel. They found this explanation useful.

Doing One's Duty to the Deceased

This task may involve following through on promises made before an individual died, taking up causes or activities the deceased was involved in, or, in the case of questionable deaths, investigating causes of the death and searching for justice. However, seeking to avenge a death or tirelessly taking up a deceased's cause only out of guilt will not facilitate grief.

Regaining a Sense of Control

Loss of a loved one and being unable to do anything about it is very disempowering. Grieving individuals may feel as though they no longer have control over anything, including their own emotional response to the loss. Although it may seem paradoxical, feelings of guilt may be an effort to regain a sense of control. Many survivors come to believe that if they had just asked the doctor to run one more test, treated the deceased with more respect, just been a better person, then maybe the deceased wouldn't have died, died so soon, or suffered so much. Believing that one may have been able to prevent the death or prevent suffering implies that the bereaved had some control over the situation. Guilt may be somewhat helpful in the short term to prevent the shattering of the world as they knew it. It may take time and talking with a good friend or therapist to sort out feelings of guilt.

Finding a Sense of Purpose

For many grieving people, and particularly those whose life centered around the deceased, this task becomes paramount. Finding a sense of purpose can be particularly challenging for older adults who were caring for the deceased for an extended period before death.

Relearning the World

Particularly for an older adult who had a relationship with the deceased for many years, one part of relearning the world is mentally and practically coming to terms with living without them. Practical tasks may involve learning to negotiate the bus system or pay bills. Those whose worldview was shattered by the death may have more mental or emotional relearning to do. For example, if one's long-held belief was that children outlive parents and a child dies, it may rattle an entire belief system. The same may be true for someone who expected to die before a spouse or believed that spouses are together forever. Developing a new belief system about the world can be a very daunting task. This may be particularly difficult for older adults who have lived a long life and had their belief system shattered in later life.

STUG Reactions

Many people experience grief and come to feel as though they have returned to a normal state of functioning, only to experience a sudden flash of seemingly unbearable sadness. This resurgence leaves many who have struggled through the grieving process feeling as though they have lost all gains they had made. Therese Rando (1988) called these experiences STUG reactions: sudden temporary upsurges of grief. These reactions are often triggered by a situation, a place, a holiday, or a scent that reminds the survivor of the deceased. Most often, STUG reactions are brief and do not indicate that the individual is experiencing pathological symptoms. Bereaved persons can be reassured that these reactions are normal and may occur periodically but typically become less intense and taper off over time.

WHAT CAN YOU DO?

When faced with a grieving senior or family member, there are several things that may be helpful for you to do:

- Be aware of your own attitudes toward dying, death, and grief. Death is such a taboo topic in so many cultures that most people do not think about or discuss it with others. Some activities that may be helpful to you to familiarize yourself with death and dying:

95

—Visit or volunteer in a hospice or a nursing home. Expose yourself to those near the end of life.

—Have a conversation with someone close to you about your coming death or the death of a loved one.

—If you are still struggling with a loss of your own, talk with a therapist about the experience and what it means to you.

- Most people are very uncomfortable talking about death or listening to someone else talk about it. Grieving people often feel alone in their experience and do not want to burden others with discussion of death. Giving a grieving person an opportunity to share personal feelings can be a very powerful experience. Encourage the expression of feelings, needs, and beliefs, and listen closely to what is being expressed. Whether an individual is experiencing denial, anger, confusion, fear, or guilt, the listener should remain calm, even when the emotions of the grieving person are intense.

- Do not take anger or irrational outbursts personally. Remember that the individual is grieving. Reacting to anger with anger will only escalate the situation.

- Because each person experiences grief very differently, do not tell a grieving person that you know what they are feeling or understand what they are going through. In all likelihood, you do not. Tell them instead that you are sorry for their loss and offer your sympathy and support.

- Do not try to talk individuals out of their feelings. People experience intense emotions following a loss and need a safe place to express them. Use active listening skills, like responding to statements without agreeing, challenging, or disputing the other person's perspective. Listen carefully and acknowledge what you have heard the person say.

- Allow an individual time to think about the loss. This is especially true for older adults who may be processing information more slowly.

- Have a list of area bereavement services available for your clients and their families. If the grief is interfering with daily functioning for more than two months after the loss, referral to a therapist may be beneficial.

TRAUMATIC GRIEF

Although most people are able to function normally following bereavement, some experience what has been called traumatic grief (TG). Traumatic grief is a relatively new diagnosis and has not yet been included in the Diagnostic and Statistical Manual of Mental Disorders (DSM-IV, American Psychological Association). A growing body of literature has demonstrated that TG is a distinct syndrome and predicts poorer functioning, lower energy, and poorer mental health than normal grieving (Silverman et al., 2000). One study showed that 57 percent of older adults with TG had suicidal thoughts, compared to 24 percent of bereaved older adults without TG (Szanto, Prigerson, Houck, Ehrenpreis, & Reynolds, 1997). Another study found that older adults with TG had higher rates of cancer, heart trouble, high blood pressure, and changes in eating habits than those without TG one to two years after the death of a terminally ill spouse (Prigerson et al., 1997). As many as 20 percent of older adults may experience traumatic grief following the loss of a spouse (Prigerson & Jacobs, 2001).

Traumatic grief is a syndrome with two clusters of symptoms. The first cluster reflects *separation distress* symptoms, including searching and yearning for the deceased, having intrusive thoughts about the deceased, and experiencing excessive loneliness since the death. In TG, these symptoms occur at least daily or to a marked degree. The second cluster of symptoms reflects the *trauma response*, with symptoms similar to those in posttraumatic stress disorder. In response to the death, 6 of the following 11 symptoms are experienced at least daily or to a marked degree as part of TG:

- purposelessness, feelings of futility about future
- subjective sense of numbness, detachment, or absence of emotional responsiveness
- difficulty acknowledging the death (disbelief)
- feeling that life is empty or meaningless
- feeling that a part of oneself has died
- shattered worldview (lost sense of security, trust, control)
- assumption of symptoms of harmful behaviors of, or related to, the deceased
- excessive irritability, bitterness, or anger related to the death
- avoidance of reminders of the loss
- shocked or daze from the loss
- feeling that life is not fulfilling without the deceased

As with defining normal grief, the most controversial component of the TG diagnostic criteria is the length of time that symptoms are present before they are considered pathological. As a general rule, however, if a person is experiencing the symptoms of TG for longer than two months after the death of a loved one and those symptoms impair the individual's ability to carry out daily activities, referral to a mental health professional is recommended.

Mental Health, Grief, and Loss in Later life: Summary

Later life presents a host of challenges and losses, but older adults do not come empty-handed to the process of understanding and dealing with them. As with younger adults, a small portion of older adults will develop mental health problems. Some of these disorders and their treatments have unique characteristics in later life. Major depressive episodes and anxiety disorders are the most common mental disorders and, when detected, can be effectively treated. Substance abuse is increasing among older adults. Later life comes with a variety of losses, but most adults cope very well with them. Losing a spouse in later life can result in profound grief that may require treatment. If you have a general awareness of mental illness and grief, you can help refer older adults for appropriate treatment.

You should be knowledgeable about:

- common mental health problems of older adults
- prevalence and course of mental health problems
- treatment options that are available for mental illness in later life
- losses associated with later life
- normal grief versus traumatic grief
- resources for you, your clients, and their families

References

Alexopolous, G. S., Meyers, B. S., Young, R. C., Campbell, S., Silbersweig, D., & Charlson, M. (1997). "Vascular depression" hypothesis. *Archives of General Psychiatry, 54*, 915–922.

Almeida, O. P., & Fenner, S. (2002). Bipolar disorder: Similarities and differences between patients with illness onset before and after 65 years of age. *International Psychogeriatrics, 14*, 311–322.

American Psychiatric Association. (1994). *Diagnostic and statistical manual of mental disorders* (4th ed.). Washington, D.C.: American Psychiatric Association.

Andreason, N. C., & Black, D. W. (2001). Delusional disorder and other psychotic disorders. In N. C. Andreason & D. W. Black (Eds.), *Introductory Textbook of Psychiatry* (3rd ed.). Washington, DC: American Psychiatric Association.

Baltes, P. B., Smith, J., & Staudinger, U. M. (1992). Wisdom and successful aging. In T. B. Sonderegger (Ed.), *Nebraska symposium on motivation 1991, Vol. 39: Psychology and aging*, pp. 123–167. Lincoln, NE: University of Nebraska Press.

Bartels, S. J., Dums, A. R., Oxman, T. E., Schneider, L. S., Arean, P. A., Alexopolous, G. S., et al. (2002). Evidence-based practices in geriatric mental health care. *Psychiatric Services, 53*, 1419–1431.

Bonnano, G. A., & Kaltman, S. (2001). The varieties of grief experience. *Clinical Psychology Review, 21*, 705–734.

Christenson, R., & Blazer, D. G. (1994). Epidemiology of persecutory ideation in an elderly population in the community. *American Journal of Psychiatry, 141*, 1088–1091.

Emery, E., & Pargament, K. (2002). *Effects of social roles among elders in assisted living facilities*. Poster presentation at the annual meeting of the Gerontological Society of America, Boston, MA.

Erikson, E. H., Erikson, J. M., & Kivnick, H. Q. (1986). *Vital involvement in old age*. New York: Norton.

Fillip, S. H. (1996). Motivation and emotion. In J. E. Birren & K. W. Schaie (Eds.), *Handbook of the psychology of aging* (4th ed.), pp. 218–235. San Diego, CA: Academic Press.

Finlayson, R. E. (1995). Misuse of prescription drugs. *International Journal of Addictions, 30,* 1871–1901.

Gretarsdottir, E., Woodruff-Borden, J., Meeks, S., & Depp, C. A. (2003). Social anxiety in older adults: Phenomenology, prevalence, and measurement. *Behaviour Research and Therapy, 42,* 459–475.

Harris, M. J., & Jeste, D. V. (1988). Late-onset schizophrenia: An overview. *Schizophrenia Bulletin, 14,* 39–55.

Hays, J. C., Gold, D. T., & Pieper, C. F. (1997). Sibling bereavement in later life. *Omega, 35,* 25–42.

Hidalgo, R. B., & Davidson, J. R. T. (2000). Posttraumatic stress disorder: Epidemiology and health-related considerations. *Journal of Clinical Psychiatry, 61* (Suppl 7), 5–13.

Hyer, L., Summers, M., Braswell, L., & Boyd, S. (1995). Posttraumatic stress disorder: Silent problem among older combat veterans. *Psychotherapy, 32,* 348–364.

Jette, A. M. (1996). Disability trends and transitions. In R. H. Binstock & L. K. George (Eds.), *Handbook of aging and the social sciences*, pp. 94–114. San Diego, CA: Academic Press.

Jung, C. (1958). *Psychology and religion, Vol. 11. The collected works of C. G. Jung* (R. F. C. Hull, Trans.). Princeton, NJ: Princeton University Press.

Koenig, H. G., Meador, K. G., Goli, B., Shelp, F., Coehn, H. J., & Blazer, D. G. (1992). Self-rated depressive symptoms in medical inpatients: Age and racial differences. *International Journal of Psychiatry in Medicine, 22,* 11–31.

Kübler-Ross, E. (1969). *On death and dying.* New York: MacMillan.

Lehman, D. R., Wortman, C. B., & Williams, A. F. (1987). Long-term effects of losing a spouse or child in a motor vehicle crash. *Journal of Personality and Social Psychology, 52,* 218–231.

Marottoli, R. A., Ostfeld, A. M., Merrill, S. S., Perlman, G. D., Foley, D. J., & Cooney, L. M., Jr. (1993). Driving cessation and changes in mileage driven among elderly individuals. *Journals of Gerontology, 48,* S255–S260.

McClure, F. S., Gladsjo, J. A., & Jeste, D. V. (1999). Late-onset psychosis: Clinical, research, and ethical considerations. *American Journal of Psychiatry, 156,* 935–940.

McLeod, A. (1994). The reactivation of posttraumatic stress disorder in later life. *Australian and New Zealand Journal of Psychiatry, 28,* 625–634.

Moos, R. H., Mertens, J. R., & Brennan, P. L. (1994). Rates and predictors of four-year re-admission among late-middle ages and older substance abuse patients. *Journal of the Study of Alcohol, 55,* 561–570.

Moss, M., Lesher, E. L., & Moss, S. Z. (1986). Impact of the death of an adult child on elderly parents: Some observations. *Omega, 17,* 209–218.

Moss, M. S., Moss, S. Z., & Hansson, R. O. (2002). Bereavement and old age. In M. S. Stroebe, R. O. Hansson, W. Stroebe, & H. Schut (Eds.), *Handbook of bereavement research.* Washington, DC: American Psychological Association.

Neugarten, B. L. (1977). Personality and aging. In J. E. Birren & K. W. Schaie (Eds.), *Handbook of the psychology of aging*, pp. 626–649. New York: Van Nostrand Reinhold.

Norris, F. H., & Murrell, S. A. (1990). Social support, life events and stress as modifiers of adjustment to bereavement by older adults. *Psychology and Aging, 5,* 429–436.

Parker, G., Roy, K., Hadzi-Pavolvik, D., & Pedic, F. (1992). Psychotic (delusional) depression: A meta-analysis of physical treatments. *Journal of Affective Disorders, 24,* 17–24.

Prigerson, H. G., Bierhals, A. J., Kasl, S. V., Reynolds, C. F., Shear, M. K., Day, N., et al. (1997). Traumatic grief as a risk factor for mental and physical morbidity. *American Journal of Psychiatry, 154,* 616–623.

Prigerson, H. G., & Jacobs, S. C. (2001). Caring for bereaved patients: "All the doctors just suddenly go." *Journal of the American Medical Association, 286,* 1369–1375.

Rando, T. A. (1988). *Grieving: How to go on living when someone you love dies.* Lexington, MA: Lexington.

Reynolds, C. F., III, Frank, E., Perel., J. M., Imber, S. D., Cornes, C., Miller, M. D., et al. (1999). Nortriptyline and interpersonal psychotherapy as maintenance therapies for recurrent major depression: A randomized controlled trial in patients older than 59 years. *Journal of the American Medical Association, 281,* 39–45.

Rigler, S. K. (2000). Alcoholism in the elderly. *American Family Physician, 61,* 1710–1716.

Sadavoy, J., & LeClair, J. K. (1997). Treatment of anxiety disorders in later life. *Canadian Journal of Psychiatry, 42* (Suppl 1), 28S–34S.

Silverman, G. K., Jacobs, S. C., Kasl., S. V., Shear, M. K., Maciejewski, P. K., Noaghiul, F. S., et al. (2000). Quality of life impairments associated with diagnostic criteria for traumatic grief. *Psychological Medicine, 30,* 857–862.

Stanley, M., & Beck, J. (2000). Anxiety disorders. *Clinical Psychology Review, 20,* 731–754.

Szanto, K., Prigerson, H. G., Houck, P., Ehrenpreis, L., & Reynolds, C. F. (1997). Suicidal ideation in elderly bereaved: The role of complicated grief. *Suicide & Life Threatening Behavior, 27,* 194–207.

Thase, M. E., Greenhouse, J. B., Frank, E., Reynolds, C. F., III, Pilkonis, P. A., Hurley, K., et al. (1997). Treatment of major depression with psychotherapy or psychotherapy-pharmacotherapy combinations. *Archives of General Psychiatry, 54,* 1009–1015.

Thompson, L. W., Gallagher-Thompson, D., Futterman, A., Gilewski, M. J., & Peterson, J. (1998). The effects of later-life spousal bereavement over a thirty-month interval. In M. P. Lawton & T. A. Salthouse (Eds.), *Essential papers on the psychology of aging.* New York: New York University Press.

Thorpe, L. (1997). The treatment of psychotic disorders in later life. *Canadian Journal of Psychiatry, 42* (Suppl 1), 19S–27S.

van Gerpen, M. W., Johnson, J. E., & Wistead, D. K. (1999). Mania in the geriatric population: A review of the literature. *American Journal of Geriatric Psychiatry, 7,* 188–202.

Vickio, C. (1999, March). Together in spirit: Keeping our relationships alive when a loved one dies. *Death Studies, 23*(2).

Webster, J., & Grossberg, G. T. (1998). Later-life onset of psychotic symptoms. *American Journal of Geriatric Psychiatry, 6,* 196–202.

Weintraub, E., Weintraub, D., Dixon, L., Delahanty, J., Gandhi, D., Cohen, A., et al. (2002). Geriatric patients on a substance abuse consultation service. *American Journal of Geriatric Psychiatry, 10,* 337–342.

Weissman, M. M., Bruce, M. L., Leaf, P. L., Florio, L. P., & Holzer, C., III. (1991). Affective disorders. In L. N. Robins & D. A. Regier (Eds.), *Psychiatric disorders in America: The Epidemiologic Catchment Area Study*, pp. 53–80. New York: The Free Press.

Wells, L. E., & Stryker, S. (1988). Stability and change in self over the life course. In P. B. Baltes, D. L. Featherman, & R. M. Lerner (Eds.), *Lifespan development and behavior, Vol. 18*, pp. 191–229. Hillsdale, N.J.: Lawrence Erlbaum Associates.

Resources

Suggested Reading—Annotated

Feeling Good Handbook, David Burns, Plume Books, 1999, ISBN 0452281326. Burns adapts cognitive therapy to deal with a wide range of problems. *Feeling Good Handbook* teaches its readers how to remove the mental obstacles that bar them from success—from test anxiety and fear of public speaking to procrastination and self-doubt to depression.

Full Catastrophe Living: Using the Wisdom of Your Body and Mind to Face Stress, Pain, and Illness, Jon Kabat-Zinn, Delta Trade Paperbacks, 1990, ISBN 0385303122. Kabat-Zinn is the founder of the Stress Reduction Clinic at the University of Massachusetts Medical Center. His book details ways in which meditation has helped hospital patients deal with illness and can help anyone deal with stress and gain a calmer outlook on life.

Grief Recovery Handbook, John W. James & Russell Friedman, Perennial Press, 1998, ISBN 0060952733. Drawing from their own histories as well as from others', the authors illustrate what grief is and how it is possible to recover and regain energy and spontaneity. *Grief Recovery Handbook* offers grievers specific activities that help them complete the grieving process and accept loss.

Widow to Widow: Thoughtful, Practical Ideas for Rebuilding Your Life, Genevieve Davis Ginsburg, Fisher Books, 1997, ISBN 1555612261. *Widow to Widow* answers the number-one question asked by widows: "Why didn't anyone ever tell me it would be like this?" Writing from her own experiences as a widow, author Davis Ginsburg dispels the myths and disputes the rules, encouraging widows to begin their new lives in their own way and in their own time.

Services

AARP. http://www.aarp.org/griefandloss/support. Find a local grief support group at this page.

Alcoholics Anonymous (AA). http://www.aa.org

Grief & Loss Resource Centre. http://www.rockies.net/~spirit/grief/grief.html

Grief Recovery. http://www.grief.net

Griefnet. http://rivendell.org

Hospice Foundation of America. http://www.hospicefoundation.org/grief

National Alliance for the Mentally Ill (NAMI). http://www.nami.org

Chapter 5

The Experience of Aging

Hope is a waking dream.

Aristotle

A woman we will call Susan told the following dream to gerontologist and philosopher Harry Moody. After a decade of careful planning, Susan and her husband had recently moved to a luxury retirement community in Hilton Head, South Carolina.

> *I dreamed I was back in high school at a dance and it was time to go home. I needed a ride and I went around frantically asking everyone I knew for help. But no matter what I did, I couldn't get a ride home.*

After waking, Susan realized that the dream was a strong message to acknowledge that she and her husband had made a bad decision when they moved to Hilton Head. Soon after her dream they relocated to Asheville, North Carolina, and to a very different kind of community, where they have lived happily for many years. They fulfilled their dream of retirement. Their clue to life planning came to them in the form of a dream.

Introduction

Even with careful thought and rational planning, people may not fully understand their own goals or sources of satisfaction. In this case, Susan felt dissatisfaction, but only through a powerful dream did she realize that she and her husband needed to change course.

Prior to Susan's dream, she and her husband had spent several months pretending that they loved their new home. We know from cognitive psychology that people often rationalize their choices and resist acknowledging contradictory feelings aroused by their choices. Interestingly enough, psychologists have also learned that presenting more information doesn't necessarily result in better decisions (Schwartz, 2004). In fact, just getting a lot of information can actually paralyze choice and result in procrastination.

A knowledgeable CSA can be helpful in providing just the right amount of information at just the right time. Like messages delivered in dreams, inspiration about your clients comes from many different kinds of knowledge beyond verbal or rational statements alone. In this chapter, we'll examine how you can better understand the experience of aging in order to become more effective in your work with seniors.

Five Myths of Aging

As we grow up, we learn to cope successfully with the challenges we face in life. We enter school, we make friends, we prepare for a career, and many of us establish families of our own. It is common to recognize that people do better or worse in coping with these challenges. Is it possible to think of coping with the tasks of later life along the same lines? To do so demands overcoming myths that are very common in our society.

Rowe and Kahn, in their pathbreaking book *Successful Aging* (1999), identify a number of stereotypes about older people, false beliefs they designate as the Five Myths about Aging.

Myth 1: To Be Old Is to Be Sick

As with other stereotypes, the link between illness and aging is based on a grain of truth. While recent decades have seen great improvement in rates of chronic illness and disability, the risk for developing both conditions does increase with age. But even if they develop functional deficits, most older people are still able to live independently in their own homes until they reach very advanced age. Despite limitations in activity, seniors adapt—for instance, by relying on a cane or walker or by using a hearing aid. (We examine age-adaptive strategies in more detail below.)

Myth 2: You Can't Teach an Old Dog New Tricks

Most of us have heard the claim that as years go by people "lose a million neurons every day." It is not true. Neurobiology has shown that the human brain actually retains a high degree of neuroplasticity, the ability to learn new things, even into advanced age (Diamond, 1988). One practical implication is that older people can make changes to improve their lives. For instance, large numbers of adults have quit smoking, even beyond middle age. Epidemiologists now point to data showing how changes in health behavior have delayed disability and diminished the need for long-term care (Manton & Gu, 2001).

For you as a CSA, the facts about neuroplasticity and lifelong learning are good news. For example, the old stereotype that older people will never change to new brands is not true. Your role is to provide new knowledge that can help people make better decisions in later life.

Myth 3: The Secret to Successful Aging Is to Choose Your Parents Wisely

There is growing awareness of the role of genetics as an influence on our health. But Rowe and Kahn (1999) point out that genetics are not the only factors determining how we age. The good news is that social and behavioral fac-

tors within our control also play an important role in shaping health and well being. As your clients learn more about these facts, lifelong learning and healthy behavior are within their reach.

MYTH 4: THE HORSE IS OUT OF THE BARN

It's natural to be pessimistic about changing behavior if people believe "it's just too late" to do any good. Yet we now understand that adopting healthy lifestyle behaviors can provide a payoff at any age. For example, after a person quits smoking, human lung function begins to approach normal after only a few years, even for those who quit after middle age.

But opportunities for change are not limited to health behavior. It is also entirely possible to make positive changes in saving and spending patterns later in life.

MYTH 5: THE ELDERLY DON'T PULL THEIR OWN WEIGHT

A stereotypical image of aging is Whistler's mother, sitting on a rocking chair. The reality is quite different. More and more older people are attracted by what is called *productive aging*, whether by extending years of paid employment or by engaging in productive roles in their families and communities (Bass, 1995; Morrow-Howell, Hinterlong, & Sherraden, 2001). If older people believe they have little to contribute, then they may overlook ways in which their expertise and life experience can be useful to others. As education levels rise and guaranteed pension income becomes more uncertain, we're likely to see more and more older people attracted to productive aging and continued work beyond what was previously the "normal" age of retirement.

A major conclusion from the work of gerontologists like Rowe and Kahn (1999) is that we need carefully and repeatedly to examine our attitudes toward aging and to challenge the common stereotypes and myths. This critical thinking is important for two reasons: (a) aging itself typically evokes attitudes of avoidance or denial, which makes long-range planning more difficult; and (b) the actual character of later life itself has changed dramatically and will change further in the 21st century, as described in chapter 1, Trends in Aging.

You, therefore, in your role as CSA, need to take two steps. First, work hard to overcome stereotypes and question outdated ideas about aging. Second, become better informed about the varieties of aging experience in order to give the most helpful consultation to your individual clients.

Understanding the Experienced World of Aging

The subjective world of old age is different from the typical world of people who are young or in midlife. This fact is important because you may be considerably younger than your clients. You'll have to work hard to understand the subjective world of aging. The first and most important task is to recognize how the world of old age is different from the world of youth or middle age and to become skilled in responding to differences. Psychologists tell us there are different developmental tasks for each of the seasons of life (Levinson, 1978).

During young adulthood through midlife, human beings are typically concerned with establishing themselves in the wider world. For example, financial tasks during this time include home ownership, paying for children's education, and making challenging decisions about career and family, such as moving to another part of the country or going back to work after taking time to raise children. Each of these developmental tasks forces us to explore our deep personal values. That process of exploration continues into the later years; it does not stop.

Some of the key developmental tasks that many seniors face in later life are:

1. leaving traditional work;
2. using leisure time as a source of meaning;
3. taking on caregiving;
4. facing chronic illness, disability, and death;
5. leaving a legacy.

LEAVING TRADITIONAL WORK

In later life, new developmental tasks typically include leaving traditional work roles, perhaps for leisure or perhaps for new productive roles, such as volunteerism. The transition to retirement, whatever form it takes, requires complex decisions—for instance, when to start drawing on pension income or whether to move to a new part of the country. You can be helpful with these decisions.

LEISURE TIME AS A SOURCE OF MEANING

Many people look forward to later life and retirement as a time to escape from the stress of the workplace and finally enjoy themselves. Old age is typically a time when the work role becomes less important and leisure takes on more significance in life (Leitner & Leitner, 1996). We sometimes think of leisure as free time, which obviously becomes more available after retirement. But leisure can be defined as any activity enjoyed for its own sake, pursued as an end in itself. Some older people are unaccustomed to leisure, so when they leave the role of work, they may try to replace it with lots of activity. "I'm busier than ever," is a statement sometimes heard from people who are retired (Ekerdt, 1986).

Does leisure in retirement actually replace the work role? Does it become a source of meaning in its own right? The answer depends on the quality of subjective experience during leisure. Leisure may be an end in itself, but moments of leisure also have a developmental pattern that is rich with purpose. Leisure, in short, can be serious business. For example, if we play sports or perform music or read a book, each moment leads to the next in some purposeful developmental pattern. By contrast, other common leisure activities, like television viewing, take up a lot of time but are passive and less demanding. In advising older people about the use of free time in retirement, we need to recognize it can vary tremendously in its meaning and purpose.

There is a common stereotype of retired people playing shuffleboard or hitting the golf course. Actually, as people get older they usually continue the same activities they engaged in earlier in life (Atchley, 1999), a fact recognized by the *continuity theory* of aging. True, with advancing age, there tends to be an overall decline in participation rate in many kinds of activities, whether going to church or going to the golf course. But it's a mistake to resort to stereotypes about "old people's" activities, such as bingo or singing old-time songs. Age alone does not serve as a good predictor of what people will do with their leisure in later life—old people are not all alike (O'Rand & Henretta, 1999). Variations and individual differences, along with the influence of gender and socioeconomic status, play a big part.

TAKING ON CAREGIVING

Caregiving of spouses and aging parents is often a task of later life. For example, clients might ask you, "Should I put my husband in a nursing home where he can receive better care for his Alzheimer's? We promised each other we would never go to a nursing home." Or, "How can I find reliable professionals to take care of my mother while I go to work?" Such questions don't have easy answers, but professional guidance can be vital in such situations. For just that reason, new professions have sprung up, such as elder law attorneys and private geriatric care managers. These professions were completely unheard of a generation ago.

Caregiving decisions today also present complexities unknown to previous generations. It is no longer unusual to find a 60- or 70-year-old client who has one or more living parents. Caregiving presents enormous challenges for persons of any age, but especially for multigenerational families, with four or even five generations alive at the same time. As Americans today marry and have children at later ages, in the future it will no longer be unusual to see people who are approaching retirement while at the same time paying for college tuition or helping out adult children who face their own stresses as they enter their 20s.

FACING CHRONIC ILLNESS, DISABILITY, AND DEATH

As people move into more advanced ages, the likelihood of chronic illness, disability, and death increases. Your clients may be faced with decisions about paying for expensive health care costs, including long-term care. They may be concerned with framing or reframing their wills. These decisions become increasingly intertwined with concerns about protecting assets and estate planning. For these reasons retirement planning can never be approached in purely financial terms. Much more is at stake emotionally in such decisions.

LEAVING A LEGACY

A large developmental task of later life is what Erik Erikson called *generativity*— giving attention to one's legacy for future generations (Erikson & Erikson, 1998; Kotre, 1999). Leaving a legacy is much more complex than financial planning alone. For example, along with a property will (for assets) and a living will (for health care decisions), some seniors are now drawing *ethical wills*, the systematic writing down or communicating one's intangible legacy of values to children and family members (Baines, 2001). This process of life review, whether expressed verbally or in a written statement, can be an important and healing part of later life.

Strategies toward Aging

What do people think about growing older? Your professional consultation with older clients requires acknowledgment of deep, often unconscious feelings about aging on the part of both the client and yourself. These attitudes can have profound effects on life planning and choices for dealing with advancing age. Harry Moody has grouped strategies toward aging into four major

categories: age denial, age adaptation, age irrelevance, and age affirmation. All four attitudes affect the experience of aging.

AGE DENIAL

Prejudice and rejection of aging in our society is so widespread that it has been given a name of its own: *ageism* (Nelson, 2002). In light of that prejudice it is not surprising that there are many products on the market that promise to overcome aging, for example, so-called anti-aging medicine and cosmetic surgery. Because of the power of age denial, there will be clients who reject any kind of professional service or transaction if it means they have to identify themselves as old. This attitude can be a big problem. Fear and denial of aging can be paralyzing and lead to procrastination: "No, I've never written a will, but I'm planning to get to it one of these days." Age denial can pose a serious barrier to benefiting from your CSA services.

> *Sam and Cindy, a couple both in their early 70s, were sitting in the office of a CSA for a consultation when they got into an argument so heated that it seemed like they might come to blows.*
>
> *"I just don't want to move in with all those old people," shouted Sam angrily. "And I'm not even retired."*

Sam was a piano teacher and occasional performer who loved his music. Cindy was eager to move into a continuing care retirement community (CCRC). Cindy dragged Sam to meet with the CSA.

"Senior Advisor," he snorted. "Are you putting me out to pasture, or what?"

In the discussion that followed, Sam repeatedly found reasons why moving into the CCRC wasn't feasible: What if they changed their minds? Weren't they in good health right now? What about hidden costs in the financing arrangement? The CSA spent hours in this and other meetings in a fruitless attempt to help Sam and Cindy plan for the future. No matter what the option was, Sam refused to consider anything based on his declaring himself to be old.

AGE ADAPTATION

While some people deny age, others approach it with acceptance. With advancing age, there are changes in the body, social life, and financial conditions that call for changes in behavior. In other words, acceptance doesn't necessarily mean being passive to whatever happens to come along. Adapting to new circumstances is a key strategy for successful aging (Dall, Ermini, Herrling, Meier-Ruge, & Stahelin, 1995).

But age adaptation is not easy. For instance, there are certain financial products—such as long-term care insurance—that may be helpful but appear threatening and unfamiliar to clients. While most people have experience with car insurance or homeowners insurance, very few know much about long-term care insurance.

Understanding a client's motivation is a key to working with older clients. In the case of long-term care insurance, the incentive for buying might be to avoid being a burden on one's children or to preserve an estate. Still another more positive motive might be to maximize autonomy and choice in the future. A similar mix of motives appears in housing decisions. After children have left home or work obligations recede, people commonly begin to think about moving to a smaller house or renegotiating finances to draw down home equity. But they find themselves pulled in different directions: aging in place versus making an adaptive change. An age-adaptive product—such as a reverse mortgage—may arouse ambivalence for someone who has long had a goal of paying off the mortgage. An important role for you is to help clients work through mixed motives as they adapt to age-related life changes, as the following story suggests.

Mildred Macon was worried about the future. At age 85, she was grateful for having lived a long life, but more and more the past was looking better than the future. In the past year, Mildred had fallen several times, bruising herself badly. She felt lucky that she hadn't broken any bones, but who could say what might happen next time?

Mildred's daughter Amy lived about half an hour away and visited her Mom at least once a week. But for the next six months, her job was going to keep her temporarily in another state and it would be impossible to visit. Calling on the phone was fine to keep in touch, but what happened if her Mom fell again?

Mildred recognized the problem and arranged to receive an emergency alert device that would permit her to call for help if she fell or became disabled. Amy also found a local geriatric care manager who agreed to look in on Mildred for a fee. Mildred also agreed to put her name on a waiting list for a very attractive assisted living facility. She wasn't ready to move into one right away, she said, but just in case. Besides, she reasoned, it made Amy more comfortable and would make her feel less guilty about being away for the new job.

AGE IRRELEVANCE

In view of the power of ageism, we sometimes find that it's best to downplay aging altogether. For example, there are dimensions of financial behavior, such as saving for the future, that can be promoted in an age-irrelevant manner. David Wolfe has argued that marketers generally do better by positioning their products as "ageless" (Wolfe & Snyder, 2003). We know from studies of age identification that as wealth and socioeconomic levels rise, people are less and less inclined to relate to life options according to age. This fact has important implications for you as you help clients plan for the future. Even if a product is age-adaptive, we may do better by approaching the decision in terms of age irrelevance or ageless marketing. By ignoring any explicit link to chronological age we can sometimes bypass fear and avoidance in order to deal with a client's needs in a way that is approached independent of chronological age.

Ed Walton was always a careful planner. He was the kind of guy who mailed his income taxes in by February and managed to get a refund back from the IRS. Ed says, "Better to have them withhold too much than risk a penalty."

By the time Ed reached age 65, he had retired from his job with the utility company, but he began growing a little concerned about his pension. Ed insisted that he just didn't feel old, but he realized it was time to look over his portfolio. He consulted a financial planner, a CSA who gave Ed some very valuable advice.

"How long do you expect to live?" asked the CSA.

"Who knows?" replied Ed.

"Well, how long did each of your parents live?"

"Both my mom and dad lived into their 90s—Mom died just last year," replied Ed, who was obviously a vigorous and healthy man.

In the discussion that followed it became clear that Ed had planned for everything except for living a long time. Using a life expectancy calculator the financial planner estimated that Ed, a non-smoker, could easily live into his 90s, like both his parents. The planner pointed out that most of Ed's retirement funds were in bonds and other fixed-income investments, which might not be wise for a 20- or 30-year time horizon. The CSA didn't approach Ed Walton's problem as a matter of retirement planning but as a matter of investment planning over a longer-than-expected time horizon.

Ed found this approach congenial and started approaching his investment decisions in the same methodical way he'd always done his taxes. It surprised him that he found investing an interesting subject, and before long he had joined an investment club consisting of people of all ages who helped each other learn more about the stock market. Ed continued to consult with his CSA financial planner and was always grateful that he'd been given a push to take a more active role in preparing for his financial future. He felt younger than ever, he insisted.

AGE AFFIRMATION

We shouldn't overemphasize the negative aspects of age avoidance. After all there are, in fact, many hopes for later life—such as retirement travel or pension eligibility—that are both positive and explicitly linked to chronological age. Taken together all these hopes make up our dream for a good old age. Skillful marketers understand the power of hopes and dreams, and they try to tap into that positive motivation. For example, the marketing appeals of retirement communities, such as Sun City, Arizona, usually emphasize features and benefits of retirement living such as leisure time and the opportunity to fulfill long-cherished fantasies for the good life (Freedman, 2002). You need to help clients identify goals that are age-affirmative in order to motivate them to take steps now to plan for the future.

> Jim and Jill Howard had always been travelers. They met when they were kids in a youth hostel in Belgium, and during the previous 40 years of their marriage they never missed an opportunity to travel and learn about foreign countries. When they turned age 55, they started participating in Elderhostel, and they even got award pins as frequent hostelers because they'd been on a total of 25 different trips overseas. In their late 60s, the future looked great for them—until Jim had a stroke. As brain events go, it wasn't devastating. But it left Jim with serious balance problems. Air travel was not an option anymore. Both Jim and Jill worried that their traveling life might be over.
>
> The Howards loved the Elderhostel trips and the people they met there. The two of them had never considered moving into a retirement community. That attitude changed the day that Jill found out that Golden Gardens community had its own Learning in Retirement Institute. Jim's first comment was that he didn't like joining clubs.
>
> "It's not a club," Jill replied. "It's like Elderhostel in one place."
>
> As it happened, Golden Gardens was located in a town not far from them, so by moving there, they could still be in touch with family and old friends. It turned out that among the residents of Golden Gardens were lots of other Elderhostelers, people attracted by the same atmosphere as the Howards. Within the first year of moving in, Jim had become chairman of the Curriculum Committee and was organizing classes. He could not travel the way he and Jill used to, but he felt excited about life and happy to be a part of Golden Gardens.

Fears about Later Life

As we've seen, ageism denotes a stereotyped view of later life as a period of decline and disaster. But not all fears about old age are based on prejudice or imagination. Some fears are all too real, and you need to take account of those fears in helping people plan for the later years.

While not a given, advancing age increases the probability of chronic illness, dementia, and death. A quick look at life insurance rates will tell you that mortality is a realistic fear for elders. Yet survey research suggests that older people are actually less afraid of death than younger people (Cicirelli, 2001).

So what *are* they afraid of? Older people typically express fears of dependency and loss of control. In comparison, death may even seem preferable. For example, the history of assisted suicide in Oregon, the only state where it is legal, suggests that very few people, even with terminal illness, actually make use of the option. When they do, it is mostly not for reasons of pain, but because they fear dependency and loss of autonomy (Sullivan, Hedberg, & Fleming, 2000).

Fear of dependency is also the reason behind common attitudes about nursing homes. It is not unusual for older people to say, "I'd rather die than go into a nursing home." Ironically, many who do enter long-term care facilities adapt to the situation and may even find more opportunities for activities, social contact, and support. But the fear of being "put away in a nursing home" is still widespread.

Another important fear among seniors is that of *impoverishment*—outliving one's income or assets. Here again, the fear is not unrealistic because poverty rates rise dramatically among the oldest-old (people over age 80).

Lastly, there is the fear of losing one's mind, an informal way of referring to dementia or diminished mental capacity. Unfortunately, rates of dementia do rise dramatically among the oldest-old. However, developing dementia is not inevitable in older age.

The overall picture of fears in later life was captured well by Shakespeare's play *King Lear*, which is probably the greatest literary work ever to depict the tragedy of age (Deats, 1999). Lear is a king who tries to prepare for his retirement, but finds himself in a state of extreme dependency. Two of his adult daughters fail to provide for him, and he ultimately loses his mind and is destroyed. Shakespeare understood that, no matter how powerful we are, old age can bring with it a loss of power and therefore greater vulnerability.

You can help people take steps—like sound financial planning—that reduce the likelihood of tragedy in old age. But planning can never offer complete assurance. Therefore, be sensitive to fears about old age.

Aging and the Search for Meaning

The most important task for you as a CSA is to learn to listen to your senior clients. Listen to the voices of older people themselves: What are their hopes and dreams? Consider the following passages from a journal kept by author Florida Scott-Maxwell during the last years of her life, during which she lived in a nursing home:

Age puzzles me. I thought it was a quiet time. My seventies were interesting, and fairly serene, but my eighties are passionate. I grow more intense as I age. To my own surprise I burst out with hot conviction. Only a few years ago I enjoyed my tranquility; now I am so disturbed by the outer world and by human quality in general that I want to put things right, as though I still owed a debt to life.

Later on she added that she has reached a "place beyond resignation, a place I had no idea existed until I had arrived here" (Scott-Maxwell, 2000, p. 32). These passages remind us that aging has many phases and seasons, and older people find meaning in new ways.

WHAT GIVES MEANING TO LIFE

What do older people themselves say about what gives meaning to their lives? When a sample of participants at a senior center was asked that question, nearly 90 percent of respondents described their lives as meaningful (Burbank, 1992). For most of them (57 percent) the meaning came from human relationships, an answer followed by service to others (12 percent), religion, and leisure activities. Another study revealed that the most damaging threat to well-being in later life is loss of life purpose and boredom, not fear of absolute destitution or poor health. Responses show that people find purpose or meaning in a variety of ways: work, leisure, grandparenting, and intimate adult relationships. Respondents reported that unless they were sick or depressed, they didn't feel old (Thompson, 1993).

From this empirical research we can identify two important ideas about how older people find meaning in their lives. First, *being* old (by chronological age) is not the same thing as *feeling* old. Unless people are sick or depressed they are unlikely to feel old. Instead they will experience themselves as the same person they were years before. Florida Scott-Maxwell wrote precisely this in her journal when she observed that even though she may look "drab outside," still inside she has the same strong feelings that make her the person she always was.

The second point is that older people will find meaning in many different ways—some from continued activity, others from a need to be needed, and still others from religion and beliefs that help them cope with suffering, accept themselves, and be reconciled to the world around them. Self-acceptance at any age is not easy, and in later life it may involve struggling with difficult questions. You can never avoid or escape from such questions about meaning because they greatly impact how seniors make decisions. By understanding the recurrent—indeed, nearly universal—developmental tasks of later life, you will be in the best possible position to be a good listener, to listen attentively, which is where professional training and understanding of aging are crucial.

DIVERSITY IS THE NORM

Many factors—too many to cover in this chapter alone—affect the experience of older age. For example, many older women live with the double whammies of ageism and sexism. And many older minority women face the triple whammies of ageism, sexism, and racism. How does this affect the experience of aging? What is growing older like for 85-year-old Corrine Gable who, like 47 percent of black women on their own (Vierck & Hodges, 2003), lives in poverty? For that matter, what is the experience like for multimillionaire Albert Myers, who at age 75 started yet another business?

What is the experience of aging like for people who are in two parent–two children families? For those who are gay? Single? Childless? What is it like for the hale and hardy? For seniors who are in pain? Disabled? For those who are coping with a terminal illness? The loss of a spouse? The loss of a child? What is it like for people with Alzheimer's disease? For Florence Ross, who at age 81 earned her doctorate ("81-year-old," 2004) in dispute resolution?

In order to communicate the experience of growing older to professionals working with seniors, this chapter has described some common themes about the experience. However, it is important to remember that, in truth, there are as many styles of aging as there are seniors.

The Experience of Aging: Summary

This chapter opened with a dream that signaled to an older woman that, despite a great deal of planning, she had made an unfortunate decision about retirement living. The actual experience of aging may turn out to be different from what a senior expected. As Florida Scott-Maxwell wrote, it is "a place I had no idea existed until I had arrived here." Successful aging involves more than gathering facts and advice; it requires overcoming stereotypes and asking deeper questions about values, about the meaning of life, about fears, hopes, and dreams. This is also the task for you in your practice as a CSA.

References

81-year-old grandmother earns PhD in dispute resolution. (2004, February 20). *Newport Plain Talk.* p. 12B.

Atchley, R. C. (1999). *Continuity and adaptation in aging: Creating positive experiences.* Baltimore, MD: Johns Hopkins University Press.

Baines, B. (2001). *Ethical wills: Putting your values on paper.* New York: Perseus.

Bass, S. (Ed.). (1995). *Older and active: How Americans over 55 are contributing to society.* New Haven, CT: Yale University Press.

Burbank, P. M.(1992, September) Exploratory study: Assessing the meaning in life among older adult clients. *Journal of Gerontological Nursing, 18*(9), 19–28.

Cicirelli, V. G. (2001, December) Personal meanings of death in older adults and young adults in relation to their fears of death. *Death Studies, 25*(8), 663–683.

Dall, J. L. C., Ermini, M., Herrling, P. L., Meier-Ruge, W., & Stahelin, H. B. (Eds.). (1995). *Adaptations in aging.* San Diego, CA: Academic Press.

Deats, S. M. (1999). The dialectic of aging in Shakespeare's *King Lear* and *The Tempest,* in S. M. Deats & L. Lenker (Eds.), *Aging and identity: A humanities perspective.* Westport, CT: Praeger.

Diamond, M. (1988). *Enriching heredity: The impact of the environment on the brain.* New York: Free Press.

Ekerdt, D. J. (1986, June). Busy ethic: Moral continuity between work and retirement. *Gerontologist, 26*(3), 239–244.

Erikson, E., & Erikson, J. (1998). *The life cycle completed.* New York: Norton.

Freedman, M. (2002). *Prime time: How baby boomers will revolutionize retirement and transform America.* New York: Public Affairs.

Kotre, J. (1999). *Make it count: How to generate a legacy that gives meaning to your life.* New York: Free Press.

Leitner, M. J., & Leitner, S. F. (1996). *Leisure in later life.* New York: Haworth Press.

Levinson, D. J. (1978). *The seasons of a man's life.* New York: Knopf.

Manton, K. G., & Gu, X. (2001, May 22). Changes in the prevalence of chronic disability in the United States black and nonblack population above age 65 from 1982 to 1999. *Proceedings of the National Academy of Sciences, 98*(11), 6354–6359.

Morrow-Howell. N., Hinterlong, J., & Sherraden, M. (Eds.). (2001). *Productive aging: Concepts and challenges.* Baltimore, MD: Johns Hopkins University Press.

Nelson, T. (Ed.). (2002). *Ageism: Stereotyping and prejudice against older persons.* Cambridge, MA: MIT Press.

O'Rand, A. M., & Henretta, J. C. (1999). *Age and inequality: Diverse pathways through later life.* Boulder, CO: Westview Press.

Rowe, J. W., & Kahn, R. (1999). *Successful aging.* New York: Dell.

Schwartz, B. (2004). *The paradox of choice: Why more is less.* New York: Ecco.

Scott-Maxwell, F. (2000). *The measure of my days.* New York: Penguin.

Sullivan, A. D., Hedberg, K., & Fleming, D. W. (2000, February 24). Legalized physician-assisted suicide in Oregon—The second year. *New England Journal of Medicine, 342*(8), 598–604.

Thompson, P. (1993, August). "I don't feel old": The significance of the search for meaning in later life. *International Journal of Geriatric Psychiatry, 8*(8), 685–692.

Vierck, E., & Hodges, K. (2004). *Aging: Demographics, health, and health services.* Westport, CT: Greenwood.

Wolfe, D., & Snyder, R. (2003). *Ageless marketing: Strategies for reaching the hearts and minds of the new customer majority.* Chicago: Dearborn Trade Publishing.

Part 2

AGING WITHIN THE FAMILY AND COMMUNITY

Without a sense of caring, there can be no sense of community.

Anthony J. D'Angelo

Even as the cell is the unit of the organic body, so the family is the unit of society.

Ruth Nanda Anshen

Part 2 examines the family and community context of aging. As you will see in chapter 6, relationships with family and friends are important for seniors, who often look to them for emotional support and caregiving. While some seniors remain self-sufficient throughout their lives, others require assistance with activities of daily living such as bathing, eating, and personal care. Most often family, friends, and community programs provide such assistance. The chapters in this section cover these issues and options and provide important information that you can use to assist your senior clients with receiving quality care in the housing of their choice.

Chapter 6

The Family and Social Support Systems

Kate Hixon, 79, rises early every morning to read the paper and drink coffee on her porch as the sun comes up over the bayou. Her neighbor and friend Sam Houston, 76, likewise gets up early and takes his dog Charlie for a walk. Neighbors for 52 years, they know each other's daily habits and unconsciously monitor these patterns to check in with one another. If one doesn't see the other one by mid-morning, they put in a call, followed by a visit. When Kate fell five years ago and broke her leg, it was Sam who found her and got her to the hospital in less than four hours. Likewise, last year when Sam got a bad case of the flu, Kate came by with hot soup and a caring hand to see him through. They each have children and grandchildren who regularly visit, but they do not live nearby; in the day-to-day business of living and in times of need, they have come to rely on one another.

Goldie Steinberg, 86, knew as a young girl she wanted to be a doctor. Therefore, it came as no surprise to her family and friends the day she announced that she had made a decision to pursue a career in medicine. Although she never married, Goldie has never lived alone nor regretted her decision to be single. As a young woman, she lived with her aunt in New York City, then later with another doctor that she worked with at the hospital. In midlife, Goldie bought a large home in Brooklyn with a plan of helping young female interns by offering them inexpensive room and board. Officially retired for 20 years, she has remained active in the field by volunteering at a neighborhood clinic and traveling overseas with Doctors Without Borders. She continues to have a close relationship with her sister and her children, as well as a close circle of friends that she sees regularly. "Goldie's girls" continue to come and go as resident doctors, but never lose touch with Goldie. On her 85th birthday, 85 of her old roommates gave her a surprise party to celebrate her life and their unique family of women doctors.

Introduction

*Call it a clan, call it a network, call it a tribe, call it a family.
Whatever you call it, whoever you are, you need one.*

Jane Howard

By birth, adoption, marriage, or other social arrangement, nearly everyone belongs to a family. From the cradle to the grave, most of us depend on our families for love, care, support, guidance, a sense of identity, and a feeling of belonging. We play a variety of family roles over the course of our lifetime—child, sibling, cousin, spouse, parent, in-law, grandparent, or even great-grandparent and great-great grandparent. Family members may live separately, with a partner, or in a *nuclear family, extended family,* or *blended family* household. While what constitutes a family varies by historical time, region, and circumstance, the family group is universally the most basic of social institutions.

Families play an important role in *social support systems*—the family, friends, and organizations that we turn to in times of need for emotional support, financial assistance, personal care, household help, and any other assistance (Atchley & Barusch, 2004; Himes, 1993). *Social support* provides people with a sense of being loved and cared for, esteemed, and valued. It allows us to receive and to give to others reassurance, affirmation, and assistance, especially during difficult times.

Strong family bonds and close ties with friends help seniors cope with the life events commonly associated with aging, such as retirement, widowhood, decreased mobility, and poor health. An increasing body of research suggests that social support is an important factor of successful aging (Rowe & Kahn, 1998). Older adults with strong social support systems are more likely than those without such support to experience better physical health (Bosworth & Schaie, 1997), better mental health (Krause, 2001), a lower risk for long-term care placement (Freedman, 1996), and longer lives (Seeman, Kaplan, Knudsen, Cohen, & Guralnik, 1987).

Over the past few decades, social, demographic, and economic factors have significantly altered the structure of the American family. For example, more mothers are working outside the home, people are living longer—many with limited mobility or cognitive impairment—and families are more geographically dispersed. Not surprisingly, these changes in family structure affect family relationships and the types of support provided to older family members. In spite of these challenges, the large majority of Americans strive to continue to meet the needs of their elders (Atchley & Barusch (2004); Bengtson, Putney, & Wakeman, 2004).

It is important to note that due to constraints of space, we have generalized much of the information about families to reflect that of the majority of Americans or the national average. Family patterns differ widely among racial and ethnic groups, as well as by income and other factors. For example, the national average of female-headed households with children is 8 percent. This, however, varies considerably by race and ethnicity. In 2002, about 5 percent of non-Hispanic white and Asian households were female-headed households with children, compared to 14 percent Hispanic households and 22 percent of African American households (Ameristat, 2003).

The interdependence and deep emotional feelings between family members create an intricate and often delicate web that you will need to understand and navigate in order to best serve your senior clients and families. This chapter provides readers with an overview of the American family—dispelling some of the myths and affirming the realities of where we have been, where we are today, and how things are likely to change in the future. It also reviews the importance of friends in social support systems. You will learn about some of the key challenges that elders and their families face and resources that can help fill in those gaps. This knowledge on the social support systems of elders will also help you identify potential problems, locate resources, and make referrals without overstepping boundaries or getting enmeshed in family conflicts.

Family: In Crisis or Transition?

American families have always shown remarkable resiliency, or flexible adjustment to natural, economic, and social challenges. Their strengths resemble the elasticity of a spider web, a gull's skillful flow with the wind, the regenerating power of perennial grasses, the cooperation of an ant colony, and the persistence of a stream carving canyon rocks. These are not the strengths of fixed monuments but living organisms. This resilience is not measured by wealth, muscle, or efficiency but by creativity, unity, and hope. Cultivating these family strengths is critical to a thriving human community.

Ben Silliman

Much has been written in recent years of the American family in crisis. Unquestionably, we live in an increasingly complex world that requires families to face new challenges. Greater geographic distances between family members, the need for two income earners to maintain a middle-class lifestyle, a growing number of divorces and blended families, and the demands of caring for parents while still raising children are just a few of the issues families must confront, especially in meeting the needs of aging relatives. In addition, today's world *seems* to face more social problems—drug and alcohol abuse, a failing Social Security and health care system, high crime rates, and a general decline in personal responsibility and moral values. How families—and society—respond to these challenges affects everyone, but especially those who are the most vulnerable and dependent for support and care: children, elders, and seriously ill persons.

How well are we meeting these challenges? In the popular press and in academia we have seen over the past two decades a polarization and politicization of the changes in family dynamics. Some argue that the decline in the number of "traditional" American families—working father, stay-at-home mother, and children—is the root of many of our social problems today (Popenoe, 1999). Others argue that many of the changes in families, such as women working outside the home and the dissolution of unhappy marriages, overall are better for individuals as well as for other family members (Stacey, 1998). Still others take a more neutral position that historically it is the nature of family groups to reinvent themselves in order to meet their current needs (Bengtson et al., 2004; Elkind, 1994; Kain, 1990).

The debate about the state of the American family is beyond the scope of this chapter. It is important to note, however, that family diversity is a topic that evokes strong feelings—remember the public outcry brought on by Dan Quayle's memorable speech condemning television character Murphy Brown for her choice to be a single mother? Regardless of your personal preferences and beliefs regarding family, it is important for you to understand and be sensitive to the diversity that exists among your senior clients and their families.

THE GOOD OLD DAYS NEVER WERE

Things ain't what they used to be and probably never was.

Will Rogers

Many people distressed with the current status of the American family wish for a return of the good old days of the traditional family—when men earned an honest day's living to provide for their families, women lovingly upheld the hearth and home, and well-mannered children attended school and did as they were told. In this idealized version of family life, older adults were venerated, while aging and ill family members were cared for in extended family households. Like most nostalgic thinking, however, such wishful thoughts are only marginally based on historic fact (Coontz, 2000; Hareven, 1993). In understanding family structure and dynamics today, as well as future family trends, it is imperative to understand the roads that have led us here. Since so much of our past has been glorified in nostalgia, it's particularly important to separate out the fact from the fiction, so that we do not fall into the trap of holding ourselves up to a standard that never existed.

Even in Plymouth Colony, Families Had Problems

Research based on the examination of legal records, family letters and diaries, census data, and other historical documents reveal that the golden age of the American family as described above has never really existed. Since the *Mayflower* arrived (and before), communities have fretted over the state of the American family (Demos, 1978; Hareven, 1993). Historic records show that there have always been unhappy marriages, out-of-wedlock children (or hasty marriages with a pregnant bride), rebellious youth, substance abuse, gambling, truancy, and child and spousal abuse (Coontz, 2000; Mintz & Kellogg, 1989; Newman, 1999). In fact, some of these problems were worse in earlier times than they have been more recently. For example, rates of alcohol abuse, child abuse, truancy, and dropping out of school were higher in the 19th century than they are today, and murder rates were higher in 1933 than they were in the 1980s (Coontz). Not only have social problems always existed, but in many cases they were not even considered morally or legally wrong, as in the case of corporal punishment of wives and children by their husbands and fathers throughout much of early American history (Newman). So, while there have always been traditional nuclear families in the sense of mother, father, and children, there has not been a documented historical period when the majority of families were more stable, more harmonious, and happier (Zinn & Eitzen, 1987).

The Waltons Were the Exception

Another popular myth proven false by historical research is that in earlier times, families lived together in multigenerational or large extended family households (Coontz, 2000; Hareven, 1993). Part of the explanation here lies in sheer demographics: Until the 1940s, little overlap existed between first and third generations. Life expectancy during the colonial period was only about 40 years. Many mothers died from complications related to childbirth (about one in eight births ended in maternal death), which in part explains the low life expectancy, but also limited the interaction in many families between generations. By 1900 life expectancy still remained at only 48 years—only about 4 percent of the population was 65 or older. Looked at another way, in 1900, only one-fifth of 30-year-olds had at least one grandparent still alive. In 2000, approximately three-fourths of Americans the same age had one or more living grandparents (Quadagno, 2002).

Like today, the three-generation family has existed throughout American history, particularly among poor and immigrant families. During hard times, such as the Great Depression and World War II, families moved in together out of necessity. In but a few cases did multigenerational families create the life depicted on the popular 1970s television show *The Waltons*. In fact, hard times like the Depression tended to create more family turmoil and strain intergenerational relationships (Coontz, 2000; Newman, 1993). According to a 1948 film on family problems of the day, "No home is big enough to house two families, particularly two of different generations, with opposite theories on child training" (Coontz).

The preferred domicile arrangement has always been nuclear families, with parents or other relatives living close by—"intimacy from a distance" (Demos, 1970; Hareven, 1993). This does not mean, however, that older adults lived alone. Most elders did their best to preserve their autonomy by staying the head of the household, rather than moving in with family (Hareven). Sometimes this arrangement was accomplished by the voluntary agreement of an adult child to remain in the home or return home to care for aging parents. Other times it was mandated by a formal agreement. For example, in colonial America, aging parents used legal contracts with inheriting sons to guarantee their support and care in old age (Demos, 1978). Likewise, in the 19th and early 20th centuries, parents used the legal leverage of inheritance and the social obligation of *reciprocity* to guarantee their care in old age. Less appealing options included moving into a child's household, taking in boarders, or boarding with others in the community (Hareven).

Whatever Happened to "Respect Your Elders"?

Most social historians agree that aged persons were revered and venerated during the American colonial period (Aachenbaum, 1978; Demos, 1970; Fischer, 1978). It is debatable, however, if this atypical tradition of respect applied to all elders or primarily to older, white, middle-class men (Atchley & Barusch, 2004; Quadagno, 2002). Economics played a role in respecting one's male elders, as older men tended to be the ones who controlled the family property and were most experienced in trade and commerce (Aachenbaum; Demos, 1970). Religious beliefs of the period also influenced behavior. Puritans and pilgrims believed that old age was a sign of God's favor; therefore, male elders were at the top of the hierarchy as community and religious leaders (Demos, 1970; Fischer).

In his research, Fischer (1978) found that not just male church and political elders, but *all* older people in the colonies were given special consideration. For example, in church the oldest members of the congregation were assigned seating near the pulpit, with the other members seated according to age behind them. Younger people were in such awe of elders that the fashions of the day emulated them—powdered hair, white wigs, and clothes tailored to make young people look older than their age were popular until around the Revolutionary War (Fischer).

Other scholars believe that age did not assure one of prestige and power, particularly within the context of the larger community. Older women, Native Americans, African Americans, and immigrants may have held some respect within their own families, but this rarely extended beyond familial ties (Quadagno, 2002).

In historical terms this period of respect for elders was brief. By the mid-1800s, attitudes toward the aged turned progressively more negative, although historians disagree over the timing and causes of this transition (Quadagno, 2002; Atchley & Barusch, 2004). Styles changed to emphasize a youthful appearance, and where once the young might have claimed to be older than their years, they began to allude to being younger (Fischer, 1978). Terms of respect, such as *gaffer* and *fogy*, became derogatory jeers. Henry David Thoreau captured the feeling of the day when, in 1847 at the age of 30, he wrote

> I have lived some 30 years on this planet and I have yet to hear the first syllable of valuable or even earnest advice from my seniors. They have told me nothing and probably cannot teach me anything.

So much for respect for one's elders. The revolt against age grew into the cult of youth by the 20th century.

Those Fabulous '50s

Today, it is often the 1950s that are idealized as the era of the perfect nuclear family and the high point of traditional family values (Coontz, 2000). Popular television sitcoms such as *Ozzie and Harriet* and *Father Knows Best* idealized and exemplified the good life American families strove for during the Cold War period. While it is true that during this decade a record number of American households consisted of a working father, stay-at-home mom, and several young children and that it was the boom years of the middle class, it was not an era without social problems. The 1950s also produced the McCarthy inquisition, institutionalized racism, and the Cold War. Nearly half of all marriages that began in the 1950s ended in divorce, and despite the prosperity for many during the decade, nearly a quarter of Americans were poor (Council on Contemporary Families, 2003). Alcoholism, out-of-wedlock births, spousal abuse, homosexuality, and other family skeletons were abundant but safely guarded in the closet (Coontz).

The 1950s were a particularly hard time for many older Americans. The affluence of the period largely bypassed minorities and older adults. The postwar era saw the first great migration of Americans away from their parents and families in the cities and rural areas to the growing number of suburbs. Further, the American population 65 years and older mushroomed from 3 million in 1900 to over 12 million in 1950, doubling from 4 to 8 percent of the population (Medicare Rights Center, 2004). While Social Security and a growing number of pensions provided some income guarantee, nearly two-thirds of older Americans had annual incomes of less than $1,000, and only 1 in 8 had health insurance (Medicare Rights Center). By 1965, 60 percent of older Americans lived at or near poverty level, and 80 percent relied solely on their Social Security for income (Atchley, 1972). For America's older minorities, the picture was even bleaker. Prior to the mid-1960s and the passage of bills such as the Medicare Act and the Older Americans Act, government-funded services and financial support to America's poor or elderly largely did not exist: There were no meals on wheels, adult day care centers, home and community-based services, or subsidized housing. In short, outside of family assistance little help existed for seniors.

A BRIDGE TO THE FUTURE

In every conceivable manner, the family is the link to our past, bridge to our future.

Alex Haley

Perhaps you found the preceding section interesting but are wondering, "What's the point? What does this have to do with families today, and what does it have to do with my interactions with seniors and their families?" There are several reasons why it is important for you to have a historical appreciation of the American family, as well as be able to distinguish between some of the facts and the fiction of the "good old days" and their romantic lure.

In every generation, there are those who believe that their parents or grandparents grew up in the good old days—a time when families were more stable, the world was safer, and life was less complicated. While these longings may be real and worthy of consideration, they shouldn't be taken literally (Coontz, 2000). People who wish life were more like the 1950s usually do not mean that they want the whole package. Family historian Stephanie Coontz sums it up succinctly:

> What most people really feel nostalgic about has little to do with the internal structure of the 1950s families. It is the belief that the 1950s provided a more family-friendly economic and social environment, an easier climate in which to keep kids on the straight and narrow, and above all, a greater feeling of hope for a family's long-term future, especially for its young. The contrast between the perceived hopefulness of the '50s and our own misgivings about the future is key to contemporary nostalgia for the period. . . . People today understandably feel that their lives are out of balance, but they yearn for something totally *new*—a more equal distribution of work, family, and community time for both men and women, children and adults. (p. 34)

Advisors who understand that nostalgia has its pitfalls but is more than cheap sentiment have an advantage—they understand that seniors and family members who talk of the way things used to be are giving important clues of what they hope for, what they fear, and what is currently missing in their lives. Talking about the past can be a way to relate in a deeper, more meaningful way with clients—it helps us to understand what they value about family and relationships, what their familial expectations are, as well as how they view their obligations. If, in remembering their childhoods, seniors confide that it was far less than perfect, you can reassure them that many Americans feel the same way and that few families have ever lived like the Andersons in *Father Knows Best*.

A historical perspective reveals and emphasizes that today's aging population is not a homogeneous group. Each cohort has been shaped by its own unique historic events, as well as economic, demographic, and social characteristics. Factors such as race, gender, socioeconomic background, and education further differentiate the aging experience both between and within each of these groups.

Taken together, these aspects have a profound effect on people's attitudes, behaviors, and life decisions (Hareven, 1993). For example, people who came of age during the Great Depression often have a different view of finances than those who came of age during the prosperity of the 1950s and 1960s. Knowing the conditions that people faced early in life informs us as to how they are likely to adapt in later life, including their "views of family relations, their expectations of support from kin, and their ability to interact with welfare agencies and institutions" (Hareven, p. 9).

Facts Correcting Popular Misconceptions about America's Families

- *In 1960, one child in three lived in poverty.*

- *Fewer than half the students who entered high school in the late 1940s ever finished.*

- *From 1950 to 1959 there were 257,455 cases of polio, mostly in children; 11,957 died.*

- *In 1940, 1 child in 10 did not live with either birth parent. Today, the figure is 1 in 25.*

- *A higher proportion of people report their marriage is happy today than did in 1957.*

- *A woman over 35 has a better chance of marrying today than she did in the 1950s.*

- *In the mid-1950s, 25 percent of the total population—and 50 percent of black families—lived below the poverty line.*

- *In 1952, there were 2 million more wives working outside the home than at the peak of World War II.*

- *Women in the 1950s who failed to conform to the June Cleaver stereotype of housewife and mother were severely criticized, and men who failed to marry were considered immature and selfish.*

- *Half of the marriages that began in the 1950s ended in divorce.*

- *During the 1950s, more than 2 million married couples lived separately.*

- *In 1957 there were more than twice as many births to girls and young women ages 15 to 19 than in 1983.*

- *The number of illegitimate babies put up for adoption rose 80 percent from 1944 to 1955.*

- *In 1959, one-third of American children—and one-fourth of all Americans—were poor.*

Source: Used with permission from the Council on Contemporary Families, http://www.contemporaryfamilies.org

---

While this section does not offer a comprehensive history on the American family, it can provide you with a big-picture view of how families have changed over the years and how history and other factors shape an individual and a cohort. You can employ personal reminiscence, as well as historical perspective, to build a bridge from the past into the future, by dispelling the myths of the way we never were and building on what we know to be true, for ourselves and for our families.

Today's Family: Diversity in the New Millennium

We have become not a melting pot but a beautiful mosaic. Different people, different beliefs, different yearnings, different hopes, different dreams.

Jimmy Carter

When asked to describe the typical American household, most people will answer, "Mom, dad, and the kids"—the nuclear family (Newman, 1999). The answer to this question illustrates a major gap between the public perception and the reality of the composition of most American households.

According to the 2000 United States Census, married-couple households with their own children represented only 24 percent of all American households, compared to 40 percent of all households in 1970 (Census Bureau, 2001. See Figure 6.1.) Given that the census includes *blended families* in the definition, the number of *biological nuclear families* constituted even less than a quarter of all American households in 2000. The proportion of all households estimated to be the *traditional nuclear family* represented only about 8 percent of American households in 1998 (Smith, 1999).

HOUSEHOLD TYPE DEFINITIONS

- *housing unit:* an apartment, house, trailer, or any other structure designed for people to live in.
- *household:* all the people who occupy a housing unit. A household includes related family members and all the unrelated people, if any, such as boarders, foster children, etc., who live together. A person living alone or a group of unrelated people living together, such as partners or roommates, also counts as a household.
- *family household:* a group of two people or more related by birth, marriage, or adoption and residing together, and any unrelated people who may be living in the housing unit.
- *non-family household:* a person living alone or two or more people who live together but who are not related, such as roommates or boarders.
- *married-couple households with own children:* a husband and wife living together with children—by birth, adoption, or marriage (stepchildren)—who are under the age of 18 and never married.

128

- *blended families:* a husband and wife living together with children that one or both partners bring to the family from previous marriages or relationships; may also include children from their union.
- *biological nuclear family:* a husband and wife living together with children by birth or adoption only (i.e., does not include blended families).
- *traditional nuclear family:* a husband and wife living together with children by birth or adoption only, in which the father is the sole breadwinner and the mother is a full-time homemaker.

Figure 6.1 Households by Type: 1970 to 2000

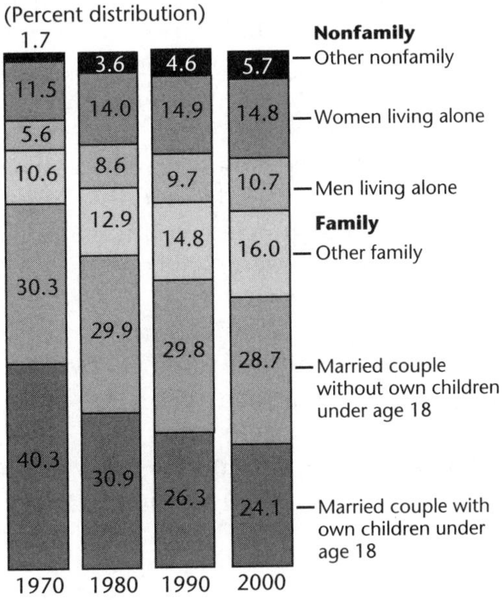

(Percent distribution)

1970	1980	1990	2000	
1.7	3.6	4.6	5.7	**Nonfamily** — Other nonfamily
11.5	14.0	14.9	14.8	— Women living alone
5.6	8.6	9.7	10.7	— Men living alone
10.6				**Family** — Other family
	12.9	14.8	16.0	
30.3	29.9	29.8	28.7	— Married couple without own children under age 18
40.3	30.9	26.3	24.1	— Married couple with own children under age 18

Source: U.S. Census Bureau Population Survey, March: 1970 to 2000.

If this all sounds confusing, it is. Even some demographers and family historians cannot agree on which definitions or proportions should be used in talking about family trends. The proportions given in this comparison are based on census data from *all* households—both family and non-family. Notably, whether discussing proportions of households or proportions of families, married couples with own children have been in steady decline since 1970. Since the American family has become so politicized, both sides use statistics to bolster their argument, leaving many confused: Is the traditional family in decline or recovery? When you are working with families, it is helpful to know the difference between the facts, the rhetoric, and the media spin put on census data.

In talking about household type in relationship to older adults, it's important to include both non-family households and family households, as they are intricately interwoven. For example, the decline in the proportion of family households is in part related to the increase in non-family households, such as single households and couple households with no children, both of which include a high proportion of older adults (Klein, 2004). Changes in household and family structure have important implications for seniors because they affect the makeup and quality of an older person's social support network (Bengtson, Burton, & Rosenthal, 1990). Furthermore, because many of today's seniors are living in the midst of this family evolution, there is a great discrepancy between the families in which they grew up and what families are today. The sidebar of the Barkley family history illustrates these changes in size and dynamics over time.

The Barkleys

The Barkley family provides an overview of some of the typical changes experienced by most American families in just a few generations. Like most young Americans at the beginning of the century, Millie and Robert married in their early to mid-20s, began a family soon after, and had several children throughout their marriage, with not all of them making it to adulthood. While they did not have their parents for social support, they could depend on their siblings and other extended family in good times and bad. Their children grew up among this big extended family—only two generations deep, but comprised of many aunts, uncles, siblings, and cousins. Like more than half of all marriages of the era, theirs ended with the death of a spouse before all the children had left home (Newman, 1999). Robert Barkley lived long enough to see his first daughter married and his first grandchild out of diapers. He was still working and still had children living at home when he passed away; there had been no retirement years, no empty-nest years with Millie. In her time of financial and emotional need, Millie turned to her siblings and extended family for support. In her elder years, she turned to her children, particularly her son, his wife, and children, who lived with her in the family home until her death.

The Morgans

In contrast, Millie's granddaughter Eva, like most women after World War II, married young and completed childbearing early in her life as well as in her marriage. Unlike Millie's day, when middle-class mothers stayed home to raise children and keep house, it was socially acceptable for Eva in the 1950s to take a part-time job once the kids were in school. Also unlike her grandmother, all of Eva's children survived childhood and most graduated college. Furthermore, she has had over 30 years with her husband after the children moved out, nearly 20 years and counting in which they both have been retired. Eva and Dave have known their children as youths, young adults, and now as middle-aged parents. They have seen some of their grandchildren grow from infants to parents and are enjoying a third round of babies as great-grandparents. While each generation has had fewer children in and across families, there are now four generations living.

But all has not been perfect for Eva and Dave Morgan either. They have had their own marital problems, as well as watched from the sidelines the failed relationships of their children. Rather than depend on family for assistance in later life, Eva and Dave have financially planned for in-home care and resident long-term care when the time comes. Unlike Eva's mother Ann and grandmother Millie, who grew up with and depended on their extended

130

Case Study: The Barkley and Morgan Families

In 1905, Millie Hardin, 23, and Robert Barkley, 25, married in Wilmington, Delaware. Robert earned a good income at DuPont, so after they were married they bought a house and started a family. Over the next 15 years, Millie and Robert had six children, although two died before their first birthday. Millie's mother died young at 29 in childbirth, but her father lived to be 58, and lived nearby, along with her three sisters and their families. Both of Robert's parents died before he was married, but his five brothers and their families also lived in the area. The extended families got together regularly, with sometimes upwards of 50 cousins playing together on summer evenings at the Barkley home. In 1927, the oldest Barkley daughter, Ann, 21, married and had a daughter Eva, followed by two other children. In 1929, Robert Barkley, 49, died of a heart attack, leaving Millie with two sons still under 18 years old at home. The extended families pooled resources to help Millie raise the boys, and her oldest son, Bob, remained in the home to help Millie as she grew older and frail with health problems. Family members came frequently to visit and were an integral part of daily life. When she passed away at 69, Bob and his family took over the house.

Eva, like many of her cousins and other young women after World War II, married young at 18 years old. She was the first of all her siblings to move away from Wilmington, when her husband, Dave Morgan, 22, was accepted at the University of Virginia on the GI Bill. Dave got a job in 1950 at the State Department, and with the help of a VA loan, bought a house in the suburbs of Washington, D.C. Eva had four children, two boys and two girls, before she turned 25 years old. When the youngest started school, Eva took a part-time job to buy some luxuries, such as a second car and a television set.

All four children graduated high school, and the three youngest attended college. In 1969, Eva, 42, became a grandmother, and her mother Ann, 63, became a great-grandmother when Eva's daughter Mary, 19, had a baby girl, Amy, with her live-in boyfriend.

Eva's mom Ann developed disabling arthritis, so Ann moved in with her daughter's family until she died in 1974.

Throughout the 1970s, the Morgan children attended graduate school, worked, and entered in and out of relationships. After two years, Mary left her child's father and became a single mother on welfare while going back to school. Mary's younger sister, Susan, has never married nor had any children, but she enjoys a close network of friends and has quickly climbed the corporate ladder. Both older brothers Will and John lived with a succession of girlfriends before finally marrying in their late 20s. Today Will is divorced and shares custody of his son. John is step father to a son and the biological father of two daughters. The Morgan siblings live in different parts of the country and rarely all get together, although most usually see their parents once a year. Mary calls her parents daily and is the family's informal distance caregiver.

Eva and Dave, now in their late 70s, are great-grandparents. Dave recently had a bad stroke. So far, with a long-term care policy paying for in-home help, Eva has managed his care. However, they are talking of moving soon to a continuing care retirement center.

families for support of all types, Eva and Dave's siblings and their families rarely see each other and do not feel comfortable calling one another if they need help. While any of the Morgans' four children would certainly provide help if they were asked, Eva and Dave feel strongly about their independence and do not want to be a burden.

Family Structure

The Barkley family has a fairly typical, white, middle-class, suburban family history. The typical story for African Americans, Hispanics, and other minority groups in the United States over the past 100 years would undoubtedly be different—as likely would be white, working-class, rural Americans. In talking about family structure and households, its important to emphasize again that these are national averages and vary greatly by race, ethnicity, socioeconomic background, and other variables.

THE DEMOGRAPHIC TRANSITION

The structure and dynamics of the American family have changed in several significant ways over the past century, particularly in the last 40 years. One of the greatest changes to occur to family structure is the *demographic transition*—the change in population structure identified with developing countries and associated improvements in public health and medicine. According to the demographic transition theory, as countries become developed, they experience a shift in growth rate from rapid population growth, to slow growth, to

zero growth, and finally to a reduction in population. Some European countries, such as Hungary and Germany, are actually experiencing a population decline today.

In addition to a declining population, most of these countries are also experiencing their population aging, that is, the country's proportion of adults 65 and older is increasing. As discussed in chapter 1, Trends in Aging, the American senior population has increased from 4 percent of the population in 1900 to over 12 percent of the population today, and is expected to grow to 20 percent of the population by 2030. Furthermore, among those 65 and older, the greatest growth is in the oldest-old age category, those 85 years and older. Therefore, not only is our nation aging, but the aging population itself is getting older.

The Beanpole Theory

Noting the simultaneous impact of decreased mortality and decreased fertility (the outcome of the demographic transition) to family structure, social scientists theorized that as people lived longer *and* had fewer births, it should result in a *verticalization* of the family (Bengtson et al., 1990). In other words, as people live longer, it should increase the number of generations living at the same time; but within each generation, there should be fewer siblings and cousins because of decreases in fertility. Consequently, the family structure should change from the *horizontal* or *pyramid family structure* (two or three living generations, but many siblings and kin within a generation) to a *vertical* or *beanpole family structure* (four or five living generations, but only a few siblings and kin within a generation).

Changes in the family structure are predicted to be far-reaching, from the number of kin in a *generation*, to the number and complexity of family roles, to the duration of time spent in roles and family relationships (Bengtson et al., 1990). Consequently, the *beanpole theory* has captured the attention of the gerontology and social science communities (Treas, 1995). Some of these changes have been documented. For example, due to parents' increased longevity since 1800, daughters in 1980 had on average fourfold the number of years to spend with both parents alive (Bengtson et al., 1990). And certainly the United States Census has determined that families are having fewer children, down from an average of four children in 1900 to two children today. However, the major premise that families today increasingly consist of four or five generations is debatable (Farkas & Hogan, 1995; Uhlenberg, 1995; Treas). Research involving 10,000 people in seven countries, including the United States, found only 1 percent of the sample with five-generation families and only 2.4 percent of families with four or more generations (Farkas & Hogan). Rossi and Rossi (1990) found in their study that the large majority, 80 percent, of all adults were in lineages of three or fewer generations, and more were in two-generation families than in four- or five-generation families.

Even still, the beanpole theory has generated a number of questions, the answers to which should be of interest and value to you. For example, with fewer siblings to care for aging parents, will social support become intergenerational, with grandchildren and even great-grandchildren providing and receiving support?

Pyramid family structure

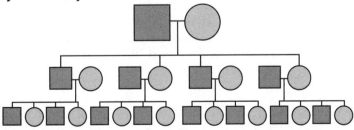

This stylized model of the pyramid family illustrates a typical American family structure prevalent in the twentieth century. Note the pyramid shape, narrow at the top and wider at the bottom, with the grandparents represented at the top by the square (grandfather) and circle (grandmother), their four children and their spouses presented in the middle of the diagram, and their sixteen grandchildren on the bottom.

133

Bean-Pole family structure

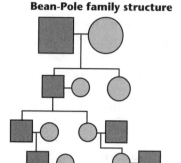

The beanpole family structure is becoming more prevalent today, as couples choose to have fewer (or no) children and people live longer. In this stylized model, the number in each generation is cut in half, as the grandparents have only two children, and their children have only two children. While each generation has fewer members within it, it is more likely that there will be four or even five generations alive at the same time as people live longer lives.

A Multiplicity of Family Forms

The second greatest change to family structure is the multiplicity of family forms. In America today, there is no typical family—diversity has become the hallmark feature. While many still believe that the nuclear family provides the best environment for raising families, a growing number of citizens also believe that *alternative families* provide loving homes and good foundations for children. Furthermore, in courtrooms and boardrooms across the country, alternative families are slowly getting legal recognition and support.

Social and legal sanctions in support of alternative family forms are in stark contrast to the conformity of the 1950s and early 1960s. Then, marriage and the traditional nuclear family were considered the ideal and the norm, and variations such as out-of-wedlock children or homosexuality were socially scorned, if not legally prohibited. Family forms that have become increasingly more prevalent today include single mothers, teen mothers, single fathers, childless couples, cohabiting couples, gay parents, blended or stepfamilies, and grandparents raising grandkids. Each of these emerging family forms brings unique gifts and challenges to the intergenerational relationship.

The consequences of structural changes in the family are profound and far-reaching. For older Americans today, it means that family relationships are potentially more complex, diverse, and richer than those experienced by prior generations. Family relationships form the foundation for most seniors' social, emotional, and instrumental support in later life.

The Ties that Bind

The person who tries to live alone will not succeed as a human being. His heart withers if it does not answer another heart. His mind shrinks away if he hears only the echoes of his own thoughts and finds no other inspiration.

Pearl S. Buck

Love and the ability to form interpersonal relationships form the foundation of our humanity. These relationships are essential for our survival—we need them to learn, work, and procreate. While human relationships vary considerably, the most powerful, enjoyable, satisfying, even sorrowful are those that we have with family, friends, and loved ones. "Within this inner circle of intimate relationships, we are bonded to each other with 'emotional glue'—bonded with love" (Perry, 2004).

Atchley and Barusch (2004) identify three types of bonds that foster close relationships: interdependence, intimacy, and belonging. *Interdependence* is a mutual, reciprocal relationship between two or more people, whereby people get their needs met better together than they would alone. Interdependence can also increase the resources available to a person. For example, the crew selected for each space shuttle mission brings different sets of expertise to the flight, reducing the number of tasks any one crew member needs to do or know how to do.

Intimacy refers to the mutual exchange of "affection, trust, and confidence" (Atchley & Barusch, 2004, p. 188). When we share secrets or inside jokes with longtime trusted friends or family we experience intimate moments. Intimacy can also be in the form of sexual and sensual interaction.

Belonging fulfills our need to be part of a group that shares and validates our values and beliefs and offers an environment in which we feel safe, secure, and free to be ourselves.

How we bond with others usually involves one or more of these three relationship ties. Whom we bond with outside of our families and the intensity of the relationship varies over the life course. Many people form close, lifetime friendships as youths in school or as young adults working or attending college. Others develop meaningful relationships later in life through religious activities, special interests, or parental involvement. A long relationship does not necessarily foster a deep one, and a short one is not necessarily shallow. The diversity and number of relationships increase through midlife, due to the cumulative effects of a lifetime of interacting with others. In later life, long-term close relationships wane as friends and relatives die. Still, even at very old age, most people still have one or two close relationships (Atchley & Barusch, 2004).

All the relationships an individual has with family, friends, coworkers, neighbors, and people in groups to which a person belongs make up a *social network*. A subset of the social network includes those individuals who form a *social support system* and provide *social support*—positive and reassuring presence, emotional support, affirmation and validation, information, and financial and personal assistance. Social support is both an ongoing need as well as situation-specific: the types, amounts and sources of support needed vary with the situation, time, place, and health of the person receiving the support (Sutherland & Murphey, 1995). There are four basic types of social support: *Emotional support* includes confiding, comforting, reassuring, and listening; *informational support* provides advice and information (e.g., in decision-making about medical issues, selling or buying a home, and long-term care options); *instrumental support* involves, for example, babysitting, housework, transportation, shopping, and personal care; and *financial support* includes such things as direct money transfers, assistance with banking and check writing, and housing assistance. For the purposes of this chapter, we have collapsed the first two, emotional and informational, into one category—emotional support; and the last two, instrumental and financial, into a second category, instrumental support.

The Complexity of Support

It is important to emphasize that not all members of a social network offer social support; not even all members of a social support system offer support at the time, place, and in the way that the recipient needs it. This distinction between social networks and social support is often blurred, the assumption being that whenever family or friends are present, there is support (Morgan, 1989). For example, when a spouse dies, it is often assumed by others that family members provide the primary support in overcoming this private family loss. In coping with grief and loss, however, research indicates that non-family relationships are cited more often and more favorably than family relationships in adjusting to this role transition (Blanchard, 1998; Morgan). In Morgan's study, references to family members were more often negative than positive, although these behaviors were usually unintentional. The lack of providing social support can be benign, wherein a person does not recognize the need, so doesn't offer to help; it can be intentional, wherein a need is identified but purposely denied; or it can be unintentional, in which someone thinks they are providing support, but it is not perceived as support by the recipient (Blanchard).

Blanchard (1998), in an extensive review of the literature on the relationship between older persons, their family and community ties, and social support, drew the following conclusions from current research: First, the quality and quantity of social relationships (social network) and social support significantly influence the well-being of older people. Second, these influences can be both positive and negative. Third, social support is complex and sensitive to numerous factors, such as time, place and circumstance. Fourth, the presence of someone in a social network, regardless of the relationship, does not necessarily indicate that person provides social support in a given situation or in general. Fifth, the negative aspects of social relationships can be as important as the supportive aspects. Finally, social support and networks are strengthened through reciprocity, by promoting feelings of independence and the self-esteem gained through meaningful social exchange (p. 44).

This discussion describes the key roles of family, friends and other relationships of older Americans and their importance in providing social support to seniors. Understanding how marital status and family role influence social support will help you work with seniors and their families. For example, in working with a senior who recently lost his wife, you will know that men are less likely than women to have a good social support system. Furthermore, men are less likely to seek out or ask for emotional or instrumental support. Considering that in the first two years following a death, a widowed person is at higher risk for adverse health problems and institutional placement, you would want to assist such a client by making referrals to social support groups, encouraging him to reach out to family and friends, and (depending on the closeness of the relationship) offering to be available for support, including informally checking in.

Marriage

The primary relationship for many older adults is their spouse. In later life, marriage often provides companionship, affection, personal and sexual intimacy, interdependence, belonging, and financial security. Notably, older married couples who have weathered life's ups and downs are survivors; by definition they are a select group (Huyck, 1996). Likewise, what we know about marital patterns and satisfaction is somewhat select. Historically, research comes from studies that are largely voluntary and represent only the views of one spouse. Furthermore, they overwhelmingly represent non-Hispanic white couples from middle- and upper-class socioeconomic backgrounds (Huyck). Still, across studies and over time some general conclusions can be drawn regarding marriage in later life.

Marital Satisfaction

Numerous studies reveal that marital satisfaction follows a U-shape pattern: It starts high in the early years of marriage, wanes in middle age with the raising of children and associated financial pressures, and then steadily increases after children leave home (Bengtson et al., 1990). In the later years of marriage many couples rediscover or even redefine their relationship. For some, this manifests in more egalitarian division of household chores; for others it represents new joint interests or activities. As couples have more time to focus on their relationship separate from the competing demands of work and family, they tend to draw closer together. The dual effect of retirement and an empty nest has been theorized to improve marital satisfaction by reducing other commitments, role conflicts, and time constraints, and by increasing opportunities for companionship.

Several studies of long-term marriages identified factors that contribute to a successful marriage: viewing one's mate as a best friend, liking one's spouse as a person, sharing life goals and values, sharing similar interests and activities, maintaining a sense of humor and playfulness in the marriage, and practicing good conflict management skills (Alford-Cooper, 1998; Atchley & Miller, 1983; Lauer & Lauer, 1986; Bengtson et al., 1990; Lauer, Lauer, & Kerr, 1990). Commitment to one's spouse and to the institution of marriage has also been rated high as a reason marriages are successful and otherwise have held together (Lauer & Lauer).

Compared to their unmarried counterparts, older married couples tend to report greater happiness and life satisfaction (Mastekaasa, 1994), better health (Pienta, Hayward, & Jenkins, 2000), and longer lives (Litwak & Messeri, 1989). A major California study (comparing middle-aged couples married 15 or more years with older couples married 35 or more years) found that older couples experienced more pleasure and less conflict than middle-aged marriages (Levenson, Carstensen, & Gottman, 1993). In general, whether comparing older marriages to younger marriages or older married couples to unmarried people, the picture that emerges is a positive one of greater happiness and satisfaction, better health, and longer lives. In addition, a long and lasting marriage gives many couples a sense of accomplishment, security, and comfort.

Of course a long marriage does not necessarily mean a happy or satisfying one. Couples stay together for any number of reasons—economics, the sake of family unity or duty, convenience, or religious beliefs. According to one study, marital dissatisfaction in later life is not any more frequent than it is at any other age (Herman, 1994). Divorce, however, is less likely to be a resolution than in earlier years of marriage; only about 1 percent of all divorces occur after the age of 65 (Quadagno, 2002). Dissatisfaction with sexual relations, poor communication, and the presence of children in the home appear to be highly correlated with unhappy couples. Sometimes happy marriages deteriorate in later years as a result of declines in physical or mental health. Dementia, in particular, can devastate the foundation of the best marriage. Prolonged care-giving has also been correlated to decline in marital satisfaction, particularly if the caregiving spouse experiences health problems.

Gender

Gender (as well as race and ethnicity) significantly impacts marital status in later life. While over half of Americans 65 and older are married, men are much more likely to be so than women. According to 2000 census data (Census Bureau, 2003), more than three-quarters (77 percent) of men ages 65 to 74 are married, compared to a little over half (53 percent) of women the same ages. The disparity becomes greater with age: about two-thirds (67 percent) of men 75 and older are married, compared to less that one-third (29 percent) of women.

If men are more likely to be married, women are more likely to be widowed. In 2000, nearly a third (31 percent) of women ages 65 to 74 were widowed, compared to less than one-tenth (8 percent) of men. The gap widens with age. Of Americans 85 years and older, 79 percent of women and 38 percent of men were widowed. Gender differences in marital status can be attributed primarily to men's shorter life spans.

In contrast to widowhood, divorce or separation occurs about equally between the sexes in the 65 and older population, accounting for only 9.1 percent of all seniors in 2003. Notably, over the past decade these numbers have nearly doubled from 5.4 percent in 1990.

Gender has also been correlated to marital satisfaction and well-being. In general, compared to their wives, husbands report greater marital satisfaction (Huyck, 1996). Some research indicates that this may be because, after children leave home, wives are more likely to become dissatisfied about marital issues that they once tolerated, while husbands are more likely to be in denial or gloss over the existence of problems and the resulting tensions (Huyck).

Social Support in Marriage

Most successful couples' relationships over time nurture mutual inter-dependence, intimacy, and belonging (Atchley & Barusch, 2004). As time goes by, they come to value and rely on each other more for emotional and instrumental support. Lauer et al. (1990) found in their study of couples married 45 years or longer that the emotional support and intimacy between partners increased in intensity over the marriage. The vast majority found their spouses to be more interesting to them today than they were at the beginning of the marriage; they confided in one another, laughed together, and kissed nearly every day.

Some studies indicate that spouses become more interdependent in instrumental support over time, often sharing chores around the house, gardening, shopping, and doing other errands that may have once been the wife's duty. Other studies counter that while this shift may not happen with baby boomers, who already practice more egalitarian household responsibilities, most seniors today maintain a more traditional division of labor—husbands mow the lawn, keep the car tuned, and tackle household repairs while women cook, clean, and do the laundry.

Late-life couples also become more interdependent on one another for personal assistance, particularly in times of illness. When illness becomes a permanent state, the likelihood greatly increases that the spouse will become a caregiver. The spouse is the main provider of care for those who need assistance getting dressed, bathed, fed, and so forth. Often at the point that it becomes caregiving, it is no longer an interdependent relationship; rather, it becomes dependent. Feelings of resentment, helplessness, guilt, and other negative emotions often cloud the relationship. Studies show that prolonged caregiving can lead to burnout, poor health for the caregiver, and even poor care for the care recipient.

Not all marriages, even those self-defined as happy marriages, meet both spouses' social support needs all the time, if ever. For example, while a husband may meet the emotional support and intimacy needs of his wife, her need for social validation and belonging may best be met by her peer group (Gupta & Korte, 1994).

Husbands report receiving more emotional and social support in their marriages than do wives (Quadagno, 2002). Studies show that men throughout the life course have smaller social support systems than women, including fewer and less intimate friendships (Courtenay, 2000). In particular, husbands are less likely than wives to have a confidant besides their spouse. Research shows that men overwhelmingly confide in their wives, whereas women confide more often in their children or friends (Quadagno).

Divorce

Beginning in the 1970s, changes in cultural values and divorce laws saw a rise in divorces that continued to increase until the 1990s before leveling off. The number of divorced people 18 years and older exploded from 4.3 million in 1970 to 18.3 million in 1996 (Census Bureau, 2002). The number of people divorced and not remarried is a cumulative number, making the divorced population one of the fastest growing marital status categories (Census Bureau, 2002).

For the senior population, the proportion divorced is also rising. While only 8 percent of all seniors in 2000 were *ever divorced*, that percentage is likely to keep increasing in the coming years due to the *cohort effect*. Research based on cohort analysis demonstrates that the leading age of baby boomers born between 1945 and 1954 are about twice as likely as to be divorced by their 40th birthday as the cohort born between 1925 and 1934. They are about twice as likely to remarry—about 32 percent versus 15 percent, respectively (Census Bureau, 2002). The most rapid rise in divorces today is in the age group of 55 to 64 years (Snyder, 2000). The proportion of divorced Americans 65 and older is expected to reach 50 percent by 2010 (Quadagno, 2002).

In a recent landmark study by AARP (2004), more than 1,000 men and women who divorced in their 40s, 50s, and 60s were interviewed about their divorce experience in midlife. The study revealed some startling facts. For example, contrary to the popular belief that older men leave their wives for younger women, the study found wives (66 percent) were more likely than husbands (42 percent) to initiate divorce. Furthermore, men reported being more caught off-guard by the news, with 26 percent of men stating "they never saw it coming" compared to only 14 percent of women. Other key findings from this study include:

- People age 40 or older generally feel that divorce is more emotionally devastating than losing a job, about equal to experiencing a major illness, and nearly as devastating as a spouse's death.

- Verbal, physical, or emotional abuse leads the list of causes of divorce (34 percent), followed by differences in values and lifestyles (29 percent), cheating (27 percent), and not being in love anymore (or having "no obvious problems") (24 percent).

- The majority of respondents divorced in their 40s (73 percent), followed by 50s (22 percent) and 60s and older (4 percent).

- Nearly half (45 percent) of respondents named being alone their greatest fear of divorce, followed by fear of failing again (31 percent), financial destitution (28 percent), and never finding someone to marry or live with (24 percent). Women especially fear being financially destitute.

- Among both men and women, the main reason for delaying a divorce was for the sake of children.

- Of those divorced, 56 percent have remained divorced or are separated, 31 percent have remarried, 9 percent are living with a partner, and 5 percent are widowed.

- Despite the worry, torment, and fear they go through in making the decision and going through the divorce process, most people cope fairly well with life after divorce. Three in four (76 percent) claim they made the right decision in divorcing. Their buzzwords are "freedom," "self-identity," and "fulfillment."

Social Support after Divorce

The implications of a growing divorce rate in matters of social support are enormous for middle-age and older men and women, particularly if they don't remarry. For both parties, if they don't remarry they lose what many consider to be the main source of social support in later life—their spouse. Men are particularly at risk in this aspect because, as previously pointed out, they tend to have smaller social support systems and rely more exclusively on a spouse for support. Divorced fathers are also more likely than mothers to have less contact with adult children and live farther away (Shapiro, 2003). They also tend to have weaker emotional bonds (Bengtson et al., 1990). As one large study summed it up, men appear to gain more from marriage and lose more from divorce than women (Curran, McLanahan, & Knab, 2003).

That is not to say women get off easy. Women who do not remarry not only lose the social support of a spouse, but are more likely to be worse off economically (Bengtson et al., 1990). In general, women 65 and older are twice as likely as men to be living in poverty (Older Women's League, n.d.). Many divorced (and widowed) women 65 and older never worked outside the home, or if they did work, it was part-time or for hourly wages with minimum benefits. Consequently, few qualify for a private or public pension plan or other retirement benefits such as health plans. Women married to the same man for 10 or more years are eligible for a spousal benefit. However, that amount is equal only to one-third the Social Security benefit if the couple were still married (Older Women's League).

Several studies over the past 20 years show that compared to adult children from two-parent families, children of divorced parents generally feel less obligation to their parents, perceive a lower quality relationship with them, and have significantly less contact (Cicirelli, 1983; Bengtson et al., 1990; Aquilino, 1994; Webster & Herzog, 1995). When support is given, mothers are more likely than fathers to receive emotional, instrumental, and financial support (Wright & Maxwell, 1991).

Widowhood

Marriages that survive through the years ultimately end with the death of a spouse. In the United States, like most Western countries, life expectancy is longer for women, resulting in more widows than widowers. As previously mentioned, the likelihood of a wife becoming a widow increases significantly with age.

Despite its inevitability, death of a spouse is one of the most difficult family transitions families go through—emotionally, socially, and financially. While death of any family member is tragic, the death of a longtime spouse is particularly devastating. Along with grieving the loss of the individual, the spouse is dealing with the loss of the role and identity of being a spouse and part of a couple, "potentially one of the most pervasive, intense, intimate, and personal roles that they have ever had in their life" (Lund & Caserta, 2004).

Widowhood for both spouses is associated with increased physical and mental health problems, as well as increased risk for serious illness, hospitalization, long-term care placement, and death (Laditka & Laditka, 2003; Pienta et al., 2000; Prigerson, Maciejewski, & Rosenheck, 2000; Smith, Zick, & Duncan, 1991). The death of a spouse is an intensely personal experience and is influenced by a number of factors, such as how close the couple were before death, whether it was sudden or the result of a prolonged illness, the presence of health issues with the surviving spouse, and the use of hospice services. Noting the tremendous variation among individual experiences, it is still possible to highlight some generalizations between how men and women cope with the loss of their spouses.

Social Support in Widowhood

Men are often taken by surprise by their wife's death, as noted by this 79-year-old man (Lund & Caserta, 2004):

> I just can't believe this happened. My wife was healthy. She was strong. She took me to the emergency room three times last year. I almost died twice. All of a sudden she has a heart attack and she's dead. I'm here and she's gone. This is crazy. Nobody thought I'd be the one to live the longest.

Since most men do not expect to outlive their wives, they are usually less prepared at every level to deal with their loss. Often having relied solely on their wives for emotional support, and feeling like they need to put up a strong front for their children, husbands often have no one to share their grief with in an intimate way. If it had been a traditional marriage, simple household chores such as meals and laundry can become overwhelming. Furthermore, men are less likely than women to ask for help, attend counseling or self-help groups, or seek other support services.

Men who are widowed are more likely than women to remarry. In 1990, elderly widowed men were seven times more likely than elderly widowed women to remarry (AAGP, 1999). In contrast to women, men are rarely worse off financially with the loss of their spouses.

In general, women seem to cope better emotionally than men with the death of a spouse. Psychologically, they are more likely prepared to outlive their husbands. Most women over 65 know a neighbor, a friend, or someone else in their social network who is widowed, and they have likely been a source of social support through that transition. Women are more likely to have a strong social support system and are more willing to ask for and receive help from others. Friends and children are key sources of social support to widows.

In one study, women reported feelings of freedom after the loss of their spouse and alluded to being reluctant to give that up by remarrying (Davidson, 2001). This wish to maintain autonomy may be because women caregivers or those with overly dependent husbands feel as if they were tied down with responsibility, sometimes for years preceding the death (Davidson; Gierveld, 2004). Because women are often dependent on their husbands' retirement benefits, they do tend to fare considerably worse financially after they lose their mates. According to one study, the greatest contributor to a widow's drop in income and subsequent backslide into poverty was a decrease in Social Security and pension income as a result of the husband's death (Hungerford, 2001).

Some studies indicate that the risk for adverse health outcomes diminishes after about two years or if the person remarries (Laditka & Laditka, 2003). Coping strategies found to be effective for both husbands and wives include ongoing social support from family, friends, and peers; participation in social activities; faith-based activities (such as religious attendance and prayer); and counseling services (such as provided by support groups and hospice) (Hegge & Fischer, 2000; Lee, DeMaris, Bavin, & Sullivan, 2001; Michael, Crowther, Schmid, & Allen, 2003; Utz, Carr, Nesse, & Wortman, 2002).

Remarriage

Older adults, particularly women, are less likely than their younger counterparts to remarry following divorce and, to a lesser degree, the death of a spouse. Still, about 250,000 people over 50 remarry each year. Increases in the number of middle-age and older adults, increases in those who are single or divorced, longer life expectancies, and changes in values of the baby boomers entering retirement age portend that remarriage will occur more frequently in the future. Yet, little research exists on remarriages in later life (Pasley, 1998; Atchley & Barusch, 2004).

Social Support in Remarriage

The most-cited reason for remarriage in later life by both men and women is companionship (Bulcroft, Bulcroft, Hatch, & Borgatta, 1989; McKain, 1969). Women are also likely to remarry for economic security. Men tend to remarry more often than women; one study estimated that men are twice as likely as women to remarry (Burch, 1990).

Men's higher propensity to remarry is attributed to a number of factors. First, particularly for today's population 65 and older, it is more socially acceptable for men to remarry and to choose significantly younger wives (Burch, 1990). Second, men are more likely to meet a suitable mate, as they have a much bigger pool of mates from which to choose. Third, men gain more from the emotional support of a marriage than women; women are more likely to already have a good social support system, including emotional support from children, other family, and friends (Vinick, 1979). Indeed, women with successful careers or close relationships with friends and family, or those who value their autonomy and freedom prefer *not* to remarry.

Older adults who do remarry are likely to face a number of unique challenges. Unlike most first marriages, subsequent marriages bring to the relationship people with entirely different histories, in which they have already established a life, home, social network, career, and often a family. Where they will live, what their relationship will be to children and other family members, and inheritance and other financial dealings represent just the tip of the iceberg of a number of issues.

One of the greatest obstacles older couples face in remarriage, however, is the negative attitudes and dissuasion of friends and family. In one study (McKain, 1969) about one in four couples almost did not marry because of negative social pressure, particularly from their adult children. Other research shows that negative reaction from peers presents an even more deterring influence (Vinick, 1979). Much has changed over the last 25 years regarding social attitudes toward blended families. Some evidence suggests that cultural views are changing, particularly with regard to more positive support from children toward a parent's remarriage (Vinick & Lanspery, 2000).

For many remarriages the approval of friends and family is more than a hurdle—it predicts the success of the marriage. Other factors found to be associated with successful remarriages in later life include home ownership of both parties prior to marriage, estate planning that reassures spouses they will be taken care of and reassures children they will not lose all their inheritance, a solid friendship of several years before the marriage, and common interests and activities (McKain, 1969; Vinick & Lanspery, 2000).

Non-Traditional Couples

In addition to married couples, other types of couples exist among older populations.

Cohabiting Couples

As baby boomers age and social mores around cohabitation relax, an increasing number of older heterosexual couples live together and enjoy sexual intimacy but never marry. For some couples, it makes financial sense: widowed or divorced women may lose some of their retirement, pension or Social Security benefits if they remarry. For others cohabitation offers a degree of autonomy, flexibility, and independence (Gierveld, 2004). In terms of social support, cohabitating couples appear to have more support than divorced, widowed, or single persons, but less than married couples.

Nonsexual Couples

Another type of couple relationship consists of good friends, usually of the same sex, who do not have a sexual relationship. A recent article in the *New York Times* (Gross, 2004) offered anecdotal evidence that a number of baby boomer women are making concrete plans to live with one another in retirement in order to pool financial resources and maximize social support. In general, however, little is known about nonsexual, cohabitating couples and how they impact social support systems (Atchley & Barusch, 2004).

Homosexual Couples

Gay and lesbian couples represent another category of couple relationship. Most social scientists argue that statistical information about gay and lesbian relationships in general, and among older couples in particular, are tenuous at best (Huyck, 1996; Kimmel, 1993). Recently, however, researchers estimated the prevalence of same-sex couples based on intensive review of 2000 U.S. Census data (Bennett & Gates, 2004). According to this study, more than 1 in 10 same-sex couples include a partner age 65 or older; nearly 1 in 10 couples are comprised of two people 65 or older. Two-thirds of these couples have lived together in the same house for five years or more, and more than four out of five own their home. The proportion of same-sex couples is significantly higher if the age of 55 is used: nearly one in four same-sex couples include a partner 55 or older, and nearly one in five couples are comprised of two people 55 or older.

Social Support in Gay and Lesbian Couples

Gay and lesbian couples have unique social and legal barriers to social support. Despite great strides over the past few decades in social acceptance of homosexuality in some parts of society, it is by no means universal. Prejudice still exists on the streets and in the courts. By and large, gay and lesbian couples lack the same legal and social recognition given to heterosexual couples. In the past few years, some cities and states have begun to pass laws that recognize domestic partners (also includes heterosexual cohabiting couples) for some benefits. In addition, some states have passed laws to legally allow same-sex marriages, but in every case these laws are being challenged in court. Without legal rights, gay and lesbian couples face formidable challenges in forming and dissolving families, financial and estate planning, health care decisions, and other legal affairs. If you work with gay or lesbian couples, take extra care that their wishes are spelled out in legal documents.

Gay men and lesbians differ from heterosexuals with respect to their social support system. In some cases, gay and lesbian individuals are estranged from family members who do not accept or support their sexual identity (Quadagno, 2002). In such cases they may have little, if any, contact with a traditional system of social support. Instead, many form their own families of friends, significant others, and possibly some biological family members, including their own children, to be their social support system (Kimmel, 1993). One recent study found that gays comfortable and open with their sexuality were more likely to use and be satisfied with the social support available to them (Farberman, 2003). Moreover, these individuals reported more commitment to their relationships with their significant others or partners (Farberman).

Not all gay men and lesbians are estranged from their families of origin. Kimmel (1993) noted that sometimes by virtue of their social position, gay men and lesbians have special roles within the family. For example, they may be "elected" to be the caregiver for an aging relative because they are unmarried, can easily travel, or simply possess the willingness to do so. They may also be perceived as having more financial resources to help with an aging parent or with other family situations. Finally, they may be called upon to provide counsel or emotional support, especially to younger family members.

Never Married

In the United States, less than 5 percent of those 65 and older have never been married, and that percentage has stayed relatively stable over the past 50 years (Census Bureau, 2003). That is not to say, however, that never-married seniors have lived alone most of their lives, or that they are lonely or socially isolated. Research shows that many never-married older people have lived with others throughout their lives—friends, family, even lovers (Choi, 1996; Rubinstein, 1987; Simon, 1989). In fact, in at least one study, never-married people were more likely to be living with others, especially siblings, than were divorced persons (Choi). Some evidence suggests that what never-married people may have missed in having a spouse and children, they have made up for in social activities, satisfying careers, friends, and *fictive family* (Genevay, 1993; Simon). Furthermore, never-married women tend to be better off financially than those their age who are widowed or divorced (and never-married men appear to be no worse off financially than divorced men) (Choi).

Up until recently, those who never married, particularly women, were often pitied—or viewed with suspicion: "I wonder what's wrong with ___ that she can't find a mate?" Even in the gerontology literature, older single people have been presented as loners (Troll, Miller, & Atchley, 1979), lifelong isolates (Gubrium, 1975), and living lives without love—as in "it may be easier to have never loved than to have loved and lost" (Troll et al.). This negative social perception about single life has been especially true for women. Men, on the other hand, have been perceived as remaining bachelors "because they want personal freedom from involvement" (Troll et al.). Several books in recent years about women who came of age in the early 19th century counter this viewpoint (Delany, Delany, & Hill Hearth, 1993; Kuhn, 1991; Simon, 1989). For many people, especially women, not marrying was a conscious choice for a different type of life, usually a career, but sometimes it was simply a choice *not* to be a wife and mother. Maggie Kuhn, founder of the Gray Panthers and a lifelong social activist, articulates: "Many people ask why I never married. My glib response is always: sheer luck! When I look back on my life, I see so many things I could not have done if I had been tied to a husband and children."

Social Support in Never-Married Life

Most people who have chosen to stay single throughout their lives have a strength and resiliency that actually may serve to help them cope better in later life with living alone (Troll et al., 1979). Never-married older women have particularly strong social ties with family, friends, and social organizations (Choi, 1996; Simon, 1989). On the other hand, never-married older men tend to have weaker social ties across the board (Arber, 2004; Perren, Arber, & Davidson, 2003).

Currently, frail adults that do not have a partner or children turn to siblings, extended kin, fictive kin, and friends for social support (Goldberg, Kantrow, Kremen, & Lauter, 1986). Some studies find never-married men and women, however, are less likely than married or divorced people to have a caregiver in times of illness (Choi, 1996) and are in more need for emotional and instrumental support (Keith, Kim, & Schafer, 2000).

Parent-Child Relationship

The two most primary family relationships are between husband and wife, and between parent and child. Most older adults, 84 percent, have living children and consider them to be key members of their social support system

(Atchley & Barusch, 2004). Increases in longevity mean that parents are spending longer periods than ever before with their adult children, most of it spent after the children have moved out of the home. Increasingly, parents, particularly mothers, can expect to have a relationship of 50, 60, even 70 years or more with a "child." In fact, about 10 percent of parents have adult children aged 65 or older (Atchley & Barusch). The length of time spent in relationship to one another has resulted in a number of complex and overlapping roles, including parent, grandparent, confidant, caregiver, co-resident, and so on. As the complexity and number of roles increase, so do the opportunities and challenges for providing intergenerational social support.

A common misperception today is that adult children have turned their backs on their aging parents, leaving them socially isolated and in need of care (Atchley & Barusch, 2004). The majority of research demonstrates otherwise. Generally speaking, adult children are very much involved in their parents' lives, even if it is at a distance. While some parents may initially move away when they retire, as health problems surface or one parent gets seriously ill or dies, they tend to move back to be near one or more of their adult children. Likewise, adult children may move away to pursue careers or interests, but this does not mean they have abandoned their parents. Studies indicate that distance is not a factor in the quality or closeness of the parent-child relationship (Uhlenberg & Cooney, 1990; Lin & Rogerson, 1995). Frequency of in-person visits varies with travel time, with those living closer dropping by more often but for shorter periods of time than those who visit from out of town. Estimates vary, but in one large-scale study, more than half of the adult children with both parents alive and living together lived within 30 miles of their parents (Rogerson, Weng, & Lin, 1998).

Social Support in Parent-Child Relationships

Social support occurs throughout the life cycle between parents and children. Contrary to the myth that older people are only recipients of support, research shows social support is by and large equal and reciprocal, flowing in both generational directions (Atchley & Barusch, 2004; Bengtson et al., 1990). The type and flow of social support provided varies to some degree by timing in the life course.

Much of the research on social support in families has traditionally focused on the caregiver relationship between parent and adult child, unfairly weighting the conclusion that older adults are the primary recipients of care. Recent research, however, shows that healthy parents up until age 80 are often the primary givers of support across all categories—instrumental, emotional, informational, and financial (Bengtson et al., 1990; Hoyert, 1991). The pendulum usually swings after age 80, widowhood, serious illness, or chronic poor health, at which time adult children appear to give more support. Most parents and children believe that in the end, the support given is equal or greater to the support they have received (Atchley & Barusch, 2004).

The type of support that parents provide varies with age, need, and ability, as well by socioeconomic status, race, and ethnicity. In general, parents between the ages of 65 and 74 are likely to help their young adult children with financial assistance, such as a down payment for a car or house, and household aid, such as babysitting and housework (Atchley & Barusch, 2004). Parents also provide significant emotional support, particularly in times of serious illness, death of a spouse or child, or divorce. In recent years, an increasing number of parents also help their young adult children, mostly 18 to 35 years of age, by providing housing. Called *boomerang kids*, the grown children of this phenomenon have been attributed to the poor economy, slow job market, high costs of housing, and increasing number of adult children getting divorced.

Adult children provide parents with care as well. In a national study with more then 7,000 participants, one-third of seniors 70 years and older with physical limitations received regular assistance from their children with activities of daily living (eating, bathing, dressing, etc.), although only 7 percent receive help most of the time (Lo Sasso & Johnson, 2002). The importance of this assistance is noteworthy: Those who received regular help with basic care from their children were 60 percent less likely to use nursing home care over the next two years than similar elders who did not receive family assistance (Lo Sasso and Johnson). In addition to direct personal care, adult children also provide a wide variety of other assistance—shopping, transportation, balancing the checkbook and paying the bills, house and yard work, and so forth. Proximity is a factor for many of the tasks that need to be done, but those who live at a distance also provide a substantial amount of care.

Siblings

"Letting go of you was the hardest thing I've ever done," said 107-year-old Sarah "Sadie" Delany regarding the death of her beloved sister, Elizabeth "Bessie," at age 104. About two years older than Bessie, Sarah never expected to survive her sister: "It doesn't seem natural that I outlived you . . . learning that I am a separate human being . . . for the first time in my life" (Delany & Hill Hearth, 1997). For more than 100 years, the Delaney sisters, who chose careers over marriage, lived together—outliving their parents and siblings. While their lives are truly extraordinary, the deep bonds they shared are representative of those that often occur between siblings as they age, especially sisters.

About 85 percent of people in middle age have a living sibling, compared to 78 percent of adults 60 years and older (Cicirelli, 1995). Even at age 80, however, most people still have at least one sibling alive (Cicirelli, 1995). Siblings share a unique relationship. They are born in the same generation, they share the same family history, and their relationship lasts a lifetime. The collective memories and experiences of siblings become more meaningful over time, providing deep roots to the past and reinforcing personal identity (Gold, 1989). According to eminent gerontologist Robert Butler (1963), reminiscing about the past is an important part of *life review*, a universal process that provides a way for older adults to make sense out of their life experiences. Butler found that people reminisce more often in later life with siblings than with any other family member. The review process helps to resolve old conflicts, allows seniors to accept life as it is today, and contributes to better adjustment in old age.

Sibling relationships often follow a pattern of being close in youth, growing apart in midlife as families and careers take precedence, and growing closer again in later life (Brubaker, 1984). Often a critical incident, such as the death of a parent or spouse, divorce, or illness, serves as the catalyst for renewing contact in mid- or later life (Brubaker). Earlier rivalries or conflicts may be put aside in order to rekindle relationships.

Social Support in Sibling Relationships

Those who establish close relationships with siblings in later life tend to experience greater life satisfaction, healthier psychological well-being, higher morale, less depression, and a greater sense of emotional security in old age (Cicirelli, 1995). Most siblings report close emotional bonds, a tie that does not diminish over distance. Cicirelli (1995) in her study of older adults, found that about 26 percent of siblings lived in the same town, and another 56 percent lived within 100 miles of one another. Those who lived close by reported weekly contact, while those that lived farther away still maintained frequent contact by phone, letter, or email. Sister-to-sister sibling relationships showed the greatest amount of contact in later life, followed by sister-brother. Brother-to-brother relationships had the least amount of contact (White & Riedmann, 1992).

Social support between older siblings, particularly those who are married or have children, is most likely to consist of emotional support. While Cicirelli (1995) found that 60 percent of respondents said they would help a sibling if they needed their assistance, only 7 percent had ever turned to a sibling for primary assistance during a crisis. However, knowing that they are there if needed provides most seniors with a sense of security (Bengtson et al., 1990). For siblings without a spouse or children, such as the Delaney sisters, social support becomes more comprehensive and often includes instrumental support as well as emotional support (Atchley & Barusch, 2004).

Grandparenthood

Grandparenthood as a separate identity is a fairly recent phenomenon. Up until the beginning of the 20th century, grandparenting and parenting often overlapped. High fertility rates and lower life expectancy meant that many parents were still raising children when the first grandchild arrived. Therefore, there was little novelty in having a baby around—much less, time, energy, or other resources. As couples began marrying and starting families earlier and their parents began living longer and having fewer children, a new family life stage emerged—grandparenthood (Newman, 1999).

Grandparenting Style

In a study of more than 500 grandparents, Cherlin and Furstenberg (1986) identified three types of grandparenting styles: remote, companionate, and involved.

Remote grandparents (30 percent) were not closely or intimately involved in their grandchildren's lives. Most of them did not visit their grandchildren frequently, usually because either they lived far away or because the parents were divorced, a factor found to be especially true for the grandparents on the father's side.

Most (55 percent) of respondents were *companionate grandparents*. They described their relationship as being close, affectionate, and playful. Companionate grandparents tend to live close by and regularly interact with their grandkids. They fit the profile of the ideal grandparent for most people—being there when they were needed, loving and close to the children, but not interfering with respect to disciplining and parenting the child. They viewed their role to be friends with the grandkids and to have fun.

The *involved grandparents* were the minority (16 percent) of the respondents and were often drafted for the role they had in their grandchildren's lives through crisis or difficult situations, such as parental death or divorce. Involved grandparents play an active parenting role, setting limits, enforcing them, and disciplining grandchildren when necessary.

Social Support in Grandparenting Relationships

The type of support that grandparents give their grandchildren depends on numerous factors, such as distance, their age and health, relationship with the parents, and so forth. Atchley and Barusch (2004) identified several important functions or roles that grandparents play in the lives of their grandchildren. First, the simple act of being there provides emotional support to grandchildren and children alike. The presence of grandparents provides a sense of continuity, security, and longevity in the family. A second role of grandparents is that of family historian. Grandparents are often the keepers of the family knowledge and traditions, passing down the stories that map out a family's larger journey through time. Third, grandparents often serve as family crisis managers. Divorce, death, severe illness, accidents, or other disasters can strike and create chaos in the lives of their children and grandchildren. Grandparents often step in and provide assistance—child care, housing, transportation, money, and—perhaps most important—love, a shoulder to cry on, and their attentive presence. Fourth, grandparents sometimes act as arbitrators in disputes between children and grandchildren. Having a grandparent willing to listen about family matters can be a way for children and grandchildren to safely blow off steam, and grandparents may in turn be able to mediate on behalf of both parties. Fifth, grandparents also may be a source of values. In one study, children identified the time they spent with their grandparents as being key to forming their personal identity, including their moral beliefs and family ideals (Roberto & Stroes, 1992). Finally, in extreme cases, grandparents can become caretakers or surrogate parents of grandchildren.

Grandparents Raising Grandkids

Over the past few decades the United States has witnessed a steady rise in grandparent-headed households, more than doubling in number since 1970. According to the United States Census Bureau, in 1970, 2.2 million (3.2 percent) American children lived in a household maintained by a grandparent (Casper & Bryson, 1998). By 2000, this number had risen to 4.5 million (6.3

percent) children (AARP, 2004). In about one-third of these homes, the grandparents were the primary caregivers and no parent was present (AARP).

Most grandparent caregivers are between the ages of 55 and 64, with about 23 percent over age 65 (AARP, 2004). About half (51 percent) identify themselves as white, 38 percent as African American, and 13 percent as Hispanic. One-fourth of grandparent caregivers had income levels below poverty. A number of reasons have been given for the rise of grandparent-headed households, including increasing drug abuse among parents, teen pregnancy, divorce, the rapid rise of single-parent households, mental and physical illnesses, AIDS, crime, child abuse and neglect, and incarceration (Casper & Bryson, 1998).

Grandparent caregivers face a number of challenges. Often they do not have recognized legal status, which makes it difficult for them to enroll the grandchildren in school or make medical decisions for them. As such, grandparents find themselves in the position of having to navigate the legal and welfare systems for help, negotiating Medicaid, Social Security, or foster care funding. Grandparents who are still working must juggle work schedules with day-care and after-school programs. For many grandparents, the struggle is simply the issue of keeping up with young people. Not surprisingly, many grandparents experience higher than normal stress levels and poorer health status than before they took on the caregiving role. Even still, most grandparents raising grandchildren report that they do not regret their decision and appreciate the love and companionship the children bring into their lives (Quadagno, 2002).

Friends

Well, I would consider her my best friend. She lives just right across the boulevard from me. I met her when we were taking driving lessons together, about seven years ago. We had never known each other before but there again she's a very friendly person and when I got to class, we would talk, you know; quite a bit when we would see each other at school. And then later when I passed my test, she was one of the first persons I called to tell her about it. And I think that since then we started to be friends together. Now we call each other every day. (Matthews, 1986)

Friends are unique in social support networks. Other than our spouses, we don't get to choose family members. Friends, on the other hand, we bond with freely based on common interests, values, goals, and so forth. Most people gravitate toward people they consider to be their social equals (Atchley & Barusch, 2004). Factors that promote equality and provide common ground include growing up together, living in the same neighborhood, attending the same school or religious institution, and belonging to the same social clubs or civic organizations.

In later life, friendships complement the social support provided by family members. Unlike family support, which is often obligatory by nature, support in friendship is usually given freely. Important aspects of friendship do not appear to change over time and include enjoyment, understanding, trust, affection, respect, acceptance, and spontaneity (Davis & Todd, 1985). According to Antonucci and Akiyama (1996), a review of the literature indicates "although

Coping with Loneliness

Loneliness and social isolation are not the same as being alone or experiencing solitude. Everyone is alone from time to time. Some people choose to spend a great deal of time in solitude—they enjoy their own company and may wish to socially interact with others only on an occasional basis. Other people enjoy companionship and prefer daily contact with friends, family, and others. Being alone is often a matter of conscious choice and preference.

In contrast, loneliness often feels as if it is not a choice, but a subjective feeling caused by dissatisfaction with social relationships. Loneliness is often accompanied by feelings of sadness, helplessness, and depression. A passive state, it can often be overcome by action. The following steps can help seniors overcome feelings of loneliness and social isolation.

Recognize lonesome feelings and express them. *The first step to addressing loneliness is naming it. This sounds simple, but often it is difficult for people to admit or recognize that they are feeling lonesome. Encourage seniors to talk about their feelings, write in a journal, or write a letter to a fictitious friend to help them clarify their feelings.*

Reach out across distance and time. *Sometimes seniors may feel that all of their friends and family are gone, when in fact they just no longer live nearby. Social interaction does not need to be face to face to be meaningful. Phone calls and writing letters and email provide good alternatives of communication with others. The notion that too much time has passed to contact a distant relative, old friend, or other previous relationship may be another obstacle for seniors to overcome. Once contact is made, most people are delighted and flattered to be remembered.*

Pursue an activity or hobby. *Sometimes seniors think they are too old to take up something new, but the truth is that no one is too old to learn. Pursuing an old or new hobby or activity is a natural way for seniors to meet others with similar interests.*

Join a group. *There are thousands of different types of groups and volunteer opportunities available for people of all abilities and interests. Religious, civic, environmental, political, and social groups abound and can be readily found through such sources as Area Agencies on Aging, senior centers, the newspaper, bulletin boards, and the Internet.*

Help others. *Volunteering to serve others is an excellent antidote to loneliness. It provides not only meaningful social interaction, but also self-esteem and confidence.*

Compiled by Janice Blanchard, 2004

family members are close and intimate members of most elderly people's network, friends are named as the people with whom they enjoy spending time, engage in leisure activities, and have daily or frequent contact and who have the most significant positive impact on well-being" (p. 361).

Social Support in Friendships

Throughout our lives, friends are key providers of emotional support. Compared to men, women have a greater number of friends, do more to maintain these friendships, contact friends more frequently, and give and receive more support (Antonucci, 1990; Atchley & Barusch, 2004). This appears to be a mixed blessing, as some research indicates that larger social support systems and a higher number of intimate relationships increase the demands that a person will have placed on them, raising the probability of conflict (Antonucci).

While family members are very important providers of social support (particularly instrumental support), some studies indicate that seniors prefer friends as support providers. Furthermore, research indicates that friendships, more so than family relationships, play a crucial role in the well-being, morale, and autonomy of older adults (Antonucci, 1990; Atchley & Barusch, 2004). It should be noted that the line between family and friendship is often blurred, with many seniors considering family members among their friends (Atchley & Barusch).

Reciprocity is an important dimension of social support in friendships. Relationships in which exchanges were viewed to be equitable were more satisfying and more positive (Antonucci, 1990). Interestingly, in most comparative studies, seniors hold different standards for families and friends when it comes to providing social support. Whereas family are expected to provide support in times of need, friends are not expected to, and therefore the support they do provide is more appreciated (Antonucci).

Social Support: The Role of the CSA

Working with seniors and their families can be a gratifying job. It is enormously satisfying to recognize an issue that needs to be addressed and be able to make the referrals and provide the resources to clients to get the assistance they need. On the other hand, you can lead a horse to water but you can't make it drink. It can be equally frustrating to see a family in need of assistance, refer them to resources that could sort out and ameliorate the situation, and yet see the client not follow through on the recommendations. Worse still is to try and help families work through a crisis only to get caught in the web of family pathologies.

This section starts out by discussing healthy and unhealthy family behaviors, followed by strategies for you to help seniors and their families find resolutions without overstepping boundaries or getting enmeshed in family conflicts.

HOW TO TELL A HEALTHY FAMILY FROM A TOXIC TRIBE

Families are dynamic and interdependent systems. How family systems operate deeply affects the developmental processes of children. In healthy family systems, family members are bonded with love, tempered by respect, and governed by rules that work to protect and enhance the welfare and development of each person. Communications between members are open, opinions and ideas are encouraged, and rules are flexible and enforced fairly and consistently. In healthy families, children build on the bedrock of a solid core group of values—they know the difference between right and wrong, establish personal boundaries, and emulate positive social roles and patterns of interaction. Children feel cared for, valued, and validated as they are encouraged to communicate their needs and wants, and feel they have the right to speak up in family matters. As a consequence, these children usually develop a positive and confident self-identity.

An unhealthy family system is spawned by one or more members, usually a parent, who has a serious problem, such as mental illness or alcohol or drug addiction, that impacts every other family member. In these families, communication is strained and distorted, opinions and ideas are ignored or discouraged, and rules are inflexible, unrealistic, and enforced unfairly and inconsistently. In an unhealthy family, children are confronted with a shifting sandbar of mixed messages and conflicting ideas. As a result, they often have a harder time distinguishing between appropriate and inappropriate behavior, develop poor personal boundaries, and lack the knowledge and the skills of participating in loving, reciprocal relationships. Children in unhealthy families frequently feel unloved, abandoned, guilty, and shamed. Consequently, they suffer low self-esteem and depression and are more vulnerable themselves to addictions and destructive behavior patterns.

Signs of an Unhealthy or Dysfunctional Family

- substance abuse
- perfectionism
- overprotection
- mental illness in one or both parents
- compulsive-obsessive behavior
- neglect
- emotional, physical, verbal, or sexual abuse
- religious or political fanaticism
- blurred boundaries and roles
- denial or trivialization about erratic behavior

Source: Compiled by Janice Blanchard, 2004

CLOSE ENCOUNTERS OF THE DYSFUNCTIONAL KIND

Sooner or later, you likely will encounter a family in crisis. Precipitated by a loved one's fall, onset of serious illness, death, or other emergency, family members are called together, often from far away, and in a restricted time frame try to handle delicate and potentially volatile issues.

Whether the family system is healthy or unhealthy can sometimes be difficult to discern during a time of crisis; even healthy family members become understandably upset by the circumstances and don't always handle stressful situations well. Unless you have counseling credentials, you are cautioned not to get into the business of diagnosing or treating a family in conflict. However, it is useful to have at least a working knowledge of what constitutes an unhealthy or dysfunctional family in order to make your own general personal assessments in working with clients.

Healthy or Unhealthy: The Adams Family

The following is a fictitious meeting between attorney David Cohen and the Adams children—daughter Lisa, 54, daughter Jill, 52, and son Sam, 48, to discuss placement options for their mother, Ellen, 79, after a prolonged stay in a rehabilitation center for hip replacement surgery.

> *David: As you know, in two days your mother will be released from the rehabilitation center. She has limited mobility and must use a walker for the foreseeable future. Before talking to your mother about placement options, I thought it important to discuss the situation with you. Basically, Ellen has the following options: (a) she can continue to live at home with home health care or family assistance; (b) she can move in with one of you, either temporarily or permanently; or, (c) she can sell the house and move into an assisted living facility or other long-term care center.*
>
> *Lisa: I always promised Mama that I would never make her sell Shady Grove and certainly that she would never have to go in one of those old folks' homes! So that is just not an option.*
>
> *Jill: Well, Lisa, this is not all about what you promised Mother—I never made that promise and as the only one still living here in town, it's all going to fall back on me, as it always does. You want mom to stay at home—well then, you need to leave your fancy country club life and move back to little old Lakeland!*
>
> *Sam: OK, you two, please don't get started—this is about Mom and what is best for her. I think the best thing to do is to sell the house and she can move in with me. You both are married with families and busy lives, and since I am not, I can devote more time to her.*
>
> *Lisa: You mean you can devote more time to spending her money!*
>
> *Jill: Yeah, Sam, who do you think you are talking to here? We know all about your little gambling problem, and there is no way we are going to let you spend all of her money at the track!*
>
> *Sam: Now wait one minute! I haven't been to the track in over a year—that's behind me now. And, we are not talking about me, we are talking about Mom!*

In less than five minutes, the Adams family meeting has devolved into innuendo, accusations, and hurt feelings. While hypothetical, this narrative illustrates the sibling friction that often emerges when families face a crisis. Unresolved tensions and old patterns surface as the adult children find themselves replaying their historical roles in the family. Poor communication skills, sibling rivalries, martyrdom, hostility, jealousy, and a gambling addiction suggest underlying family dynamics that are in conflict and dysfunctional.

Given the preceding scenario, what could David Cohen have done differently that may have given him more control from the beginning of the meeting, or would have helped him recapture control of the meeting and focus on the task at hand, placement for Mrs. Adams?

CONFLICT RESOLUTION 101

Regardless of how close and loving a family may be, all families go through conflict. Estate and legacy planning, end-of-life decisions, living arrangements, medical preferences, and driving ability are typical issues that seniors and their families disagree on. Conflict often occurs most intensely during times of crisis.

Family conflict is unique for several reasons. There is high emotional attachment between family members, and these underlying feelings can quickly intensify differences; family relationships are long-term and often in close proximity, requiring daily interaction; and, families are private and insular, beholden to their own norms and rules, and often resistant to outside intervention (Melak, 2003). In cases involving adult children and their parents, these characteristics can be amplified by the seriousness of the situation and the healthiness of the family system. In most cases, with planning, a set of rules, and a neutral third party guiding the process, even unhealthy families can have a meeting that is under control, structured, and productive.

Planning a Family Meeting

The following guidelines for planning a family meeting were adapted from a variety of resources on conflict resolution and family mediation (Melak, 2003; Waggoner, 2000). Due to the nature of a crisis, one cannot always plan ahead in detail. However, there are general ground rules that can maximize the productivity of family meetings and minimize conflict. The main goal of the first meeting is to create an action plan to work together as a team—or at the least, to call a temporary truce to a family feud.

To begin, whenever possible, include all the core family members. If a sibling, for example, cannot physically be present, consider arranging for a conference call. If the meeting concerns making decisions about the fate of an aging parent or relative, it is best in the first meeting to not have that person present. This gives everyone the opportunity to state their feelings, ideas, and limitations without fear of hurting or upsetting their loved one. Also consider having relevant third parties present. For example, if long-term placement options are being considered, having the senior's financial planner, long-term care insurance agent, and a geriatric care manager available can enhance everyone's understanding of what resources are available.

Second, select a comfortable, neutral, and private location for the meeting. Anticipate that the meeting might get heated, so if your office does not offer a private conference room, consider holding the meeting elsewhere, such as a hotel conference room.

Third, determine the major purpose of the meeting and set a short agenda, including a set time for each person to offer their solutions as well as their opinions on other people's answers. In setting the agenda, keep it simple. It is better to address just one major issue at a time, rather than seek to solve every issue in one meeting.

Fourth, if there is time beforehand, collect and share information. For example, if your client has been diagnosed with Alzheimer's-type dementia, contact family members with this information beforehand to ensure everyone has the same working knowledge of the disease. Distributing short fact sheets at the meeting, along with writing paper and pens, may also be helpful. In addition, include the agenda and a short set of the rules.

Finally, if your personality type is such that you do not feel you can actively manage the meeting, consider enlisting or hiring someone more comfortable with the mediator role, such as a geriatric care manager or professional mediator.

Conducting a Family Meeting

The following guidelines for conducting a family meeting were also adapted from a variety of resources on conflict resolution and family mediation (Melak, 2003; Waggoner, 2000). Begin by introducing yourself, your relationship to the client, and the main reason for the meeting. In this statement, you set the tone for the meeting, so you will likely want to strike a balance between concerned, open-minded, and professional. If other third parties are present, allow them to introduce themselves and what perspective they might be able to offer the family.

Next, review the guidelines and rules for the meeting, especially if you think the family may have unhealthy patterns of interaction. This can be done very informally, such as in the following statement: "We have a lot of ground to cover in just two hours, so to begin I would like to remind everyone that we will be addressing only the items on the agenda. I know this is an emotional time and issue, and want to remind everyone to try and stay focused on the topic and to be respectful to one another. Also, I will be keeping time and track, so if we veer off course, I may need to bring you back to the primary purpose of our meeting—to consider the best living arrangements for your mother after she leaves the rehabilitation center next Monday."

Other common rules include no name-calling, only one person speaking at a time, speak only for oneself, keep the conversation relevant to the topic and not bring up the past, and write down questions or comments to bring up at the end.

The third step in the meeting process would be to have each person state his or her opinion and concerns about the issue, within a specified time limit. Keep a list of each major concern as it comes up, noting whether more than one person voiced a particular concern.

The fourth step is to take the list you have generated and have the group prioritize the concerns. Take on each issue in the order of urgency rather than in order of preference. Try to reach some closure on each item or set a next step. For example, if placing mother in a nursing home is an item and the family is divided, list as a next step what nursing homes are available in the vicinity within the price range.

At the end of the meeting, if a resolution has not been reached, decide for yourself if you think resolution could be reached in one or two more meetings, and if it is reasonable for you to be involved. If it is, set a time and place for the next meeting. Otherwise, be ready beforehand to refer the family to an elder mediator, geriatric care manager, or other professional that may be better able to address the family dilemma.

On a final note: often the first meeting can be rough. Don't take it personally if a final resolution can't be reached the first time around.

The Family and Social Support Systems: Summary

On a cold winter's evening in 1800, a 12-year-old boy was found wandering in the woods of southern France. Naked, unkempt, and unable to communicate with his captors, the boy was assumed to have lived in the wild for at least six years, and likely more. Named Victor, the boy was brought to Paris, where scientists of the day were fascinated with the prospect of studying a human being raised in almost complete social isolation. Dr. Jean-Marc-Gaspard Itard dedicated himself to educating the "wild child of Aveyron," but to no avail. Victor never learned to speak, was unable to distinguish right from wrong, and was extremely limited in his ability to socially interact.

The story of Victor compels us to consider the essence of our humanity. While an extreme example of social isolation, it nevertheless illustrates the basic human need for social interaction and support. Just as people need shelter and food, we need love and support from others to survive as human beings. Moreover, as this chapter illustrates, people who sustain good social support systems experience better physical and mental health and overall well-being than those who do not have close interpersonal relationships. As we grow older, these social relationships become increasingly important to our ability to lead independent and meaningful lives. Paradoxically, as we age and develop greater need for social support systems, we experience at the same time an increased risk of losing key members of those systems.

Social isolation and loneliness are associated with growing older for a variety of reasons: Children, family, and friends may move away or pass away; disability or illness of ourselves or others may limit mobility; retirement and withdrawal from social activities may limit social interaction with others; and making new friends may become more difficult. Just as the presence of strong social support systems is positively correlated with good health outcomes, social isolation and loneliness are associated with poorer health, greater risk for institutional placement, and a greater risk of death.

You need to know that family and friends in later life are not just perks—seniors need and depend upon their social support systems. Work toward being able to recognize potential situations in which senior clients are at risk of inadequate social support or social isolation, and be able to offer referrals and resources to counter the problem.

This chapter has emphasized that there is a significant gap between the public perception and the reality of American families past, present, and future. By understanding the myth of the golden age of the American family, you are better prepared to help clients appreciate their families and not hold

THE FAMILY AND SOCIAL SUPPORT SYSTEMS

themselves or others to a standard that has never really existed. Furthermore, you can learn how to use conversations about childhood and family reminiscence, as well as a historical perspective, to relate to clients in a deeper and more meaningful way.

This chapter has also emphasized the diversity and complexity of today's family structure. The change from a pyramid to a beanpole-type family structure has changed the number of kin in a generation, the number and complexity of family roles, and the duration of time spent in roles and family relationships. A major point for you to remember is that there is no typical American family—families may be comprised of one or two parents who may be single, married, unmarried, or remarried. There may be no children, biological or adopted children, full or half-siblings, or no blood relationship at all. The reality is, less than a quarter of American households today consist of the two-parent nuclear family with own children, and it is likely that this trend will not substantially change in the future. You need to know that recent changes in family structure profoundly affect seniors' social support systems as well as their financial stability, particularly for women. Senior advisors who understand the risks and benefits of marriage, singlehood, childlessness, blended families, and so forth, are in a better position to assist clients in planning for the future. At the same time, educated CSAs are also more apt to help clients recognize and address family or personal dilemmas that arise in the present. Regardless of your personal preferences and beliefs regarding family, it is important for you to understand and be sensitive to the diversity that exists among seniors and their families.

Changes in family structure significantly affect family dynamics, which in turn influence the social support systems of older men and women. In particular, these changes have implications for the availability of potential caregivers and the likelihood of receiving family support in old age (Bengtson et al., 2004). In most cases, children have not abandoned their elders and willingly provide informal care as needed. Most families have reciprocal social support relationships throughout the life cycle. Divorce and remarriages, however, have increasingly blurred the lines of responsibility between adult children and their parents and stepparents. For example, as previously detailed, divorced fathers are less likely to receive emotional or instrumental support from adult children. If they don't remarry, they are at a greater risk of having an inadequate social support system, and more likely to experience the resulting negative consequences. Divorced older women, on the other hand, are less likely to remarry and more likely to be having financial difficulties, to the extreme of living in poverty. They are, however, more likely to receive emotional, instrumental, and financial support from their adult children. The degree to which adult children feel obligated to stepparents or relatives is not yet clear. It may be that the increases in number of relatives by marriage will make up for some of the social support lost due to divorce and lower fertility rates (Bengtson et al., 2004).

Finally, you need to be able to identify potential family problems, locate resources, and make referrals without overstepping boundaries or getting enmeshed in family conflicts. The ability to distinguish between a healthy and an unhealthy or dysfunctional family is a skill that will serve you well when working with clients and their families. Making such an assessment, however, should serve only to guide your interactions and inform your strategy for working with a family; you are cautioned to refrain from trying to diagnose or treat a family unless you are specifically trained to do so. Through planning, establishing rules, and using a neutral third party to guide the process, even unhealthy families can take part in meetings that are controlled, structured, and productive.

References

Aachenbaum, W. A. (1978). *Old age in the new land.* Baltimore, MD: John Hopkins University Press.

AARP. (2004). *The divorce experience: A study of divorce at midlife and beyond* [Electronic version]. Retrieved July 22, 2004, from http://research.aarp.org/general/divorce.pdf

Alford-Cooper, F. (1998). *For keeps: Marriages that last a lifetime.* Armonk, NY: M. E. Sharpe.

AAGP (American Association of Geriatric Psychiatry). (1999). Marriage and divorce in later life [Electronic version]. *American Journal of Geriatric Psychiatry, 7,* 185–187. Retrieved August 1, 2004, from http://www.gmhfonline.org/p_c/marriage.asp

Ameristat. (2003, March). *Diversity, poverty characterize female-headed households.* Population Reference Bureau. Retrieved July 28, 2004, from http://www.ameristat.org/Content/NavigationMenu/Ameristat/Topics1/Marriageand Family/Diversity,_Poverty_Characterize_Female-Headed_Households.htm

Antonucci, T. C. (1990). Social supports and social relationships. In R. H. Binstock & L. K. George (Eds.), *Handbook of aging and the social sciences* (3rd ed.). New York: Academic Press.

Antonucci, T. C., & Akiyama, H. (1996). Convoys of social relations: Family and friendships within a life span context. In R. Blieszner & V. H. Bedford (Eds.), *Aging and the family: Theory and research.* Westport, CT: Praeger.

Aquilino, W. S. (1994). Later life parental divorce and widowhood: Impact on young adult's assessment of parent-child relations. *Journal of Marriage and the Family, 56,* 908–922.

Arber, S. (2004). Gender, marital status, and ageing: Linking material, health, and social resources. *Journal of Aging Studies, 18*(1), 91–108.

Atchley, R. C. (1972). *The social forces in later life.* Belmont, CA: Wadsworth.

Atchley, R. C., & Barusch, A. S. (2004). *Social forces and aging: An introduction to social gerontology* (10th ed.). Stamford, CT: Wadsworth.

Atchley, R. C., & Miller, S. J. (1983). Types of elderly couples. In T. H. Brubaker (Ed.), *Family relationships in later life.* Beverly Hills, CA: Sage.

Bengtson, V., Burton, L., & Rosenthal, C. (1990). Families and aging: Diversity and heterogeneity. In R. H. Binstock & L. K. George (Eds.), *Handbook of aging and the social sciences* (3rd ed.). New York: Academic Press.

Bengtson, V. L., Putney, N. M., & Wakeman, M. A. (2004, March). *The family and the future: Challenges, prospects, and resilience.* Paper presented at the Conference on Public Policy and Responsibility Across the Generations, Boston College, Boston, MA.

Bennett, L., & Gates, G. J. (2004, January). *The cost of marriage inequality to gay, lesbian and bisexual seniors: A Human Rights Campaign Foundation report.* Retrieved July 22, 2004, from the Human Rights Campaign Web site: http://www. hrc.org/Template.cfm?Section=Get_Involved1&Template=/ContentManagement/ContentDisplay.cfm&ContentID=16569

Blanchard, J. (1998). Owning wellness: An evaluation of the Older Women's Wellness Centre. (Master's thesis, University of South Florida, Tampa, FL, 1998).

Bosworth, H. B., & Schaie, K. W. (1997). The relationship of social environment, social networks, and health outcomes in the Seattle Longitudinal Study: Two analytic approaches. *Journal of Gerontology: Psychological Sciences, 52B*, 197–205.

Brubaker, T. H. (1984) *Later life families.* Beverly Hills, CA: Sage Publications.

Bulcroft, K., Bulcroft R., Hatch L., & Borgatta, E. (1989). Antecedents and consequences of remarriage in later life. *Research on Aging, 11*(1), 82–106.

Burch, T. (1990). Remarriage of older Canadians. *Research on Aging, 12*(4), 546–559.

Butler, R. N. (1963). The life review: An interpretation of reminiscence in the aged. *Psychiatry 26*, 65–76.

Casper, L. M., & Bryson, K. R. (1998). Co-resident grandparents and their grandchildren: Grandparent maintained families. Population Division Working Paper No. 26. Retrieved July 18, 2003, from the United States Census Bureau Web site: http://www.census.gov/population/www/documentation/twps0026/twps0026.html

Census Bureau. (2001, June). America's families and living arrangements: Population characteristics. *Current population reports*, P20-537. Retrieved July 30, 2003, from http://www.census.gov/prod/2001pubs/p20-537.pdf

Census Bureau. (2002, February). Number, timing, and duration of marriages and divorces: 1996. *Current population reports*, P70-80. Retrieved July 22, 2003, from http://www.sipp.census.gov/sipp/p70s/p70-80.pdf

Census Bureau. (2003, October). Marital status: 2000. *U.S. Census briefs.* Retrieved July 28, 2003, from http://www.census.gov/prod/2003pubs/c2kbr-30.pdf

Cherlin, A. J., & Furstenberg, F. F., Jr. (1986). *New American grandparent: A place in the family, a life apart.* New York: Basic Books.

Choi, N. G. (1996). Never-married and divorced elderly: Comparison of economic and health status, social support, and living arrangement. *Journal of Social Work, 26*(1–2), 3–25.

Cicirelli, V. G. (1983). Comparison of helping behavior to elderly parents of adult children with intact and disrupted marriages. *Gerontologist (26)*3, 619–625.

Cicirelli, V. G. (1995). *Sibling relationships across the life span.* New York: Plenum Press.

Coontz, S. (2000). *The way we never were: American families and the nostalgia trap* (Rev. ed.). New York: Basic Books.

Council on Contemporary Families. (2003). Facts versus fictions. Retrieved August 20, 2004, from http://www.contemporaryfamilies.org/public/education.php#facts

Courtenay, W. H. (2000). Behavioral factors associated with disease, injury, and death among men: Evidence and implications for prevention. *Journal of Men's Studies, 9*, 81–142.

Curran, S. R., McLanahan, S., & Knab, J. (2003). Does remarriage expand perceptions of kinship support among the elderly? *Social Science Research, 32*(2), 171–190.

Davidson, K. (2001). Late life widowhood, selfishness and new partnership choices: A gendered perspective. *Ageing and Society, 21*(3), 297–317.

Davis, K. E., & Todd, M. J. (1985). Assessing friendships: Prototypes, paradigm cases, and relationship description. In S. Duck & D. Perlman (Eds.), *Understanding personal relationships: Sage series in personal relationships, Vol. 1*, pp. 17–37. Beverly Hills, CA: Sage.

Delany, S. L., Delany, A. E., & Hill Hearth, A. (1993). *Having our say: The Delany sisters' first 100 years*. New York: Kodansha International.

Delany S. L., & Hill Hearth, A. (1997). *On my own at 107: Reflections on life without Bessie*. San Francisco: Harper San Francisco.

Demos, J. (1970). *A little commonwealth: Family life in Plymouth Colony*. New York: Oxford University Press.

Demos, J. (1978). Old age in early New England. In J. Demos and S. Boocock (Eds.), *Turning points: American Journal of Sociology, 84*(Suppl.), S247–S287.

Elkind, D. (1994). *Ties that stress: The new family imbalance*. Cambridge, MA: Harvard University Press.

Farberman, R. (2003). Degree of "outness" key to social support for gays and lesbians. APA Online, *Monitor on Psychology*. Retrieved August 1, 2004, from http://www.apa.org/monitor/apr03/degree.html

Farkas, J. I., & Hogan, D. P. (1995). The demography of changing intergenerational relationships. In V. L. Bengtson, K. W. Schaie, & L. M. Burton (Eds.), *Adult intergenerational relations: Effects of societal change*. New York: Springer Publishing.

Fischer, D. H. (1978). *Growing old in America*. New York: Oxford University Press.

Freedman, V. A. (1996, March). Family structure and the risk of nursing home admission. *Journals of Gerontology Series B: Psychological Sciences and Social Sciences, 51*(2), S61–S69.

Genevay, B. (1993). "Creating" families: Older people alone. In L. Burton (Ed.), *Familes and aging*. Amityville, NY: Baywood Publishing Company.

Gierveld, J. (2004). Remarriage, unmarried cohabitation, living apart together: Partner relationships following bereavement or divorce. *Journal of Marriage and Family, 66*(1), 236–243.

Gold, D. (1989). Sibling relationships in old age: A typology. *International Journal of Aging and Human Development, 28*(1), 37–51.

Goldberg, G. S., Kantrow, R., Kremen, E., & Lauter, L. (1986). Spouseless, childless elderly women and their social supports. *Social Work, 31*(2), 104–112.

Gross, J. (2004, February 27). Older women team up to face future together. *New York Times.* Retrieved August 21, 2004, from http://www.nytimes.com/2004/02/27/national/27RETI.html?ex=1164258000&en=499ac9c1a9380607&ei=5035

Gubrium, J. F. (1975). Being single in old age. *International Journal of Aging and Human Development, 6,* 29–41.

Gupta, V., & Korte, C. (1994). The effects of a confidant and a peer group on the well-being of single elders. *International Journal of Aging and Human Development, 39*(4), 293–302.

Hareven, T. K. (1993). Family and generational relations in the later years: A historical perspective. In L. Burton (Ed.), *Familes and aging.* Amityville, NY: Baywood Publishing Company.

Hegge, M., & Fischer, C. (2000). Grief responses of senior and elderly widows: Practice implications. *Journal of Gerontological Nursing, 26*(2), 35–43.

Herman, S. M. (1994). Marital satisfaction in the elderly. *Gerontology and Geriatrics Education, 14*(4), 69–79.

Himes, C. L. (1993). Social demography of contemporary families and aging. In L. Burton (Ed.), *Familes and aging.* Amityville, NY: Baywood Publishing Company.

Hoyert, D. L. (1991). Financial and household exchanges between generations. *Research on Aging, 13,* 205–225.

Huyck, M. H. (1996). Marriage and close relationships of the marital kind. In R. Blieszner & V. H. Bedford (Eds.), *Aging and the family: Theory and research.* Westport, CT: Praeger.

Hungerford, T. L. (2001). Economic consequences of widowhood on elderly women in the United States and Germany. *Gerontologist, 41*(1), 103–110.

Kain, E. L. (1990). *The myth of family decline: Understanding families in a world of rapid social change.* New York: Simon & Schuster.

Keith, P. M., Kim, S., & Schafer, R. B. (2000). Informal ties of the unmarried in middle and later life: Who has them and who does not? *Sociological Spectrum, (20)*2, 221–238.

Kimmel, D. C. (1993). The families of older gay men and lesbians. In L. Burton (Ed.), *Familes and aging.* Amityville, NY: Baywood Publishing Company.

Klein, H. S. (2004). *A population history of the United States.* Cambridge, MA: Cambridge University Press.

Krause, N. (2001). Social support. In R. H. Binstock & L. K. George (Eds.), *Handbook of aging and the social sciences* (5th ed.). San Diego, CA: Academic Press.

Kuhn, M. (1991). *No stone unturned: The life and times of Maggie Kuhn.* New York: Ballantine.

Laditka, J. N., & Laditka, S. B. (2003). Increased hospitalization risk for recently widowed older women and protective effects of social contacts. *Journal of Women and Aging 15*(2–3), 7–28.

Lauer, R. H. & Lauer, J. C. (1986). Factors in long-term marriages. *Journal of Family Issues, 7*(4), 382–390.

Lauer, R. H., Lauer, J. C., & Kerr, S. T. (1990). Long-term marriage: Perceptions of stability and satisfaction. *International Journal of Aging and Human Development, 31*(3), 189–195.

Lee, G. R., DeMaris, A., Bavin, S., & Sullivan, R. (2001). Gender differences in the depressive effect of widowhood in later life. *Journals of Gerontology: Series B: Psychological Sciences and Social Sciences, 56B(1)*, S56–S61.

Levenson, R. W., Carstensen, L. L., & Gottman, J. M. (1993). Long-term marriage: age, gender, and satisfaction. *Psychology and Aging 8*(2), 301–313.

Lin, G. E., & Rogerson, P. A. (1995). Elderly parents and the geographic availability of their adult children. *Research in Aging, 17*(3), 303–331.

Litwak, E., & Messeri, P. (1989). Organizational theory, social supports, and mortality rates: A theoretical convergence. *American Sociological Review, 54*, 49–66.

Lo Sasso, A. T., & Johnson, R. W. (2002). Does informal care from adult children reduce nursing home admissions for the elderly? *Inquiry, 39*(3), 279–297.

Lund, D. A., & Caserta, M. S. (2004). Older men coping with widowhood. *Geriatrics and Aging, 7*(6), 29–33.

Mastekaasa, A. (1994). Marital status, distress, and well-being: An international comparison. *Journal of Comparative Family Studies 25*, 183–206.

Matthews, S. H. (1986). *Friendships through the life course*. Beverly Hills, CA: Sage.

McKain, W. C., Jr. (1969). *Retirement marriage*. Storrs, CT: Storrs Agricultural Experiment Station, University of Connecticut.

Medicare Rights Center. (2004). The history of Medicare and the current debate. Retrieved July 7, 2004, from http://www.medicarerights.org/maincontenthistory.html

Melak, C. (2003). *Family conflict*. Retrieved August 2, 2004, from Conflict Research Consortium Web site: http://www.crinfo.org/ck_essays/ck_family_conflict.cfm

Michael, S. T., Crowther, M. R., Schmid, B., & Allen, R. S. (2003). Widowhood and spirituality: Coping responses to bereavement. *Journal of Women and Aging, 15*(2–3), 145–165.

Mintz, S., & Kellogg, S. (1989). *Domestic revolutions: A social history of American family life*. New York: The Free Press.

Morgan, D. L. (1989). Adjusting to widowhood: Do social networks really make it easier? *The Gerontologist, 29*(1), 101–107.

Newman, D. M. (1999). *Sociology of families*. Thousand Oaks, CA: Pine Forge Press.

Older Women's League. (n.d.). The state of older women in America. Washington, DC: Older Women's League.

Pasley, K. (1998). Research findings: Divorce and remarriage in later adulthood. Retrieved July 18, 2004, from http://www.saafamilies.org/faqs/findings/7.htm

Perren, K., Arber, S., & Davidson, K. (2003). Men's organisational affiliations in later life: The influence of social class and marital status on informal group membership. *Ageing and Society, 23*, Part 1.

Perry, B. (2004). *Bonding and attachment in maltreated children: Consequences of emotional neglect in childhood*. Retrieved July 27, 2004, from http://teacher.scholastic.com/professional/bruceperry/bonding.htm

Pienta, A. M., Hayward, M. D., & Jenkins, K. R. (2000). Health consequences of marriage for the retirement years. *Journal of Family Issues, 21*(5).

Popenoe, D. (1999). *Life without father: Compelling new evidence that fatherhood and marriage are indispensable for the good of children and society.* Cambridge, MA: Harvard University Press.

Prigerson, H. G., Maciejewski, P. K., & Rosenheck, R. A. (2000). Preliminary explorations of the harmful interactive effects of widowhood and marital harmony on health, health service use, and health care costs. *Gerontologist, 40*(3), 349–357.

Quadagno, J. (2002). *Aging and the life course: An introduction to social gerontology* (2nd ed.). New York: McGraw-Hill.

Roberto, K., & Stroes, J. (1992). Grandchildren and grandparents: Roles, influences, and relationships. *International Journal of Aging and Human Development, 34*, 227–239.

Rogerson, P. A., Weng, R. H., & Lin, G. (1998). Spatial separation of parents and their adult children. *Association of American Geographers Annals, 3814*, 656–671.

Rossi, A., & Rossi, P. (1990). *Of human bonding: Parent-child relations across the life course.* New York: Aldine de Gruyter.

Rowe, J. W., & Kahn, R. L. (1998). *Successful aging.* New York: Random House.

Rubinstein, R. L. (1987). Never married elderly as a social type: Re-evaluating some images. *The Gerontologist, 27*, 108–113.

Seeman, T. E., Kaplan, G. A., Knudsen, L., Cohen, R., & Guralnik, J. (1987). Social network ties and mortality among the elderly in the Alameda County study. *Annals of Epidemiology, 126*(4), 714–723.

Shapiro, A. (2003). Later-life divorce and parent-adult child contact and proximity: A longitudinal study. *Journal of Family Issues, 24*(2), 264–285.

Simon, B. L. (1989). *Never married women.* Philadelphia: Temple University Press.

Smith, K., Zick, C., & Duncan, G. (1991). Remarriage patterns among recent widows and widowers. *Demography, 28*(3), 361–374.

Smith, T. W. (1999, November). *The emerging 21st century American family.* National Opinion Research Center, University of Chicago. General Social Survey Social Change Report No. 42.

Snyder, D. P. (2000). There is more to this boom than boomers: The information revolution has entered its prosperity-enhancing phase. Retrieved July 21, 2004, from http://www.davidpearcesnyder.com/there_is_more_to_this_boom_than_boomers.htm

Stacey, J. (1998). *Brave new families: Stories of domestic upheaval in late-twentieth-century America.* Berkeley, CA: University of California Press.

Sutherland, D., & Murphey, E. (1995). Social support among elderly in two community programs. *Journal of Gerontological Nursing, 21*(2), 31–38.

Treas, J. (1995). Beanpole or beanstalk? Comments on "The demography of changing intergenerational relations." In V. L. Bengtson, K. W. Schaie, & L. M. Burton (Eds.), *Adult intergenerational relations: Effects of societal change.* New York: Springer.

Troll, L. E., Miller, S. J., & Atchley, R. C. (1979). *Families in later life.* Belmont, CA: Wadsworth.

Uhlenberg, P. L. (1995). Demographic influences on intergenerational relationships. In V. L. Bengtson, K. W. Schaie, & L. M. Burton (Eds.), *Adult intergenerational relations: Effects of societal change.* New York: Springer.

Uhlenberg, P. L., & Cooney, T. M. (1990). Family size and mother-child relations in later life. *The Gerontologist, 30*(5), 618–625.

Utz, R. L., Carr, D., Nesse, R., & Wortman, C. B. (2002). Effect of widowhood on older adults' social participation: An evaluation of activity, disengagement, and continuity theories. *Gerontologist, 42*(4), 522–533.

Vinick, B. H. (1979). Remarriage. In R. H. Jacobs & B. H. Vinick, *Re-engagement in later life.* Stamford, CT: Greylock.

Vinick, B. H., & Lanspery, S. (2000). Cinderella's sequel: Stepmothers' long-term relationships with adult stepchildren. *Journal of Comparative Family Studies, 31*(3), 377–384.

Waggoner, M. (2000). *Using family meetings to resolve eldercare issues.* Retrieved August 1, 2004, from http://www.ec-online.net/Knowledge/Articles/familymeetings.html

Webster, P. S., & Herzog, A. R. (1995). Effects of parental divorce and memories of family problems on relationships between adult children and their parents. *Journals of Gerontology, Series B: Psychological Sciences and Social Sciences, 50B*(1), S24-S34.

White, L. K., & Riedmann, A. (1992). Ties among adult siblings. *Social Forces, 71*, 85–102.

Wright, C. L., & Maxwell, J. W. (1991). Social support during adjustment to later-life divorce: How adult children help parents. *Journal of Divorce and Remarriage, 15*(3–4), 21–48.

Zinn, S. D., & Eitzen, M. B. (1987). *Social problems.* Boston: Allyn and Bacon.

Resources

Family Support

Children of Aging Parents. http://www.caps4caregivers.org, P.O. Box 7250, Penndel, PA 19047, 800-227-7294.

Stepfamily Association of America, Inc. http://www.saafamilies.org, 650 J St., Ste. 205, Lincoln, NE 68508, 800-735-0329.

Well Spouse Foundation. http://www.wellspouse.org, 63 W. Main St., Ste. H, Freehold, NJ 07728, 800-838-0879.

Care Managers

National Association of Professional Geriatric Care Managers. http://www.caremanager.org, 1604 N. Country Club Rd., Tucson, AZ 85716, 520-881-8008.

National Association of Social Workers. http://www.naswdc.org, 750 First St. NE, Ste. 700, Washington, DC 20002-4241, 800-638-8799.

Support Groups

Adult Children of Alcoholics. http://www.adultchildren.org, P.O. Box 3216, Torrance CA 90510, 310-534-1815.

Co-Dependents Anonymous, Inc. http://www.codependents.org, P.O. Box 33577, Phoenix, AZ 85067-3577.

Family Caregiver Alliance—Online Support Groups. http://www.caregiver.org, 690 Market St., Ste. 600, San Francisco, CA 94104, 415-434-3388, 800-445-8106.

Chapter 7

Caregivers and Caregiving in America

Invest in the human family. Invest in people. Build a little community of those you love and who love you. In the beginning of life, when we are infants, we need others to survive right? And at the end of life when you get to be like me, you need others to survive right?

Then Morrie's voice drops to a whisper. "But here is the secret: in between we need each other as well."

From *Tuesdays with Morrie* by Mitch Albom

There are only four kinds of people in the world—those who have been caregivers, those who currently are caregivers, those who will be caregivers, and those who will need caregivers.

Rosalynn Carter

Caregiving can start abruptly with the onset of a serious illness such as a heart attack or stroke; or the need for care can begin when a person experiences slight limitations associated with growing older . . .

Caregivers face a number of challenges. These include learning basic health care skills; coping with physical, emotional, and financial stress; understanding legal options; assessing the service system; and learning how to balance conflicting demands while dealing with potentially stressful family dynamics.

Some caregivers handle these challenges better than others. Caregiving responsibilities can lead to feelings of love, generosity, and a strengthening of family ties. Some caregivers are thankful for the opportunity to provide care and to share in the final days of the older person's life.

For others these responsibilities can be overwhelming and lead to isolation, physical illness, financial devastation, and loss of employment. In severe cases, caregiver exhaustion can lead to elder abuse—the financial exploitation, neglect, or mental or physical abuse of an older person.

Louise Fradkin and Angela Heath (1992, pp. 3, 6)

Introduction

Caregiving is one person giving care to another. It is a process that often involves a tremendous sacrifice of time, energy, and money. It is often emotionally charged and demanding. Because the majority of your senior clients will, at some point in their later years, be both caregivers and care receivers, it is important for you to understand the caregiving process and how to help your clients cope with and manage it.

In all its diversity, caregiving is a global issue, as countries around the world face aging populations. In America, caregiving provided outside of institutions is the backbone of the long-term care system. The value of unpaid care for adults is estimated to be $257 billion annually (AARP and National Alliance for Caregiving, 2004). "Based on 17.9 weekly hours of care at $8.18 hourly wage and 25.8 million caregivers, the mid-range national estimate of the economic value of informal care in 1997 was $196 billion. Comparing it to available national spending for home care ($32 billion), nursing home care ($83 billion) and total health care ($1 trillion), we see that the economic value of informal care is equivalent to approximately 18 percent of national health care spending and exceeds spending for home care and nursing home care combined" (Tennstedt, 1999).

In addition to its economic impact, caregiving exacts a toll on caregivers, who often suffer compromised health, personal financial strain, and intense emotional stress.

A Profile of Caregivers

In April 2004, the National Alliance for Caregiving and AARP published the results of their comprehensive random telephone survey about caregiving. Funded by the MetLife Foundation, the study, *Caregiving in the U.S.*, sought to update and expand the body of knowledge about caregivers' activities, the perceived impact of caregiving on their daily lives, and the unmet needs of the caregiver population. In sum, 6,139 adults were surveyed, and 1,247 caregivers were identified and interviewed. The caregiver sample included an over-sampling of 200 African American, 200 Hispanic, and 200 Asian American caregivers, in an effort to better understand ethnic and racial differences in responses (AARP and National Alliance for Caregiving, 2004).

The study defined a caregiver as someone who provides unpaid care to another who requires help with activities of daily living (ADLs) or instrumental activities of daily living (IADLs). ADLs include basic physical maneuvers that healthy individuals perform daily without assistance: bathing, dressing, using the toilet, transferring oneself (from the bed to a chair, for example), and feeding. IADLs define another range of tasks considered instrumental to one's self-sufficiency. They include shopping, cooking meals, performing household tasks, doing laundry, managing money, using the telephone, and taking medications by oneself. ADLs and IADLs are most often used to identify caregivers, to measure the level and type of work that caregivers perform, and to understand care recipients' needs (so as to determine their eligibility for public programs or services).

WHO PROVIDES CARE?

- About 44.4 million Americans (21 percent of the adult population) act as caregivers.

- An estimated 17 percent, or 18,539,500 households in the United States, contain at least one caregiver who provides care to someone age 50 or older.

- An estimated 4 percent, or 4,362,200 households, contain a caregiver of someone 18 to 49 years old.

- Eighty-three percent of caregivers are related to their care recipients; 17 percent came from outside the family.

- A typical caregiver is female (61 percent), approximately 46 years old, has at least some college experience (66 percent), and spends an average of 20 hours or more per week providing care to someone age 50 or older (79 percent) (see Figures 7.1 and 7.2).

- Male caregivers are more likely to be working full-time (60 percent) than female caregivers (41 percent).

- Asian caregivers are more often male than female, a higher proportion than any other ethnic background surveyed. (Fifty-four percent of Asian caregivers are men, compared to 41 percent of Hispanics, 38 percent of whites, and 33 percent of African Americans giving care.)

Figure 7.1 Age of Caregivers

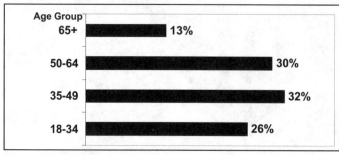

Source: AARP and National Alliance for Caregiving, 2004.

Figure 7.2 Employment Status of Caregivers

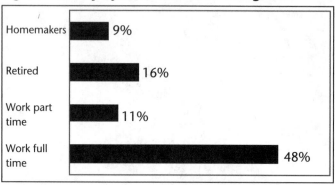

Source: AARP and National Alliance for Caregiving, 2004.

- The majority of caregivers are married or living with a partner (62 percent), and most have juggled work with caregiving responsibilities at some point during their roles as caregivers.

WHO RECEIVES CARE?

- Most care recipients are female (65 percent) and many recipients are widowed (42 percent).
- Nearly 8 out of 10 care recipients are age 50 or older.
- The average age of all care recipients over age 50 is 75 years old.
- Caregivers who provide care for someone 50 or older tend to be helping their mothers (34 percent), grandmothers (11 percent), or fathers (10 percent). Sixty-five percent of these caregivers say other unpaid caregivers assist them in their role. Forty-six percent said they also employed paid help within the past year.
- Of those caring for someone 50 or older, the most commonly cited primary problem or illness that the person they care for has is "aging" (15 percent of those surveyed), followed by diabetes, cancer, and heart disease.
- One quarter of caregivers for those 50 or older report the person they care for is suffering from Alzheimer's, dementia, or other mental confusion, but only 8 percent say it is their main illness.
- More than half of care recipients (55 percent) live in their own homes.

- More than 9 out of 10 (92 percent) care recipients 50 or older take prescription medicine.

AMOUNT AND TYPE OF CARE PROVIDED

The *Caregiving in the U.S.* researchers utilized the "Level of Burden Index" to measure the challenges caregivers face. The index combines the number of ADLs and IADLs that require help, as well as the amount of time devoted to caregiving. There are five levels of caregiver burden, with a level 5 rating signifying the highest degree of responsibilities. Level 5 caregivers have formidable, even onerous roles, and are likely to need significant emotional support and respite. Below are notable findings from the study about the various types of care provided:

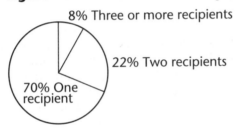

- Most caregivers (69 percent) say they care for one person, but about 30 percent also care for two or more adults (see Figure 7.3).

Figure 7.3 Number of Care Recipients

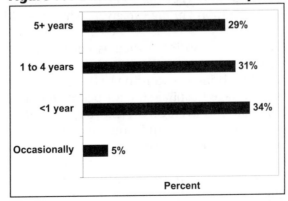

- Nearly half of all caregivers (48 percent) provide eight hours or less of care per week.
- One in five caregivers reported providing more than 40 hours of care a week.
- The average duration of caregiving is 4.3 years.
- About three in ten caregivers say they have been providing care for five or more years. Another three in ten say they have been providing care for one to four years (see Figure 7.4).

Figure 7.4 Duration of Care for Recipient

Duration	Percent
5+ years	29%
1 to 4 years	31%
<1 year	34%
Occasionally	5%

Percent

- Female caregivers are more likely to provide care at the highest level of burden (5), whereas men are more likely to provide care at the lowest level of burden (1).

- Only 10 percent of caregivers provide care at the highest level of burden. Their intense caregiving is complicated by the fact that they are usually older themselves and their health is only "fair" relative to that of other caregivers.

- Thirty-seven percent of caregivers say no one else provided unpaid help to the person they care for within the past 12 months.

- Caregivers tend to live near the people they care for. Among caregivers who do not live with the care recipient, 85 percent live within one hour's travel.

- About one in four caregivers (24 percent) say the person they care for lives with them.

We will revisit this survey later in the chapter to examine the stressful aspects of caregiving and what kinds of support are helpful to caregivers.

Trends in Caregiving

Several trends have changed the caregiving landscape and made the role of those who support seniors living in their homes and communities even more critical. Family members no longer all live in the same zip code, much less the same state. This raises the issue of who will care for aging parents, or how children will care for parents from a distance. Blended, divorced, and non-traditional family structures also complicate the provision of care to aging or disabled family members, often blurring responsibilities.

Along with changes in family structure, health care advances have created new care needs. While more people than ever before are surviving infectious diseases, traumatic injuries, and chronic illnesses, these conditions often create a need for long-term care to assist those now living with disabilities. Carol Levine, director of the Families and Health Care Project for the United Hospital Fund, also provides care for her husband, who was severely brain-damaged in an automobile accident in 1990. "After that," says Levine, "I spent about five years trying to piece together care for my husband. I felt totally abandoned by a system that had worked heroically to save his life but then said, 'Here, you take him now. We've done our job'" (Levine, 2003, p. 4). Levine's sense of bewilderment and isolation is common among caregivers who are suddenly thrust into their roles.

Caregiving needs have also intensified as efforts to contain health care costs have shortened hospital stays and shifted greater responsibilities outside of hospital walls and into homes. According to the Centers for Disease Control and Prevention, the average hospital stay for people 65 or older in 2001 was 5.8 days, less than half the average of 12.6 days in 1970 (Levine, 2003). Furthermore, medication regimens and home care technology can be dizzyingly complex, requiring sophisticated monitoring. Altogether, the scope of caregiving has broadened, and pressures on caregivers have mounted. The need to recognize and support caregivers is fundamental to your role as a CSA, and your knowledge can be a valued service to families facing the challenges of providing care.

CONSIDERING CARE RECIPIENTS

When seniors begin experiencing disability or illness, they face a host of new concerns. In general, many seniors are not used to or comfortable with asking for help. When seniors require caregiving, they must often deal with the grief associated with physical decline, the difficulty of being in pain, and the frustration of being unable to do tasks that were once simple to execute. As many caregivers are children caring for parents, the reversal of roles may be initially uncomfortable for both parties. Seniors may also worry about depleting their financial resources, becoming a burden to their families, or losing their dignity or control over their own care. Seniors, especially care recipients, fear losing their independence more than anything. You, as well as caregivers, should be cognizant of this, and make every effort to affirm the dignity and independence of your senior clients.

Here are some facts that demonstrate the need for caregivers:

- By the time adults reach age 65, they are frequently dealing with at least one chronic illness, such as arthritis, diabetes, or fibromyalgia.
- By the time seniors are 75, they often must deal with two chronic illnesses. At 85, they may struggle with three or four illnesses.
- The 85-and-older age group is the fastest growing segment of our population.

About half of seniors *not* living in institutions have a disability (Vierck, 2003). In other words, they have one or more long-lasting physical, mental, or emotional condition that impairs their ability to perform daily tasks, although they still reside in the community. Despite these hurdles, seniors are often reluctant to consider themselves disabled, just as they do not consider themselves old, per se. While you, your clients' families, and caregivers can assist seniors as they face the physical changes that the years can bring, you should focus on seniors' strengths, abilities, and gifts—not their limitations. With modifications and help, many older adults with disabilities continue to lead productive and enjoyable lives.

WHO ME? I'M NOT A CAREGIVER

Despite the significant portion of society that provides care—about 21 percent of households (AARP and National Alliance for Caregiving, 2004)—many caregivers are hesitant to identify themselves with that term or may not perceive that the work they do is caregiving. For some, this is due to personal and cultural contexts that shape their understanding of the task. African American and older Latino caregivers may consider the term *family caregiver* strange or redundant, believing that caring for an ill family member is an unquestioned responsibility for everyone in a family (Dobrof & Ebenstein, 2003).

Some dislike the term *caregiver* because it signifies that they have officially taken on a new role and the identity (with some negative connotations) that goes along with it. Others may balk at the word *caregiver* because to say one is a caregiver acknowledges the care recipient's loss of independence, a tough task for many children caring for their parents. Similarly, a wife may not want to admit that her relationship to her husband of 47 years has become fundamentally different.

However, those who do not associate with the term *caregiver* also may not recognize that they are not alone or that many services exist to support them. Health care and social service professionals often wish to identify caregivers so they can manage their own health, both physical and emotional, and learn of resources such as caregiver support groups (Dobrof & Ebenstein, 2003). You can encourage caregivers to recognize just what it is they are doing—providing a critical service that unites them with many other families, which can be alternately blessed and stressful, but which requires support so that caregivers do not become ill themselves.

While some caregivers are summoned because of a decisive incident, such as a fall or a stroke, others may not realize when the increasing level of support they provide crosses over to the realm of "true caregiving." Aneshensel and colleagues, in their description of caregiver transitions, write, "Whereas people know precisely when they enter a job, entry into caregiving might be gradual and insidious, in some instances becoming a fait accompli before one is fully aware of it" (Aneshensel, Pearlin, Mullan, Zarit, & Whitlatch, 1995). One caregiver named Judy, a full-time executive in Minnesota who coordinates the care decisions for her mother in a nursing home, says she initially took on some tasks because she was available, seemed to be the most concerned, and had experience talking with the doctors. Eventually her seven brothers and sisters began to look to her to do everything, even when she pleaded for help. Even though they lived much closer to their mother, Judy felt that because she had first accepted the role of caregiver, the rest of the family thought it had become hers to keep.

Beyond Function—The Caring Relationship

The methods of measuring ADLs (and later, IADLs) were originally developed in the 1950s and 1960s to describe the functional abilities and limitations of those with disabilities (Levine, Reinhard, Feinberg, Albert, & Hart, 2003). More than 40 ADL and IADL instruments have been created since the 1970s. Yet some have criticized the ADL/IADL indices as incomplete ways to understand the work of caregivers, believing it to be an overly medical model. True, caregivers do assist with many ADLs and IADLs, but they also perform complex tasks and bear emotional burdens far beyond them. From Family Caregivers on the Job: "Caregivers do not think of what they do in terms of performing tasks related to ADLs and IADLs; they do whatever needs to be done. Then they watch and wait until the next thing needs to be done, and the next, and the next" (Levine et al., 2003). E. K. Abel (1990) also noted, "The chores that family and friends perform do not exist in a vacuum; rather, they are embedded in intimate personal relationships . . ."

These relationships, even if warm and strong, pose challenges, as caregivers and recipients have to perform unfamiliar roles outside of a lifetime of more familiar interactions. The relationships can also be more challenging:

176

Personal Reflection

Before you continue reading this chapter, consider your beliefs, attitudes, and assumptions about caregiving. Answer the following questions in the space provided below.

- *Were either of your parents ever caregivers?*

    Yes - Eva

- *Whom did they care for?*

    Eva for Dad

- *How did they feel about it?*

    Martyr. No choice

- *Do you think you will ever be asked to be a caregiver?*

    Yes

- *How do you feel about caring for your parents or older adult relatives?*

    Totally fine. I will feel honored

- *How do you feel about caring for your spouse or your best friend?*

    Totally fine

- *Would you feel comfortable having an older adult parent move in with you?*

    Yes

- *What would your concerns be?*

    Craig's mindset

As you read and consider the content of the chapter, come back to this page and make additional comments.

"The caregiver may encounter disruptive behavior, particularly when the care recipient feels confused, threatened, or insulted, or if he or she is physically uncomfortable. The care recipient may also perceive certain acts, like being moved into the bathroom, undressed, and washed, as physical or sexual abuse and may respond with combative behavior. If the care recipient suffers from arthritis or other mobility problems, he or she may resist going into the bathroom because movement is painful" (Levine et al., 2003). Consequently, the response of the recipient to care—whether helpful, compliant, passive, resistant, hostile, belligerent, or cognitively impaired—can greatly affect the caregiver's tasks.

Caring for someone with dementia requires incredible patience, perseverance, and vigilance. It can also be an utterly consuming job, as Leah, a caregiver from Florida relates:

> I packed a bag for my mother and took her to my brother's house. He promised to take over for the weekend so that I could have the first real break since my mother came to live with me three years ago. I dropped her off about 8:30 Friday night. I couldn't wait to get home and take a nice long bath. I used to love this, but hadn't been able to relax with Mom in the house. She has dementia, and I never knew what she would do.
>
> About 10:30, I heard this pounding on the door. I ignored it, and it got louder and louder. I went to the door to find my mother—suitcase and all! Alone! My brother had always inferred that all the problems and chaos were my fault. Now, Mr. Know-It-All brought her back, but couldn't face me, so he ran when I came to the door. I had the satisfaction of knowing he couldn't even last two hours, but my weekend was ruined.
>
> After I put Mom to bed, I wondered if I should have talked to him about her attitudes and habits. Maybe he would have tried longer if he had been expecting whatever happened. Maybe he would have agreed to do it again. I cried for hours. (Beerman & Rappaport-Musson, 2002, p. 163)

Waves of the caring relationship affect the whole family boat. Caregiving demands often conflict with individual opinions of how various family members want to lead their lives, especially with regard to future plans, privacy, vacations, money, and social interaction. Relationships among spouses, adult siblings, and children can suffer as members compete for attention and time. Occasionally, caregiving leads to reactivation of old intra-family rivalries. Even stable family relationships and positive perceptions of care recipients can become distorted as the demands of caregiving increase.

CARING FOR DIFFICULT OR TOXIC ADULTS

Difficult care recipients can be excessively demanding, angry, manipulative, or critical. Caregivers may respond with anger, guilt, or exhaustion. Depression, anxiety, anger, and pain can drain caregivers who must interact regularly with toxic individuals (i.e., those who are abusive, belligerent, or combative).

In some cases, toxic individuals are so difficult to deal with that, as a CSA, you will typically talk instead with their representatives. For example, an elder law attorney may want to work not with a toxic senior, but with an adult child of the senior, to discuss important matters such as power of attorney or conservatorship. The following counsel offers advice for caregivers and professionals who work with toxic older adults (Dykes, 2000):

- Respect that toxic seniors must initiate their own healing process. They cannot be "fixed."
- When encountering a toxic senior, first acknowledge to yourself your own hurt or disgust. Then put it aside and get on with the work you must do with that person.
- Center yourself. Clear out your own feelings.
- Accept toxic seniors where they are. When you recognize the behavior for what it is, you can better understand the person you are dealing with and tailor your response.
- Questions are less helpful than listening and observation.
- Never lie to toxic care recipients. Mean what you say.
- Be gentle but strong. Set firm limits; stick to them.

Setting and Maintaining Boundaries

In her book *Working with Toxic Older Adults: A Guide to Coping with Difficult Adults* (1999), Gloria M. Davenport writes:

> Surrounding toxic adults with steadfast boundaries and love means to be there, to be a presence but detached and free from seductive toxic hooks and games. It means setting personal limits and boundaries. It means loving yourself enough to quell your own fears and defenses, enabling and empowering you to sustain objective support.

Boundaries are "psychological fences" because they define emotional limits. They delineate what is "in bounds" and what is "out of bounds." In healthy relationships, boundaries act as operational parameters that outline how the caregiver/care recipient relationship works. Boundaries perform critical functions, including:

- helping caregivers define what they will and will not accept in their behavior and the behavior of their care recipient;
- assisting caregivers in defining and respecting their "no's";
- reminding caregivers of their responsibility to behave consciously;
- helping caregivers get priority needs met—in order to set boundaries, it is vital for caregivers to rank their priority needs;
- outlining the framework for how they will connect and share their energy with the care recipient;
- telling others who they are.

Also see Appendix A: Expressing Love Through Setting Limits.

REWARDS OF CAREGIVING

Caring for an older parent, friend, or relative can be joyous and enriching. "[The] provision of emotional support . . . the expression of the caregiver's love and concern . . . are the usual motivations for assuming the caregiving role" (Levine et al., 2003). These ministrations of love can create a time and space for increased sharing, a renewal of the special closeness that may have slipped away over the years, or discovery of family history. Old wounds that may have festered from childhood or adolescence can finally be healed. Friendships can be renewed. Caregivers can gain wisdom from care recipients as they tell their stories and what they have learned in life. The majority of caregivers gain satisfaction from knowing that their care recipients are receiving help and remaining in the community.

Many view their caregiving as having spiritual dimensions as well. Nearly all religions and sacred texts extol the virtues of service and self-sacrifice that caregiving entails (Doka, 2003). Caregiving allows individuals to practice these spiritual habits and cultivate their sense of empathy. Other spiritual gifts caregiving can initiate include "a newly found or appreciated closeness and intimacy or even a reaffirmation of relationships so easily overlooked in the stress and bustle of everyday life" (Doka, 2003). However, the burden of caregiving can be multiplied by an overemphasis on caregiving's spiritual rewards, while ignoring the immense sacrifices it also requires. Some caregivers have said they felt that comments such as "God never gives you burdens you cannot bear" are demeaning, and can make caregivers feel inadequate and unable to ask for needed help.

"The most critical aspect of spiritual support," Doka writes, "requires that the spiritual needs that arise as part of caregiving must be addressed. The illness, accidents, or disasters that make caregiving necessary raise profound spiritual and existential questions. These questions may threaten or shatter spiritual assumptions about the fairness of life, the nature of the world, or even the goodness of whatever one believes and identifies as God. . . . Spiritual support means that one journeys with the caregiver as he or she struggles with these questions, eschewing easy answers or banal affirmations" (Doka, 2003).

CAREGIVER STRESS

While there are deep rewards for caregiving, closer to the surface caregivers are exposed to a wide range of stressors, including strains on the emotional, physical, and financial aspects of their lives. We return now to the *Caregiving in the U.S.* survey to gain a better understanding of the stressful impact of caregiving on individual lives (AARP and National Alliance for Caregiving, 2004):

- Three factors have the greatest effect on caregivers' emotional stress, physical strain, and financial hardship due to caregiving. They are: the level of burden (defined earlier), whether caregivers feel they had a choice in the decision to become caregivers, and caregivers' reported health status.

- More than half (57 percent) of working caregivers say they have had to go to work late, leave early, or take time off during the day to provide care.

- Women contribute more hours of care, provide higher levels of care, and feel they have less of a choice in assuming the caregiving role than men. These factors increase women's risk for emotional stress and a diminished quality of life.

- Of those who are level 5 caregivers, 84 percent say they have less time for friends and family; 76 percent report less time for vacations, hobbies, and social activities; and 49 percent say they are getting less exercise than before becoming a caregiver. Thirty-four percent of level 5 caregivers (who are generally older) say caregiving has made their health worse.

Physical and Emotional Stress

The chore of caregiving can exact very tangible physical and emotional aches, pains, and even illnesses. This is not surprising considering that caregivers are positioned amidst grief and loss and, depending upon the number of outside supports, may feel emotionally isolated and physically overextended in their work.

Several identified risk factors may lead to or compound the stress of caring for an older adult. For example, gender plays a role. More women work while delaying childbearing, experiencing divorce, and becoming single parents, potentially leaving them with responsibility of caring for several generations. Caregiving can increase anxiety and distress, particularly when the responsibilities of work, marriage, child rearing, and parental caregiving collide.

The stressful aspects of caregiving most commonly cited are caring for incontinent care recipients, caring for people suffering from dementia, and giving baths. Most caregivers also yearn for additional free time. Such routine respite provided by volunteers, other family members, or professional caregivers is vital. Live-in caregivers cannot work 24 hours a day, seven days a week—the strain is just too great. Plus, feeling trapped in a house with limited social engagements demoralizes caregivers.

Caregiving Across the Life Cycle, a report prepared by the National Family Caregiver's Association (NFCA) and Fortis Long-Term Care, suggests that family caregivers often find themselves in precarious positions (NFCA, 1998). Respondents report experiencing increases in certain physical and psychological conditions after assuming caregiving duties: depression (reported by 61 percent of caregivers, a rate six times the national average), sleeplessness (51 percent), back pain (41 percent), stomach disorders (24 percent), headaches (15 percent), and colds. (See Resources section for information on *Caregiving Across the Life Cycle*.)

Caregivers also commonly experience anxiety, feelings of helplessness, lowered morale, and both emotional and physical exhaustion. In particular, caregivers assisting older adults with Alzheimer's disease (AD) report three times as many emotional stress symptoms as the general population. These caregivers are two to three times more likely than a noncaregiver to take psychotropic drugs. People caring for recipients with AD are also chronically fatigued because one of the symptoms of AD is day-night reversal—patients sleep during the day and remain awake at night.

Caregivers of recipients in clear decline experience anticipatory grief. The closer the bond between caregivers and care recipients, the more stressing and fatiguing is the specter of death. Proximity to the death process may be more stressful to informal caregivers than to professionals who, by training and experience, are better prepared for dealing with death.

Financial Stress

The financial stress of caregiving can compound the problems of already burdened caregivers. The personal resources of both recipients and providers can be seriously drained by prolonged needs for care. Financial compensation for family caregivers can come from insurance or benefits such as the Aid and Attendance Allowance from the Veterans Administration. Federal Child and Dependent Care Credit provides limited tax credit. Some state programs reimburse family members for care, in a very limited fashion. Decreases in funding and increased utilization lead many agencies to direct their services toward private pay clients, making these services even less available to those with low incomes.

Costs associated with caregiving can be a hardship for many. Following is an overview of service costs:

- home health care—can be very expensive, but typically is more affordable than nursing home care
- Medicare—provides limited coverage for home health care or nursing home care; regulations are tight
- Medicaid—helps cover nursing home costs for very low-income people; home and community-based services are covered in many areas; states vary
- senior center programs—often free or offered on a modest fee basis

- home-delivered meals—low cost and sometimes free, based on the ability to pay
- volunteer services—friendly visitors, telephone reassurance, home repair; often free
- hospice care—fully covered by Medicare, if it is a Medicare-certified program and the physician has diagnosed terminal illness
- adult day care services—costs vary; can be free or on a sliding fee basis; some people qualify for Medicaid; states vary
- personal emergency response systems (PERS)—privately purchased from manufacturer; monthly service fees; local hospitals, fire departments, and rescue services sometimes lend or install these systems

OLDER ADULT ABUSE AND NEGLECT ISSUES

Abuse and neglect of older adults can be related to the stresses of caregiving. Federal definitions of elder abuse, neglect, and exploitation first appeared in the 1987 Amendments to the Older Americans Act. Legislatures in all 50 states have passed elder abuse prevention laws. In most states, elder abuse is considered a crime. Certain emotional abuse and neglect cases are subject to criminal prosecution. Self-neglect, however, is not a crime in all jurisdictions.

Categories of Elder Abuse

Domestic elder abuse is the mistreatment of an older person by someone who has a special relationship with the elder (spouse, sibling, child, friend, or caregiver) in the older person's home or in the home of the caregiver.

Institutional abuse is the mistreatment of an older person who lives in a residential facility (e.g., nursing home, foster home, group home, or board and care facility). Abusers are usually people who have a legal or contractual obligation (e.g., as paid caregivers, staff, or professionals) to provide the elder victim with care and protection.

The behavior of some older adults themselves threatens their health or safety. This situation, called *self-neglect*, includes such activities as refusing or failing to acquire adequate food, water, clothing, shelter, personal hygiene, medication, or safety precautions.

How to Spot Abuse

Abuse can take many forms: physical abuse, the use of physical force resulting in pain, injury, or impairment; sexual abuse, nonconsensual sexual contact of any kind; and emotional or psychological abuse, the infliction of anguish, pain, or distress through verbal or nonverbal acts. Furthermore, abuse can occur through neglect, the refusal or failure to fulfill any part of one's obligation or duty to seniors, or abandonment, the desertion of an elderly person by individuals with responsibility for providing care. Last, you and your clients' families should be watchful for financial or material exploitation, the illegal or improper use of a senior's funds, property, or assets.

Here are the major signs and symptoms of abuse:

- dehydration, malnutrition, untreated medical conditions, or poor personal hygiene

- hazardous or unsafe living conditions (no indoor plumbing, no heat, no running water, improper wiring, etc.)

- unsanitary or unclean living quarters (animal or insect infestation, no functioning toilet, fecal or urine smell)

- inappropriate or inadequate clothing; lack of necessary medical aids such as eyeglasses, hearing aids, or dentures

- grossly inadequate housing or homelessness

- sudden changes in bank account (withdrawal of large sums by a person accompanying the elder)

- abrupt changes in a will or other financial documents

- unexplained disappearance of funds or valuable possessions

- sudden appearance of previously uninvolved relatives claiming rights to an elder's affairs and possessions

- writing checks for unnecessary or inappropriate provisions

If you or others suspect elder abuse, contact your state Adult Protective Services (APS) agency to investigate. (Note: The APS agency provides services only if the older adult agrees or has been declared incapacitated by the court and a guardian has been appointed.)

Signs of Stress

Stress appears differently in different people, but may exhibit itself in some of the ways detailed below.

- **Physical changes.** Caregivers can experience changes in appetite, gastrointestinal distress, changes in frequency of urination, pounding hearts, and dry mouths. Typically, heart and respiratory rates increase and muscles tighten. Humans respond to threatening situations by invoking the "flight or fight" response—the body's internal mechanism to either stand and fight a threat or flee from the danger.

- **Emotional changes.** Caregivers can exhibit emotional instability, crying without cause, laughing inappropriately, anxiety, anger, agitation, irritability, indecision, apathy, or fatigue.

- **Behavioral Signs.** Caregivers may neglect responsibilities at home, with children, or on the job. Alcohol abuse or self-medication may occur, as can neglect of personal hygiene. In general, changes in behavior, habits, and performance occur as stress mounts.

Tools to Support the Caregiver

The *Caregiving in the U.S.* survey provides some useful statistics on how care-givers are currently coping, finding support, and meeting their changing needs (AARP and National Alliance for Caregiving, 2004):

- More than 8 out of 10 (84 percent) African American caregivers say they cope with caregiving stress by praying, compared to 79 percent of Hispanics, 71 percent of whites, and 50 percent of Asian caregivers.

phone calls –

- About 60 percent of caregivers talk with or seek advice from friends or rela-tives to relieve stress, and 44 percent say they read caregiving books to do so.

- When needing information about some aspect of caregiving, 29 percent say they would first turn to the Internet for answers, and 38 percent would seek out a doctor, nurse, or other health professional.

Meals on Wheels

- Almost half of caregivers utilize support of outside services, such as trans-portation, adult day care, Meals on Wheels, and respite care.

Time for self

- Caregivers' most frequently reported unmet needs were "finding time for myself" (35 percent), "managing emotional and physical stress" (29 per-cent), and "balancing work and family responsibilities" (29 percent). (Level 5 caregivers report much higher rates.)

- About 30 percent of caregivers need help "keeping the person I care for safe," and about 20 percent desired help talking to doctors and other health care professionals, as well as making end-of-life decisions.

Among the study's conclusions is this powerful statement, which has implications for you and all CSAs: "If we are going to protect the health and well-being of caregivers who are at risk, it is important to help them fulfill their needs so that they do not sacrifice themselves in the service of others" (p. 17).

Two of the greatest needs of caregivers are *information* and *assistance*. Here is where you can help as a CSA. While you can't control a caregiver's choices, you *can* provide an array of options. Caregivers need resources, both profes-sional and volunteer, that exist in their geographical area. New parental care-givers often have many questions about their roles. How do I act? What do I say to doctors? Do I go into the doctor's office with my parent? Do I assume responsibility for paying the care recipient's bills? What else should I be doing for the care recipient?

Providing them with copies of the tools in this chapter and in the appendix can get new caregivers started on the right path of developing a tool-box and knowing they do not have to struggle in isolation with this new role.

RESOURCES FOR CAREGIVING HELP

Education and support services can be located through general aging orga-nizations, such as the Administration on Aging, or through disease-specific organizations such as the Alzheimer's Association. (For more information on how to locate services, see chapter 9: Home and Community-Based Services.) Some resources to consider:

- home health aides
- housekeeping and chore services
- care managers
- financial advisors
- insurance managers
- neighbors
- church volunteers
- senior centers
- transportation services
- friendly visitors or companions
- telephone reassurance programs
- home maintenance and repair services
- gatekeeper or home observation programs
- personal emergency response systems (PERS)
- hospice care
- adult day care or night care programs
- delivered meals

Geriatric Care Manager

Carol, a caregiver from New Jersey, exults about her source of assistance, a geriatric care manager: "She gives me my only peace of mind. She is my eyes and ears. She is quickly able to get whatever is needed . . . home health aides, consults with specialists, and she facilitates interactions with facilities and agencies" (Beerman & Rappaport-Musson, 2002, p. 29).

STRESS RELIEF

Caregivers must be attuned to their own needs. They must recognize what causes stress and establish a plan that will mitigate the stress. Stress reduction takes place physically, emotionally, spiritually, and mentally. Caregivers need to assess how they are doing on a daily basis. Below are some strategies your clients who are caregivers can use to seek balance and regain peace:

- Pace yourself.
- Delegate responsibilities to others, especially when fatigue or stress levels are high.
- Vent feelings to friends, colleagues, or professionals.
- Keep a log or journal to get powerful emotions on paper.
- Attend classes, workshops, or conferences to obtain new information and ways to cope with stress.
- Have and follow a plan; update it as necessary.
- Participate in leisure activities such as outings to museums or lunches with friends.

- Seek wise counsel from clergy or professionals who work with older adults.
- Join a support group.
- Create a joke book.
- Compile relaxation techniques, funny stories, or a video library that can be used as diversions during moments of stress.

Sometimes, redistributing burdens can sensitize other family members to a caregiver's situation. Family meetings can be a useful tool to assess individual needs and gather some support. (See Appendix B: The Value of Family Meetings.) Blossom, a caregiver from Maine, explains how she found family support:

My sister lives in another state, and she really doesn't understand what is going on with Dad. I finally decided that I couldn't handle all of the problems, and I asked her to come out for a visit. We spent three very long and difficult days with Dad. Now she really understands what I am dealing with every day. Before I could even ask, she offered to do whatever she can to help me. We made a list of things that she could handle for Dad by telephone such as following up with doctors, making appointments, and taking care of some of his financial questions and paperwork. What a difference for me knowing that she supports my efforts and she can help. (Beerman & Rappaport-Musson, 2002, p. 29)

RESPITE CARE

Respite care is one form of caregiver assistance. It involves family members, professionals, or volunteers who come to care recipients' homes to provide relief for the caregiver. Sometimes care recipients can leave the home to attend day care programs for specified periods of time, which allows caregivers the opportunity to run errands or get away for a while. Charmaine, a caregiver from Florida, describes the importance of the respite she received:

I had sitters come in once a week for four hours while I went out and tended to grocery shopping and did what I had to do. Four hours is not enough. It's a mad rush. You come home, you're just totally wiped out, and then you still have to do your caregiving duties. Four hours twice a week was a godsend. It gives you time to go out, have a leisurely lunch, and maybe go to the library. Do things for yourself. Take your mind off what's going to be facing you when you get home. (Beerman & Rappaport-Musson, 2002, p. 161)

Choice of respite care depends on a variety of factors. Can the care recipient leave home? Does the community respite program have the necessary equipment to support the care recipient? Does the care recipient value social interaction? Are programs available in the community? Can the caregiver or family afford the respite program?

The cost of respite care often depends on the service provided. Community alternatives include local churches, associations, or day care facilities, as well as other family members or friends. Respite care reduces the incidence of caregiver burnout and, over time, can allow the care recipient to stay at home longer.

Preparing a care recipient for a respite worker takes time. Initial visits occur with the caregiver present. When the care recipient feels comfortable, the caregiver can leave. Savvy caregivers maintain a positive, upbeat attitude and discuss any fears ahead of time.

PRIORITIES FOR CAREGIVERS

The following suggestions will help your clients establish priorities as caregivers.

- *Allow care recipients to remain as independent as possible for as long as possible.* Caregivers must resist the impulse to rush in and try to fix things. Caregivers who respect seniors' needs to remain independent will allow them to do what they can do, even if their actions may not be up to "normal" standards. Focus on capacity (what the care recipient can do) rather than incapacity (what the care recipient can't do).

- *Intervene gracefully and only when necessary.* Caregivers must strive to make decisions *with* care recipients and not *for* them. Caregivers must respect the autonomy and sovereignty of care recipients who, unless they are seriously mentally incapacitated, have the right to make decisions about their own care and their own activities. Respectful support means that caregivers let go of many of their expectations. Care recipients may take longer to do everything—caregivers must accommodate to the slower pace.

- *Get and give up-to-date information on health issues.* Good information helps caregivers understand the course of illnesses and how best to manage them. When caregivers have knowledge of care recipients' illnesses, they will be better able to communicate with attending physicians.

  Caregivers are encouraged to attend medical appointments with their care recipients. Encourage care recipients to be honest and explicit about symptoms at home and during medical exams. In fact, caregivers can facilitate openness during medical exams by faxing information to physicians before appointments to advise them of symptoms or concerns, or about changes that seniors may not see (e.g., growing forgetfulness, negligence of daily chores, trouble with routine tasks). Additionally, by attending appointments, caregivers will be better able to comply with medication directives and watch for possible side effects addressed by physicians.

- *Don't take on too much responsibility.* Care usually falls on the shoulders of one person—the primary caregiver. Though the caregiving responsibility is often too much for one person to adequately handle, rarely is it shared. This creates the possibility of *serial caregiving*, where each successive caregiver burns out and then another person takes over. It's important to be honest about the burdens involved and make a plan as to how they will be distributed across several helpers and how the primary caregiver will receive relief.

- *Manage stress.* Most caregivers experience enormous stress, which can wear on their health and lead to inadequate care for the recipient. Caregivers must mitigate their own stress, realize their limits, and set boundaries with their care recipient.

- *Get help when you need it.* Some caregivers believe that asking for help demonstrates weakness or character flaws. Yet caregivers need respite, routine breaks from care, and life-enhancing activities to mitigate their stress so they can continue in their important work.

Should You Be a Caregiver?

Not everyone is suited to caregiving. Before assuming caregiving duties, it is important that caregivers participate in a process that Bernie Siegel, the physician who specializes in self-care for cancer therapy, calls "carefrontation," a time of introspection to help potential caregivers determine if they can legitimately embrace the role. Introspection is an honest appraisal of capabilities when caregivers take a hard and truthful look at who they are and what they can handle physically, emotionally, and mentally. The fundamental question that must be asked is, What is the most loving choice for the care recipient, the potential caregivers, and the members of the respective families? (See Appendix C: Are You Cut Out for Caregiving?)

An impulsive or reactive choice to be a caregiver can lead to abuse of the care recipient, nervous breakdowns, poor health, or fiscal fraud. Determining how much time can be spent performing caregiving tasks, how much money can be contributed, or what special skills can be offered is an important part of reflection. Another consideration is emotional support—how much the caregiver will need as well as how much the caregiver can provide for the care recipient. Importantly, those who have been abused at the hands of a parent or other individual should not serve as a caregiver for their abuser, for the sake of both parties' safety and mental health.

Caregivers and Caregiving in America: Summary

Caregivers say having someone to listen, help them organize their thinking, and reassure them is a valued service. However, it is important to allow caregivers to define their experience for themselves.

There are many opportunities for you to serve caregivers:

- If your agency has a newsletter, allocate a column for caregivers.
- Publicize upcoming events for caregivers.
- Keep books, newsletters, videos, and resources in your library to lend to caregivers.
- Cosponsor educational programs for caregivers.
- Encourage libraries and schools to maintain special sections on caregiving issues.

- Organize support groups to encourage caregivers to discuss issues with others who have had similar situations.
- Invite caregivers to serve on advisory boards and provide program input that they would deem beneficial. Since time is often scarce for caregivers, allow for their participation via letter, telephone, or conference call.

Above all, the most essential actions you and others can take on behalf of a caregiver are to:

- acknowledge the difficulty and importance of the role;
- listen to a caregiver's needs and experiences;
- refer the person to informational and educational resources when appropriate;
- follow up with the person and support the caregiver in expressing his or her own solutions.

Throughout the United States, caregivers perform heroics on a daily basis, without pay and largely without recognition. You are uniquely positioned and even charged to appreciate the needs of caregivers and their families and support them in their work. By caring for caregivers, you can create ripples of benefits for their care recipients, their families, employers, and society at large.

Appendix A: Expressing Love Through Setting Limits

It is vital that caregivers keep themselves in the equation of their own lives. Because caregiving is a difficult endeavor and often requires extraordinary commitment, energy, and time, caregivers can ignore their own needs. Over time, as they become absorbed in the care of their recipient, they can cease to demonstrate concern for their own well-being. In their loving devotion to the care recipient, they can become increasingly unloving to themselves.

One important way that caregivers can express concern for their own needs is to establish and maintain loving limits. Loving limits requires establishing flexible and changeable boundaries. Loving limits requires that people honestly give care. Loving limits requires that caregivers act authentically by speaking their truth without blame or judgment.

Caregivers who discount their own needs eventually burn out. Anger and frustration often accompany this phase. Burnout can develop when (a) boundaries have been ill-defined or nonexistent, and (b) open, honest, and direct communication with the care recipient has not occurred.

Setting loving limits requires that caregivers understand the difference between needs and wants. Needs are the essential requirements for life. Wants are the "it would be nice if" sorts of experiences. Conscious caregivers strive to meet each of the fundamental needs. Most caregivers find it impossible to meet every care recipient's wants without ignoring their own needs.

Boundaries define emotional and behavioral limits. They act as operational parameters that define how caregiver–care recipient relationships work. Boundaries are personal prescriptions that delineate what an individual will and will not accept in their own and others' behavior. Ill-defined or nonexistent boundaries set up the caregiver for unnecessary problems and powerful negative emotional responses.

If boundaries are unclear or nonexistent, it is possible to change the situation and establish clear and reasonable boundaries.

- Explore the reality of what is. Are you comfortable with the boundaries you have established? If so, congratulations. If not, read on.
- Determine if boundaries are weak, inconsistent, or nonexistent. Decide where boundaries (if nonexistent) need to be established or (if weak) strengthened. If inconsistent, ask yourself, "Why am I vacillating?"
- Ascertain the care recipient's authentic needs. Are you meeting his or her needs? How many wants are you meeting? Are you meeting your own needs?
- How are you feeling? Are you often angry or frustrated? Do you feel burned out? If so, something in the caregiving routine must change. Caregivers cannot continue indefinitely when they are feeling strong negative emotions. Ask yourself where the emotions are coming from. Look at the situations that elicit strong emotions. These are probably areas where you will choose

to establish stronger, more consistent boundaries. Remember, boundaries are often *felt out* rather than *figured out*. Listen to your feelings!

- Determine a plan of action for setting boundaries and maintaining them. Have a face-to-face, heart-to-heart conversation with the care recipient to discuss what is and is not working and why things need to change. There are three important aspects of this communication: First, define what is happening; second, describe how you are feeling; and third, define what you need to change to feel better. Explain how the two of you need to openly address issues and problem-solve situations together. Describe your relationship as a partnership.

- Take a personal time out on a regular basis (at least once a day). Scan your body, your mind, and your emotions. Answer this question: "How am I doing today?" Follow it up with "What do I need to do differently to improve my well-being?"

- Give yourself permission to change the routine. If your guilt buttons are consistently getting pushed, and you cannot give yourself this vital permission, seek professional counsel. Caregivers who love their care recipients and also love themselves will be healthier and more at peace as they strive to honor their caregiving roles.

Appendix B: The Value of Family Meetings

By M. J. Oberhausen

Introduction

Family meetings, sometimes called family conferences, are like task forces in business that meet to solve problems. A certain group of people who bring strengths and resources to the work team focuses on establishing a plan to solve a dilemma. In essence, holding a family meeting requires creating a family task force.

In family meetings, the goal is to establish a strategy for the management of care of older parents or family members who need ongoing care. Meetings may occur once or multiple times. They can be informal, or they can utilize the services of a professional mediator. Meetings can be in-person, over the phone, on a conference call, or a combination of in-person with some members on phones. Consider the following eight steps.

STEP ONE: WHY THE TASK FORCE IS CREATED

A family meeting is often scheduled when there has been a crisis or a marked change in the health of an older adult family member. Most times, siblings or the spouse of the care recipient will coordinate the meeting, but coordinators must not take matters into their own hands and dominate a meeting or control the agenda. Shortcuts in the process can have disastrous consequences. A bossy coordinator may instigate a mutiny, and the care recipient who is already under a great deal of stress can become overwhelmed with negativity and dissension in the family. A family meeting is a forum for open, honest, and direct communication.

STEP TWO: ATTENDEES—WHOM TO INVITE

- Who should come? The people most involved with the care and who are concerned about the outcome of the decision-making process.
- Remember—shared decisions generally produce the best results. All participants will feel as if they own the outcome.
- Create opportunities for multigenerational dialogue. Siblings, children, grandchildren, spouses, and loving friends can all be involved.
- Don't assume that family members should be left out just because they live far away and haven't been very involved in past family affairs. Excluding a member can be potential sabotage: A faraway son who wasn't invited to a meeting may say, "Mom, I would have never let them do this to you had I been there."
- Are sons- and daughters-in-laws to be included in the meeting? What about grandchildren?
- Generally use three criteria: Who is most concerned? Who is most affected? Who has resources to offer?
- Exclude the "cousin Bobs" who only want to give advice, judge, and criticize.
- Send letters to all concerned outlining the necessity for the meeting. In a crisis or medical emergency, make phone calls.
- A coordinator who expects a contentious attitude out of one or more family members should find a professional facilitator who will agree to coordinate the meeting. Establish a neutral meeting site if necessary, where family members will be on their best behavior. Note: If family members have *never* gotten along or there are major unresolved issues (physical or sexual abuse), a facilitator will probably be necessary.

STEP THREE: PREPARING FOR THE MEETING

- Attendees should prepare for the meeting by reviewing their beliefs, attitudes, and assumptions about what it means to be a loving and dutiful child, grandchild, friend, spouse, etc.
- The coordinator can prepare a list of questions. (See Appendix C: Are You Cut Out for Caregiving? for a list of questions attendees can answer prior to the meeting.)

STEP FOUR: AT THE MEETING—GIVING THE FLOOR TO ALL

- Set up ground rules at the beginning of the first meeting: speak for yourself, don't interrupt, one person talks at a time. Post the ground rules for all participants to see. Review these ground rules before additional meetings.
- Everyone should have a chance to speak his or her mind, including the care recipient whenever possible.
- Consider suggestions and options from each participant.
- Lay the groundwork for full participation. How will everyone be heard?
- In contentious families, expect storms in the early sessions or in the first part of the meeting.
- Family meetings are not the time to resolve old conflicts.
- Clear the air and listen to what other participants share.

STEP FIVE: IDENTIFYING THE PROBLEM—WHAT'S GOING ON? WHAT'S OUR REALITY?

- Gather information about the issues. Is the older adult safe in his or her home? Contact professionals such as geriatric physicians, geriatric social workers, folks from aging services, and mental health workers who specialize in the geriatric population for reality checks.
- Define the problem: "Mom is not safe anymore. She almost burned the kitchen down." Major resistance in this step can be denial that older adult has "the dwindles" or is going downhill fast.
- Don't panic if things seem overwhelming. Direct energies to find specific options to the challenges that the care recipient faces.

STEP SIX: DISCOVERING WHO WILL MAKE COMMITMENTS

- The *zero hour*—who does what, when, how much? Who contributes money? What are family members and friends willing to do?
- This is often when task force members drop out (temporarily or permanently). Self-confrontation is often painful. Family members may need to participate in introspection (i.e., a personal reflection about one's perceived duties and obligations to one's parent or older adult relative). Religious beliefs and family values will come to the surface.
- Create a window in which to alter decisions: "We'll do this for three months and then revisit the situation and see how everyone is doing. At that point we can change the plan if we need to."
- At each step of the commitment process, check in with the care recipient to establish his or her comfort level with the decisions.

STEP SEVEN: PARTICIPATE IN THE PROCESS OF INTROSPECTION

- Members separate from the task force. Members of the meeting do a reality check by looking at what's on their life plates. They review other commitments and ask themselves if they can live with the choices and commitments they are going to make. The commitments may be determined by the relationships family members have with the care recipient.

- Tell fellow task force members the truth, announcing in advance the limits of involvement is better than copping out later.

STEP EIGHT: SET PERSONAL PRIORITIES AND REACH A FAMILY AGREEMENT

- Members make decisions and establish a workable agreement with a commitment written out in the form of a group contract. This may be vastly different than what members anticipated.
- Allow room for change in the future as the care recipient's condition changes or other life events come to the forefront.
- Check in again with the care recipient to make certain he or she is comfortable with the plan.

FAMILY MEETING ROADBLOCKS

Here are five common roadblocks in the family meeting process:

- Family members may say things they don't mean.
- Family members may keep secrets. Everyone must be encouraged to speak the truth without blame or judgment. Family members who tell the truth about their perspective will positively influence the decisions of the group. If a family member has been abused by the care recipient and can't handle supporting him or her, it is vital that the collective hear what happened so they will understand the person's reasons for balking at becoming involved in care.
- Family members may hide feelings. Some family members will hide their feelings because they focus on what "good" people should feel, instead of what they actually feel.
- Family members may make promises or commitments they do not intend to keep or may not be able to keep if circumstances change, such as, "You won't *ever* go to a nursing home," or "We promise to call you every day." Avoid using the words *always* and *never*.
- Family members may jump the gun and make hasty decisions that don't honor the wishes of the care recipient. The process can be staged out based around the care recipient's needs.

When There's an Impasse

- Stick with the basics. Follow the rules of process established by the family members. Take a 10-minute break and come back with fresh eyes and ears.
- Keep your heart open to the process. Don't let fear rule your decisions.
- Get a trusted family friend to act as a facilitator or a trained professional to facilitate subsequent meetings.

Conclusion

- The family task force must be ready to adapt the original agreement based around the needs of the care recipient.
- The task force composition may change because of divorce, relocation, illness, withdrawal, etc.
- Setbacks won't destroy the task force unless the members give up.
- Working together can produce the most effective action.

Appendix C: Are You Cut Out for Caregiving?

Introspection Questions

1. Are you a nurturer?
2. What in your background supports being a nurturer?
3. Do you have any unresolved and deep-seated anger over how the potential care recipient treated you as a child, teenager, or adult?
4. Were you physically or sexually abused by the potential care recipient?
5. How is your health and stamina? Do you have the energy to be a principal caregiver?
6. What is your prime motivation for caregiving—guilt, family obligations, or love?
7. What duty and obligation do you believe you have to the potential care recipient?
8. Have you rid yourself of emotional baggage and owned your vulnerability?
9. Can you express your feelings and your opinions even when they are unpopular?
10. Can you comfort friends and family members when they are in distress?
11. How well have you cared for yourself in your life? Do you know your limits, and do you honor them?
12. Do you respect your priority needs and seek to get them met?
13. Do you know how to relax and mitigate stress? Do you actively incorporate wellness activities in your life? How well do you take care of yourself? Are you last on the priority rung?
14. What role do religion and spirituality play in your life? Is it an anchor and a support for you?
15. How well would your family and home handle the addition of a parent or grandparent?
16. Do you work at home? Is your workspace separated from living space?

National Council on Aging (NCOA). http://www.ncoa.org, 800-424-9046. A private, nonprofit association of agencies, senior centers, employment services, and more, the association provides research, best practices, and workplace development information.

National Family Caregivers Association (NFCA). http://www.nfcacares.org, 800-896-3650. NFCA supports family caregivers and publicly represents this constituency. They promote self-advocacy and self-care.

National Hospice Organization. http://www.hospiceinfo.org, 800-658-8898. This Web site contains information about the national hospice program and includes links to many other sites on this subject.

National Institute on Aging (NIA). http://www.nia.nih.gov, 410-496-1752. This institute leads the federal effort on aging research.

National Institute of Neurological Disorders and Stroke (NINDS). http://www.ninds.nih.gov, 800-352-9424 or 301-496-5751. NINDS conducts and supports research on brain and nervous system disorders.

Chapter 8

Housing

The first time that Fern, Betty's mother, fell in her apartment, help came quickly. Thankfully, Fern was wearing her emergency-alert bracelet. But Fern has fallen a number of times since then, and she has not always been as lucky. Once she fell in the middle of a busy street and sprained her ankle.

The stress on Betty is getting to be too much. She says, "I have lost count of how many times I have left work or dinner with my family because of an emergency with my mother."

The last straw came when Fern disappeared for a whole afternoon. Betty is now looking for help in making decisions about how to find supportive housing for her mother. But she doesn't know where to start.

. . .

Terry and Adam have lived happily in the same home for more than 50 years. At ages 88 and 87, they plan to stay "right where we are as long as possible." In fact, they have hired a renovation expert to convert a den on the first floor of their two-story Colonial to a bedroom and bathroom in case one of them cannot climb stairs in the future. They are also widening doorways and making the new rooms handicap-accessible in case they need wheelchair access. Terry says, "We are preparing for the future as best we know how and enjoying life the way we always have. We have the best of everything right now."

Introduction

These two stories represent the extremes of housing options for seniors. Fern is at one end of the spectrum. She needs long-term care and has not planned ahead, leaving the decision to her badly stressed daughter. Terry and Adam are at the other end of the spectrum. They are a healthy and happy couple who are planning ahead and enjoying life in their family home.

Where one grows old matters (Golant, 1984). The decision where to live is one of the most important choices seniors make when deciding how to meet their changing needs. The quality of their housing, neighborhood, and the communities they live in influence whether they have satisfying and rewarding lifestyles and achieve their everyday needs.

Housing is so intimately linked with the comings and goings of seniors that it can give us clues about their well-being. Changes in how seniors occupy or use their homes may signal changes in their physical and mental capabilities. A fall on the stairs, signs of housing neglect, or poorly maintained landscaping may be an indication that a senior is having difficulty adapting to problems related to aging.

To assess the housing options of your senior clients, you may use the following checklist:

1. Does the senior view his or her present housing situation positively or negatively?
2. Which shelter and care qualities are the most important to the senior?
3. What housing alternatives are available, how do they differ, and what are their strengths and weaknesses?

You can help seniors understand their housing choices and the extent to which they are likely to be compatible with their lifestyles and capabilities, particularly their level of hardiness and financial resources. In order to help you achieve these goals, this chapter addresses why it can be difficult to help seniors make housing choices, the federal laws that govern housing options, staying put versus relocating, financial strategies, and housing types. It also provides practical information on how to assess the needs of seniors and how to aid them in their decision-making.

QUESTIONS TO ASK SENIORS ABOUT THEIR HOUSING

Among the most important questions you can ask about the housing situations of your senior clients are (Golant, 1984; Regnier, 2002):

- *Owner or renter.* Is the housing owned or rented, and is that status in the best interests of the older person?
- *Affordability.* To what extent are housing costs a financial burden on the household?
- *Asset wealth.* How necessary will it be for the senior to rely on the equity in the residence (selling value of dwelling after a mortgage is paid off) to meet future financial needs?
- *Physical comfort.* Is the residence a comfortable place to live, as indicated by the number of rooms and their sizes, inside temperatures, noise level, lighting, colors, furniture, ambience, sources of stimulation, and other architectural and design features?
- *Maintenance/upkeep.* Does the residence appear to be well maintained, as judged by working appliances, air and heating systems, plumbing and electrical systems, condition of roof, and myriad other structural and operating features?
- *Ease of use and safety.* Can the senior easily and safely use all the space and features of the residence, including upper floors or a basement,

—unexpected absence of a family member to help;

—major change in financial status;

—significant change in health status;

—significant change in mental well-being (for example, depression, confusion);

—new difficulties with ADL or IADL abilities.

- Housing opportunities or solutions are not the same everywhere. Not all places offer:

—similar housing and care options with the same features;

—affordable housing and care options;

—equal opportunities to occupy housing and care facilities made affordable by government funded programs.

Housing for Older and Impaired Persons Is Defined by Federal Laws

The types and quality of housing for seniors vary throughout the United States. Nonetheless, two federal laws—the Fair Housing Act and the Americans with Disabilities Act—identify a set of basic housing requirements that local governments, architects, developers, property owners, rental managers, and other professionals must follow when accommodating older adults, particularly the impaired (Hyatt, 2001; U.S. Department of Housing and Urban Development, 2003b).

THE FAIR HOUSING ACT

Since 1968, The Fair Housing Act (Title VIII of the Civil Rights Act of 1968) has protected consumers of any race, color, sex, religion, or national origin seeking to buy and rent housing of their choice. The Fair Housing Amendments of 1988 (FHA) further added "handicap" and "familial status" to the grounds for prohibiting discrimination.

Adults Only

Congress passed The Fair Housing Act to stop housing providers from discriminating against families with children when renting or selling their homes, but the law also recognized *housing for seniors* as an exempt category. By so doing, it gave seniors the option of living primarily with persons the same age as themselves, and gave housing developers the motivation to target seniors as an exclusive consumer market. This category included:

- housing occupied by one or more persons created by any state or federal program (for example, Section 202 government-assisted rental program);
- housing intended for, and solely occupied by, persons 62 years of age or older;
- housing in which 80 percent or more of the occupied units in the housing facility (or community) were occupied by at least one person age 55 and older, so long as the senior housing property published and verified policies and procedures that demonstrated an intent to be for seniors. (The Housing for Older Persons Act of 1995 [HOPA] eliminated what was an earlier and confusing requirement that age 55 and older housing had to have "significant facilities and services" for seniors.)

Protecting the Disabled from Housing Discrimination

Physically impaired older renters sometimes find themselves in an apartment or rental building with unhelpful or unsafe design features that need modification. Some examples of such features include lack of grab bars, difficult walking environments, hard-to-reach shelves and closets, shower and sink features that are difficult to use, poor or absent wheelchair access, hard-to-use common areas (Wylde, Baron-Robbins, & Clark, 1994). The property owner, though, may prohibit any changes. And older renters may also have difficulty complying with the tenant rules in the building. Again, maybe the property owner will not yield. Worse still, seniors may have to confront rental managers who seek to evict them because they convey the "wrong" marketing image and pose greater insurance liability risks.

The Fair Housing Act protects disabled persons against various such types of discrimination. (*Disabled persons* broadly includes those who have any physical or mental impairment that substantially limits one or more of their major life activities.) Its provisions applied to all residential buildings with four or more dwelling units, including many types of planned senior housing. The list below details its major provisions:

- A property owner must allow disabled persons to make "reasonable modifications" to residences so that they can fully enjoy them. The tenants, however, must pay for these changes. Examples include installing grab bars, replacing doorknobs with lever handles, widening doorways for wheelchair access, or installing a ramp at the entrance to the building. When the tenant vacates the dwelling, he or she may also have to restore the premises to its original condition.

- A property owner cannot refuse to make "reasonable accommodations" in the building's rules, policies, practices, or services to ensure disabled persons can use and enjoy their residences like the other residents. For example, a property owner would be expected to waive a rule against keeping pets for a tenant who is emotionally dependent on the pet or uses the pet as a service animal; to waive a no-guest rule for a tenant who needs a live-in aide; or to change parking rules to make it more convenient for a tenant with disabilities to park.

- Rental managers/owners/landlords are prohibited from making inquiries about the disability status of an applicant unless they are related to the applicant's "ability to meet the requirements of ownership or tenancy" and are asked of all applicants.

- Multifamily dwellings occupied after March 13, 1991, with four or more units with an elevator are required to contain certain handicap-accessible features to make them usable for persons with disabilities. The accessibility guidelines include seven broad technical requirements (U.S. Department of Housing and Urban Development, 1998):

  —accessible building entrance on an accessible route

  —accessible and usable public and common use areas

  —usable doors

  —accessible route into and through the covered dwelling unit

  —light switches, electrical outlets, thermostats, and other environmental controls in accessible locations

  —reinforced walls for grab bars

  —usable kitchens and bathrooms

- Local zoning and land-use restrictions often limit the location of facilities serving frail or disabled seniors. The Fair Housing Act prohibited the arbitrary application of special requirements through land-use regulations, restrictive covenants, and conditional or special-use permits that had the effect of limiting the ability of handicapped individuals to live in the residence of their choice in the community.

AMERICANS WITH DISABILITIES ACT OF 1990

The Fair Housing Act's design requirements and disability discrimination provisions applied to most conventional residential housing and planned senior housing properties. The Americans with Disabilities Act (ADA) protects against similar sources of discrimination in the nonresidential areas or public accommodations of privately owned senior housing complexes. These might include a restaurant, bar, auditorium, sales or rental office, laundromat, barber or beauty shop, professional offices of a health care provider, library, or exercise and recreation sites. ADA regulatory guidelines specifically cover long-term care facilities and nursing homes.

Staying Put, Aging in Place, or Moving: Fundamental Decisions of Seniors

Seniors move less frequently from their current housing than any other age group (Schachter, 2004). This residential inertia is not surprising. They typically own their dwellings (80 percent of seniors do) and most occupy comfortable quarters in familiar neighborhoods and communities. Often they are also psychologically attached to their homes, which symbolize their having "made it" (Golant, 1984, 2003).

Seniors who develop physical or cognitive impairments are especially unequivocal about staying put. Nursing homes and even more desirable alternatives, such as assisted living facilities, are last on their list of choices. They prefer to remain in their familiar homes where they can package together a combination of family assistance with home and community-based professional care. This has given rise to the concept of *aging with choice* (also called *aging in place*). The phrase *aging with choice* involves more than seniors simply staying in their homes. It also implies that seniors can cope successfully with their vulnerabilities, either by themselves or with the assistance of family or professional caregivers (Golant, 2004).

Professionals and scholars often romanticize the desirability of seniors staying in their own homes. However, doing so can have several downsides, even for healthy and active seniors (Golant, 2003; U.S. Department of Housing and Urban Development, 2003a). For example:

- An excessive share of seniors' monthly incomes may go to pay for their housing expenditures.
- Homes purchased much earlier in life may now be much larger than needed.
- Housing may be in physical disrepair, making for an uncomfortable or unsafe setting.
- Residences may lack design features (for example, grab bars, accessible closets) appropriate for a less agile, older resident.
- Residences may be older and poorly insulated, making them very expensive to heat or cool.
- Familiar neighbors may have moved away.
- Without a car in a suburban or rural setting, seniors may find it very difficult to reach desired locations.
- Neighborhoods may have become unsafe to walk alone.

Seniors staying in their homes and also trying to cope with their physical and cognitive declines may have difficulties for these reasons:

- Family caregivers or hired care professionals may be unavailable when needed.
- Family members may be inept caregivers.
- Caregiving demands may simply be too demanding or difficult to fulfill.
- Seniors or family members may find it too costly to hire the amount of necessary professional care to address impairment needs.
- Family members may psychologically or physically abuse an older person.
- Even if caregiving needs will be satisfied, seniors may feel alone or socially isolated much of the time.

Just as the concept of seniors staying in their own homes defies simple generalizations, moving can be disruptive and stressful, but also rewarding, satisfying, and empowering. This is not surprising, given that older people move for at least four different reasons (Longino, 2002):

- *Amenity moves.* Seniors desire a new location that better fits their changing recreational or leisure lifestyle preferences (for example, moving to an active adult retirement community or to a rural county close to the mountains).
- *Environmental modification moves.* Seniors want to relocate to a home that is smaller and easier to maintain, or to a neighborhood closer to everyday needs that is safer or more socially compatible.
- *Light assistance moves.* Seniors want or need a residential setting that offers light housekeeping, meals, and a little personal assistance.
- *Heavy assistance moves.* Seniors require a residential setting that offers a lot of personal assistance and often nursing care.

Major "Aging with Choice" Strategies for Older Adults in Their Own Homes

Seniors can benefit from three types of strategies to more successfully stay in their own homes, age with choice, and enjoy a better quality of life (Golant, 1994). This chapter examines two of these: financial strategies and housing adaptation strategies, while chapter 9 examines a third, home and community-based assistance services. (Another financial strategy, the reverse mortgage, is discussed in chapter 16.)

FINANCIAL STRATEGIES

Property Tax Relief Programs

A large property tax can result in financial stress for seniors (Golant, 2003). States offer various tax abatement programs to alleviate this problem. Many of these are available to all taxpayers, some are targeted to poor persons, and others are specifically earmarked for the elderly. Property tax relief comes in three different forms (National Conference of State Legislatures, 2002): homestead exemptions and credits, circuit breaker programs, and property tax deferral programs.

Homestead Exemptions and Credits

Forty-eight states and the District of Columbia offer these programs. Homeowners get relief because the amount of their property taxes is not based on their total assessed property value, but rather on some smaller dollar amount. Similar relief is offered by homestead credits, but some dollar amount is subtracted from the actual property tax rather than from the assessed value. In 17 states, the elderly and non-elderly receive the same tax relief benefits; in 12 states, only seniors receive benefits; and in 12 other states and the District of Columbia, both seniors and non-seniors receive benefits, but the former are more generous. The actual dollar value of the tax relief depends on a particular state's program.

Circuit Breaker Programs

These programs give refunds to lower-income and disabled homeowners and renters when their estimated property taxes (or imputed taxes for renters) overload (i.e., exceed) some percentage of their income. Most states target the elderly. The amount of tax relief will depend on the size of the household's income and the amount of its property taxes. Twenty-six states and the District of Columbia offer property tax relief programs to both renters and homeowners; five states (Idaho, Oklahoma, South Dakota, Washington, and Wyoming) offer these programs only to homeowners; and Alaska and Oregon offer tax relief only to renters.

Property Tax Deferral Programs

These programs allow homeowners to put off paying their property taxes by borrowing on the equity in their homes. These deferred taxes and the accrued interest then become a lien on the value of the home. When home-owners sell their dwellings or die, the debt becomes due. This type of financial relief shares similarities with reverse mortgages. Twenty-four states and the District of Columbia offer this program. The age eligibility of seniors, their income caps, and the upper amount of deferred taxes vary by state.

Older Homeowners' Use of Property Tax Relief Programs

An AARP investigation found that older homeowners applied for home-stead exemption programs more often than circuit breaker and homestead credit programs. Property tax deferral programs were the least used. Seniors reported that they did not apply for these programs because they did not know about them or because they needed help with the applications. AARP argued for the need for further outreach efforts (Baer, 1998).

Sale-Leaseback Plans

Even when older homeowners have difficulty paying for their housing costs, they are very reluctant to move. The sale-leaseback plan allows them to stay put but get money from the equity in their homes (Golant, 1992). A sale-leaseback plan works this way: A family member or friend, but conceivably an investor or a nonprofit organization, buys the home from the older persons. Although the older homeowner becomes a renter, the new owner guarantees the seniors the right of lifetime tenancy. The new owner in turn views the purchased home as an investment property that will yield a favorable return, especially in a rapidly appreciating housing market. Thus, the new owner treats property taxes and maintenance costs as tax-deductible cost items.

If the older seller chooses to hold a mortgage note on the house, he or she will receive part of the dwelling's equity in the form of an initial cash down payment from the new owner and the remainder as monthly pay-ments (principal plus interest). Alternatively, if the buyer financed the house purchase through a commercial lender, the older person will immediately receive all of the home's equity from the new owner. In either instance, the older person can invest the up-front cash or purchase an annuity from an insurance company.

Cautions About Sale-Leaseback Plans

Sale-leaseback plans are laden with potential financial and legal pitfalls for the unwary. Their appropriateness depends on whether the monthly mortgage payment (principal plus interest) adequately covers the older resident's costs of living, especially the monthly rent. If rent increases are excessive, there is the danger that the older resident will be paying out more for rent than is received in mortgage payments or the interest returned on the investment.

Seniors assume all the usual risks of renters, though more is at stake given their reluctance to move. They must be assured of lifetime tenancy, that their rent increases will not be excessive, that their dwellings will be appropriately maintained, that the new owner will tolerate their taking in of a caregiver or boarder, and that they will retain their right of residency during a short-term absence, such as during a hospital or nursing home stay.

If seniors hold a mortgage note, they must also scrutinize the financial implications of their receiving a new source of monthly income. New income may change their eligibility for Supplemental Security Income, Medicaid, or food stamps.

This method of releasing a home's equity is not especially popular with either private investors or financial institutions that consider the life-tenure lease provisions too restrictive because they cannot easily increase rents or sell the property. On the other hand, a sale-leaseback approach might be advantageous to family members who want a strategy by which they can increase the monthly cash income of their older mother or father. The Internal Revenue Service, however, must view the home sale as a legitimate, for-profit commercial venture. Thus, it must not appear that the rent charged is too low or that the buyer is not assuming investment risks or costs such as taxes, insurance, and repairs.

Reverse Mortgages

Financial planners are likely to encounter clients facing potential retirement-income shortfalls while having substantial equity in a home or condominium. When this situation prevails, the clients may wish to explore the opportunity of obtaining additional retirement cash through a reverse mortgage.

For many seniors their most valuable asset is their home. Therefore, your senior clients may want to consider reverse mortgages. They allow seniors over age 62 to enter into a type of loan that converts part of their home equity into tax-free income. Reverse mortgages are covered in detail in chapter 16.

HOUSING ADAPTATION STRATEGIES

Home Sharing with Nonrelatives

Why would a senior open up the doors of his or her house or apartment to a stranger such as a boarder or live-in tenant? In fact, only a very small percentage (just over 2 percent) of seniors share their households with someone unrelated to them (Federal Interagency Forum on Aging-Related Statistics, 2000), but their reasons for doing so may be compelling. Among the benefits (Golant, 1992) are:

- an additional source of income;
- companionship and not having to live alone;
- a greater probability of getting help in the event of a disabling accident or medical emergency;
- assistance with everyday minor home maintenance, household chores, and grocery errands;
- assistance with personal care needs including bathing, dressing, meal preparation, walking, and getting around.

Currently, home sharing is not a popular housing option. However, some communities feature home share programs sponsored by nonprofit organizations that assist seniors if they choose to share a home with others.

Physical Modifications to the Home

In the year 2000, seniors ages 65 and older experienced 1.8 million falls, resulting in emergency room visits costing $16.4 billion in medical and long-term care costs. About 55 percent of these falls occurred inside the house, while an additional 23 percent occurred outside but near the house (Kochera, 2002a). Falls are caused by dizziness, fainting, seizure, impairment of motion, lack of strength of arm or leg, gait impairment, arthritis, vitamin deficiencies, bad vision, poor balance, and the failure to use appropriate assistive devices such as walkers and canes. The side effects of medications are often culprits. Some, but not all, experts believe that falling could be reduced by environmental modifications—for example, reducing cluttered pathways, removing badly placed electrical cords, eliminating loose throw rugs, modifying slippery surfaces (such as in showers), reducing the height of out-of-reach cabinets and closets, and through the installation of grab bars, ramps, and handrails.

The 1995 American Housing survey from the United States Department of Housing and Urban Development (HUD) showed that over half of seniors with impairments (and thus at greater risk of falling) had made no home modifications, and that another fourth had introduced but one. Just less than one in four reported they had made at least two modifications, including extra handrails or grab bars, widening of doors and hallways, adding ramps, and adding other accessibility features in the bathroom and kitchen, such as modifying the sink faucets and cabinets (Census Bureau, 2001).

Seniors are often hesitant to make home modifications because they are afraid of dealing with contractors or repair personnel who overcharge or do inadequate work. Lower income seniors would be especially likely to participate if there were more affordable government programs, less-confusing eligibility requirements, a simpler application process, home modification assessments coordinated with other social services such as home care, or if professionals working with seniors had more knowledge about the potential benefits of home modifications. Currently, city and county governments fund home modifications through subsidies received from the Community Development Block Grant programs and from Title III Older Americans Act programs. Private foundations and voluntary groups such as United Way and Rotary Clubs also financially support home modification programs (Pynoos, Liebig, Overton, & Calvert, 1997).

TECHNOLOGY THAT CAN SUPPORT INDEPENDENCE FOR SENIORS

New technologies can help seniors stay independent in their own homes. They include assistive devices, monitor and response systems, and communication aids. Please see chapter 9 for information on such technologies.

Major Housing Relocation Options

Seniors can select from different relocation strategies to realize a residential setting that is more consistent with changes in their lifestyle or level of frailty (Golant, 1994):

- the household of a family member
- a government-subsidized rental property
- an active-adult community
- independent living/congregate living facility
- assisted living facilities, board and care, or continuing care retirement communities
- a nursing home

HOUSEHOLD ALTERNATIVES INVOLVING FAMILY

Although a less popular alternative than in the past, about 7 percent of men and 17 percent of women ages 65 and older now live with family members other than their spouses, usually in the dwelling of an adult child. Over a quarter of women ages 85 and older occupy this type of living arrangement. The proportion of African American, Asian, and Hispanic elderly persons opting for this choice is much higher—about 16 percent of minority elderly men and 34 percent of minority elderly women (Federal Interagency Forum on Aging-Related Statistics, 2000).

An older parent living alone who is having difficulty coping with his or her frailties is usually the motivation for this housing choice. It is especially the alternative of choice for those adult children who feel guilty about not "doing enough." In the case of minorities, it may be motivated by their strong cultural values that emphasize multigenerational helping relationships.

This is often not an easily implemented alternative, and being a caregiver is inevitably stressful (see chapter 7). This living arrangement is most successful when adult children recognize their limitations and make good use of adult day care, friendly visitor programs, and respite care services to reduce their physical and emotional stresses.

An adult child can accommodate an older parent in one of three distinctive housing arrangements: a spare bedroom, an accessory apartment, or an Elder Cottage Housing Opportunity (ECHO) unit. These are more than bricks-and-mortar adjustments, and each can differently affect the social and emotional worlds of adult child and older parent alike (Golant, 1992).

Spare Bedroom

When adult children take in an older parent, often their own children have departed, thereby opening up a spare bedroom. This is the least demanding of the options for renovating a household. At most, architectural modifications will involve the addition of another bathroom or perhaps only adaptations to an existing one. This might include the installation of grab bars or the introduction of a seat in the bathtub. HUD's Fair Housing manual offers useful design specifications for such modifications (U.S. Department of Housing and Urban Development, 1998).

This household arrangement obviously produces the most intimate of family relationships, but it has downsides. It can result in dramatic assaults on the host family's lifestyles. The physical closeness will often infringe on their private time, and decisions must continually be made—for some these will be wrenching judgments—when to include the older parent in their everyday activities.

Living in a spare bedroom also has pros and cons for the older person. Physical security and emotional closeness are a plus, but on the minus side, the bedroom becomes the only space that belongs exclusively to the older parent. Thus, the older person must always wonder when the family will welcome his or her presence. Conflicts will arise if an older parent feels put off when the host family refuses his or her help with household chores or if the family unrealistically assumes that an older boarder can assist with babysitting a grandchild.

Accessory Apartment, In-Law Suite, or Second Units

The host family can minimize some potential privacy and control problems by creating a physically separate living space for the older parent. Owners of single-family homes can convert an already existing basement, garage, sun room, spare bedroom, or porch into a self-contained suite with its own private entrance to the outside (like a studio apartment with kitchen and bathroom). The host family can also introduce extensive physical design adaptations to make this suite more accessible and easier to use. It can also install an intercom or a camera surveillance system to monitor the status of an older parent, though privacy issues might arise. HUD's Fair Housing manual again will offer useful information.

Again, there are downsides. First, such a conversion requires a building permit, and zoning regulations may not automatically allow this use in many single-family neighborhoods. Also, this is an expensive strategy, and dealing with subcontractors and workers is rarely fun. Nearby residents may communicate loudly their distaste of allowing boarders. The added residential space will also result in higher property taxes, home insurance, and utility costs.

When an older parent lives in such separate quarters, his or her entering or occupying the main family home may constitute a major event. New questions arise: Why are you here at this time? When do you plan to leave? Should you be here when I give my party? Thus, the accessory apartment arrangement may require more formalized visiting rules.

ECHO (Elder Cottage Housing Opportunity) Housing

The ultimate physical separation is achieved by installing a completely self-contained housing unit (prefabricated or modular structure or manufactured home with all utility hookups) in the backyard or side yard of the single-family house. This may be impractical in most neighborhoods, however, because the lot is too small or zoning regulations prohibit the introduction of a separate residential structure on a single-family lot. These regulatory hurdles are less likely to occur in neighborhoods that already have mixed (residential and nonresidential) land uses, are in rural areas, or are, paradoxically, in very high-end neighborhoods, where the occupants already tolerate such residential buildings as the quarters of paid household staff.

The ECHO option shares many of the same advantages and disadvantages of the accessory apartment, but it has two additional drawbacks. First, when the host family no longer needs this structure, there may be no buyers, and the original costs will be lost. Second, the caregiver has to navigate between different buildings, especially if the older person has impairments demanding more supervision and hands-on care. This can make the monitoring and assistance tasks that much more inconvenient, time-consuming, and physically exhausting, especially during bad weather.

AFFORDABLE RENTAL HOUSING OPPORTUNITIES

The likelihood of seniors finding affordable rental housing in the private market depends much on their locale's rental housing costs. In the year 2004, a recently occupied mid-price two-bedroom apartment (rental units at the 40th percentile) cost $1,420 in Oakland, California, $707 in Tucson, Arizona, $752 in Cleveland, Ohio, and $580 in Gainesville, Florida. If seniors were not expected to pay more than 30 percent of their income on their rent, they would need to have annual incomes, respectively, of $56,800, $28,280, $30,080, and $23,200.

Low-income seniors who find the private rental housing market too expensive may be able to secure affordable accommodations if they apply successfully to the rent-assisted housing programs administered by federal, state, or local governments. Typically, eligible households (those headed by people ages 62 and older) are not expected to pay more than 30 percent of their adjusted annual income, which is primarily their earned and asset income, minus an amount allowed for certain expenses (U.S. Department of Housing and Urban Development, 2003a).

Most government-sponsored health and social programs determine who is poor by comparing their incomes to federal poverty thresholds that vary by household size, but not by location. In contrast, most government-assisted rental housing programs determine eligibility by whether households of particular sizes have incomes that are sufficiently below the median family income of the local area (metropolitan area or non-metropolitan county).

Eligible households usually must have an income that is below 80 percent of the area's median income. Some housing programs target seniors with extremely low incomes, below 30 percent of their area's median income, while others consider households eligible if they have incomes below 50 percent of their area's median income. Because some places are more expensive to live in than others, a household might be considered poor in one place but not in another (National Low Income Housing Coalition, 2003). An older person living alone, for example, satisfying the very low income eligibility threshold limit in the cities cited earlier, could have an income as high as $29,000 in Oakland, $14,200 in Tucson, $21,000 in Cleveland, and $18,250 in Gainesville.

A variety of federal, state, and local government programs offer affordable rental housing, and most are administered by HUD. Finding a suitable apartment can be a daunting task, however. In some communities, seniors could be on a waiting list for years. It is useful to distinguish among the different types of rental housing programs: Public (Local) Housing; Tenant Based Section 8 Housing; Section 202 Housing and the Section 515 Program; the Low Income Housing Tax Credit Program; and State, County, and City Affordable Housing Programs (Golant, 2003; Kochera, 2001, 2002b; U.S. Department of Housing and Urban Development, 2003a).

Public Housing

This is the oldest subsidized housing program in the United States. County- or city-based Public (Local) Housing Authorities own and operate rental buildings that charge lower rents (project-based subsidized rental units). People ages 62 and older occupy approximately one-third (1.1 million) of these apartments. Key factors when considering this option include:

- Some buildings are older and run down and not in the best of neighborhoods.
- Families of all ages occupy most buildings, and the older person must consider the pros and cons of living among younger families with children.
- Some buildings are not well maintained.
- Some buildings are dedicated to seniors, but the apartments are very small.
- Seniors-only buildings are more likely to have service coordinators on staff, persons who assist seniors in finding the home and community-based services they need.

Tenant-Based Section 8

Public Housing Authorities also administer the Housing Choice Voucher program (the merged Section 8 Certificate and Voucher programs), referred to as *tenant-based assisted housing*, which makes it possible for eligible low-income applicants to afford rental housing available in the private market. They receive financial assistance in the form of a rent subsidy (the sum is actually paid directly to the property owner) valued roughly at the difference between what applicants can afford (i.e., 30 percent of their income) and the market rent of an apartment (within 90 percent to 110 percent of HUD fair housing rent guidelines). Age 62 and over households occupy roughly 15 percent of the 1.4 million subsidized units in this program. Key considerations are:

- In higher-priced rental housing markets with a low vacancy rate, it is often difficult for seniors to find apartments that charge a low enough rent that would qualify under this program.
- Tenants of all ages will often occupy these apartment buildings, and seniors may find such mixed-age buildings undesirable.
- Because of the mixed ages of their tenants, seniors in these buildings are less likely to enjoy the benefits of service coordinators, supportive services, or accessible design features.

Affordable, Privately Owned and Managed, Multifamily Buildings (Section 202 Housing)

A variety of HUD programs have encouraged the construction of rental projects available to households with low incomes (80 percent or less of their area's median income). They are variously owned by for-profits and non-profits, the latter often faith-based organizations. One such highly lauded program is named Section 202. Section 202 is restricted to nonprofit organizations and specifically targets low-income seniors. Age 62 and over households occupy just over half of the over 1.6 million subsidized units in all these HUD programs. Some of these seniors-only buildings may be more attractive to some seniors because:

- families with children will not occupy them;
- the buildings are more likely to have service coordinators on staff, community space for social and recreational facilities, on-site meal programs, housekeeping services, and transportation assistance;
- the buildings have security systems—front, door, and "in apartment" call system.

However, the more attractive buildings are likely to have the longest waiting lists. For example, Section 202 programs have nine applicants for every vacant unit.

The Section 515 Program

This program is administered by the Rural Housing Service (formerly known as Farmers Home Administration), part of the Department of Agriculture. It offers low-rent apartments in rural areas to households with low incomes (80 percent or less of area's median income). Age 62 and older households occupy roughly 42 percent of its more than 450,000 rental units. Seniors considering this type of housing should be aware that:

- these buildings may be less geographically accessible to the medical and shopping needs of seniors because they are located in rural America;
- many of these projects are very small and there is sometimes no on-site manager for older occupants to report building-related problems;
- these buildings often lack design features or staffing that could be helpful to more frail seniors.

The Low Income Housing Tax Credit Program

Many new affordable rental units are produced under this program, which is typically administered by a state's housing finance agency. Households earning up to 60 percent of their area's median income are eligible. Older households occupy roughly one-quarter of its more than 433,000 units (Kochera, 2002b). Key considerations:

- Most properties in this program have an average waiting list of eight months.

218

- Housing projects targeted to elderly occupants, rather than mixed-age occupants, are more likely to have special design accessibility features in their units.
- Projects vary considerably as to whether they offer services to seniors such as transportation, group meals, or housekeeping.
- Over 42 percent of the properties for seniors are located in rural areas.

State, County, and City Affordable Housing Programs

A variety of other state and local affordable housing programs, particularly federal block grant programs, will fund the building of new affordable rental units. They will be more available in some states and communities than others.

ACTIVE ADULT COMMUNITIES

Developers market active adult communities (AAC, also called retirement communities) to seniors who would enjoy living in a planned community that offers organized leisure and recreation activities. The community's responsibility for the outside and inside maintenance of the units is also a plus. Even as they downplay this aspect, developers design these communities primarily for seniors, but the current practice is to leave off the "retirement" label. Children are welcome, but usually only as temporary guests, and some communities even have specially designated recreation facilities such as swimming pools for this younger group (Suchman, 2001).

Typical occupants of AACs are persons in their late 50s through early 70s who are healthy and have active lifestyles with no significant impairments. Married couples predominate, but the percentages of divorced, single, or widowed occupants are on the rise. These seniors tend to be more affluent, and many have sold their previous homes and are able to pay cash for their smaller, but often luxuriously designed, new dwellings. For the less well-off, cooperative-owned units, attached row housing, or manufactured homes are available.

At one end of the spectrum are smaller residential subdivisions or high-rise apartment and condominium complexes that offer scaled-down recreation amenities, such as clubhouses and health clubs, hobby areas, tennis courts, or swimming pools. At the other end of the spectrum are the large, self-contained, recreation-rich retirement complexes—truly towns—such as Sun City, Leisure Village, or The Villages, in states such as Arizona, California, and Florida that tens of thousands of seniors call home. These residential complexes can be spread over thousands of acres, offer recreational activities that make the social programs of even the most luxurious cruise ship look meager, and offer all the establishments and services found in a larger town or small city. Although they come with such traditional amenities as golf courses, tennis courts, clubhouses, and swimming pools, the newer communities also offer fitness centers, spas, computer and investment clubs, educational classes, softball leagues, movie theaters, jogging and bicycle trails, water aerobic classes, cross-country skiing and ice-skating (in the Midwest or Northeast, of course). In these larger communities, the means of transportation is also distinctive: In one large Florida retirement town, 9 out of 10 residents get around in golf carts.

Although these communities are often associated with the warmer climates of Florida, Arizona, Texas, Nevada, and California, seniors can easily find them in northeastern and midwestern states, such as New Jersey, Michigan, Virginia, Illinois, and New York. These developments are targeting retirees who seek to remain in their familiar states and communities—despite the unfavorable weather—to be close to family, friends, and their favorite clubs. Many states seeking the positive economic impact of this age set—Mississippi, North Carolina, South Carolina, Alabama, Maine, and Tennessee—are now aggressively marketing their communities to older consumers (Golant, 2002a).

These places are more attractive to certain groups of seniors than others. Their security and predictable future are certainly pluses. Along with their security guards, these planned communities have strict population and land-use controls. They will also appeal to seniors who are not enamored with all the trappings of a youth-oriented society or who dislike comparing their looks and vitality with 20- and 30-year-olds. Rather, they enjoy being with others with similar life histories, backgrounds, and interests.

However attractive this type of community may be to some, it is obviously not for everyone. Some seniors cannot easily pull up stakes from where they have lived for a long time. Also, some people get bored engaging in the same leisure activities every day and interacting with the same people. Other seniors seek neighborhoods where they can live among younger people. Then there are seniors whose circumstances change while living in a recreation-focused community. The onset of a debilitating health condition or the loss of a spouse may suddenly make it unattractive.

Choosing between a Multi-Age Setting and a Seniors-Only Community

Clearly, there are benefits to each type of development—a community peopled with a variety of ages, possibly including children, or a retirement community for seniors only. It is important for you to advise your senior clients who are considering a move to carefully weigh the pros and cons of each housing option against their personal desires. Among the items to consider:

- individual values, preferences, and desires
- hobbies and other interests
- religious or spiritual practices and communities
- health and future possible medical needs
- access to transportation
- financial resources
- access to and types of support from family, friends, and others

PLANNED SENIOR APARTMENT, INDEPENDENT LIVING, AND CONGREGATE LIVING FACILITIES

Tired of dealing with a larger house and no longer tied to their current community, some seniors downsize and look for residences that are easier to maintain. Some will head to suburban subdivisions or rural locales occupied by persons of all ages. Others, however, will look to planned residential developments targeted to seniors.

These seniors are still independent and ambulatory, but they may have minor physical impairments and health problems. They no longer want responsibility for the usual home and household chores, and they are attracted by the prospects of new social opportunities to combat their loneliness in a secure environment (Brecht, 2002).

Historically, nonprofit sponsors usually owned these facilities, but since the early 1980s, developments by for-profit sponsors are more common. High-rise apartment complexes, small patio homes, and cottages on small lots may all populate this category, and some residential complexes will contain a mix of these building types. All types of tenant arrangements are possible. Rental apartments may offer monthly or yearly contracts, but condominiums and cooperatives are increasingly popular.

When they were first developed, the services of planned living settings were often limited to building and grounds maintenance. Later versions offered a fuller array of services, including housekeeping, security, demand-responsive transportation, planned social and recreational activities, exercise fitness centers, and wellness checks. In other complexes, it is usual to find a common dining room where all the residents of the building can eat together. The presence of this communal space is sometimes the basis for labeling these options as congregate living as opposed to independent living facilities or senior apartments, the latter labels being preferred by the private sector.

Some of these residential complexes may accommodate a frailer group of seniors than others and offer more supportive services if they are in states with less stringent licensing care criteria. On the other hand, liability and insurance concerns may discourage a facility from offering such supportive services. This category also includes some affordable rental properties with supportive services that are funded by government-assisted housing programs.

The options of planned living residences vary in their size and luxuriousness. Some will offer scaled-down housing accommodations (smaller rooms, kitchenettes), but higher-end buildings can offer relatively large two- or three-bedroom apartments with all possible amenities. The number of units in these facilities can vary dramatically, ranging from 20 to well over 300 units, and the architectural aesthetics can vary, as well. Monthly rents can range from less than $1,000 to more than $5,000.

From the outside, these planned residential alternatives are generally indistinguishable from other housing. Inside, their communal areas may consist of a simple large room where meals are served and occasional lectures are held. Additionally, they can include libraries, craft rooms, and spacious and well-appointed common areas for formal dining, lectures, and social

events. Office space may be available for the activities of social workers or case managers. The apartments may contain design features sensitive to the needs of an older population, such as grab bars in the bathrooms and kitchens designed with safety and ease of use in mind, and including some type of emergency alert system—pull cords or emergency response systems.

A final distinction is important: Some of these properties stand by themselves, while others are connected to adjoining buildings that offer assisted living and nursing care. Seniors who seek accommodations for the here and now will prefer stand-alone facilities. Alternatively, seniors who feel comfortable knowing that more supportive accommodations are nearby in the event of their becoming impaired may find comfort in occupying a multilevel facility.

ASSISTED LIVING FACILITIES

These facilities target seniors with physical or cognitive impairments that make it difficult for them to perform an average of two ADLs without assistance (Golant, 2004). The typical occupants of assisted living facilities are women living alone in their late 70s or 80s. These shelter and care options are known by different and confusing labels: residential care facilities, personal care homes, catered living facilities, retirement homes, adult care homes, board and care homes, domiciliary care homes, rest homes, community residences, and sheltered care. Since the 1980s, however, the private sector has favored the *assisted living* label to distinguish its professionally managed residences from the board and care option serving poor seniors (as discussed a little later in this chapter). Most assisted living facilities are owned by for-profits or are publicly held. Most for-profit facilities are stand-alone and for seniors only, while nonprofit assisted living facilities are usually part of an age continuum. State governments increasingly recognize assisted living facilities as a distinct seniors housing category in their regulations (Mollica, 2002).

Eligibility for Assisted Living Facilities

To properly advise your senior clients, it is important that you know about the state laws and regulations that determine eligibility for being accepted into an assisted living facility.

In addition, you should tell your senior clients who are considering moving to an assisted living facility that it is extremely important for them to read and understand all the terms and conditions of the facility's contract. They would also benefit from legal and tax advice before they sign the contract.

Assisted living facilities offer all the services—meals, housekeeping, and planned social and recreational activities—of congregate living facilities. What distinguishes this alternative is its on-site staff, who are available 24 hours, seven days a week for protective oversight to meet both the scheduled and unscheduled needs of their more frail residents. Thus, assisted living facilities distinguish themselves from most home care delivered by professional agencies that offer assistance only at scheduled fixed times and for minimum blocks of time.

Even as they need assistance with several of their everyday activities and may require some nursing services, seniors in assisted living facilities tend to be less impaired and have fewer health problems than nursing home residents. Most assisted living facilities are unable to deal with the medical conditions of residents who require continuous assistance and monitoring. Thus, they will not accept residents who need around-the-clock skilled nursing procedures or who require ongoing supervision because they get confused, wander, or have memory, judgment, or behavioral problems. Generalizations must be made carefully, however, because a growing share of assisted living facilities now accommodate persons with dementia in designated sections of their properties (Golant, 2004).

Assisted living facilities come in all sizes and range from one-story buildings to high-rises. They may be freestanding or part of a building or campus that also contains a nursing home or a congregate living facility. On average, they consist of just over 50 units (or beds). They generally appear more residential or hotel-like than nursing homes. Their accommodations typically include two-bedroom apartments or studios with kitchenettes or comfortably furnished private rooms with their own baths or showers, doors that lock, and individual temperature controls. They are likely to have grab bars in their bathrooms, some type of emergency call system, and design features sensitive to the needs of physically frail clientele, but they will eschew nursing stations, long corridors, and institution-like tile floors (Brecht, 2002; U.S. Senate Special Committee on Aging, 1999).

A unique philosophy of care also distinguishes assisted living facilities from nursing homes. Assisted living facilities seek to treat residents with dignity and respect and allow them to have more say over planning their assistance and care, and to give residents more independence and privacy without jeopardizing their safety or security.

"If You've Seen <u>One</u> Assisted Living Facility, You've Seen <u>One</u>."

An overview of the assisted living alternative is hardly enough to use in making a decision, though. You must be aware of why selecting an appropriate facility may be very difficult.

Assisted living facilities can deviate spectacularly from each other. Absent federal regulations, each state regulates its own version of this option. Within any state's guidelines, individual assisted living operators operate very different facilities.

The result is that assisted living facilities can have very different design, management, safety, and, most important, admitting standards. Some will have architectural styles and design features that resemble either upscale or bargain-rate hotels. Others will look more like nursing homes because of their hospital-like appearance and because residents must share their rooms and toilet and sink facilities. Some assisted living facilities will admit residents with frailty profiles that resemble those of nursing homes, while others will only accept or accommodate less impaired and healthier residents.

Thus, seniors and their families must make two critically important judgments:

- Ascertain whether a prospective assisted living facility will accept and continue to care for or accommodate their physical and mental impairments even if they worsen. Will an assisted living facility be their last residence or merely a temporary stop on their way to a nursing home?
- Decide whether even the most desirable stay in an assisted living facility can justify the considerable time and energy demanded by moving again (American Health Care Association, 2004; Coalition of Institutionalized Aged and Disabled & Nursing Home Community Coalition, 2003). A good source of information is CareGuide, mentioned in the Resources section at the end of the chapter.

Some seniors will have no decision to make because of this option's high costs. The 2003 monthly base fee for assisted living units averaged $2,379 (MetLife Mature Market Institute, 2003a). Potential residents must also scrutinize carefully what services are included in this base rate. Often, when residents become more impaired, the facility will charge them substantially higher monthly costs to pay for heavier duty care. Monthly fees may also increase just because of ordinary cost-of-living increases.

Be Alert to Cost Creep

The fact that costs and fees can increase over the base rate is called *cost creep*. Advise your senior clients exploring the possibility of moving into an assisted living facility to examine the facility's contract carefully to determine if it allows cost creep to occur. Seniors should seek counsel from their lawyers and tax advisors in making their final decisions. Although many assisted living facilities do *not* operate this way, other facilities do.

Most occupants will pay for the assisted living alternative out of their own pockets because Medicare, Medicaid, and many long-term care policies do not offer coverage. Some states subsidize the costs of these accommodations through their Medicaid Waiver program, but these affordable units are scarce.

Residents typically handle their costs for assisted living by one or a combination of the following:

- relying on their incomes (typically, interest on investments, Social Security, and private pensions)
- drawing on their savings (often from the earlier sale of their homes)
- receiving financial assistance from their grown children

BOARD AND CARE

The board and care residence is the poor cousin to the assisted living facility, although their names are sometimes used interchangeably. Most board and care residences are licensed under their state laws and regulations (though some states license both options under their same regulatory umbrella), and it is important for you to know what your state says about this level of care. That information will enable you to help your senior clients think through the advantages and disadvantages of this option for their particular situations.

Board and care facilities are typically smaller and offer fewer private accommodations and physical amenities (Morgan, Eckert, & Lyons, 1995). The board and care residential setting is often a large, conventional single-family house consisting of multiple bedrooms, each occupied by one person, or alternatively by two to four residents. Residents may have to share the toilet and bathroom facilities, and most activities will occur in the building's common living areas. Special design features and some type of emergency call system are often unavailable. Three or more unrelated adults—but usually fewer than 20 or 30—who pay a monthly fee or rent typically occupy these residences. It is often difficult to differentiate board and care from adult foster care homes. The latter is typically distinguished by its having fewer than three residents.

Unlike assisted living facilities, these mom-and-pop board and care facilities are less likely to be professionally managed and may not be licensed by their states. Typically, a married couple or a single person who lives on premises operates them and typically manages everything from housekeeping, meals, and laundry to the care of the residents. The professional qualifications, specialized training, or education of proprietors can vary greatly.

Older residents of board and care facilities may be relatively independent or need personal assistance and care comparable to residents of assisted living facilities. They typically have the lowest incomes and depend solely on their Social Security or their Supplemental Security Income monthly checks. The average monthly fee can be as low as $450. Operators of these facilities may receive additional financial assistance from their state governments.

CONTINUING CARE RETIREMENT COMMUNITIES

Continuing care retirement communities (CCRCs), once referred to as life-care communities, offer a full continuum of housing and services within the same community. Thus, they cater to seniors ranging from those who are relatively active to those who suffer from serious physical and mental disabilities and chronic health problems. Over the course of their CCRC stay, older residents could conceivably occupy a rental apartment in a congregate housing facility, a room or apartment in an assisted living facility, and a bed in a skilled nursing home. As a senior housing expert put it, "Visitors who tour the different levels of shelter and care found in a well-run, full-service CCRC often feel as if they are watching the aging process unfold before them" (Golant, 1992, p. 26).

These various levels of shelter and care are housed on different floors or wings of a single high-rise building or in physically adjacent buildings (garden apartments, cottages, duplexes, mid- and low-rise buildings) or spread out in a campus setting. Some CCRCs are especially luxurious and resemble upscale ski resorts.

The average CCRC contains just over 330 units, made up of 231 independent or congregate living units, 34 assisted living beds, and 70 skilled nursing home beds. On average, an older resident will live in the congregate living facility for just over three years, the assisted living facility for one year, and the skilled nursing facility for nine months (ASHA, 2002).

CCRC Services

Seniors are attracted to the CCRC option because of its promise that for the rest of their lives they will receive appropriate personal assistance and nursing care in attractive residential settings, regardless of the current seriousness of their impairments or chronic health problems. Thus, they (or their family members) will not have to conduct a frantic search for an assisted living facility or a nursing home to cope with unexpected declines in their health or functioning. Indeed, CCRC residents often indicate that not being a burden on their children or friends was an important reason for their residency (Hunt, 2003; Krout, Moen, Holmes, Oggins, & Bowen, 2002).

A recent trend among CCRCs is to offer more apartment services to reduce housing moves within the community and better meet the desires of residents. Many CCRCs are downsizing their skilled nursing staff and increasing home-delivered services.

Three Types of CCRC Contracts

Residents typically sign contracts that specify the shelter arrangements, residential services, personal and health care, and nursing care that they are guaranteed during their stay in the CCRC. These agreements also specify the present costs to the residents of living in its community and using its resources, the conditions under which costs may be increased, and the conditions under which residents must transfer among its levels of care. These contracts are designed to protect the rights of the older residents, but they also give the owners of CCRCs considerable influence as to what long-term care benefits older residents receive.

The American Seniors Housing Association (ASHA) distinguishes three principal contract types: life care (also known as extensive or all-inclusive); modified; and fee-for-service (ASHA, 2002).

These contracts reflect the differences in the way CCRCs charge for personal assistance and nursing care and the extent to which they guarantee the availability of this care without additional costs to residents. In practice, CCRCs will often offer residents contract arrangements that represent a blend of these three contract types. A very small percentage of CCRCs also offer their residents the opportunity to own their units. This is an attempt to capture that market of seniors who consider real estate ownership a critical prerequisite for occupying a CCRC.

Life Care and Modified Contracts

CCRCs offering either life care or modified contracts guarantee their residents shelter, residential services, and amenities along with personal assistance and nursing care for the rest of their lives in return for an initial entrance fee and a monthly payment schedule. CCRCs usually offer these contracts to seniors who initially occupy their congregate or independent living units. Entrance fees vary greatly from a low of $50,000 to well over $500,000. Monthly fees can range from less than $1,000 to more than $5,000. The entry fees may be nonrefundable or partially refundable depending on the length of the resident's stay.

Life care and modified contracts differ financially in an important way:

- Under the life care contract, residents who move to the assisted living or nursing home accommodations of the CCRC continue to pay a monthly fee similar to what they had for their independent living accommodations. CCRCs agree to increase these fees only to compensate for normal operating cost increases.
- Under the modified contract, when residents move to a higher level of care, the CCRC agrees to charge the independent living rate for only some specified time period, after which residents must pay either a full or a discounted per diem rate.

You should be aware that, while some seniors are currently living under life care contracts, *new issuances of life care contracts are disappearing* because it is a difficult business model to manage effectively.

Fee-for-Service Contracts

Fee-for-service contracts often do not require an entrance fee. Under this plan, residents receive priority or guaranteed admission to the CCRC's higher levels of care, but they are not entitled to any discounted health care or assisted living services. Rather, on entering the CCRC's assisted living facility or nursing home, they pay the regular and usually higher per diem market rate. Older residents admitted directly into a CCRC's assisted living facility or nursing home would typically sign fee-for-service contracts.

The payment of an entry fee usually does not give the older resident any ownership rights to a living unit. Rather, it is more akin to a long-term care insurance premium that guarantees the resident the right to receive the benefits associated with the facility's assisted living and nursing care accommodations when he or she needs them and at some specified price. CCRCs typically rely on the entrance fees to pay for their debt financing and operating expenses and to build up financial reserves to cover their future costs of providing services and care.

Differences Among CCRCs: Types of Assistance and Care

The types of assistance and care residents are entitled to in return for their monthly fee may not be obvious or simply related to the contract type. How much is charged will depend on the operator's cost of running the facility, the luxuriousness of the accommodations, the size of the occupied unit or room, and whether one or two persons occupy a unit. It will also depend on what residential, assisted, and nursing care services the CCRC includes in its base plan. Some CCRCs, for example, will charge residents extra to receive more hands-on or skilled care to address more serious impairments or health problems. CCRCs will also differ as to whether their entrance fee or their monthly fees include medical coverage distinct from long-term care services such as personal assistance and nursing services. Medical reimbursements, for example, may be limited to routine checkups and minor medical treatments.

Most CCRCs require seniors who initially enter their independent or congregate living facilities to undergo a medical examination to assess their physical and mental status. They may also require prospective residents to have Medicare Part A and B coverage and sometimes Medigap coverage. (See chapter 19 for more information about Medicare.) Selected pre-existing ADL impairments or health conditions may cause a CCRC to reject some seniors as residents in their independent facilities. Residents will also be required to prove they have sufficient assets and income to cover the entry and monthly fees. Some CCRCs will prefer residents with certain ethnic, religious, or fraternal order affiliations.

Different state and federal laws may regulate the assisted living facilities and nursing homes of CCRCs. CCRCs often come under the purview of their state's department of insurance because of their unique financial and legal features. Some CCRCs are accredited by the Continuing Care Accreditation Commission; this accreditation guarantees the facilities have met certain minimum shelter, care, and financial standards. The absence of such accreditation, however, does not necessarily imply that they have not met these standards.

CCRC Issues for Seniors

The unique financial and lifetime commitments that seniors must make to the CCRC ownership and management require them to be especially vigilant. Specifically, seniors should consider the following questions (Golant, 1998):

- Would seniors be comfortable living with residents like themselves, and would the everyday rhythm of activities in the CCRC be to their liking?

- Are seniors familiar with the record of accomplishment of the organizations (which may be multiple, separate entities) that own and manage the facility?

- Do seniors have confidence in the financial solvency of the CCRC and its ability to keep its shelter and care promises (insurance benefits) without inordinately raising its fees because it has failed to estimate accurately its future long-term care obligations?

- Are seniors fully cognizant of how the CCRC makes its shelter and care resident transfer decisions? They must be clear under what circumstances such a move might be only temporary. For example, when might a stay in a nursing home be shortened and the residents allowed to return to independent living units if they have recovered from an earlier health problem? This is important because of the growing trend among seniors to delay as long as possible their permanent relocation from their independent living quarters to assisted living or nursing home accommodations.

- Are seniors knowledgeable about the circumstances under which it will be possible for CCRC management to deliver personal care and home health services into their congregate facility apartments, so that they can exercise their preferences for aging with choice?

- Will seniors have effective means of communicating dissatisfactions or concerns to the management?

- What about a worst-case scenario? What if, at some future point, seniors have difficulty paying their monthly fees? How will the CCRC likely respond? Does it, for example, have any contingency funding to deal with this situation?

The bottom line: Before signing a CCRC contract, seniors should receive counsel from their accountant and lawyer.

NURSING HOMES

Nursing homes (also known as nursing facilities and skilled nursing homes) provide shelter and care for seniors (9 out of every 10 nursing home residents) who have more serious health problems, functional impairments, or cognitive deficits and who often require 24-hour skilled nursing care. On average, their residents need at least some assistance with an average of 3.8 ADLs—notably bathing, dressing, toileting, and transferring. More than 56 percent of the residents will be cognitively impaired (for example, dementia as from a stroke or Alzheimer's disease), almost 50 percent will be wheelchair bound, and 6 percent will be bedfast. Residents admitted to nursing homes typically have more than one health problem, most frequently a combination of cardiovascular disease, mental and cognitive disorders, and disorders of the endocrine system, usually diabetes or hypothyroidism (American Health Care Association, 2001).

The nursing home population has become older and sicker (Sahyoun, Pratt, Lentzner, Dey, & Robinson, 2001). The average age of admission is now 82.6 years. More than 51 percent of the residents are age 85 and over. They need help with a higher average number of ADLs and have multiple health problems. Nursing homes have responded by adding specialized wings and levels of care to accommodate residents with Alzheimer's disease and those in need of special types of rehabilitation therapies, subacute care, and hospice services. An increasing percentage of nursing home residents are minorities (7 percent), with African Americans now having a higher rate of nursing home admission than whites (American Health Care Association, 2001).

Elderly Americans have reduced their use of nursing home care because of the greater availability of noninstitutional group shelter and care options, their strong distaste for this option, and because they can cope with their frailty needs in their own homes (Bishop, 1999). It is, however, a more likely option for seniors who live alone, cannot depend on family, or cannot afford costly professional care. Home-based caregiving demands may simply become overwhelming if an older person requires the help of two persons when transferring between bed and toilet or needs continuous nursing care. Aging with choice may also be precluded when persons with Alzheimer's disease exhibit behaviors such as hitting, wandering, or putting themselves in danger, for example by touching a hot stove.

Just fewer than 5 percent of seniors now occupy nursing homes, ranging from 1.1 percent of 65- to 74-year-olds to just over 18 percent of the 85-plus group. On average, women enter a nursing home around age 80 and men around age 75. The average length of stay is about 2.4 years. About half of the older women will stay for less than a year, while 31 percent will stay for 1 to 5 years and 15 percent will stay from 5 to 10 years. From a more realistic lifetime risk perspective, the proportion of age 65-plus elders who will eventually be nursing home occupants ranges from 39 percent to 49 percent. Importantly, the nursing home stay may not be permanent. Nursing home discharge data reveal that 30 percent recuperated and went back to the community (short-term rehabilitations after a hospital stay), 36 percent moved to a hospital or another nursing home, 25 percent died, and 9 percent left for destinations unknown (American Health Care Association, 2001).

For-profit companies now own the majority (67 percent) of nursing homes, and well over half are owned or operated by a national multifacility chain. About 1 in 10 is operated by a hospital. Though the average nursing facility has 108 beds, the numbers can vary dramatically. Twenty-five percent have fewer than 100 beds, 52 percent have 100 to 199 beds, and 19 percent have 200 beds or more.

Nursing home care is expensive. In the United States in 2003, the average daily rate for a private nursing home bed was just more than $181, or more than $66,000 a year. For a semiprivate room the daily rate was just more than $158, or almost $58,000 a year. These charges vary dramatically across cities and states, however, and the most expensive nursing homes charge more than $600 a day—more than $220,000 a year (MetLife Mature Market Institute, 2003b).

Because of their high costs, it becomes crucial whether nursing home beds are eligible to be filled by recipients of Medicare (discussed in chapter 19) and Medicaid (discussed in chapter 20). About 45 percent of the beds are certified for both the Medicaid and the Medicare programs, just over 3 percent are certified for Medicare only, 46 percent are certified for Medicaid only, and 6 percent are uncertified for either federal program. As testimony to the importance of the Medicaid program as a financing source, more than two-thirds of the residents in nursing homes now receive Medicaid, only 9 percent are Medicare beneficiaries, and 24 percent pay through private or other payer sources (for example, private insurance plans) (American Health Care Association, 2001).

Even though nursing homes are the most regulated of all shelter and care options available to American seniors, and their overall quality has improved, evidence of lax enforcement and poor quality care persists. Nursing homes have suffered from lower Medicaid reimbursement rates, understaffing (especially among nurses), high staff turnover, and in some states, such as Florida, from high insurance liability costs. Evidence suggests that for-profit homes, especially chain-owned homes, and those with more Medicaid residents have lower registered nurse and licensed practical nurse staffing levels and overall deliver a lower quality of care than nonprofit facilities (Centers for Medicare & Medicaid Services, 2004; Harrington, Woolhandler, Mullan, Carrillo, & Himmelstein, 2001).

Families and professionals can now readily obtain information on the Internet about the size and ownership, patient profiles, staffing characteristics, and quality of care indicators of specific nursing homes. Medline Plus, a service of the National Institutes of Health, compiles and furnishes that information. See the Resources section at the end of this chapter

TRENDS IN NURSING HOME CARE

Use of nursing homes is declining. This trend is fueled by increasing availability of home and community-based services (discussed in chapter 9), assisted living, in-home technology that makes it easier for physically and cognitively impaired seniors to remain in their homes, and society's general preference that we remain in our own homes as we age.

Some nursing homes are attempting to change their appearance and philosophy of care. The most publicized effort is the Eden Alternative, developed by Dr. William Thomas. It aims to eliminate residents' feelings of loneliness, helplessness and boredom—the "three plagues." Along with changing the physical ambience of nursing homes by including plants, animals, birds, and visits from children, an Eden Alternative nursing home promotes a more flexible management style with greater staff empowerment (especially among nurses aides and housekeepers) and advocates less rigid scheduling of activities and care plans, which encourages a stronger atmosphere of spontaneity.

In the spirit of the Eden Alternative, new nursing home initiatives are springing up throughout the country. Most notably, in 1997 a group calling themselves "nursing home pioneers" started a movement called the Pioneer

Network to change the culture of nursing homes. The group included nursing home reform leaders from around the United States such as Dr. Thomas.

The Pioneer Network envisions a culture of aging that is life-affirming, satisfying, humane, and meaningful wherever seniors live. This approach is called *culture change*, which expresses the move to change the way seniors are treated whether in nursing homes or other residences. It is a major step toward providing comfortable living and humane care for seniors, particularly frail seniors.

In its first seven years, the Pioneer Network has produced results throughout the country (Pioneer Network, 2004):

- Nine states have started "culture change coalitions" composed of long-term care professionals and others working to change the way seniors are treated and cared for. Many others are forming coalitions.

- Several multifacility organizations have committed their homes to culture change. Among them are Apple Health Care, Pinon Management, AGE Institute Holdings, Inc., and The Evangelical Lutheran Good Samaritan Society.

- The Center for Medicare and Medicaid Services has produced a $2\frac{1}{2}$-hour video about the Pioneer Network values, principles, and practices.

- Nursing home providers who are implementing cultural change are reporting lower turnover of direct care workers and are reporting positive outcomes in resident quality of care and quality of life.

Housing: Summary

As a CSA working with seniors on housing issues, you have three difficult tasks:

- You must fully understand the unique circumstances of your clients and their housing situations in terms of both deficiencies and virtues.

- You must be fully aware of the housing options that are available, their features, their costs, and their drawbacks.

- Last, and most challenging, you must put these two complicated pieces of the puzzle together and help your clients find an appropriate residential match. For you, this often means knowing the resources that are available in your area and where you and your client can turn for assistance. The Resources section of this chapter has many sources to investigate.

References

American Health Care Association. (2001). *Facts and trends: The nursing facility sourcebook.* Washington, DC: American Health Care Association.

American Health Care Association. (2004). *Planning Ahead: A consumer's guide to assisted living facilities.* Washington, DC: American Health Care Association, National Center for Assisted Living. Retrieved June 28, 2004, from http://www.longtermcareliving.com/planning_ahead/assisted/assisted1.htm

ASHA (American Seniors Housing Association). (2002). *The state of seniors housing, 2002.* Washington, DC: National Investment Center.

Baer, D. (1998). *Awareness and popularity of property tax relief programs.* Washington, DC: AARP. Retrieved June 28, 2004, from http://research.aarp.org/econ/9803_tax_1.html

Bishop, C. E. (1999). Where are the missing elders? The decline in nursing home use, 1985 and 1995. *Health Affairs, 18*(4), 146–155.

Brecht, S. B. (2002). *Analyzing seniors' housing markets.* Washington, DC: Urban Land Institute.

Census Bureau. (2001). *Current housing reports, series H151/95-1, supplement to the American Housing Survey for the United States in 1995.* Washington, DC: U.S. Government Printing Office.

Centers for Medicare & Medicaid Services. (2004). *Guide to choosing a nursing home.* Baltimore, MD: Centers for Medicare & Medicaid Services. Retrieved June 28, 2004, from http://www.medicare.gov/publications/pubs/pdf/02174.pdf

Coalition of Institutionalized Aged and Disabled, & Nursing Home Community Coalition. (2003). *Thinking of moving to an assisted living residence? A guidebook for finding choice and independence.* New York: Coalition of Institutionalized Aged and Disabled. Retrieved June 28, 2004, from http://www.nhccnys.org/news/documents/alguidepotresfinal.pdf

Federal Interagency Forum on Aging-Related Statistics. (2000). *Older Americans 2000: Key indicators of well-being.* Washington, DC: U.S. Government Printing Office.

Golant, S. M. (1984). *A place to grow old: The meaning of environment in old age.* New York: Columbia University Press.

Golant, S. M. (1991). Matching congregate housing settings with a diverse elderly population: Research and theoretical considerations. In L. W. Kaye A. and Monk (Ed.), *Congregate housing for the elderly: Theoretical, policy, and programmatic perspectives* (pp. 21–38). New York: Haworth Press.

Golant, S. M. (1992). *Housing America's elderly: Many possibilities, few choices.* Newbury Park, CA: Sage Publications.

Golant, S. M. (1994). Aging in place or moving: The multiple meanings of retirees' housing. In A. Monk (Ed.), *The Columbia retirement handbook.* New York: Columbia University Press.

Golant, S. M. (1998). Continuing care retirement communities. In W. van Vliet (Ed.), *The encyclopedia of housing* (pp. 86-88). Thousand Oaks, CA: Sage Publications.

Golant, S. M. (2002a). Deciding where to live: The emerging residential settlement patterns of retired Americans. *Generations, 26*(11), 66–73.

Golant, S. M. (2002b). The housing problems of the future elderly population, Appendix G-1. In Commission on Affordable Housing and Health Facility Needs for Seniors in the 21st Century (Ed.), *A quiet crisis in America: A report to Congress* (pp. 189–370). Washington, DC: U.S. Government Printing Office.

Golant, S. M. (2003). Government-assisted rental accommodations: Should they accommodate older homeowners with unmet needs? *Maine Policy Review, 12*(2), 36–57.

Golant, S. M. (2004). Do impaired seniors with health care needs occupy U.S. assisted living facilities? An analysis of six national studies. *Journal of Gerontology: Social Sciences, 59B*(2), S68–S79.

233

Harrington, C., Woolhandler, S., Mullan, J., Carrillo, H., & Himmelstein, D. U. (2001). Does investor ownership of nursing homes compromise the quality of care? *American Journal of Public Health, 91*(9), 1452–1455.

Hunt, B. (2003). *Continuing care retirement communities.* Philadelphia, PA: Xlibris Corporation.

Hyatt, W. S. (2001). Legal considerations. In D. R. Suchman (Ed.), *Developing active adult retirement communities* (pp. 139-161). Washington, DC: Urban Land Institute.

Kochera, A. (2001). *A summary of federal rental housing programs, Fact Sheet #85.* Washington, DC: AARP.

Kochera, A. (2002a). *Falls among seniors and the role of the home: An analysis of cost, incidence, and potential savings from home modification.* Washington, DC: AARP, Public Policy Institute. Retrieved June 28, 2004, from http://research.aarp.org/il/ib56_falls.html

Kochera, A. (2002b). *Serving the affordable housing needs of older low-income renters: A survey of low-income housing tax credit properties.* Washington, DC: AARP.

Krout, J. A., Moen, P., Holmes, H. H., Oggins, J., & Bowen, N. (2002). Reasons for relocation to a continuing care retirement community. *The Journal of Applied Gerontology, 21*(2), 236–256.

Longino, C. F., Jr. (2002). The geographical mobility of retirees. *Contemporary Gerontology, 9*(1), 2–6.

MetLife Mature Market Institute. (2003a). *The MetLife market survey of assisted living costs.* Westport, CT: MetLife Mature Market Institute. Retrieved June 28, 2004, from http://www.metlife.com/WPSAssets/16670870001065792597V1F2003 Assisted Living Survey.pdf

MetLife Mature Market Institute. (2003b). *The MetLife market survey of nursing home and home care costs.* Westport, CT: MetLife Mature Market Institute. Retrieved June 28, 2004, from http://www.openminds.com/indres/metlifehomesurvey.pdf

Mollica, R. (2002). *State Assisted Living Policy: 2002.* Portland, ME: National Academy for State Health Policy.

Morgan, L. A., Eckert, J. K., & Lyons, S. M. (1995). *Small board-and-care homes: Residential care in transition.* Baltimore: Johns Hopkins Press.

National Conference of State Legislatures. (2002). *A guide to property taxes: Property tax relief.* Washington, DC: National Conference of State Legislatures.

National Low Income Housing Coalition. (2003). *Out of reach 2003: America's housing wage climbs.* Washington, DC: National Low Income Housing Coalition. http://www.nlihc.org/oor2003/

Pioneer Network. (2004). Values, vision, and mission. Retrieved June 28, 2004, from http://www.pioneernetwork.net/index.cfm/fuseaction/content.display/page/Values VisionMission.cfm

Pynoos, J., Liebig, P., Overton, J., & Calvert, E. (1997). The delivery of home modification and repair services. In S. Lanspery & J. Hyde (Eds.), *Staying put: Adapting the places instead of the people* (pp. 171–192). Amityville, NY: Baywood Publishing Co.

Regnier, V. (2002). *Design for assisted living: Guidelines for housing the physically and mentally frail.* New York: Wiley.

Sahyoun, N. R., Pratt, L. A., Lentzner, H., Dey, A., & Robinson, K. N. (2001, March). The changing profile of nursing home residents: 1985–1997. *Aging Trends, No. 4.*

Hyattsville, MD: National Center for Health Statistics. Retrieved June 28, 2004, from http://www.cdc.gov/nchs/data/agingtrends/04nursin.pdf

Schachter, J. (2004). Geographical Mobility: 2002 to 2003. *Current Population Reports, P20-549*, 1–15. Retrieved June 28, 2004, from http://www.census.gov/prod/2004pubs/p20-549.pdf

Suchman, D. R. (2001). *Developing active adult retirement communities.* Washington, DC: The Urban Land Institute.

U.S. Department of Housing and Urban Development. (1998). *Fair Housing Act design manual: A manual to assist designers and builders in meeting the accessibility requirements of the Fair Housing Act.* Washington, DC: U.S. Department of Housing and Urban Development. Retrieved June 28, 2004, from http://www.huduser.org/publications/destech/fairhousing.html

U.S. Department of Housing and Urban Development. (2003a). *Trends in worst case needs for housing, 1978–1999: A report to Congress on worst case housing needs.* Washington, DC: U.S. Department of Housing and Urban Development. Retrieved June 28, 2004, from http://www.huduser.org/Publications/PDF/trends.pdf

U.S. Department of Housing and Urban Development. (2003b). Fair housing—It's your right. Retrieved June 28, 2004, from http://www.hud.gov/offices/fheo/FHLaws/yourrights.cfm

U.S. Senate Special Committee on Aging. (1999). *Shopping for assisted living: What customers need to make the best buy. Hearings before the Special Committee on Aging.* Washington, DC: U.S. Government Printing Office.

Wylde, M., Baron-Robbins, & Clark, S. (1994). *Building for a lifetime: The design and construction of fully accessible homes.* Newtown, CT: Taunton Books & Videos.

Resources

Suggested Reading

CareGuide. *Guide to assisted living facilities: What is an assisted living facility?* http://www.careguide.com/modules.php?op=modload&name=CG_Resources&file=article&sid=882

Medline Plus, Nursing Homes, http://www.nlm.nih.gov/medlineplus/nursinghomes.html

Services

AARP, http://www.aarp.org

American Association of Homes and Services for the Aging (AAHSA), http://www2.aahsa.org

American Seniors Housing Association (ASHA) http://www.seniorshousing.org

Assisted Living Federation of America, http://www.alfa.org/

Assistguide, http://www.assistguide.com. Connecting senior and disability markets through innovative online systems.

Consumer Consortium on Assisted Living, http://www.ccal.org

The Continuing Care Accreditation Commission, http://www.ccaconline.org

The Eden Alternative, http://www.edenalt.com/welcome.htm

Elderweb, http://www.elderweb.com

National Association of Home Builders, http://www.nahb.org

National Center for Assisted Living, http://www.ncal.org

National Cooperative Bank Development Corporation, http://www.ncbdc.org

National Council on the Aging, http://www.ncoa.org

National Investment Center for Seniors Housing & Care Industries, http://www.nic.org

National Multi Housing Council, http://www.nmhc.org

Pioneer Network, http://www.pioneernetwork.net

Chapter 9

Home and Community-Based Services

In 1984 Dotty Strum, age 72, fell while getting out of the shower and broke her hip. The surgery to pin her hip back together went well, but her recovery was complicated by diabetes. After Dotty left the hospital, she moved to the home of her daughter, Brenda Jones, so Brenda and her own daughters could care for her full time. This meant that Brenda's 26-year-old daughter had to give up her bedroom and move into her teenage sister's room. After a couple of months, living in close quarters became unbearable for the Jones family, and with great reluctance, Brenda moved Dotty to a nursing home, where she died six months later.

In 2003 Brenda, by then 73, fell while carrying groceries into the kitchen and shattered her hip. Her surgery went well, but, like her mother, her recovery was complicated by diabetes. Brenda's rehabilitation, however, has been quite different than her mother's was almost 20 years earlier.

Because she had access to services based in her community, Brenda was able to remain in her own home where an aide, Dana, came every day and helped her around the house, ran errands, and prepared meals. She also had help from a physical therapist who came twice a week for several weeks. When Brenda needed to visit her doctor, Linda, a person known as a friendly visitor, came and picked her up, accompanied her to the doctor's office and the pharmacy to purchase prescriptions, and then drove her back home. And, because of the emergency response system that her daughters had installed in her home, she was comfortable staying alone at night.

Now recovered, Brenda still receives assistance from Dana and has become good friends with Linda, who stops in to see her regularly.

. . .

Cheryl's fiercely independent and elderly aunt, Jan Tompkins, is widowed and lives alone in a rural area in upper New York state, 350 miles away from Cheryl's home in Virginia. Cheryl is the only family member Jan has. Jan was a lifetime smoker,

---

Unless otherwise noted, facts and figures in this chapter are from the United States Administration on Aging.

and emphysema is now slowly robbing her of her ability to breathe. Cheryl does not know what type of care her aunt needs or where to look for help. She is afraid that she will have to arrange for her to go into a nursing home to be watched over 24 hours a day, seven days a week. Such a move would be very hard on Jan.

Luckily, one of Cheryl's coworkers had a similar experience with her elderly mother, who lived several states away. She suggested Cheryl get in touch with the Area Agency on Aging closest to Jan's home. Cheryl called the Tompkins County Office for the Aging, which put her in touch with a geriatric care manager.

The manager assessed Jan's situation and arranged for the appropriate home health care services. He also calls Cheryl once a week and gives her an update on how her aunt is doing. For now, Jan can remain in her home, and Cheryl has the peace of mind of knowing that her aunt is being cared for and a professional is watching over her.

Introduction

In the 1970s and 1980s social policy makers in the United States became aware that the long-term care system needed far-reaching change to effectively serve the needs of the burgeoning senior population. The system was fragmented and limited. Often the only available option for seniors like Dotty Strum and Jan Tompkins was entering a nursing home. Since that time services that enable seniors to remain independent in the housing of their choice have flourished across the country.

Home and community-based services (HCBS) are popular in the field of aging because they exemplify a social policy away from nursing homes and toward independent living and consumer control. Many communities now have an impressive continuum of long-term supportive services available for seniors. The goal of these programs is to help people with physical limitations live outside of institutions and in their own homes. Some community programs have developed as the result of government funding. Many are run by not-for-profits, others are businesses. Some are free, others are available only to seniors who meet certain qualifications, and others require payment. Such programs fall under the umbrella terms of *home and community-based services* or *long-term supportive services*. This chapter will use the two terms interchangeably.

It is important for you to be aware of the long-term supportive services offered in your community so that you can refer your clients to them if and when the need arises. Armed with this knowledge, you can be instrumental in keeping your clients out of nursing homes.

Independent living is not doing things by yourself.
It is being in control of how things are done.

Judith E. Heuman

Overview of HCBS

By definition, *home and community-based services* allow people of all ages who have physical limitations to remain independent in the least restrictive settings possible and to be connected with their communities. The availability of HCBS in a community can make the difference between a senior living at home and having to live in a nursing home. Usually some form of home care is central to HCBS.

Home and community-based services usually work in conjunction with an *informal support network*. Such networks are composed of family members, friends, and neighbors who care for people of any age who face chronic illness or disability.

A recent study funded by AARP took an in-depth look at the roles of supportive services to enhance the independence of people ages 50 and older with disabilities. When the researchers asked open-ended questions about the respondents' hopes and concerns, the number-one fear they named was loss of independence. Control over decision-making was also a major theme (AARP, 2003).

The following are some of the comments made by the 53 percent of AARP's respondents who answered yes to the question, "Have there been times in the past month when you could not do something you really needed or wanted to do because of your disability or health condition?" (AARP, 2003, p. 7):

"I would like to just go for a ride."

"Walk on the beach."

"Pay my bills, nothing else."

"Make a minor car repair, walk to the corner, get something off a high shelf, tie my shoes."

"Just get out of bed."

"Just get back and forth to the store."

"I can hardly go to visit relatives because of the stairs."

"Go to the park with my grandchildren."

These responses reflect the daily challenges faced by seniors with physical limitations.

MODELS OF CARE

HCBS may be delivered through a medical or a personal model. The majority of funded services are provided under the *medical model*, in which health care workers provide services under the supervision of physicians and nurses.

Another option that is growing in popularity is the *personal model*, also known as *consumer-directed personal assistance services*. Under this model, seniors receive services in their homes from personal assistants who are not supervised by medical professionals. Typically, the senior (or a family member, friend, or representative) advertises for assistants, interviews them, and develops the job description and terms of the position. The senior receiving the service is considered a self-directed consumer and not a patient. They hire, train, supervise, and fire their personal assistants. In the personal model, seniors are in control of their care.

Unhappily, this model is readily available only to those seniors who can pay for services out of their own pockets and to some Medicaid recipients who live in states that permit payment for care under this model. However, an increasing number of states are moving their services in this direction, and many analysts consider it the wave of the future.

Another way of describing HCBS is by comparing the *professionally managed services model* to the *cash model*. In the professionally managed model someone other than the senior makes the decisions about care and services. In the cash model the senior decides how to spend money for care, including purchasing services from vendors, hiring a friend to help with activities of daily living, purchasing assistive technology, or modifying the home to make it more accessible. Some states have or are developing cash programs under the federal Cash and Counseling Demonstration and Evaluation project, which is part of the White House New Freedom Initiative (see below).

> *In the struggle to live with independence and dignity as we age, everyone has a story, and each story is unique and deeply personal.*
>
> AARP, 2003, p. 7

FEDERAL PROGRAMS PROMOTING COMMUNITY SERVICES

The federal government is actively funding programs to help provide services for seniors in their communities. Under these programs, professionals in the fields of health, social services, and aging often work together to provide independence for seniors. Current programs include the following, funded through the Older Americans Act, the White House New Freedom Initiative, and Medicaid waivers.

The Older Americans Act

The Older Americans Act (OAA) was originally signed into law by President Lyndon B. Johnson on July 14, 1965. The Act created the primary vehicle for organizing, coordinating, and providing community-based services and opportunities for older Americans and their families. The OAA established a National Aging Network, headed by the United States Administration on Aging (AoA). It includes State Units on Aging (SUAs), Area Agencies on Aging (AAAs), tribal organizations, local service providers, and volunteers (see Figure 9.1).

There are 655 Area Agencies on Aging nationwide. Area Agencies on Aging offer information and assistance services providing older persons and their caregivers with specific information about services in the community. All individuals 60 years of age and older are eligible for services under the OAA, although priority attention is given to those who are in greatest need.

Figure 9.1 Snapshot of the National Aging Network

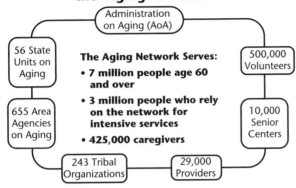

AoA Is the Federal Leader of the "Aging Network"

Administration on Aging (AoA)

56 State Units on Aging

655 Area Agencies on Aging

The Aging Network Serves:
- **7 million people age 60 and over**
- **3 million people who rely on the network for intensive services**
- **425,000 caregivers**

500,000 Volunteers

10,000 Senior Centers

243 Tribal Organizations

29,000 Providers

There are also 243 programs nationwide that administer Title VI of the Older Americans Act. The Title VI program promotes nutrition and supportive services, such as transportation, to American Indian, Alaskan Natives, and Native Hawaiians. The Title VI program also has an information and assistance service that provides specific information about services in the community.

You should be familiar with your local Area Agency on Aging and Title VI Program so you can refer clients to them if needed. Look in your telephone directory in the blue pages (government listings) or in the yellow pages under *Aging, Elders, Senior Citizens, Community Services*, or *Social Services*. If you have difficulty locating your local Area Agency on Aging, call the Eldercare Locator toll-free at 800-677-1116, or visit online at http://www.ageinfo.org/elderloc. (Also see the Resources section for more information.) The Eldercare Locator is a nationwide service to help families and friends find information about community services for seniors. The Eldercare Locator provides access to an extensive network of organizations serving older people at state and local community levels.

The White House New Freedom Initiative

The White House New Freedom Initiative was launched in 2001 to promote the goal of community living for people of all ages with disabilities. Under this initiative, the federal government initiated the Aging and Disability Resource Center Grant Program, a joint effort of the AoA and Centers for Medicare & Medicaid Services (CMS). It helps states integrate their supportive services into a single, coordinated system.

Under the initiative, grants have been awarded to 24 states to create one-stop-shopping centers to help consumers learn about and gain access to HCBS and nursing facility care. As of 2004, grants have been awarded to Arkansas, Arizona, California, Florida, Georgia, Illinois, Indiana, Iowa, Louisiana, Maine, Maryland, Massachusetts, Minnesota, Montana, New Hampshire, New Jersey, New Mexico, North Carolina, Pennsylvania, Rhode Island, South Carolina, West Virginia, Wisconsin, and the Northern Mariana Islands. If you live in one of these states, you will soon have a central coordinated system source for HCBS support resources.

The Role of Waivers

The United States Department of Health and Human Services has been allowing more disabled people on Medicaid to receive long-term supportive services outside of nursing homes. Through the use of Medicaid waivers (see chapter 20), people with disabilities can choose services in their own homes and communities. For example, Nevada has a waiver that allows about 1,700 Medicaid recipients to receive home care, personal care services, respite care, transportation, home-delivered meals, and other services to keep them at home and out of nursing homes.

HCBS Options

By definition, HCBS reflects the character, needs, and resources of local communities. A program that is available in one locale may not be available in another. As a general rule, urban and suburban residents have more options available to them than those living in rural areas. It is important for you, as a CSA, to be familiar with all of the HCBS programs in your area and know how to refer clients to them.

INFORMATION AND REFERRAL

Information and referral (I&R) services should be one of your first stops when you are getting to know your local aging network. Community information and referral programs link people and services. I&R specialists are trained professionals who assess callers' needs, determine their options and best courses of action, direct them to appropriate programs and services, provide culturally appropriate support, often intervene in crisis situations, and advocate for callers as needed.

I&R Programs for Seniors

These programs are available in nearly every community. Many State Agencies on Aging have toll-free statewide numbers that assist with linking seniors with appropriate services. Anyone, regardless of age, may telephone an Area Agency on Aging for information on services and resources available in the community to individuals 60 and over. Many programs offer additional services beyond supplying information. For example, in addition to local information and assistance, Illinois' Senior HelpLine links seniors and their caregivers to local services. Their professional staff assess needs and write referrals for a range of services such as care management, legal services, transportation, employment, and nutrition services. Senior HelpLine staff also provide elder abuse intake and accept appeals and service queries from the state's HCBS program.

In an AARP survey, an overwhelming number of older Americans somewhat or strongly agreed with the statement "What I'd really like to do is stay in my current residence as long as possible." Among those ages 55 to 64, 83 percent agreed or strongly agreed, as did 92 percent of persons aged 65 and older (AARP, 2003, p. 84).

242

2-1-1 Services

The Federal Communications Commission has designated 2-1-1 as a national, toll-free telephone number to access information and referral services. In states where the service is available, seniors and others can dial 2-1-1 on any phone and reach an information and referral specialist. The goal in many states is to make the service available 24 hours a day all year and usable by those with hearing impairments, and to provide assistance in many languages.

There are presently 130 active 2-1-1 systems in 26 states (United Way and Alliance of Information and Referral Services, n.d.). 2-1-1 serves approximately 90 million Americans—more than 32 percent of the American population.

Some state 2-1-1 programs are fully functional, while others are in their initial stages. For example, Texas currently has 24 active 2-1-1 call centers. This represents coverage for 90 percent of the Texas population. As of this writing, implementation of the final center (in El Paso) was scheduled for 2004. Upon the El Paso center's completion, Texas will have 100 percent statewide coverage. On the other hand, in Rhode Island, local I&R and other agencies are just beginning the process of developing a 2-1-1 system.

TRANSPORTATION

Access to adequate transportation is often the major factor that allows seniors to live independently at home. It is the connection to vital activities such as going to medical appointments, grocery shopping, and visiting family and friends. It is also the link to recreation, volunteering, employment, and other activities that contribute to quality of life. According to the Administration on Aging, two-thirds of older adults who stop driving say it is because of physical impairments (AoA, 2004a). One-third of older adults who do not drive rely on family and friends for their transportation.

Many communities recommend that seniors should evaluate their driving skills about every three years. You should know about and be able to refer your clients to the AARP driver safety program closest to you (see the Resources section). The refresher course is available in most communities. It was specially designed for motorists ages 50 and older. Its purpose is to help older drivers improve their skills and avoid accidents and traffic violations. Upon completing the eight-hour AARP Driver Safety Program, graduates may be eligible for an automobile insurance premium reduction or discount depending on the state they live in and the insurance company they use.

Transportation Services

The types of transportation available to your senior clients depend upon where you live. Your local Area Agency on Aging is a good place to start your search for such services. In some communities the AAA arranges, monitors, and supports programs that provide transportation for the elderly. If your local agency doesn't provide such services directly, the staff will give you assistance in locating them. In 2000, assisted transportation through State and Area Agencies on Aging provided 2.7 million trips for persons ages 60 and older (AARP, 2003). Assisted transportation can take several forms, detailed here.

Demand response, also referred to as dial-a-ride, provides transportation from one specific location to another. It requires advance reservations and often requires a payment or donation. The door-to-door service provides flexibility, comfort, and the potential for adapting to the needs of each rider. Taxicabs are a common form of demand-response transit service. Transit providers often use the term *paratransit* to describe demand-response services for riders with disabilities.

Fixed-route and scheduled services transport seniors along an established route with designated stops where riders can board and be dropped off. Reservations are not required because the vehicles stop at predetermined times and locations. Fixed-route services usually require payment of a fare on a per-ride or regular basis. For example, Easy Street, a commuter van service in Connecticut, has more than 200 routes in operation. Monthly fares cover all operating costs for the vehicle, including insurance, maintenance, and fuel.

Ridesharing programs arrange for seniors to be driven to specific destinations with volunteer drivers. There is now a national ridesharing Web site (http://www.erideshare.com) that is handy for use by people of all ages. For example, these message were recently posted on the site:

> Need ride from Washington, DC, to Arlington, Virginia, and back—several days of the week to visit sick relative. Will pay for gas.

> I live in Denver and am blind and cannot drive. I am requesting a ride to visit a relative in a nursing home in Fort Carson twice a week. Flexible hours.

Of course, if your clients use the eRideShare or other Web site, they should follow precautions for safety. All eRideShare members, for example, correspond by anonymous email. Clients' email addresses and identification remain private. In addition, the eRideShare's site includes other safety information.

Escort services provide support for seniors with limited mobility to obtain needed services. Escort services pick up clients at home, guide them through appointments, and then return them to the safety of home. Escort services are great volunteer opportunities for you. You might accompany a senior to a doctor's appointment or spend the afternoon together running errands.

CARE MANAGEMENT

Care managers help with navigation through the long-term supportive services system. (Care managers who specialize in the care of seniors are referred to as *geriatric care managers*.) They are extremely important members of long-term care supportive teams. You should know the reputations of and be able to refer clients to several care managers in your area.

Seniors can turn to care managers to learn what resources available in their areas will best meet their needs and to contract with local service providers. Families who live far away or are otherwise unable to provide care for a loved one often turn to private care managers to arrange for assistance.

Care managers meet with seniors and families, assess their needs, and develop plans to meet those needs. They also can help fill out the appropriate

Medicare, Medicaid, and insurance forms. Care managers usually follow up after providing their services to make sure that the senior is receiving the care he or she needs.

Because of their central role in long-term supportive services, care management service systems have grown enormously in the last several decades. Several important resources for locating care managers include the Family Caregiver Alliance, the National Association of Professional Geriatric Care Managers, and the Case Management Society of America.

IN-HOME SERVICES

In-home services encompass a wide range of supportive services for seniors who are homebound. Their availability often is credited with keeping seniors at home and out of nursing homes.

Home Health Care

Home health care (HHC) provides supportive care and supplies to seniors' homes. The recipient may be recovering from an illness, have a physical limitation, or be chronically or terminally ill. The types of services provided can be medical, nursing, social, therapeutic treatment, or assistance with activities of daily living. Services may be temporary, intermittent, or long-term.

Home care organizations include home health agencies, hospices, homemaker and home care aide (HCA) agencies, staffing and private-duty agencies, and companies specializing in medical equipment and supplies, pharmaceuticals, and drug infusion therapy (National Association for Home Care, 1996). In addition, some agencies now offer telehealth services.

Home care services are available 24 hours a day, seven days a week. Depending on the patient's needs and resources, they may be provided by an individual or a team of specialists on a part-time, intermittent, hourly, or shift basis.

Following are some of the types of professionals and helpers who provide home health care services, depending on the needs of the senior.

Licensed Practical Nurses

Licensed practical nurses (LPNs, known as licensed vocational nurses [LVNs] in California and Texas) exist in most states. LPNs usually have two years of training and have passed state or national boards. They can administer most medications, take blood pressure and other measurements, and perform related tasks.

Registered Nurses

Registered nurses (RNs) are professional nurses who often supervise the tasks performed by LPNs, orderlies, and nursing assistants. They provide direct care and make decisions regarding plans of care for individuals. They may have bachelor's degrees or associate degrees in nursing, but not all states have educational requirements.

ISSUE	RESOURCE
access to services	care managers Area Agencies on Aging I&R services
activities	senior centers
assistive technology	Rehabilitation Engineering and Assistive Technology Society of North America TechConnections.Org department stores
away-from-home services	adult day care
companionship	friendly visitors senior centers
coordinated care	adult day care
coordination of care	care managers social workers home health agencies
energy assistance	Low Income Home Energy Assistance Program
health insurance decisions	senior health insurance counseling and assistance programs BenefitsCheckUp
housing assistance and repair	Area Agency on Aging state housing department residential repair and renovation programs
information	I&R hotlines 2-1-1 services senior centers
in-home services	home health agencies home care aid agencies hospices rehabilitation services staffing and private-duty nursing agencies pharmaceutical and infusion therapy companies durable medical equipment companies telehealth assistive technology
legal	National Association of Elder Law Attorneys Administration on Aging legal programs legal hotlines
locating services	I&R
Medicaid questions	senior health insurance counseling and assistance programs BenefitsCheckUp
Medicare questions	senior health insurance counseling and assistance programs BenefitsCheckUp

ISSUE	RESOURCE
nutrition	Meals on Wheels congregate meals senior centers adult day care dieticians
rehabilitation	home health care physical therapists occupational therapists speech and language therapists dieticians
respite	adult day care home health care
safety	gatekeeper programs personal emergency response programs telephone reassurance adult protective services
supplemental insurance	senior health insurance counseling and assistance programs
transportation	demand response fixed route ridesharing escort services

Home Care Aides

Home care aides are trained to provide custodial care, such as helping with dressing, bathing, getting in and out of bed, and using the toilet. They may also prepare meals. They usually are not certified.

Social Workers

Social workers help people function the best way they can in their environment, deal with their relationships, and solve personal and family problems. Social workers often see clients who face life-threatening diseases or social problems. These problems may include inadequate housing, unemployment, serious illness, disability, or substance abuse. Social workers also assist families that have serious domestic conflicts, including those involving elder abuse.

Rehabilitation Services

Rehabilitation services provide care to help maximize patients' quality of life and restore them to the highest possible level of function. Such services include the roles described below.

- *Physical therapists.* Physical therapists (PTs) help restore function, improve mobility, relieve pain, and prevent or limit permanent disabilities of patients suffering from injuries or disease. PTs examine patients' medical histories and then test such measures as the patients' strength, range of motion, and balance and coordination. Physical therapists develop treatment plans describing a treatment strategy, its purpose, and its anticipated outcome.

- *Occupational therapists.* Occupational therapists (OTs) help people improve their ability to perform tasks of daily living. OTs may prescribe physical exercises or other activities to improve function. For example, a client with short-term memory loss might be encouraged to make lists to aid recall, and a person with coordination problems might be assigned exercises to improve hand-eye coordination.

  Occupational therapists sometimes use computer programs to help clients improve function. They also design or make special equipment needed at home. OTs develop computer-aided adaptive equipment and teach clients with severe limitations how to use that equipment in order to communicate better and control various aspects of their environment.

- *Speech and language pathologists.* Speech and language pathologists, sometimes called *speech therapists*, assess, diagnose, treat, and help to prevent speech, language, cognitive, communication, voice, fluency, and other related disorders. They also work with people who have difficulty swallowing.

- *Dieticians.* Dieticians working in home health agencies provide instruction on grocery shopping and food preparation to the elderly, individuals with special needs, and children.

The in-home services described above may be available in your community through one or more of the following entities.

Home Health Agencies

Home health agencies (HHAs) are usually certified by Medicare, which means that they can provide services to Medicare and Medicaid recipients. Depending on the agency, the needs of the senior, and the availability of funds or coverage, services come from a range of health care workers such as physicians, nurses, physical therapists, occupational therapists, social workers, homemakers and home care aides, durable medical equipment suppliers, and volunteers (National Association for Home Care, 1996).

Home Care Aid Agencies

Home care aid agencies provide helpers for seniors and others who need assistance in the home and with personal care. Such helpers do a variety of tasks such as cleaning house, doing laundry, and preparing meals. Often referred to as home care aides, they may also be called homemakers, caregivers, companions, or personal attendants. HCA agencies may plan meals

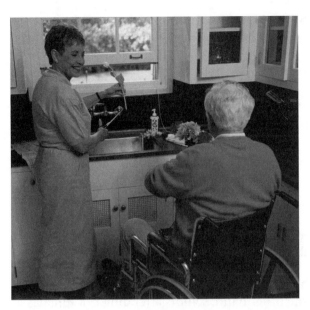

(including special diets), shop for food, and cook. They also may help clients move from bed, bathe, dress, and groom. Some accompany clients outside the home, serving as a guide and companion.

In some states HCA agencies must be licensed and meet minimum standards. Most homemaker and HCA agencies recruit, train, and supervise their personnel and thus are responsible for the care rendered.

Hospices

Hospice agencies provide programs of care that promote quality of life during a life-threatening illness. Hospices recognize dying as a normal process. Hospice care provides comfort when cure of the illness is no longer possible.

These programs neither hasten nor postpone death. Hospice care involves a core interdisciplinary team of skilled professionals and volunteers who provide comprehensive medical, psychological, and spiritual care for the terminally ill and support for patients' families. Hospice care also includes the provision of related medications, medical supplies, and equipment. Most hospices are Medicare-certified and licensed according to state requirements.

Staffing and Private-Duty Agencies

Staffing and private-duty agencies provide seniors and others with nursing, homemaker, HCA, and companion services. The best-known agencies are the Visiting Nurse Associations (VNAs). They are not-for-profit, community-based home health organizations. VNAs care for nearly 4 million people annually (Visiting Nurse Associations of America, n.d.).

Many staffing and private-duty agencies assign nurses to assess their clients' needs and to provide follow-up and supervision. Responsibility for patient care rests with each agency.

Pharmaceutical and Infusion Therapy Companies

Pharmaceutical and infusion therapy companies specialize in the delivery of drugs, equipment, and professional services for the homebound who require intravenous or nutritional therapies through specially placed tubes.

Durable Medical Equipment Suppliers

Durable medical equipment suppliers provide home care patients with products ranging from respirators, wheelchairs, and walkers to catheter and wound-care supplies.

Telehealth Service Providers

Some agencies are developing telehealth services for the homebound. Through telehealth a nurse can read a senior's vital signs over the telephone. The innovative technology uses existing telephone lines and a computer-based interactive videophone. A monitoring unit can check heart and lung sounds, blood pressure, blood oxygen level, and blood sugar, while a high-resolution camera can provide a view of wounds.

HOME-DELIVERED AND CONGREGATE MEALS

Both public and private programs deliver hot meals to seniors and provide them in congregate settings such as senior centers. The Elderly Nutrition Program is the largest public program financing such services. It is funded through the Administration on Aging. Services are provided through local Area Agencies on Aging or Tribal Senior Services.

Volunteers and paid staff who deliver meals to homebound seniors often spend some time with them, helping to brighten their day. They also check on the welfare of the senior. On the other hand, seniors attending hot lunches at

one of the senior nutrition sites can share time with friends and neighbors. The sites also offer a variety of programs such as health clinics, information and referral, recreation programs, exercise sessions, and craft classes.

The Elderly Nutrition Program's 3.1 million senior participants receive an estimated 40 to 50 percent of most required daily nutrients (AoA, 2004b). In 2000, some 144 million meals were delivered under this program (AARP, 2003). Elderly Nutrition Program participants have twice as many physical impairments as does the overall elderly population (AoA, 2004b).

The Elderly Nutrition Program also provides a range of related services through the aging network's estimated 4,000 nutrition service providers. They include nutrition screening, assessment, education, and counseling. Nutrition service providers may also include special health assessments for such diseases as hypertension and diabetes. Through additional services, older participants learn to shop, plan, and prepare nutritious meals that are economical and enhance their health and well-being.

While there is no means test for participation in the Elderly Nutrition Program, services are targeted to seniors with the greatest economic or social need, with special attention given to low-income minorities and rural older people.

A good example of an Elderly Nutrition Program is Coastline Elderly Services in Wisconsin (Coastline Elderly Services, n.d.). The program provides hot noontime meals for consumers over 60 and their spouses through two different programs—The Meals on Wheels Program for homebound elders and the Lunch Program provided at 15 senior centers in the area.

The meals provide between 700 and 800 calories with no added salt. They include one-third of the daily nutrients as recommended for older adults and no more than 30 percent of the daily fat allotment. Low-sugar desserts and low-fat milk are available. Daily menus are published in local senior and community newspapers and are announced on two radio stations.

FRIENDLY VISITORS

Often the best prescription for loneliness is friendship. Friendly visitor programs provide regular personal or telephone contact for seniors who are homebound or live alone. Usually a volunteer provides the service. Besides developing friendships, the volunteer often identifies the needs of the senior and contacts those who can help. Friendly visitors do not give personal care, provide homemaking, administer medications, or transfer patients. Some of the services friendly visitors offer include (Visiting Nurse Association of Somerset Hills, n.d.):

- friendship, companionship, and conversation
- a visit several times a month
- possible help with simple errands
- sharing conversation, memories, and interests
- reading aloud, writing notes, and helping with personal correspondence
- initiating handcrafts or playing games or cards
- going for a short walk or a drive
- celebrating holidays and birthdays

GATEKEEPER PROGRAMS

Some public utilities and government agencies offer *gatekeeper* or *home observation programs*, in which service people who visit homes regularly are trained to notice anything unusual or any indication of need and report it to the local Area Agency on Aging. For example, in Portland, Oregon, the Multnomah County Aging and Disability Services Department has trained gatekeepers in more than eight occupations, including utility technicians, postal carriers, and firefighters (Multnomah County Aging and Disability Services Department, 2002). If the gatekeepers notice a problem they call the service hotline, and the hotline personnel dispatches a care manager or other social service professional.

PERSONAL EMERGENCY RESPONSE SYSTEMS

The key to many seniors living at home is getting help quickly if an emergency occurs. A personal emergency response system (PERS, also called a medical emergency response system or medical alert system) is an electronic device designed to let users summon help in an emergency.

A PERS has three components: a small radio *transmitter* (a help button carried or worn by the user), a *console* connected to the user's telephone, and an *emergency response center* that monitors calls. When emergency help is needed, the senior presses the transmitter's panic button to send a radio signal to the console. The console automatically dials one or more preselected emergency telephone numbers. A PERS can be purchased, rented, or leased. Most systems can dial out even if the phone is in use or off the hook.

TELEPHONE REASSURANCE

Telephone reassurance provides a regular friendly and familiar voice to people who live alone. A trained volunteer calls on a regular schedule to make sure the senior is safe and to provide a sense of caring. For some seniors, a telephone reassurance call may be the only one they receive all day.

If a volunteer calls and there is no answer, the volunteer calls an emergency contact person to verify the well-being of the individual. If there is still no answer, the volunteer will call a secondary contact, and so on. If no one can reach the senior, the police are called. An officer will then be dispatched to the residence to check on the senior. Telephone reassurance is another great volunteer opportunity for you.

SENIOR CENTERS

Senior centers are community focal points for seniors. Funded in part through the Older Americans Act, there are now some 15,000 centers across the country, serving close to 10 million seniors annually. The centers typically provide nutrition, recreation, social, and educational services, as well as comprehensive information and referral. Congregate (group) meals are often served at senior centers. Many centers are adding new and innovative programs such as fitness activities, health education, and Internet training.

Most states have hundreds of senior centers that provide the typical services mentioned above, and each one characterizes the uniqueness of the surrounding community. For example, Pennsylvania has more than 650 senior centers, one of which is the Mechanicsburg Area Senior Adult Center, where some participants play in regular pool tournaments and are members of a league. Every year they put on a pool league banquet, complete with awards. Two other centers in Pennsylvania focus on different activities. The September House Senior Center in York offers computer classes. They have had more than 200 students in the past year. And participants at the Blue Ridge Senior Center in Great Bend help out Project Kidds, which aids abused and neglected children. Blue Ridge Senior Center attendees make doll clothing, wooden toys, and blocks for the children.

ADULT DAY CARE

Adult day care programs offer an alternative to institutionalization for seniors who cannot stay alone during the day but who do not need patient care. They can serve as a respite for caregivers. These programs are designed to promote maximum independence. Seniors usually attend on a scheduled basis.

Most adult day centers offer personal assistance and therapeutic activities (AARP, 2004). Services may also include:

- nursing
- social services
- restorative services
- medical and health care monitoring
- exercise sessions
- field trips
- recreational activities
- physical, occupational, and speech therapy
- medication administration
- meals
- transportation to and from the facility

According to a national survey by Partners in Caregiving, the United States presently has 3,407 adult day centers (The Robert Wood Johnson Foundation, 2004). Most centers (78 percent) are nonprofit organizations.

One of the most well-known day care centers is On Lok SeniorHealth in San Francisco. On Lok provides preventative, primary, and acute medical services and long-term care. Its primary focus is preventive measures that maintain the health and well-being of seniors. On Lok, one of the country's first senior day health centers, began in 1971 in the Chinatown, North Beach, and Polk Gulch neighborhoods. The founders' concern about the fragmented care they saw motivated them to create their own holistic senior health care plan.

The On Lok model of coordinated service delivery and innovative financing is being replicated across the country under the name the Program of All-Inclusive Care for the Elderly (PACE). Today more than 70 organizations in 30 states are in various stages of the PACE model—from start-up to full operation.

LEGAL SERVICES

Elder law is one of the fastest growing legal specialties. Elder law attorneys work specifically with the legal problems and concerns of seniors. Such issues include age discrimination, public benefits, probate and estate planning, guardianship and conservatorship, and health and long-term care planning. As a CSA, you should have contacts with and be able to make referrals to

---

On Lok: A Model Adult Day Care Program

Health benefits available to senior participants include:

- *primary medical care and specialty care as needed (such as cardiology, neurology)*
- *routine preventive care such as audiology, dentistry, optometry, and podiatry*
- *rehabilitation therapy (physical, occupational, speech) and recreational therapy*
- *home health care and personal care*
- *social services*
- *nutrition services and home-delivered meals as necessary*
- *transportation and emergency medical transport*
- *acute hospital and nursing home care*
- *nursing care and monitoring*
- *adult day health care*
- *prescription drugs and necessary health care-related equipment and supplies*

The On Lok staff includes:

- *physicians*
- *nurses*
- *social workers*
- *physical and occupational therapists*
- *dietitians*
- *transportation staff*
- *home care workers*
- *recreational activities leaders*

Source: On Lok SeniorHealth (n.d.)

---

several reputable elder law attorneys. The Web site for the National Academy of Elder Law Attorneys (NAELA) has a searchable directory of attorneys who belong to NAELA. (See the Resources section.)

Two major sources of legal advice include AoA legal services and hotlines.

AoA Legal Services

AoA legal services help seniors and caregivers receive information on public benefits, residents' rights, guardianship, health and financial advance planning, and other legal issues. There are approximately 1,000 AoA legal services providers nationwide, giving more than one million hours of legal assistance per year. AoA also funds 13 senior legal hotlines. Most clients of AoA legal programs are low-income seniors.

The following examples demonstrate the types of problems handled through AoA legal services programs.

- A 73-year-old woman contacted by a telemarketer was invited to join a discount buyers club. She told the company she was not interested. However, when her checks began bouncing, she contacted her bank and found that an electronic transfer to the buyers club had been made. Intervention by senior legal services led to a refund of all her money plus additional expenses.
- An elderly couple was charged nearly $11,000 for minor home repairs that were never completed. Legal services assisted the couple in canceling the contract.
- A lawyer assisted an elderly woman in obtaining her Social Security funds after they had been garnished from an account jointly held with her son. The son had a judgment against him, and the creditor took action against the account. The elderly woman was a resident of a nursing facility and the nonpayment of her bill might have caused her to be discharged.
- An 80-year-old man discovered that he was a proposed ward under a guardianship petition. He did not believe he needed a guardian, and his lawyer defended him against imposition of the guardianship by showing that the standards for granting it had not been met.

AoA legal services can provide alternatives to guardianship. These include medical and financial powers of attorney, living wills, and advance directives (combination of a medical power of attorney and a living will). AoA legal services providers can also represent seniors who wish to contest a guardianship petition or those who desire to modify or terminate an existing guardianship (or power of attorney).

The AoA requires each state to appoint a legal assistance developer, responsible for developing and coordinating the state's legal services and elder rights programs.

Legal Hotlines

At least 25 states offer legal hotlines that provide advice to callers. If your state has such a hotline, it may also offer services such as reviewing documents and providing legal forms. They also may make a referral to a free legal services program or private attorney. (For information on a senior legal hotline directory, see the United States Administration on Aging listing in the Resources section.)

ADULT PROTECTIVE SERVICES

Adult protective services (APS) agencies receive and investigate reports of elder abuse. Protective service workers provide crisis intervention, counseling, information and referral to clients, and liaison with the court system.

To report elder abuse, contact an adult protective services agency through your local Area Agency on Aging. The APS agency screens calls for potential seriousness, and it keeps the information it receives confidential. If the agency decides the situation possibly violates state elder abuse laws, it assigns a case-worker to conduct an investigation (in cases of an emergency, usually within 24 hours). If the victim needs crisis intervention, services are available.

STATE HEALTH INSURANCE COUNSELING AND ASSISTANCE PROGRAMS

Known as SHIPS, these programs comprise 53 state programs with nearly 15,000 trained volunteers who offer unbiased, one-on-one counseling to help Medicare beneficiaries understand their health insurance benefits and options. They do not sell insurance or recommend policies, agents, or specific companies.

The programs are funded by the federal government. SHIPs can answer your clients' questions about:

- choosing a managed care plan;
- deciding between original Medicare (fee-for-service) and managed care;
- understanding new health plan choices;
- how to understand a Medicare bill;
- how and whether to purchase additional health insurance (Medigap policy, long-term care insurance, etc.);
- understanding how to appeal payment denials;
- understanding Medicare rights and protections and how to submit complaints about medical care or treatment.

An example of a state SHIP program is Idaho's Senior Health Insurance Benefits Advisors (ISHIBA). Volunteer advocates throughout Idaho run the program. ISHIBA has a community education and outreach component. Coordinators make educational presentations on Medicare and other senior health insurance issues to community groups. They also disseminate information at hundreds of health and senior fairs throughout the state. In 1999 ISHIBA volunteers and staff served more than 49,000 clients (Idaho Department of Insurance, n.d.).

BENEFITSCHECKUP

The BenefitsCheckUp Web site was developed by the National Council on the Aging (NCOA) to help seniors find out if they are eligible for a wide range of public assistance programs, including state programs, Social Security, Medicaid, food stamps, weatherization, in-home services, and pharmacy programs. The Web site produces a printable report listing programs that users may qualify for, along with enrollment information. (See the Resources section at the end of this chapter.)

HOUSING ASSISTANCE

Housing assistance services provide seniors with a wide variety of assistance related to financing, building, maintaining, and locating housing. Services can include housing counseling, information and referral, landlord-tenant dispute resolution, home equity conversion, carpentry, minor electrical and plumbing repairs, low-cost weatherization material, and home security. In some areas short-term shelter is provided to seniors who are in need of emergency housing. Many housing assistance programs can be found through your state's housing agency or local Area Agency on Aging.

THE LOW INCOME HOME ENERGY ASSISTANCE PROGRAM

The Low Income Home Energy Assistance Program (LIHEAP) helps pay the winter heating bills or summer cooling bills of low-income and elderly people. Two-thirds of the families receiving LIHEAP assistance have incomes of less than $8,000 a year, so the program clearly helps the people who need help the most (Campaign for Home Energy Assistance, 2004).

In fiscal year 2000, about 34 percent of households receiving heating assistance included at least one elderly member, and about 36 percent of households included at least one member who was disabled. The Campaign for Home Energy Assistance's Clearinghouse provides free telephone and email referrals to people who want to know where to apply for low-income energy assistance.

RESIDENTIAL REPAIR AND RENOVATION

These programs help seniors keep the condition of their housing in good repair before problems become major. Volunteers might come to an individual's home and patch a leaky roof, for instance, or repair faulty plumbing and insulate drafty walls.

The Volunteer Senior Home Repair Program in Marshfield, Wisconsin, is a good example of the invaluable services such programs provide. The goal of the program is to make living at home safer and more comfortable for seniors (Eberhardt, 2004). Representatives go to seniors' homes and do safety check-ups. They make suggestions about necessary repairs and make arrangements to have those repairs fixed at no cost to the homeowner. Labor is free. Volunteers donate their time and talents to assist seniors whose yearly incomes are at or below $24,000 a year. Projects completed through the Marshfield Volunteer Senior Home Repair Program include repairing, installing, or replacing ramps, broken windows, door handles, steps, decks, new flooring, smoke alarms, lighting, garage doors, and chimneys.

Assistive Technology

Assistive technology includes any device that is used to improve the capabilities of individuals with disabilities. It can make a critical difference in the lives of

The terms *assistive technology* and *durable medical equipment* are often confused. Durable medical equipment describes devices that are medically necessary, such as artificial limbs and wheelchairs. Assistive technology is an umbrella term that also includes durable medical equipment. Medicare and Medicaid cover some types of durable medical equipment, but most assistive technologies are not covered by Medicare or Medicaid.

seniors with limitations who are living at home. Such assistive devices range from $5.00 low-tech bottle openers to high-tech computer-aided equipment costing thousands of dollars.

This area of services for seniors is one of the most exciting in gerontology. The availability of products has increased dramatically in recent years. In fact, there is now so much demand for assistive technologies that many devices can be purchased at stores such as Ace Hardware, Home Depot, Kmart, Lowe's Home Improvement, Target, True Value Hardware, and Wal-Mart.

One of the reasons why assistive technologies have flourished is the attention and badly needed dollars brought to the field by the Assistive Technology Act of 1998 (ATA). The ATA affirmed the federal role of promoting access to assistive technology devices and services for individuals with disabilities. The purpose of the Act is to:

- support states in sustaining and strengthening their capacity to address the assistive technology needs of individuals with disabilities;
- focus the investment in technology across Federal agencies and departments that could benefit individuals with disabilities; and
- support micro-loan programs to provide assistance to individuals who desire to purchase assistive technology devices or services.

The Rehabilitation Engineering and Assistive Technology Society of North America (RESNA) is an association of people with a common interest in technology and disability. The society is a valuable source of information about the State Assistive Technology Financial Loan Programs funded under Title III of the ATA. (See the Resources section.)

In addition to financial loans, many states have lending libraries and other organizations that lend devices to individuals. Many of these programs are funded through local or state resources. For example, the Nebraska Commission for the Deaf and Hard of Hearing offers their Assistive Devices Loan Program to residents (Nebraska Commission for the Deaf and Hard of Hearing, n.d.). Examples of the devices they lend include:

- amplified phones, which make sounds louder and clearer
- PockeTalkers, which screen out background noise, clarifying and amplifying the speaker's voice
- television decoders, which allow people to view closed captions on TV

A number of Web sites are available to help people find out about and locate assistive technologies. A major source is ABLEDATA, a federally funded project whose primary mission is to provide information on assistive technology and rehabilitation equipment available from domestic and international sources. The National Institute on Disability and Rehabilitation Research (NIDRR) sponsors the project.

Assistive Devices

The broad range of assistive devices available to enable seniors to live more independently includes:

- *alternative and augmentative communication devices such as communication boards, scanning communicators that provide voice output, and videophones*
- *assistive listening devices such as equipment that amplifies TV sound, devices that amplify the telephone, and hearing aids*
- *assistive communication devices such as TTYs (also called telecommunications devices for the deaf (TDDs) or text telephones), which enable the hard of hearing to communicate over normal telephone equipment without the requirement to hear*
- *back-saving solutions such as lumbar supports and neck pillows*
- *voice- or switch-activated controls for electronic devices such as environmental control units (ECUs), which allow individuals to control facets of their environment*
- *devices to compensate for blindness and low vision, including talking computers, computer systems for reading, audio cassette magazines, and speech synthesizers*
- *electronic aids to interact with and control appliances through voice activation, switch access, computer interface, or adaptations such as X-10 units, which transmit signals through a house's electrical wiring and allow for remote control of electrical devices*
- *gripping and grasping aids such as reachers, easy turning handles, and wall bars*
- *lifting devices such as transfer benches and overhead lifts*
- *memory and organizational aids such as pill organizers with alarms and talking picture photo albums*
- *mobility aids such as crutches, walking frames, walking sticks, wheelchairs, and scooters*
- *modifications to homes, including ramps, wider doors, wider turning areas, handrails, stair-lifts, porch-lifts, and roll-in showers—features often found in homes referred to as universal design houses*
- *modifications to telecommunication equipment, such as talking computers and amplified phones*
- *modifications to transportation equipment, such as vans with wheelchair lifts and tie-down systems*

The ABLEDATA database contains information on more than 20,000 currently available assistive devices, from white canes to voice-output programs. The database contains detailed descriptions of each product, including price and company information. The database also contains information on noncommercial prototypes, customized and one-of-a-kind products, and do-it-yourself designs.

WHAT IS AHEAD: DEVELOPING TECHNOLOGIES

A number of innovative technologies are being developed to increase the independence of seniors and people with disabilities. The following projects represent the wave of the future.

- Research funded by the National Institutes of Health and conducted by Boston University physicist and bioengineer Jim Collins and his colleagues found that seniors showed signs of better balance when they stood on a pair of battery-operated vibrating insoles (O'Hanlon, 2002). The vibrations, which cannot be felt by the seniors, amplify signals between the feet and the brain. The insoles work by reducing postural sway.

- Home Guardian LLC has installed a wireless monitoring system in apartments for senior citizens in Minneapolis (Greene, 2004). The system, which takes only about 20 minutes to install, uses sensors to pinpoint where residents are at any particular time. The system has detected at least four residents' falls.

- The Aware Home Research Initiative (AHRI) is an interdisciplinary research endeavor at the Georgia Institute of Technology. Among other projects, they are testing a program they call Digital Family Portrait (Georgia Institute of Technology, n.d.). Two people are involved in the testing: an elderly mother and her son. The senior's house has sensors under the floor that track her movements. The son has a digital picture frame, bordered by 28 butterflies and with his mother's photo in the middle. The frame picks up the level of the mother's activity along with other pertinent information. The butterfly representing the current day grows larger as the mother's activity level increases. If the activity stops without explanation, the son can call or stop by and check on his mother.

- Also at the Georgia Institute of Technology, the Gesture Pendant allows individuals to control ordinary household devices with the wave of a hand. The user wears a small pendant that contains a wireless camera. The user makes gestures in front of the pendant that controls anything from their home theater system or lighting to the kitchen sink. The system can detect loss of motor skill or tremors in the hand that might indicate the onset of illness or problems with medication. In addition, it can observe daily activities to determine, for example, if a person has been eating regularly and moving around. The device requires less dexterity, memory, and eyesight than traditional remote controls.

- The LifeWise Home, built by the National Association of Homebuilders (NAHB) Research Center in Bowie, Maryland, was designed to be accessible for seniors or disabled homeowners who are in wheelchairs, use walkers, or have physical limitations that impair mobility (National Association of Homebuilders, n.d.). Its features include a washing-and-drying toilet, with a warm-water rinse and built-in dryer, for occupants with limited range of motion.

Home and Community-Based Services:
Summary

As a CSA you come in regular contact with seniors, many of whom will eventually face the need for long-term supportive services for themselves or a loved one. You can play an important role in the lives of your clients by being informed about the services in your community that can make a difference between moving to a nursing home and staying at home.

References

AARP. (2003). *Beyond 50.03: A report to the nation on independent living and disability.* Retrieved July 6, 2004, from http://research.aarp.org/il/beyond_50_il.html

AARP. (2004, February). Adult day services. Retrieved July 6, 2004 from http://research.aarp.org/il/fs98_service.html

AoA. (Administration on Aging). (2004a). Transportation. Retrieved July 6, 2004, from http://www.aoa.gov/press/fact/alpha/fact_transportation.asp

AoA. (2004b). The elderly nutrition program. Retrieved July 6, 2004, from http://www.aoa.gov/press/fact/alpha/fact_elderly_nutrition.asp

Campaign for Home Energy Assistance. (2004). Low Income Home Energy Assistance Program home page. Retrieved July 31, 2004, from http://www.liheap.org

Coastline Elderly Services. (n.d.). Elderly nutrition program. Retrieved July 1, 2004, from http://www.coastlineelderly.org/home/wheels.htm

Eberhardt, K. (2004, June 26). Volunteer home repair available to seniors in Wood County. *Marshfield News-Herald.* Retrieved July 23, 2004, from http://www.wisinfo.com/newsherald/mnhlifestyle/289078186469666.shtml

Georgia Institute of Technology. (n.d.) The Aware Home Research Initiative. Retrieved July 22, 2004, from http://www.cc.gatech.edu/fce/ecl/projects/dfp/index.html

Greene, K. (2004, February 23). Inside the home of the future. *The Wall Street Journal*, R1. Retrieved July 31, 2004, from http:// www.cse.uta.edu/News/2004/HomeOfTheFuture_WSJ.asp

Idaho Department of Insurance. (n.d.). Shiba health. Retrieved July 6, 2004, from http://www.doi.state.id.us/shiba/shwelcome.aspx

Multnomah County Aging and Disability Services Department. (2002). Who are gatekeepers? Retrieved July 6, 2004, from http://www.co.multnomah.or.us/ads/protect/gatekeep.html

National Association for Home Care. (1996). Who provides home care? Retrieved July 1, 2004, from http://nahc.org/Consumer/wphc.html

National Association of Homebuilders. (n.d.). LifeWise Home. Retrieved July 12, 2004, from http://www.nahbrc.org/about2.asp?TrackID=&CategoryID=1830

Nebraska Commission for the Deaf and Hard of Hearing. (n.d.). Assistive devices loan program. Retrieved July 6, 2004, from http://www.nol.org/home/NCDHH/assist_device_loanpgm.htm

O'Hanlon, L. (2002, November 12). Vibrating shoes for the imbalanced elderly? *Discovery News*. Retrieved June 12, 2004, from http://dsc.discovery.com/news/briefs/20021111/shoes.html

On Lok Senior Health. (n.d.). Our services. Retrieved July 14, 2004, from http://www.onlok.org/content.asp?catid=240000183

The Robert Wood Johnson Foundation. (2004). National study of adult day services. Retrieved July 6, 2004, from http://www.rwjf.org/reports/grr/037535.htm

United Way and Alliance of Information and Referral Systems. (n.d.). National status. Retrieved July 14, 2004, from http://www.211.org/status.html

Visiting Nurse Associations of America. (n.d.). About VNAA. Retrieved July 14, 2004, from http://www.vnaa.org/vnaa/g/?h=HTML/AboutVNAA

Visiting Nurse Association of Somerset Hills. (n.d.). The Friendly Visitor Program. Retrieved July 19, 2004, from http://www.visitingnurse.org/friendly.htm#Who do friendly visitors help

Resources

Services

AARP Driver Safety Program. http:// www.aarp.org/drive. AARP's driver safety Web site provides safe driving tips and information on how seniors can participate in AARP's driver safety program.

ABLEDATA. http://www.abledata.com. 8630 Fenton St., Ste. 930, Silver Spring, MD 20910, 800-227-0216, fax 301-608-8958, TTY 301-608-8912. ABLEDATA is a federally funded project that provides information on assistive technology and rehabilitation equipment available from domestic and international sources. The ABLEDATA database contains information on more than 20,000 devices.

BenefitsCheckUp. http://www.benefitscheckup.org. BenefitsCheckUp is an online tool that screens for federal, state, and some local private and public benefits for adults ages 55 and over. It contains more than 1,200 different programs from all 50 states and the District of Columbia. On average there are 50 to 70 programs per state available to individuals. In addition to identifying the programs that a person may be eligible to receive, BenefitsCheckUp also provides a detailed description of the programs, local contacts for additional information (typically the addresses and phone numbers of where to apply for the programs), and materials to help successfully apply for each program.

Campaign for Home Energy Assistance. http://www.liheap.org, 1615 L St. NW, Ste. 520, Washington, DC 20036, 202-429-8855, fax 202-429-8857. The Campaign for Home Energy Assistance's clearinghouse provides free telephone and email referrals to people who want to know where to apply for low-income energy assistance. Those seeking help can call the National Energy Assistance Referral (NEAR) project toll-free at 866-674-6327 from 8 a.m. to 6 p.m., Eastern time, or email NEAR at energyassistance@ncat.org.

Directory of Crime Victim Services. http://ovc.ncjrs.org/findvictimservices. This is a Web-enabled, online resource sponsored by the United States Department of Justice, Office for Victims of Crime (OVC). Use the directory to locate victim services in the United States and other countries. Search by location, type of victimization, service needed, or agency type.

eRideShare. http://www.erideshare.com. eRideShare.com is a free donation-supported service for connecting commuters.

Family Caregiver Alliance. http://www.caregiver.org/caregiver/jsp/home.jsp, info@caregiver.org, 180 Montgomery St., Ste. 1100, San Francisco, CA 94104, 415-434-3388, 800-445-8106, fax 415-434-3508. The Family Caregiver Alliance works to address the needs of families and friends providing long-term care at home. FCA has programs at national, state, and local levels to support and sustain caregivers.

National Academy of Elder Law Attorneys (NAELA). http://www.naela.org, 1604 N. Country Club Rd., Tucson, AZ 85716, 520-881-4005, fax 520-325-7925. The National Academy of Elder Law Attorneys searchable directory of elder law attorneys can be found online.

National Adult Day Services Association, Inc. (NADSA). http://www.nadsa.org, email: info@nadsa.org, 722 Grant St., Ste. L, Herndon, VA 20170, 800-558-5301, 703-435-8630, fax 703-435-8631. NADSA is the voice of the rapidly growing adult day service industry in the United States. Contact NADSA to locate state associations.

National Association of Professional Geriatric Care Managers (GCM). http://www.caremanager.org, 1604 N. Country Club Rd., Tucson, AZ 85716-3102, 520-881-8008, fax 520-325-7925. With more than 1,500 members, the National Association of Professional Geriatric Care Managers is a key resource to locating geriatric care managers. The Web site has an online database searchable by location.

National Center on Elder Abuse (NCEA). http://www.elderabusecenter.org, email: ncea@nasua.org, 1201 15th St. NW, Ste. 350, Washington, DC 20005-2842, 202-898-2586, fax 202-898-2583. NCEA is a gateway to resources on elder abuse, neglect, and exploitation. The Web site includes a list of state elder abuse hotlines.

National Hospice and Palliative Care Organization (NHPCO). http://www.nhpco.org, 1700 Diagonal Rd., Ste. 625, Alexandria, VA 22314, 703-837-1500, fax 703-837-1233. NHPCO represents hospice and palliative care programs and professionals in the United States. It provides public and professional educational programs and materials to enhance understanding and availability of hospice and palliative care.

Rehabilitation Engineering and Assistive Technology Society of North America (RESNA). http://www.resna.org, 1700 N. Moore St., Ste. 1540, Arlington, VA 22209-1903, 703-524-6686, fax 703-524-6630, TTY 703-524-6639. Contact RESNA for information about the Assistive Technology Financial Loan program in your state. The Web site also has a links to state Assistive Technology Act Programs and on state projects with information and resources on assistive technology.

United States Administration on Aging (AoA). http://www.aoa.gov, email: aoainfo@aoa.gov, U.S. Dept. of Health and Human Services Administration on Aging, Washington, DC, 20201, 202-619-0724, fax 202-357-3560.

The Administration on Aging is part of a federal, state, tribal, and local partnership called the National Aging Network. The Network consists of 56 State Units on Aging (SUA), 655 Area Agencies on Aging (AAAs), 243 tribal and native organizations, 29,000 service providers, and thousands of volunteers.

To find resources and support services through the National Aging Network, contact your local Area Agency on Aging. In a few states, the State Unit or Office on Aging serves as the AAA. You can locate the appropriate AAA or local service provider through the Administration on Aging-supported, nationwide, toll-free information and assistance directory, called the Eldercare Locator. Call the Eldercare Locator at 800-677-1116, Monday through Friday, 9:00 a.m. to 8:00 p.m., Eastern time. For 24-hour access to the Locator, visit http://www.eldercare.gov

AoA's legal hotline directory is available at http://www.aoa.gov/eldfam/ Elder_Rights/Legal_Assistance/Legal_Hotline.asp

Part 3

HEALTH AND MENTAL HEALTH

And in the end it's not the years in your life that count.
It's the life in your years.

Abraham Lincoln

Nothing is inherently and invincibly young except spirit. And spirit
can enter a human being perhaps better in the quiet of old age
and dwell there more undisturbed than in the turmoil of adventure.

George Santayana

Part 3 addresses the health aspects of aging—the good news and the challenges. Health is a balance among an individual's entire set of capacities—physical, mental, emotional, and spiritual. You will learn about the chronic illnesses that occur more frequently in later life, as well as the positive side of physical aging—the dramatic benefits possible for almost all seniors through nutrition, fitness, and healthy lifestyles.

Many seniors fear that they will develop Alzheimer's disease. Therefore, it is important for you as a CSA to understand the difference between normal cognitive changes that occur with aging and the different types of dementia. Chapter 12 covers the newest research on this topic.

During later life, spirituality often increases, and many seniors develop a sense of greater assurance and fulfillment in being—rather than doing—as they become older. Chapter 13 provides insight into this important process during later life.

Finally, you will consider end-of-life issues, particularly care planning and advance directives, which help complete the cycle of life with wisdom and grace.

Chapter 10

Chronic Illness in Seniors

Hannah is a widowed former farm wife, mother of 7 children and grandmother to 18, who recently celebrated her 90th birthday with a large party in her town's community center. After the death of her husband she moved to a modest house in a small town in the Midwest. She is responsible for maintaining the house with the assistance of three of her children who also live in the area. Until recently she walked most days on a three-mile path in the town but prior to winter switched to daily use of a treadmill in her house. She has also decided to reduce her house maintenance responsibilities by selling her home and moving to a senior housing complex in the same town. She plays cards several times a week with her friends. Her health is excellent and she frequently expresses annoyance with friends who she says "spend too much time complaining about their aches and pains."

. . .

Harry is a 75-year-old retired professional who lives with his wife in an apartment in a large Southern city. Gregarious and fun-loving, he has enjoyed with family and friends social occasions, animated discussions, and fishing. Harry was first diagnosed with hypertension 15 years ago. Treatment was established with good control. However, two years ago his blood pressure began fluctuating, and controlling it became more difficult. One day on his way to a fishing outing with a friend, he suffered a massive stroke and was rushed to the hospital. He was paralyzed on the right side of his body. His speech was affected. Months of physical, occupational, and speech therapy followed. He is now able to walk with a cane, but requires much assistance from his wife with his activities of daily living. Harry is able to understand speech but unable to express himself, which leads to frustration on his part. His wife, who is dealing with health problems of her own, wonders how much longer she will be able to care for him at home.

Introduction

As Hannah's story exemplifies, today's seniors are, as a group, healthier and less limited by disabilities than previous generations. However, chronic conditions remain a significant factor for many seniors such as Harry. Understanding and supporting your senior clients requires a familiarity with the most common chronic illnesses they face, as well as signs of those diseases, symptoms, treat-

267

ments, and their potential impact on daily life. As a CSA, such knowledge will help you communicate effectively with your senior clients, appreciate the limitations that illness may bring, and support your clients during treatment and adaptation.

As medical breakthroughs and other advancements have extended and improved lives, more individuals are living longer with chronic illnesses. According to the Centers for Disease Control (CDC), the world has experienced a transition in the primary causes of death. As medicine has increasingly controlled infectious disease and acute illnesses, chronic disease and degenerative illness now account for most deaths. Treatments will undoubtedly improve and life spans will continue to lengthen, but not without exacting a huge toll on our health care system (CDC, 2004c).

SENIORS AND CHRONIC CONDITIONS

Chronic conditions are impairments or illnesses that have no cure but result in persistent or recurring health consequences that last for years. They are the most prevalent health problem and tend to be more disabling in seniors than in younger age groups. Four in five seniors have at least one chronic health problem, and one in three have activity limitation associated with those conditions (Vierck & Hodges, 2003).

While many seniors continue to lead active and productive lives even with chronic conditions, they generally notice a progression of severity as they get older. Among seniors, 45 percent of those ages 75 and older are limited in activities because of chronic conditions, compared to 34 percent of those ages 65 to 74 and 23 percent of those ages 45 to 64 (National Academy on an Aging Society, 1999). These conditions can demand extensive caregiving, whether informal (by family or friends) or formal (home care or institutional), as well as significant spending for health care.

Top Ten Chronic Conditions

Table 10.1 shows the most common illnesses faced by Americans over 65 years of age. This chapter will focus on a variety of chronic conditions affecting seniors, including heart disease, stroke, arthritis, diabetes, and cancer. Disorders such as hearing and visual impairments are covered in chapter 3, Physiological Changes of Aging.

Table 10.1 Ten Most Common Illnesses in Americans, Ages 65 and Older

arthritis	limb deformities or impairments
high blood pressure	chronic sinusitis
hearing impairments	diabetes
diseases of the heart	tinnitus (ringing in the ears)
cataracts	visual impairments

Source: National Center for Health Statistics.

The Impact of Chronic Illness

Chronic illness has a dramatic effect on seniors. Most significantly, it reduces their quality of life and ability to remain independent in their homes. It increases family pressures by placing demands for caregiving on spouses and children. It also hinders seniors' ability to enjoy favorite activities and increases out-of-pocket spending on prescription drugs, physician visits, diagnostic procedures, and hospitalizations. Often, these dollars must come from savings and retirement income.

According to a study conducted by the Alliance for Aging Research (AAR), Americans who prematurely lose the ability to live independently increase overall national health care costs by $26 billion annually (AAR, 1999). The study revealed that it is not the big killers like cancer and heart attacks that most rob seniors' independence; rather, it is under-recognized and under-treated chronic conditions such as diabetes, arthritis, cognitive impairments, and physical immobility.

It is important to recognize that health for seniors involves not just physiological aspects, but mental, emotional, behavioral, and spiritual dimensions as well. Clinical depression and other mental health conditions can develop from the stresses associated with the onset of other diseases. As such, you should refer clients seeking treatment to appropriate professionals, in addition to encouraging informal support systems that promote overall health.

Genetic predisposition, gender, and age—factors that can't be modified—make us vulnerable to developing chronic conditions. But other risk factors related to health behaviors and lifestyle choices can be modified. A high percentage of people with chronic illness have modifiable risk factors that could be treated, thus limiting the progression of the illness. Disability can be delayed as much as 10 years by practicing three basic health habits: engaging in regular physical activity, not smoking, and practicing good nutrition (CDC, 2004b, 2004c).

Figures 10.1 and 10.2 provide a visual representation of the association between chronic conditions and risk factors. Be aware of the modifiable risk factors and encourage your clients to incorporate healthy behaviors and choices into daily activities.

Figure 10.1 Percentage of 51- to 61-Year-Olds with Modifiable Risk Factors

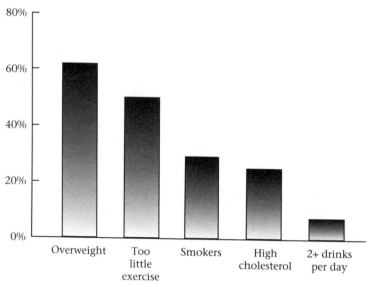

Source: National Academy on an Aging Society, analysis of data from the *1992 Health and Retirement Study*.

Figure 10.2 The Presence of Risk Factors in Seniors with Selected Chronic Conditions

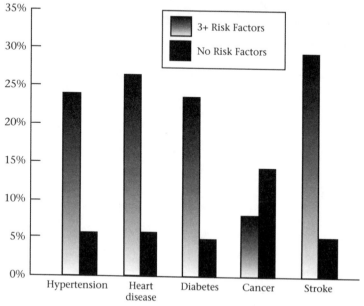

Source: National Academy on an Aging Society, analysis of data from the *1992 Health and Retirement Study*.

The Cost of Not Being Healthy

According to a study done by the Cooper Clinic in Dallas, Texas, chronic illness results in increased health care expenses (Mitchell, 2000). The clinic conducted a 20-year study of apparently healthy men, following each subject with complete physicals and extensive questionnaires at 5-year intervals. Subjects were divided into quartiles from the least fit to the most fit based on their physical exams and treadmill test results.

The least fit group spent 63 percent more on overnight hospitalizations and doctor visits each year; the extra hospitalizations alone cost $250,000. Extrapolation of the data to 97.8 million adult men in the United States shows a projected $4.1 billion increase for hospitalization costs and doctor visits for the least fit. The good news was that the most fit men were not elite athletes. Rather, they were a cross section of men who exercised 20 to 30 minutes per day, four to five times per week.

Results of this and other similar studies reinforce the importance of maintaining a healthy lifestyle to help reduce health care costs. Seniors are responsible for a disproportionate amount of health care expenses. Almost one-third of health care costs in the United States, $300 billion each year, are for older adults (CDC, 2004b). It is estimated that health care spending will increase by 25 percent between the years 2000 and 2030, during which an enormous percentage of the population passes age 65. Since poor health and chronic conditions are not inevitable as we age, healthy behaviors can be major factors in saving health care dollars.

You can play an important role by providing your clients with educational materials about the relationship of health behaviors, quality of life, and health care costs, and encouraging them to adopt healthy behaviors.

The Expression of Illness in Seniors

It is not uncommon for an illness to have different symptoms in seniors than in younger adults. It is important for you and your clients' families to know that for many seniors, *confusion* may be the initial sign of illness, thus signaling the beginning of an infection or the onset of changes in the manner in which the heart, lungs, liver, or kidneys are performing. For example, confusion may be one of the first observable symptoms of a urinary tract infection, or it could indicate that the kidneys are not excreting waste properly.

Sadly, some seniors and their families delay seeking medical treatment because they mistakenly believe the onset of confusion, sudden or gradual, or altered mental behavior is Alzheimer's disease or some other age-related cognitive change. Any change in a senior's cognitive function should be medically evaluated both to identify the underlying cause of the change and to identify amenable treatments.

Seniors may also postpone medical help for physical symptoms that they associate with "normal" aging. Acceptance of such indicators as pain, changed sleep patterns, or decreasing activity, among others, can prove detrimental to a senior and result in a worsened situation. Consultation with a health care provider should always be considered when there is a change of any kind.

271

Encourage your clients and their families to seek the advice of health care providers whenever there is an alteration in a senior's condition, physically or mentally. In situations where you see a client less often, it may be more difficult to recognize gradual changes. In such cases, it is imperative that family members who see the senior regularly be aware of the implications of physical or mental changes.

Heart Disease

Heart disease is the leading cause of death among seniors, accounting for one-third of all deaths among seniors in 1999 (Vierck & Hodges, 2003). Deaths due to heart disease become more prevalent with age. In 1999, 29 percent of deaths among those 65 to 74 years old were heart disease-related, but that number rose to 39 percent for those age 85 and older. While there are many forms of heart disease, you will most frequently encounter heart attack, more technically known as *acute myocardial infarction* (MI). To better understand heart disease, you must first understand the phenomena of hypertension, coronary arteries, and angina, and how these interact with each other in heart disease.

HYPERTENSION (HIGH BLOOD PRESSURE)

According to the National Academy on an Aging Society, high blood pressure is a leading risk factor for heart disease and stroke and is a serious health issue for about 15 percent of the adult population.

The arteries that carry blood from the heart to various organs in the body have muscles within their walls that allow the vessel to constrict or dilate in response to signals from the body. Constriction increases the pressure within the artery and restricts blood flow. During constriction, greater pressure is required to move blood through the artery. Dilation, on the other hand, increases the size of the artery, allowing blood to flow more easily and with less pressure.

Blood pressure is the force exerted by the blood against the interior wall of the artery. It is commonly reflected as a value of two numbers, the systolic and the diastolic. In a blood pressure reading of 140/90, the first or upper number, 140, represents the *systolic pressure*, or the amount of force exerted when the heart contracts to pump blood through the artery. The second or lower number, 90, represents the *diastolic pressure*, or the force within the artery between heartbeats, when the heart is at rest and there is no pressure pushing the blood through the system. A consistently high pressure within the circulatory system causes the heart to work much harder and increases the risk of heart disease, stroke, kidney disease, and blindness.

Conventionally, a blood pressure of 120/80 is considered an average reading, while a blood pressure consistently above 140/90 is termed *hypertension*. A person with a reading between 120/80 and 140/90 has *pre-hypertension* and is at high risk of developing hypertension. Numerous factors increase the risk of developing hypertension. Among the most common are smoking, high cholesterol (which clogs arteries with plaque), being overweight, and drinking too much alcohol. Figure 10.3 shows the variation in hypertension risk by age and gender.

Figure 10.3 Hypertension by Age and Gender

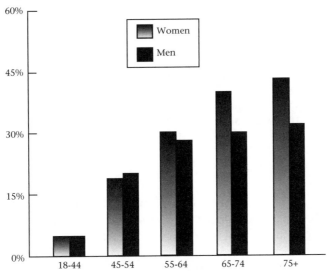

Source: National Academy on an Aging Society, analysis of data from the *1994 National Health Interview Survey.*

Fortunately, these behaviors can be controlled through lifestyle changes. Unfortunately, since high blood pressure can be present for years without any symptoms, many Americans are unaware they have high blood pressure. As such, they do not know they need to make behavioral changes or, possibly, need to take medications (antihypertensive drugs) to control their hypertension.

Knowledge about hypertension among older Americans is quite low. For example, in a survey of 1,500 people age 50 and older, the National Academy on an Aging Society discovered that 46 percent incorrectly believed stress caused hypertension and that 45 percent did not know their own blood pressure (2000). What's more, approximately 28 percent believed prescription drugs to be the only form of treatment. Clearly, such lack of knowledge prohibits full access to the measures that can lower the incidence of high blood pressure and reduce the risk of complications.

You should consider including educational materials regarding hypertension in newsletters and informational forums sent to your senior clients. You can also encourage clients to monitor their blood pressure at home or to take advantage of blood pressure screening clinics whenever possible.

WHAT ARE CORONARY ARTERIES?

The heart is a large and powerful muscle responsible for circulating blood throughout the body. It takes blood enriched with oxygen from the lungs and pumps it out to the body's organs and tissues, supplying them with the necessary nutrients. The heart muscle itself derives nutrients from *coronary arteries*. The right coronary artery and the left coronary artery, which immediately branches into the left anterior descending coronary artery, feed the front of the heart. The circumflex artery feeds the back of the heart. These arteries supply the heart muscle with both oxygen and nutrients appropriate for the amount of work being performed—the greater the exertion, the harder the heart muscle works to pump blood and the more oxygen it needs to perform satisfactorily.

Atherosclerosis is a process by which the arteries become clogged. Under normal conditions, the inner lining of the artery is very smooth and allows blood to flow unimpeded. With age and poor health habits, these arteries gradually accumulate sludge deposits consisting of cholesterol, debris, and blood platelets. These deposits attach to the artery wall and form plaque that narrows the internal lumen (diameter) of the artery, making the artery wall less flexible and more prone to developing blood clots.

ANGINA

When plaques build up, the arterial lumen becomes smaller and blood flow through the artery is reduced. Blood supply may be sufficient for the heart muscle at rest but cannot keep pace when the heart's work increases (as with exertion). Insufficient oxygen to the heart muscle leads to a type of pain known as *angina*. This is a sensation that is described variously as pain, heaviness in the chest, or tightness that feels like a band around the chest. The pain usually emanates from the center of the chest under the breastbone, but sufferers may feel it in the neck, jaw, or arm (left more often than right). The pain of angina is short in duration and goes away if activity is stopped. This allows the oxygen supply to catch up to the heart muscle's demand.

Stable angina is a chest pain that has been present at least two months, does not occur at rest, and has not changed in frequency or duration. Stable angina is usually treated medically through weight reduction, smoking cessation, and medications that reduce the work of the heart and lower oxygen demand. Conversely, *unstable angina* may be new in occurrence or reflect a change in frequency or duration of painful attacks. Unlike stable angina, unstable angina may occur even at rest. Unstable angina is associated with a worsening in the heart's condition and requires immediate medical attention.

Seniors who have stable angina may carry nitroglycerin pills. When chest pain occurs, a nitroglycerin pill placed under the tongue increases flow of blood and oxygen to the heart, reducing the heart's workload. If chest pain persists after ceasing activity and taking nitroglycerin, emergency medical attention is needed.

HEART ATTACK

As the process of atherosclerosis continues, the artery may become totally blocked, thereby cutting off blood flow entirely to a small section of the heart muscle. Without oxygenated blood, the heart muscle dies in what is commonly known as a *heart attack* or *acute myocardial infarction* (AMI). A heart attack is a medical emergency of the first order. In North America, about 500,000 heart attack deaths occur outside the hospital, compared with 60,000 deaths among those who reach the hospital (Khan & Marriott, 1996). Thus, you may save a life by recognizing the symptoms of a heart attack and summoning emergency medical services by dialing 911 immediately.

In the majority of patients, there is no identifiable event that triggers the heart attack—no one knows exactly when a coronary artery will *occlude*, or become blocked. The individual may state he or she has crushing pain, vise-like squeezing, or a heavy weight on his or her chest. The pain may be accompanied by profuse sweating, shortness of breath, nausea, or extreme weakness. The signs of heart attack in women may be more subtle or different in nature, manifested by feeling breathless, unexplained fatigue, and feelings of anxiety. Chest pain may or may not be present. If the person's blood pressure drops significantly or the heart rhythm becomes too fast or highly irregular, he or she may lose consciousness. If such an event occurs in your presence, remain with the individual and call for paramedics. Never attempt to take the individual to the hospital yourself, as the person's condition might deteriorate during transport.

TREATMENT OF HEART DISEASE

Typical treatments for coronary artery disease include angioplasty, coronary artery bypass grafts, and the emergency administration of medications to clear the clogged artery in an emergency room. Of the three treatments, the oldest is coronary artery bypass graft, or CABG (pronounced "cabbage"). When one's quality of life is eroded by the combination of chest pain and reduced levels of activity that do not respond to medications or angioplasty (explained below), a CABG offers a reasonable alternative. In this surgical procedure, the section of blocked artery is removed and is replaced by one of the patient's leg veins or internal mammary arteries. The new vein or artery is grafted into place, restoring circulation through the coronary artery. With this treatment, approximately 90 percent of patients obtain complete relief for two or more years (Khan & Marriott, 1996).

Another treatment for heart attack is angioplasty (also called percutaneous transluminal coronary angioplasty, or PTCA). Angioplasty, which has been a part of the medical arsenal for a little less than 25 years, involves passing an instrument through the skin (percutaneous) and into the artery (transluminal). The instrument is advanced into the coronary arteries, where a balloon on the tip of the instrument inflates to crush the atherosclerotic plaques. Successful reopening of an artery can be accomplished in 70 to 90 percent of patients, although about 20 to 35 percent of these patients will occlude again within six months (Khan & Marriott, 1996).

Khan and Marriott report that the most recent form of treatment focuses on dissolving clots through one of four drugs: streptokinase, tissue plasminogen activase (tPA), reteplase, and anistreplase (APSAC). Used in the emergency department, these drugs are given intravenously within a very short period of time (four to six hours) after the onset of heart attack symptoms and both dissolve the clot and reestablish blood flow to the heart muscle.

Aftercare is critical for those who have had heart surgery. Coronary heart disease patients usually undergo some type of physical therapy. Those that successfully follow through with therapy are less likely to suffer another coronary event. Regardless, any medical treatment for heart disease remains incomplete without the necessary lifestyle changes to support a healthy heart, such as losing weight, modifying the diet, quitting smoking, and exercising regularly.

Support groups such as Mended Hearts (see Resources section) can help those with heart disease meet new challenges and receive support to maintain their lifestyle changes.

The role you can play in heart disease is threefold. First, be aware that high cholesterol, high blood pressure, smoking, obesity, and sedentary lifestyle significantly increase the incidence of coronary heart disease. Encourage senior clients to seek appropriate medical assessment and make changes to alleviate these factors. Second, learn about angina and the symptoms of a heart attack, and learn cardiopulmonary resuscitation (CPR), a procedure that could be lifesaving. Third, offer assistance that supports the patient and family as the person moves through recovery toward resuming normal activities following a heart attack or bypass surgery.

Stroke

Note: The information in this section is excerpted from materials provided by the National Institute of Neurological Disorders and Stroke (2000).

Seven in 10 strokes occur among seniors (Vierck & Hodges, 2003), and strokes are the third leading cause of death among seniors (8.3 percent of all senior deaths). Those who survive a stroke often have significant physical and emotional challenges, as they seek to relearn skills that let them interact and communicate with those around them. The precipitous event of a stroke can devastate families. Consequently, you should be acquainted with the risk factors and symptoms of strokes, treatment options following a stroke, and methods to support those whose lives have been altered.

WHAT IS STROKE?

A stroke occurs when a clot suddenly interrupts the blood supply to part of the brain or when a blood vessel within the brain bursts, spilling blood into the surrounding space. As a result, some brain cells die immediately while others remain at risk of dying. These damaged cells can linger in a compromised state for several hours. Fortunately, timely treatment can save these compromised cells.

There are two forms of stroke: *ischemic stroke* and *hemorrhagic stroke. Ischemia* is the term used to describe the loss of oxygen and nutrients to brain cells when there is inadequate blood flow. An ischemic stroke occurs when an artery supplying the brain with blood suddenly becomes blocked, which decreases or stops blood flow to the brain. Ultimately, this causes a brain *infarction*, or death of brain cells. This type of stroke accounts for approximately 80 percent of all strokes. Blood clots are the most common cause of artery blockage and brain infarction.

Clotting of the blood is both necessary and beneficial because it stops bleeding and allows repair of damaged areas of arteries or veins. However, when blood clots develop in the wrong place, such as within an artery in the brain, they can cause devastating injury. Studies indicate that clotting problems become more frequent as people age. Blood clots may form in an artery within the brain or they may travel to the brain from other parts of the body. Either condition leads to identical end results: Brain tissue will die due to lack of oxygen and nutrients. Ischemic strokes can also occur if arteries within the brain become narrowed. This, too, reduces blood flow and increases the likelihood that clots will develop. Narrowed arteries are the result of the buildup of sludge (cholesterol, fatty substances, cellular debris) as commonly seen in atherosclerosis.

Hemorrhagic strokes occur when an artery within the brain bursts, spewing blood into the surrounding tissue. This upsets not only the blood supply but also the delicate chemical balance brain cells need to function. This type of stroke, which accounts for approximately 20 percent of all strokes, can occur in several ways. One common cause is an *aneurysm*, a weak or thin spot on an artery wall. These weak spots stretch or balloon out over time under high arterial pressure. The thin walls of these ballooning aneurysms can rupture and spill blood into the space surrounding brain cells. Hemorrhage also occurs when arterial walls break open. For instance, a plaque-encrusted artery wall eventually loses its elasticity and becomes thin and brittle. This makes the artery prone to cracking. Combined with high blood pressure, a brittle artery wall is at risk of giving way and spewing blood into the surrounding brain tissue.

WHO IS AT RISK FOR STROKE?

Some people are at higher risk for stroke than others are. Some risk factors can be controlled, but others cannot. Among the factors that cannot be altered are one's age, gender, race and ethnicity, and family history. The risk of stroke increases with age, so seniors are at higher risk than the general population. For every decade after age 55, the risk of stroke doubles; two-thirds of all strokes occur in people over 65 years old. What's more, people over 65 have a seven-fold greater risk of dying from stroke than the general population. And, the *incidence* of stroke is increasing proportionately with the increase in the senior population. When the relatively large baby boomer population moves into the over-65 age group, stroke and other diseases will have an even greater impact on the health care field.

Gender also plays a role in stroke risk. Although men have a higher risk for stroke (1.25 times higher), more women die from it. (Men are usually younger when they have a stroke, and therefore they have a higher rate of survival than women.)

The incidence of stroke is higher when a family history of the disease exists. Additionally, the incidence is higher in certain ethnic groups such as African Americans, whose risk is almost double that of Caucasians. Studies also show that twice as many African Americans who suffer a stroke die from the event compared to Caucasians. Among other ethnic populations in the United States, including Hispanics, Asians, and Native Americans, the incidence of stroke is similar to that for Caucasians.

Modifiable risks encompass behavioral choices and lifestyle patterns that increase one's risk of stroke. Among these risks, hypertension is by far the most potent modifiable risk factor. Maintaining proper weight, avoiding excess salt (sodium), exercising regularly, and using prescribed antihypertensive medications can all reduce stroke risk. Another modifiable risk factor is cigarette smoking, which has been linked to the buildup of fatty substances in the carotid artery, the main neck artery supplying blood to the brain. Blockage of this artery is the leading cause of stroke in Americans. Also, smoking carries many other health hazards: nicotine raises blood pressure; carbon monoxide reduces the amount of oxygen reaching the brain; and cigarette smoke makes the blood thicker, thereby increasing one's risk for clots.

Common heart disorders such as coronary artery disease, valve defects, irregular heartbeat, and enlargement of one of the heart's chambers can result in blood clots that may break loose and block vessels in or leading to the brain. To reduce risk, physicians now frequently prescribe medications such as aspirin to help prevent clot formation. In more serious cases, surgery may be recommended to clean out clogged arteries.

SYMPTOMS OF STROKE

Warning signs are clues that the brain is not receiving enough oxygen. If you observe one or more of these signs of a stroke in a senior client, call 911 immediately:

- sudden numbness or weakness of face, arm, or leg, especially on one side of the body
- sudden confusion or trouble speaking or understanding
- sudden trouble seeing in one or both eyes or having double vision
- sudden trouble walking, dizziness, loss of balance or coordination, or drowsiness
- sudden severe headache with no known cause
- nausea or vomiting

Sometimes the warning signs may last only a few moments and then disappear. These brief episodes, known as *transient ischemic attacks* or TIAs, are sometimes called "mini-strokes." Although brief, they identify an underlying serious condition that won't go away without medical help. Unfortunately, since they clear up, many people ignore them. Paying attention to these signals may save a client's life.

TREATMENT FOR STROKE

The type of stroke therapy a patient receives largely depends on the stage of disease. Generally, there are three treatment stages for stroke: prevention, therapy immediately after stroke, and post-stroke rehabilitation.

Therapies to prevent either a first stroke or a recurrent stroke are based on treating an individual's underlying risk factors. Acute stroke therapies strive to halt a stroke in progress by quickly dissolving the blood clot causing the stroke or to stop the bleeding from a hemorrhagic stroke with surgery. The purpose of post-stroke rehabilitation is to overcome disabilities that result from stroke damage.

Rehabilitation Therapy

Stroke is the number one cause of serious adult disability in the United States and can be devastating to both the stroke victim and his or her family. Some disabilities that can result from a stroke are paralysis, cognitive deficits, speech problems, emotional difficulties, daily living problems, and chronic pain. Although stroke is a disease of the brain, it often affects the entire body, so available therapies can help rehabilitate some post-stroke patients.

One common disability that results from stroke is paralysis on one side of the body, known as *hemiplegia*. A related disability, though not as debilitating as paralysis, is one-sided weakness or *hemiparesis*. Paralysis or weakness may also affect only one part of the body such as the face, an arm, or a leg.

The brain has two hemispheres, each of which controls the opposite side of the body. Because of this, a person who suffers a stroke in the left hemisphere will have right-sided paralysis or paresis. Conversely, a person with a stroke in the right hemisphere of the brain will display deficits on the left side of the body. As a result of a stroke, a person may have problems with even the simplest of daily activities—walking, dressing, eating, or using the bathroom. Motor deficits can result, affecting balance and coordination. Some stroke patients also have trouble eating and swallowing, a condition known as *dysphagia*.

For most stroke patients, physical therapy (PT) is the cornerstone of the rehabilitation process. A physical therapist combines training, exercises, and physical manipulation of the stroke patient's body to help restore movement, balance, and coordination. The goal of PT is to help the stroke victim relearn basic activities such as walking, sitting, standing, lying down, and the switching from one type of movement to another.

Like physical therapy, occupational therapy (OT) also involves exercise and training to help the stroke patient relearn everyday activities such as eating, drinking and swallowing, dressing, bathing, cooking, reading and writing, and toileting. The goal of the occupational therapist is to help the patient provide their own care by becoming independent or semi-independent.

Speech and language problems arise when brain damage occurs in the language centers of the brain. Due to the brain's great ability to learn and change (called *brain plasticity*), other areas can adapt to take over some of the lost functions. Speech therapy helps stroke patients relearn language and speaking skills or learn other forms of communication. Speech therapy is appropriate for patients who have no deficits in cognition or thinking but have problems understanding speech or written words or have problems forming speech. A speech therapist trains stroke patients to improve their language skills. If necessary, a speech therapist will help a stroke victim learn alternative ways of communicating or will assist the patient in developing coping skills to deal with the frustration of not being able to communicate fully.

With time and patience, stroke survivors should be able to regain some, and sometimes all, of their language and speaking abilities, depending on the extent of damage from the stroke. Many stroke patients develop psychological problems such as depression, anxiety, frustration, and anger. When this occurs, mental health treatment or medication may alleviate some issues. Sometimes, it is beneficial for family members of the stroke patient to also seek psychological follow-up.

Aspirin Therapy

Recent studies indicate that aspirin can reduce the risk of heart attacks and ischemic strokes and can reduce the risk of death or complications from a heart attack. Aspirin thins the blood, allowing it to circulate more easily and decreasing the likelihood of blood clots. Thus, many people believe that if someone is having a heart attack, the person should be given aspirin. Despite these apparent benefits, *aspirin therapy should be provided only under the direction of a physician who can monitor side effects and potential negative consequences.* Aspirin can be very hard on the stomach lining and may produce ulcers in some people. Reducing the blood's ability to clot can have very negative consequences when other conditions exist, such as wet macular degeneration or hemorrhagic stroke. Aspirin may also interact with other medications the senior may be taking. For people who are not at risk of heart attack or stroke, the potential dangers of aspirin therapy may outweigh the benefits. It is increasingly common for physicians to prescribe low doses of aspirin for patients who have had an angioplasty, heart attack, or ischemic stroke. The best advice is for seniors to ask their physicians about the possible value of aspirin for their specific condition.

Diabetes Mellitus

Like arthritis, diabetes mellitus is a series of diseases with a common thread. The disease results from the body's inability to properly use glucose, one of the principal sources of cellular energy. When the body converts the food we eat into glucose, insulin (made by the pancreas) helps deliver the glucose to cells and stores any excess for later use. However, whenever insulin is either insufficient or altogether absent, glucose builds up within the bloodstream and cells are unable to get the energy source needed to continue their functions.

There are two major types of diabetes, Type 1 and Type 2. *Type 1 diabetes,* previously called *insulin-dependent diabetes mellitus* (IDDM) or juvenile onset diabetes, affects approximately 16 million Americans, according to the National Center for Biotechnology Information (n.d.).

Type 1 diabetics are usually less than 40 years of age and experience a very sudden onset of symptoms. Their bodies produce no insulin and they must use insulin injections or, more recently, internal insulin pumps, to provide the insulin necessary to control blood glucose. Symptoms of Type 1 diabetes include excessive thirst, constant hunger, excessive urination, sudden weight loss for no reason, rapid or difficult breathing, sudden vision changes or blurry vision, weakness, drowsiness, exhaustion, or a fruity odor on the breath (JDF, 2004).

Type 2 diabetes, previously called *non-insulin dependent diabetes mellitus* (NIDDM) or *adult-onset diabetes*, accounts for 90 to 95 percent of cases. Most often, Type 2 diabetes appears gradually after the age of 40. Symptoms include hard-to-heal skin, gum or urinary tract infections, drowsiness, tingling of hands and feet, excessive urination, excessive hunger and thirst, and itching of skin and genitals (ADA, 2002; JDF, 2004). Nearly 11 percent of Americans ages 65 to 74 have Type 2 diabetes (ADA, 1996).

Individuals with Type 2 diabetes produce insulin but either do not make it in sufficient quantities or have cells that resist its actions. The genetic link— or tendency to run in families—is even greater in Type 2 diabetes than in Type 1. For example, an identical twin of a Type 1 diabetic has a 25 to 50 percent chance of having diabetes, while the identical twin of a Type 2 diabetic has a 60 to 75 percent chance of developing the disease (ADA, 1996). Research indicates the most important non-genetic factor in Type 2 diabetes is obesity— three-quarters of all people with Type 2 diabetes are or have been overweight (ADA, 1996). Age is also a factor, as over half of all new cases of Type 2 diabetes occur in people over age 55 (ADA, 1996). One of the most significant concerns is that Type 2 diabetes often goes undiagnosed for many years. Fortunately, a simple blood test that measures blood glucose provides the basis for making a diagnosis.

Pre-diabetes is a condition that raises a person's risk of developing Type 2 diabetes, heart disease, and stroke. About 41 million persons—40 percent of all adults in the United States—have pre-diabetes (CDC, 2004d). A person with pre-diabetes has a blood glucose level higher than normal but not yet at diabetic levels. Many pre-diabetics develop Type 2 diabetes within 10 years. It is important to identify pre-diabetes early because steps can be taken to prevent or delay the progression to Type 2 diabetes. These steps include losing weight, becoming physically active, and eating a healthy diet. If the numbers of persons with diabetes continue to grow, our health care system risks being overwhelmed with the health and economic consequences of the disease.

SENIORS AND DIABETES

More seniors have diabetes than any other group, making finger pricks and careful blood sugar monitoring a daily occurrence for many. Approximately half of all diabetes cases occur in people older than 55 years of age. According to the ADA, seven million seniors had diabetes in 2003. People with diabetes represent 18 percent of all nursing home residents and tend to be younger than residents who do not have diabetes.

DIABETES: OUR MOST COSTLY CHRONIC ILLNESS

Because diabetics are at higher risk for heart disease, blindness, kidney failure, extremity amputations, and other chronic conditions, diabetes is the costliest of all medical conditions. Estimated direct and indirect medical expenditures attributable to diabetes in 2002 were $132 billion (ADA, 2002).

TREATMENT OF DIABETES

Without regard to the type of diabetes, the primary goal of treatment is to achieve a balance between the amount of food ingested and the body's ability to manage glucose. Keeping blood glucose levels within a controlled range is critical to preventing damage to other areas such as the retina, kidneys, and circulatory system. Components of the treatment plan include a controlled diet, exercise, weight reduction, self-monitoring of blood glucose (SMBG), and medications to either supplement insulin or enhance the effectiveness of the body's own insulin supply. Approximately 30 to 40 percent of Type 2 diabetics require insulin, often in addition to oral medications (ADA, 1996).

COMPLICATIONS OF DIABETES

Complications of diabetes can be severe, life threatening, and substantially damaging throughout the body before a diagnosis is made. In order to minimize the occurrence of complications, regular screening for blood sugar levels, especially in the presence of a family history of diabetes, is extremely important in assuring the earliest possible response to abnormal blood sugar levels. Currently, it is thought that damage to body tissues from abnormal blood sugars begins early and continues, to some degree, even concurrent with external measures for controlling blood sugar. What this tells us is that even today's medical technology and pharmaceuticals are no match for the body's inherent controls. However, maintaining one's blood glucose levels within an established range can usually slow the progression of complications.

Many people first become aware that they have diabetes when they develop one of its life-threatening complications. The more common complications of diabetes, according to the ADA (2002), are described below.

- *Heart disease.* Heart disease is the leading cause of diabetes-related deaths. Adults with diabetes have heart disease death rates about two to four times higher than do adults without diabetes.
- *Stroke.* The risk for stroke is two to four times higher among people with diabetes.
- *High blood pressure.* About 73 percent of adults with diabetes have blood pressure greater than or equal to 130/80 or use prescription medications for hypertension.
- *Blindness.* Diabetes is the leading cause of new cases of blindness among adults 20 to 74 years old. Diabetic retinopathy causes from 12,000 to 24,000 new cases of blindness each year.
- *Kidney disease.* Diabetes is the leading cause of treated end-stage renal disease, accounting for 43 percent of new cases. In 1999, 38,160 people with

diabetes began treatment for end-stage renal disease. In 1999, a total of 114,478 people with diabetes underwent dialysis or kidney transplantation.

- *Nervous system disease.* About 60 to 70 percent of people with diabetes have mild to severe forms of nervous system damage. The results of such damage include impaired sensation or pain in the feet or hands, slowed digestion of food in the stomach, carpal tunnel syndrome, and other nerve problems. Severe forms of diabetic nerve disease are a major contributing cause of lower-extremity amputations.

- *Amputations.* More than 60 percent of non-traumatic lower-limb amputations in the United States occur among people with diabetes. From 1997 to 1999, about 82,000 non-traumatic lower-limb amputations were performed each year among people with diabetes.

- *Dental disease.* Periodontal (gum) diseases are more common among people with diabetes than among people without diabetes. Young adults with diabetes are often at twice the risk of those without diabetes. Almost one-third of people with diabetes have severe periodontal diseases.

- *Other complications.* Uncontrolled diabetes often leads to biochemical imbalances that can cause acute life-threatening events. People with diabetes are more susceptible to many other illnesses, and once they acquire these illnesses they often have a worse prognosis than people without diabetes. For example, they are more likely to die with pneumonia or influenza than people who do not have diabetes.

You can play a pivotal role in encouraging seniors to become aware of their risk factors for diabetes. You should also encourage them to be screened for diabetes and, if diagnosed, to make the lifestyle changes necessary to prevent the numerous complications that arise from uncontrolled blood glucose levels.

Arthritis

Arthritis is a group of more than 100 diseases and conditions affecting the joints and, in some cases, other organs as well. It is one of the most common medical problems in the United States, affecting nearly 70 million Americans, or one in three adults. Some of the most common forms are osteoarthritis, rheumatoid arthritis, fibromyalgia, gout, systemic lupus erythematosus, tendonitis, bursitis, and carpal tunnel syndrome. Each of these conditions affects different subsets of the population and has its own characteristic symptoms and changes in joint function. Juvenile rheumatoid arthritis, for example, may affect children as young as three, while osteoarthritis primarily affects older individuals.

Technically, *arthritis* means inflammation of a joint. But in reality, arthritis can result from normal wear and tear, as in osteoarthritis, or from inflammation, as in rheumatoid arthritis. Other forms of arthritis result from injury, infection, or metabolic problems. Some cases result from unknown causes. With rheumatoid arthritis, it's unclear what causes the inflammation, but possibly the body's immune system attacks the tissue lining the joints. Symptoms associated with arthritis include not just pain but also stiffness and swelling in joints, muscles, tendons, ligaments, and bones.

While arthritis affects all age ranges, it is especially prevalent among older adults. It is estimated that almost 59 percent of adults over age 65 have arthritis or other chronic joint symptoms, compared to 42 percent of those 45 to 65 years old and 19 percent of those ages 18 to 44 (CDC, 2004a).

The pain and costs associated with arthritis are staggering. It is the leading cause of disability among American adults. Twenty percent of adults with arthritis report limitations in activity; this accounts for approximately 3 million to 4 million older adults. Statistics show that arthritis costs the country $51.1 billion annually in medical expenses and another $35 billion in lost wages among those still working.

While some of the risk factors for arthritis—genetic make-up, hormone levels, and gender (women have higher incidence)—cannot be controlled, other factors such as lifestyle behaviors of weight and exercise can. The prevalence of arthritis in American adults was 44.5 percent in those who are inactive versus 28.9 percent in those who follow recommended daily activity levels. Similarly, the prevalence of arthritis was 44.6 percent in obese persons compared to 26.6 percent in those of normal weight (CDC, 2004a).

The misperception that arthritis is just a normal part of aging prevents many seniors from seeking medical advice or taking advantage of various therapies that help control pain and preserve their active involvement in life. Often, seniors assume that the pain, stiffness, and limitations of their activities are something that they simply must accommodate. But in fact, simple medications such as aspirin and acetaminophen, rest, joint protection, weight loss, muscle strengthening, and exercises to promote joint mobility are sufficient to allow many seniors to maintain normal activities with very tolerable levels of discomfort.

RHEUMATOID ARTHRITIS AND OSTEOARTHRITIS

Rheumatoid arthritis is the most common form of inflammatory arthritis, striking 0.3 to 1.5 percent of the American population (Pisetsky & Trien, 1992) and crossing all ethnic, racial, and age groups. It can cause severe pain and crippling deformities, such as gnarled, misshapen fingers. Typically, rheumatoid arthritis is diagnosed among 40- to 50-year-olds. Studies indicate that women are three times more likely to develop the condition than men (Long, 1997).

Osteoarthritis is the most common joint disease and is the major cause of disability in older Americans, affecting approximately 10 percent of the older population (Long, 1997). Also called degenerative joint disease (DJD), it is not an inflammatory process but rather the result of wear and tear on cartilage, the substance that cushions ends of bones within a joint. Over time, cartilage becomes less elastic and less spongy and, therefore, less effective in cushioning bones. Cartilage may even thin to the point that bones rub directly on each other within the joint. By age 60, over half the population has some degeneration of their joints, while the prevalence of it among those in their 80s and 90s is almost 100 percent (Pisetsky & Trien, 1992). While osteoarthritis clearly involves age-related wear and tear, other factors contribute to its development and severity, including excess weight, joint injury, and repetitive use (e.g., baseball pitching, needlework, carpentry). The weight-bearing joints such as the knee and hip may even deteriorate to the point of requiring surgical replacement.

TREATMENT FOR ARTHRITIS

The occurrence and severity of arthritic symptoms is highly variable. Sometimes it presents stiffness in the morning or when the affected joint is held in one position, with increased discomfort at the end of the day or during increased activity. Other symptoms include joint discomfort with weather changes, swelling, aching, redness, or warmth.

There is no cure for osteoarthritis. According to the Arthritis Foundation, treatment of osteoarthritis focuses on decreasing pain and improving joint movement, and may include (Arthritis Foundation, 2004):

- exercises to keep joints flexible and improve muscle strength
- heat/cold therapy for temporary pain relief
- joint protection to prevent strain or stress on painful joints
- surgery to relieve chronic pain in damaged joints
- weight control to prevent extra stress on weight-bearing joints

The Arthritis Foundation offers self-management and physical activity classes to teach the importance of staying active and how to go about it. Information about arthritis, exercise, relaxation techniques, and conditioning are some components of the classes, which have resulted in 20 percent reduction in pain and 40 percent reduction in physician visits for those completing the courses.

When it comes to arthritis, your role is to help dispel the misperceptions that arthritis is just a normal part of aging that seniors must endure. It is, in fact, a disease that can be effectively treated. Seniors should be encouraged not to simply accept pain, discomfort, and limitations on their activities. Rather, they should be advised that effective therapy is available to allow them to continue with meaningful activities. Patients who suffer from arthritis should be encouraged to seek medical evaluation and advice. You should also take steps to ensure that your office environment is user-friendly for clients with arthritis who may have limited mobility.

Osteoporosis

Another disease that greatly affects seniors' independence and mobility is osteoporosis. It is a progressive disease that causes bones to become thin, porous, and weak (WebMD, 2003). The loss of bone mass is part of the natural aging process; however, those with osteoporosis have accelerated loss. Anyone who does not develop sufficient bone mineral density in youth is apt to develop osteoporosis in later life. However, women are more likely to have the disease, evidenced by the disease's trademark hunched posture.

Osteoporosis is often called the "silent disease" because symptoms do not appear in its early stages. As the disease progresses, symptoms do emerge, including:

- back pain;
- loss of height and stooped posture;
- curved spine;
- bone fractures, especially in the hip, back vertebrae, and wrists.

A diagnosis of *osteopenia*, often called pre-osteoporosis, indicates that one's bone mineral density is lower than normal but bones have not yet thinned to the point of osteoporosis.

Treatment for osteoporosis or osteopenia includes a diet rich in calcium and vitamin D, appropriate regular exercise, and certain medications to increase bone thickness. Treatment largely mirrors the steps for prevention. The body's natural bone thinning can be reduced or delayed with healthy lifestyle habits such as not smoking, getting sufficient calcium, phosphorous, and vitamin D in the diet, and exercising regularly to strengthen bones (WebMD, 2003).

Urinary Incontinence

Urinary incontinence (UI), a common problem among the elderly, inhibits the quality of life for many seniors and creates unique caregiving demands. According to the Agency for Health Care Policy and Research (AHCPR), UI, or the unintentional loss of urine, is a problem for more than 13 million

Americans—85 percent of them women (AHCPR, 1996). Although about half of the elderly have episodes of incontinence, bladder problems are not a natural consequence of aging, and they are not exclusively a problem of the elderly.

The AHCPR guidelines on managing acute and chronic urinary incontinence indicate that for persons over the age of 60 living in the community, the prevalence of urinary incontinence can be as high as 15 to 35 percent.

Caregivers report that approximately 53 percent of the homebound elderly are incontinent, with urinary incontinence ranking as one of the 10 leading diagnoses for homebound individuals. This condition also ranks first in total charges to Medicare for nursing services per person served in home care programs. UI often leads to institutionalization, with at least 50 percent of nursing facility admissions listing a diagnosis of incontinence.

Cancer

It is estimated that 40 percent of all Americans will face a cancer diagnosis and that one in five will die of the disease. Increased public awareness and the availability of improved cancer screening techniques have led to earlier detection and consequently more successful treatment of many types of cancer. However, the bottom line is that lifestyle issues and personal behaviors that could dramatically reduce cancer death rates are still not embraced by many.

Cancer is the second leading cause of death for seniors and a major chronic condition for this age group (Vierck & Hodges, 2003). Seniors account for 59 percent of all cancers diagnosed annually. Senior men are nearly twice as likely as their female counterparts to be diagnosed with cancer.

WHAT IS CANCER?

Under normal circumstances, human cells multiply in a very tightly controlled process. When new cells are made, they remain in a specific location within the body. For example, heart muscle cells always stay in the heart and are created only in response to specific stimuli. A heart muscle cell that is damaged destroys itself through a process known as *apoptosis*—cellular suicide—to prevent the genetic error from being passed on.

Cancer cells behave quite differently in that they multiply without regard to any of the body's normal messages to stop. For example, cancer cells expand their support network of blood vessels and become larger (forming tumor masses). Cancer cells also frequently migrate through the bloodstream to establish themselves in other locations.

The following principles help explain the most common terminology used in cancer diagnoses. A *primary tumor* occurs when a genetic mutation in a cell causes it to reproduce abnormally. As this group of cells grows in size and continues to mutate genetically, it becomes large enough that it can be felt as a lump or be seen on diagnostic tests. A *cancer in situ* is one that has grown in size but remained confined in its original location. Many cancers progress to invade surrounding tissues (*invasive cancer*) or migrate to distant locations

287

(*metastatic cancer*). Invasion and metastasis are the common characteristics of malignant (harmful) tumors. The goal of detecting cancers early is to identify and treat cells that are just beginning to change their appearance (*dysplasia*) or that have not begun to invade surrounding tissues.

Although the causes of cancer are not fully understood, they are becoming much clearer at a rapid pace. What is known is that the genes we inherit from our parents contribute directly to a very small number of cancers, causing fewer than 5 percent of all cancer deaths (Trichopoulos, Li, & Hunter, 1996). In addition, many environmental factors (e.g., overexposure to sun, cigarette smoke, or chemicals) damage cells. Tobacco smoke, for instance, is the most lethal cancer-causing agent in the United States and is responsible for an estimated 30 percent of all cancer deaths (Trichopoulos et al.). Diet rivals tobacco smoke and accounts for another 30 percent of cancer deaths through the ingestion of saturated fats and red meat. Infections such as HIV, Hepatitis B, and Epstein-Barr virus account for approximately 5 percent of all cancers.

TYPES OF CANCER

Listed below are the leading types of cancer and the estimated number of cases Americans in 2003 (ACS, 2003):

- prostate (220,900)
- breast (211,300)
- lung (171,900 cases)
- colorectal (147,500)
- bladder (57,400)
- melanoma of the skin (54,200)
- non-Hodgkins lymphoma (53,400)
- uterine (40,100)
- ovarian (25,400)
- kidney (19,500)
- leukemia (17,900)

There are numerous ways to impact the development of cancer. For example, the projected number of deaths each year from lung cancer is greater than the combined total of annual deaths from colorectal, breast, and prostate cancer. Though few cases occur in the absence of a history of smoking, the elimination of tobacco smoke could almost eradicate lung cancer. Additionally we are now beginning to understand the impact of secondhand smoke on the development of lung cancer.

Early detection of cancer through screening has generated substantial progress in reducing the impact of cancer and cancer deaths. Finding a cancer when it is more responsive to treatment can result in a cure or in a significant extension of life. Testing stools, breast self-examinations, mammograms, Pap smears, rectal exams combined with blood tests for prostate-specific antigen

(PSA), and colonoscopy are common screening tests that can dramatically improve treatment results.

Medicare covers several screening measures including annual mammograms for women over 40, a Pap smear every two years, or annually for those at high risk, and both annual PSA tests and digital rectal exams for men over 50. According to current Medicare rules, annual fecal occult blood tests and flexible sigmoidoscopic exams every four years are considered the general preventive screening measures after age 50 for early detection of colorectal cancer. Medicare allows beneficiaries at high risk of colon cancer to receive a colonoscopy exam every other year. Many seniors do not take advantage of these opportunities, but you should encourage them to do so.

TREATMENT

Cancer is treated in basically one of four ways: surgery, radiation, chemotherapy, or genetically. Surgery is the most common intervention for many forms of cancer that are accessible to the surgeon's knife and have not spread throughout the body. At times, removal of the tumor with a sufficient margin (to include the edges where tumor growth may not be clearly visible) creates a major loss of function or physical appearance that is more difficult to live with than the disease itself.

Another alternative, radiation therapy, uses x-rays or gamma rays to kill tumor cells in difficult-to-reach locations. Radiation is also used to eliminate a tumor without destroying large amounts of healthy tissue. By nature, radiation therapy creates some injury to surrounding good tissue, but healing can occur over time.

Chemotherapy circulates very powerful chemicals through the body via the bloodstream to kill tumor cells. While this mode of treatment is advantageous in reaching virtually all parts of the body, it also kills a large number of good cells, which makes the patient quite sick. A person undergoing chemotherapy will experience nausea, vomiting, diarrhea, and a reduction in blood cells, which increases the susceptibility to bleeding and infection. Often these approaches are used in combination with other cancer treatments to maximize results.

The newest forms of cancer treatment involve genetic and biologic approaches that, for example, use the body's immune system to attack the cancer cells. Health Maintenance Organizations (HMOs) or insurance companies may deny coverage of these procedures due to their experimental status.

You must appreciate the psycho-emotional devastation that the diagnosis of cancer can have on seniors and their families. Naturally, coping styles vary, as does support available through different family networks. Because people often do not know what to say to a cancer patient and may withdraw from contact, isolation is one of the biggest problems cancer patients face. You may play a role in recognizing the reality of the emotional impact and helping the senior and his or her family find sources of support and information. Most important, you should stay in touch and remain supportive. Numerous formal support groups also exist for cancer patients to assist them and their families.

Pain and Chronic Illness

Pain is a common feature in many seniors' worlds. Pain may come from cancer, osteoarthritis, or some other chronic illness. Numerous studies have demonstrated that pain is frequently undertreated, leading to a substantial reduction in seniors' overall quality of life and their ability to remain functionally independent. Depression, social isolation, sleep deprivation, and decreased mobility are all adverse results of chronic pain inadequately treated.

Undertreatment of pain appears to be particularly prevalent among nursing home residents. Researchers discovered that 26.3 percent of nursing home residents studied had daily pain not due to cancer. Furthermore, residents with pain were 2.47 times as likely to have severe functional limitations and 1.66 times as likely to show signs of depression. The researchers concluded that greater emphasis needed to be placed on maximizing function and quality of life rather than on extending the duration of life.

BARRIERS TO ADEQUATE PAIN MANAGEMENT

Inadequate pain management is widespread, especially among minority groups and ethnic populations. For example, one study of outpatients with cancer revealed that 65 percent of minority patients were undertreated for pain, compared to only 50 percent of nonminority patients (McCafferey, 1999).

One factor in appropriately treating pain is making an accurate judgment about the level of pain being experienced. Because pain is experienced differently by each person, emphasis must be placed on accepting the *patients'* assessments of their pain. Today, the staff at many hospitals, nursing homes, and outpatient centers record the patients' assessments by having them rate their pain on a scale of 1 to 10, with 10 being the worst pain imaginable (or ever experienced). Cross-cultural studies indicate that a pain rating of 3 indicated the need to review and revise pain management measures, while a rating of 4 or more markedly interfered with the patient's ability to remain active and enjoy life (McCafferey, 1999). The goal is to accept the patient's self-report of pain rather than make judgments about whether the reported level of pain is appropriate to the diagnosis or patient circumstance. There is an additional challenge when assessing pain levels in clients with dementia, but facial expressions, behavior, and changed activity levels can give clues.

Fear of drug addiction is commonly thought to be a leading cause of undertreatment of pain. This fear may be present in not only health care staff but also patients and their families. Yet, numerous studies have shown that despite substantial increases in the amount of pain medication prescribed, addiction problems are very rare. Undertreatment can also result because some seniors ineffectively manage their medication, they may not use the word *pain* to describe their discomfort to health care workers, or they may mistakenly accept that pain is part of the aging process and not seek treatment.

You may find yourself serving as an advocate for senior clients who are experiencing ongoing and activity-limiting pain by encouraging them to seek additional medical care from those who recognize the validity of their pain and aggressively work to manage it.

Polypharmacy

Managing multiple prescription medications, often called *polypharmacy*, is one of the most troublesome challenges for seniors dealing with several chronic illnesses simultaneously. As an example, a senior who has a heart condition, diabetes, and chronic lung disease—a common trio of illnesses—often must take numerous medications several times a day. Seniors take, on average, 4.5 drugs at any one time and have three times more adverse drug reactions than younger adults. Nursing home residents receive three to eight medications daily. Evidence points to the number of drugs taken as the leading factor in the high incidence of adverse drug reactions (Long, 1997). Recent efforts have been directed toward reducing medications to the minimum number and lowest dosage needed to control a disease process.

According to James Long, author of *The essential guide to chronic illness*, the picture of adverse drug reactions is complicated:

- A senior's response to a particular medication may change as the aging process continues. As such, the dosage and schedule for taking the medication may need to be changed.

- Taking multiple medications increases the chance that a particular medication may react unfavorably with another medication or with a food that the senior eats regularly. If a senior is being treated by several different physicians—specialists, for example—it is possible that each is unaware of what is prescribed by the others. In addition, physicians may be unaware of the herbal or natural supplements, vitamins, and other over-the-counter remedies a senior may be taking. Seniors must maintain a complete list of all medications they take, including non-prescription and natural substances. Periodically (especially when seeking treatment for a new condition), they must ensure the list is reviewed before adding a new medication. You should encourage them to share this information with their physicians to avoid medications that counteract each other.

If a senior's eyesight or memory change, errors in dosage and scheduling of medications can occur. Visual limitations make it difficult, for example, to detect the difference in 5.0, 0.5 and .05 on a prescription label or to read the small printed instructions that come with a prescription. Seniors may forget they took their morning pills and take them again or, conversely, miss a dose, thinking that pills were taken earlier. Whenever unusual symptoms occur, it is wise to review how the patient's medications are being taken. It may be necessary to create a large, printed schedule and put pills into a container that has separate sections for morning, afternoon, evening, and bedtime of each day. Throw away old prescriptions to reduce the chances of overdose or taking the wrong pill.

You can promote safety by encouraging your senior clients to check with both their physicians and pharmacists to ensure the medications and supplements they are taking are compatible with one another, and encourage them to get recommendations from their pharmacists as to the best mode of medication reminders.

Members of the Treatment Team

GERIATRICIANS

Seniors may find that the family practice physician or internist they have relied on for years is more attuned to the problems and treatments affecting younger populations and has less awareness of the aging effects and health challenges experienced by seniors. If health problems are not being resolved by a primary physician, a senior may wish to seek an opinion from a geriatrician, or if possible, utilize a geriatrician as their primary physician.

Geriatricians are medical doctors (MDs) or osteopaths (DOs) who have completed a fellowship-training program in geriatrics. Geriatricians have developed an expanded expertise in the aging process, the impact of aging on illness patterns, drug therapy in seniors, health maintenance, and rehabilitation. They serve in a variety of roles including hospital care, long-term care, home care, and terminal care. They are frequently involved in ethics consultations to represent the unique health and disease patterns seen in seniors. The model of care practiced by geriatricians is heavily focused on working closely with other disciplines such as nurses, therapists, social workers, and pharmacists.

Unfortunately there are not enough geriatricians to meet the need. Currently there are only about 7,600 geriatricians, or 4.5 for each 10,000 persons ages 75 and over. The American Geriatrics Society estimates that by 2030, the 20 percent of the population that will then be age 65 and older will require at least 36,000 geriatricians to meet their health care needs. The training programs are not able to keep up with the demand, partly because there are too few geriatricians available to teach in the medical schools and partly because there is not enough interest in entering the field.

GERIATRIC NURSE PRACTITIONERS

Another valuable addition to the senior's health care team is the geriatric nurse practitioner (GNP). These nationally certified nurses have completed advanced clinical education (often master's degree level) that focuses on the health and disease issues faced by seniors. As established by the board of nursing issuing their licenses, GNPs work collaboratively with physicians in primary care, acute care, or long-term care settings and have authority to write prescriptions. They perform physical examinations, order and interpret diagnostic tests, establish diagnoses, prescribe medications, and counsel patients regarding health promotion, self-care needs, and disease prevention.

GNPs combine the care-based model seen in nursing with the treatment-based medical model used by physicians. Studies show that GNP care is cost effective and produces a high rate of satisfaction among patients. For example, there is an evolving system of nursing home care that is particularly committed to the use of nurse practitioners who see nursing home residents on a daily basis. Adding a GNP to the traditional health care team of a senior nursing home patient can often provide earlier detection and treatment of health problems than is seen in nursing home residents who are seen only once per month by their primary physicians.

Chronic Illness in Seniors: Summary

You will be challenged to assist seniors living with chronic illness in improving the quality of their lives. Pain management is a key area of concern for seniors because it is a major factor in the overall quality of their lives. It also has a direct bearing on the ability of the chronically ill to remain functionally independent. By taking the time to learn about the causes, natures, and characteristics of some of the most common chronic illness that affect seniors, you can better assist your senior clients and their families when a serious diagnosis is made.

But knowledge of prevention is important also. Hippocrates said, "The function of protecting and developing health must rank even above that of restoring it when it is impaired." You can play an important role in helping clients understand what puts them at risk and encouraging healthy behaviors to reduce that risk.

References

AAR (Alliance for Aging Research). (1999). *Independence for older Americans: An investment for our nation's future.* Washington, DC: AAR.

ACS (American Cancer Society). (2003). *Cancer facts and figures 2003.* Retrieved July 17, 2004, from http://www.cancer.org/docroot/STT/content/STT_1x_Cancer_Facts_Figures_2003.asp

ADA (American Diabetes Association). (1996). *Complete guide to diabetes.* Fairfax, VA: American Diabetes Association.

ADA. (2002). *Diabetes statistics.* Retrieved July 12, 2004, from http://www.diabetes.org/diabetes-statistics.jsp

AHCPR (Agency for Health Care Policy and Research). (1996). *Overview: Urinary incontinence in adults, clinical practice guideline update.* Retrieved July 17, 2004, from http://www.ahrq.gov/clinic/uiovervw.htm

Arthritis Foundation. (2004). *Osteoarthritis.* Retrieved July 17, 2004, from http://www.arthritis.org/conditions/DiseaseCenter/oa.asp

CDC (Centers for Disease Control). (2004a, April). *Arthritis: One of three U.S. adults are affected by arthritis or chronic joint symptoms.* Retrieved May 4, 2004, from http://www.cdc.gov/arthritis

CDC. (2004b, April). *Healthy aging: Effects of an aging population.* Retrieved May 10, 2004, from http://www.cdc.gov/nccdphp/bb_aging/index.htm

CDC. (2004c, April). *Healthy aging: Preventing disease and improving quality of life among older Americans.* Retrieved May 8, 2004, from http://www.cdc.gov/nccdphp/aag/aag_aging.htm#prev

CDC. (2004d, April). *National diabetes fact sheet.* Retrieved May 10, 2004, from http://www.cdc.gov/diabetes/pubs/estimates.htm#

JDF (Juvenile Diabetes Foundation). (2004b). *General diabetes facts.* Retrieved July 12, 2004, from http://jdrf.org/files/chapters_and_affiliates/greater_bay_area_chapter/general diabetes facts.pdf

Khan, M. G. & Marriott, H. J. (1996). *Heart trouble encyclopedia.* Toronto: Stoddart Publishing Co.

Long, J. W. (1997). *The essential guide to chronic illness*. New York: Harper Perennial.

McCafferey, M. (1999, Aug.). Pain control. *American Journal of Nursing. 99*(8).

Mitchell, T. (2000, Mar. 17-19). The road to Wellville. *USA Weekend*.

National Academy on an Aging Society. (1999, November). Chronic conditions: A challenge for the 21st century. National Academy on an Aging Society *Profile*, No. 1. Retrieved May 4, 2004, from http://www.agingsociety.org/agingsociety/pdf/chronic.pdf

National Academy on an Aging Society. (2000, October) Hypertension: A common condition for older Americans. National Academy on an Aging Society *Profile*, No. 12. Retrieved July 17, 2004, from http://www.agingsociety.org/agingsociety/pdf/hypertension.pdf

National Center for Biotechnology Information. (n.d.). *Diabetes type 1*. Retrieved July 13, 2004, from http://www.ncbi.nlm.nih.gov/books/bv.fcgi?call=bv.View.ShowSection&rid=gnd.section.137

National Institute of Neurological Disorders and Stroke. (2000). *Stroke: Hope through research*. Retrieved April 12, 2003, from http://www.ninds.nih.gov/health_and_medical/pubs/stroke_hope_through_research.htm

Pisetsky, D. S. & Trien, S. F. (1992). *The Duke University Medical Center book of arthritis*. New York: Fawcett Columbine.

Trichopoulos, D., Li, F. P., & Hunter, D. J. (1996, September). What you need to know about cancer: What causes cancer. *Scientific American, 275*(3), 80. New York: W. H. Freeman and Co.

Vierck, E. & Hodges, K. (2003). *Aging: Demographics, health, and health services*. Westport, CT: Greenwood.

WebMD. (2003, Dec.). *Health Guide A-Z: Osteoporosis*. Retrieved July 1, 2004, from http://my.webmd.com/hw/osteoporosis/hw131421.asp?lastselectedguid={5FE84E90-BC77-4056-A91C-9531713CA348}

Resources

Services

American Association of Diabetes Educators. http://www.aadenet.org, 100 W. Monroe St., Suite 400, Chicago, IL 60603, 1-800-338-3633. This multidisciplinary professional organization is dedicated to advancing the practice of diabetes self-management and care through education, research, and advocacy.

American Cancer Society (ACS). http://www.cancer.org, 1-800-ACS-2345. The ACS is a nationwide community-based organization headquartered in Atlanta with state divisions and more than 3,400 local offices. Its Web site provides medical information, treatment decision tools, news updates, support resources, and more. Use the Web site or look in your local phone book to find the chapter near you.

American Diabetes Association (ADA). http://www.diabetes.org, 1701 N. Beauregard St., Alexandria, VA 22311, 1-800-DIABETES (1-800-342-2383). The American Diabetes Association is the nation's leading nonprofit health organization providing diabetes research, information, and advocacy. Contact the national office to find a local chapter.

American Geriatrics Society (AGS). http://www.americangeriatrics.org, The Empire State Building, 350 Fifth Ave., Suite 801, New York, NY 10118, 212-308-1414, 212-832-8646 fax. The American Geriatrics Society is a professional organization of health care providers dedicated to improving the health and well-being of all seniors. AGS has an active membership of over 6,000 health care professionals.

American Heart Association (AHA). http://www.americanheart.org, 7272 Greenville Ave., Dallas, TX 75231, 800-AHA-USA-1 or 800-242-8721. AHA's mission is to reduce disability and death from cardiovascular diseases and stroke by providing education, advocacy, and publications. Contact the national office to find a local chapter.

American Public Health Association (APHA). http://www.apha.org, 800 I St. NW, Washington, DC 20001-3710, 202-777-APHA. Founded 125 years ago, APHA is the largest health organization for public health professionals. It provides programs, publications, education, and advocacy. The Web site contains journals and articles on many chronic illnesses.

Arthritis Foundation (AF). http://www.arthritis.org, P.O. Box 7669, Atlanta, GA 30357-0669, 800-283-7800. The Arthritis Foundation is the only national not-for-profit organization that supports people afflicted with more than 100 types of arthritis and related conditions with advocacy, programs, services, and research. Contact the national office to find a local chapter, or locate one through the Web site.

Body Health Resources Corporation. http://thebody.com, 250 W. 57th St., New York, NY 10107. This Web site is for educational purposes and offers an opportunity to ask experts questions on a variety of topics relating to HIV/AIDS.

Centers for Disease Control (CDC). http://www.cdc.gov, 1600 Clifton Rd., MS D25, Atlanta, GA 30333, 404-639-3286. CDC is the lead federal agency for protecting the health and safety of people. Up-to-date news articles appear on the site along with archived information.

The Center for Research on Chronic Illness (CRCI). http://nursing.unc.edu/crci, email crci@unc.edu. Located at the University of North Carolina at Chapel Hill and funded by the National Institute of Nursing Research, CRCI's mission is "To assist vulnerable people who are chronically ill to maximize their health." Research articles are available on the site.

Chronic Illness Research Foundation. http://www.chronicillnet.org. A multimedia Internet information source dedicated to chronic illnesses, providing information to a broad audience from researchers to patients.

Conill Institute for Chronic Illness (CICI). http://www.conillinst.org, 3535 Market St., Suite 4045, Philadelphia, PA 19104, 215-746-7267. CICI sponsors educational programs for patients and their families, employers, physicians, and other health care providers, and selected industries whose customers may have special needs.

HealingWell.com. http://www.healingwell.com, 908-203-1350. An information source for patients, caregivers, and families coping with chronic diseases with library of articles and video webcasts on chronic illnesses. A free healing newsletter is also available online.

Improving Chronic Illness Care (ICIC). http://www.improvingchroniccare.org, 1730 Minor Ave., Suite 1290, Seattle, WA 98101-1448. 206-287-2704, 206-287-2138 fax. ICIC is a national program sponsored by The Robert Wood Johnson

Foundation in Seattle. Their mission is to support providers caring for chronically ill patients with guidelines, specialty expertise, and information systems.

Mended Hearts, Inc. http://www.mendedhearts.org, email: info@mendedhearts.org, 7272 Greenville Ave., Dallas, Texas 75231-4596, 888-HEART99 (888-432-7899) information line, 214-706-1442 national office, 214-706-5245 fax. Affiliated with the American Heart Association, Mended Hearts partners with 460 hospitals and rehabilitation clinics to offers services to heart patients through visiting programs, support group meetings, and educational forums.

National Academy on an Aging Society. http://www.agingsociety.org, 1030 15th St. NW, Ste. 250, Washington, DC 20005, 202-408-3375, 202-842-1150 fax. The Academy is a nonpartisan public policy institute providing information to the public.

National Heart, Lung, and Blood Institute, http://nhlbi.nih.gov, 301-592-8573. A division of the National Institutes of Health, the National Heart, Lung, and Blood Institute provides information for patients and the public, health professionals, and researchers.

National Institute on Aging (NIA). http://www.nia.nih.gov, Building 31, Room 5C27, 31 Center Dr., MSC 2292, Bethesda, MD 20892, 301-496-1752. NIA is one of the institutes of the National Institutes of Health (NIH). Their Web site follows the efforts of the government in researching aging. They also provide extensive consumer information such as *The Resource Directory for Older People*, a database of information that includes federal and state agencies, resource centers, professional societies, private groups, and volunteer programs. NIA's *Age Pages* provide up-to-date information for seniors on issues such as heart disease and stroke.

National Institute of Neurological Disorders and Stroke (NINDS). http://www.ninds.nih.gov, P.O. Box 5801, Bethesda, MD 20824, 800-352-9424, 301-496-5751, 301-468-5981 TTY. NINDS's vision is to "Lead the neuroscience community in shaping the future of research and its relationship to brain diseases." Numerous scholarly articles appear on the site.

National Institutes of Health (NIH). http://www.nih.gov, 9000 Rockville Pike, Bethesda, MD 20892. NIH explores medical and behavioral research for the nation. In addition to speeches and legislative resources, the site includes special reports given to the director on a variety of health subjects.

PBS. http://www.pbs.org, 1320 Braddock Pl., Alexandria, VA 22314, 703-739-5000. "Who Cares: Chronic Illness in America," a PBS broadcast, appears on the Web site.

United States Department of Health and Human Services. http://hhs.gov, 200 Independence Ave. SW, Washington, DC 20201, 202-619-0257, 877-696-6775. Numerous articles appear on this site, including those addressing diseases and conditions, aging, and resource locators for senior housing.

Chapter 11

Senior Nutrition, Fitness, and Healthy Lifestyles

After a mild stroke, Rosemary stopped most of her usual activities such as joining friends for dinner dates and attending biweekly exercise class. Rosemary had lived alone all her life and had always enjoyed her solitude after long days working as a manager. But at age 76 and comfortably retired she spent almost all her time by herself.

A year after the stroke Rosemary went to visit a longtime family friend, Bob, an internist, for a checkup. Clinically Rosemary was okay, but the doctor was shocked by her appearance—she had lost a lot of weight, she was off kilter when she walked, and she had trouble getting in and out of chairs. When he gently asked, "Rosemary, how is your appetite? What are you doing for exercise? Are you getting out of the house?" she shrugged and did not answer.

"If she doesn't start eating well and exercising it is only a matter of time before this dear lady is going to fall and break something," Bob thought to himself. He referred Rosemary to a geriatric dietician; encouraged her to start walking daily, gradually building up to a mile; and asked her to come back in two months. But Rosemary never followed through.

A month and a half after Rosemary's visit to her doctor, he received a call that she was in the hospital with broken wrists.

...

Walk Across Arizona is an annual 16-week walking program designed for teams of up to 10 people. The teams have a friendly competition to see who can get their pals, neighbors, coworkers, and family out to build a healthy habit and walk for fitness. At one retirement community participating in the program, the team captain is a 90-year-old woman; one of the team members is 93 years of age, the oldest participant in the program; and 82-year-old identical twin sisters walk an average of 16 miles per week.

"We love to exercise, but it isn't to try to live to be 100," says one of the twins. "We just want good quality of life."

Introduction

Scientific research confirms that good nutrition, exercise, and healthy lifestyles are key to longevity and prevention of chronic conditions such as osteoporosis, diabetes, and heart disease. Seniors seeking overall good health and increased longevity need to address the following important components:

- proper diet and nutrition
- physical fitness
- functional fitness
- strength training
- aerobic conditioning
- muscle building and fat loss
- not smoking
- restricting alcohol intake

According to the Administration on Aging (AoA), the combination of unhealthy eating and physical inactivity is responsible for 14 percent of preventable deaths per year (AoA, 2003). Only tobacco use causes more preventable deaths in the United States.

Poor nutritional health results from a variety of factors, including eating too little or too much, eating the same foods day after day, or not eating nutritious foods such as fruits, vegetables, dairy products, and fiber. Poor health may also result from skipping meals, a practice that an estimated one in five adults performs daily.

Nutritional health can also decline due to acute or chronic illnesses that cause a change in eating habits. For instance, diseases that adversely affect oral health (i.e., mouth, teeth, gums) can make eating unpleasant or even painful. In fact, poor oral health is not uncommon in seniors. Studies show that many have missing, loose, or unhealthy teeth, making eating difficult. Poorly fitting dentures are also cited as a common problem that exacerbates eating difficulties.

Other contributing factors to poor nutrition in seniors include:

- economic hardship
- reduced social contact
- multiple medications
- involuntary weight loss or gain
- difficulty walking, shopping, or preparing food

More details on these factors are presented later in this chapter.

As a result of their health habits, many seniors experience both muscle loss (sarcopenia) and increased body fat. This combination is dangerous in that it results in an overall weakening of the body. To compound the problem, age-related changes, many of which are gradual and unseen, occur in the body's cells, bones, tissues, and organs. These changes affect the whole body. However, through proper diet, nutrition, and exercise, seniors can adopt patterns of activity (fitness of mind and body) that will increase their chances of remaining healthier as they age. Studies have shown that it is never too late to build strength, increase endurance, and enhance nutrition.

This chapter covers good nutrition, exercise, and healthy lifestyles for seniors. To facilitate this process, you are encouraged to learn and understand both normal age-related changes and positive health habits so you can spot dangerous "red flags" in your senior clients and encourage actions that promote healthier lifestyles. Because of the very nature of your business as a CSA, you can play an important role by advising your clients about actions they can take to be healthier and remain independent longer.

> *The first wealth is health.*
>
> Ralph Waldo Emerson

Nutrition and Seniors

It is well known that eating a nutritionally sound diet at any age is beneficial. Sound nutrition helps our bodies function well and may limit or reverse damage resulting from previously poor eating habits. Unfortunately, however, the U.S. Department of Agriculture (USDA) indicates that seniors are nutritionally insufficient in the following areas: intake of several nutrients including folate, vitamin C, and vitamin E; intake of vegetable and meat groups; dietary variety; and levels of certain nutrients (USDA, 2000). In addition, they are at higher risk of being underweight.

OBESITY AND SENIORS

The Food and Drug Administration (FDA) has declared our current national status as an "obesity epidemic," as 64 percent of Americans are overweight and more than 30 percent are considered obese (FDA, 2004). *Obesity* is defined as a person weighing more than 120 percent of their desirable weight. As you may already know, obesity puts us at greater risk for a variety of health concerns, including hypertension, diabetes, cardiovascular disease, functional limitations, and premature morbidity (Merck, 2004). But dying early is exactly the reason why obesity is not really considered an issue for the elderly. In fact, according to the National Institute on Aging, "Weight generally increases over the lifetime until middle age, then tends to decrease into old age with changes in muscle, fat, and bone" (NIA, 2004). After the age of 70, nutrition and risk of being underweight become bigger concerns than obesity.

EATING WELL AS WE AGE

As a result of body changes, seniors typically require fewer calories. At the same time, nutritionists urge seniors to adhere to diets rich in vitamins, minerals, fiber, and (importantly) water. To help seniors maintain balanced diets, Dr. Robert B. Russell of Tufts University and the Health and Nutrition Research Center, along with a team of nutrition specialists, developed the 70+ Food Pyramid, a new version of the well-known USDA food pyramid. The

70+ Food Pyramid has been endorsed by AARP and provides important information for seniors to consider when discussing their dietary habits with physicians. The pyramid addresses the facts that seniors tend to eat less and consume fewer calories than younger people do and that they typically do not get the recommended amount of nutrients.

At the top of the 70+ Food Pyramid is a flag that draws attention to seniors' potential need for vitamin D, calcium, and vitamin B12 supplements. Calcium and vitamin D absorption, as well as the absorption of vitamin B12 (required for normal, healthy nerve function), decreases with age. This can cause adverse effects on bone health and increases the risk of fractures. Although not every senior requires vitamin and mineral supplements, seniors should discuss their particular nutritional needs with their primary physicians.

According to the USDA, seniors, compared with other segments of the population, have impaired responses to reduced body water. Therefore, they are most vulnerable to dehydration (USDA, 2002). Research also indicates that humans lose their thirst sensation as they age. As a result, many seniors do not drink enough fluids. To make matters worse, certain medications cause fluid imbalances within the body. These circumstances can lead to dehydration, kidney problems, and constipation. Dr. Russell and his colleagues kept these facts in mind when creating the 70+ Food Pyramid. As a result, the base of the 70+ Food Pyramid contains eight glasses of water (instead of grains, rice, and pasta as is found in the current USDA food pyramid). This recommendation shows just how important fluid balance is for seniors.

According to Dr. Russell and his team, beneficial fluids include, in any combination, water, juice, milk, decaffeinated tea or coffee, and soups. Water, according to nutritionists, is the best fluid, as it does not contain the natural sugars found in other beverages, such as juice. Alcohol and caffeinated beverages such as coffee, tea, or soda, on the other hand, are not beneficial and therefore do not count toward fluid intake.

The 70+ Food Pyramid reflects the findings from a 1988-89 study that found two-fifths of seniors eat less than they did when they were younger. According to the study, compared to the standard intake of 1,600 calories or more per day, seniors consumed 1,500 calories or less per day. Experts agree that there is nothing wrong with eating less as one ages, as long as those foods still provide sufficient dietary nutrients. The study's findings support the importance of whole grains, a colorful variety of fruits and vegetables, low-fat dairy, and lean meats, fish, and poultry as part of a healthy diet. An illustration of the 70+ Food Pyramid is shown below.

The 70+ Food Pyramid

The 70+ Food Pyramid is narrower than the traditional pyramid because seniors are less active and require less food to maintain their weight. However, they do require higher levels of specific nutrients like antioxidants to defend against free-radical damage associated with aging, vitamin D and calcium to keep bones strong, and folic acid to retain mental acuity and reduce the incidence of stroke and heart disease. To get these vital nutrients, the pyramid emphasizes nutrient-dense foods like darker-colored vegetables and

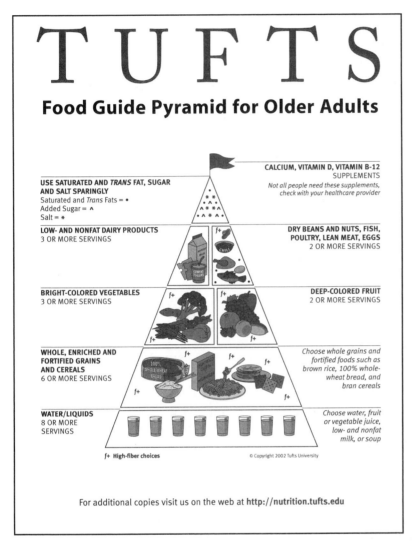

TUFTS
Food Guide Pyramid for Older Adults

CALCIUM, VITAMIN D, VITAMIN B-12
SUPPLEMENTS
Not all people need these supplements, check with your healthcare provider

USE SATURATED AND *TRANS* FAT, SUGAR AND SALT SPARINGLY
Saturated and *Trans* Fats = •
Added Sugar = ʌ
Salt = *

LOW- AND NONFAT DAIRY PRODUCTS
3 OR MORE SERVINGS

DRY BEANS AND NUTS, FISH, POULTRY, LEAN MEAT, EGGS
2 OR MORE SERVINGS

BRIGHT-COLORED VEGETABLES
3 OR MORE SERVINGS

DEEP-COLORED FRUIT
2 OR MORE SERVINGS

WHOLE, ENRICHED AND FORTIFIED GRAINS AND CEREALS
6 OR MORE SERVINGS

Choose whole grains and fortified foods such as brown rice, 100% whole-wheat bread, and bran cereals

WATER/LIQUIDS
8 OR MORE SERVINGS

Choose water, fruit or vegetable juice, low- and nonfat milk, or soup

f+ High-fiber choices

© Copyright 2002 Tufts University

For additional copies visit us on the web at **http://nutrition.tufts.edu**

fruits that have higher levels of vitamins.

Describing the pyramid, Russell says, "We suggest eating dark, leafy greens like spinach, orange and yellow vegetables like sweet potatoes and squash, and colorful fruit like strawberries and mangos that are more rich in vitamins A and C and in folic acid" (Tufts University, n.d.). Potatoes are not pictured in the pyramid because they are filling but less nutritious. Other nutrient-dense choices include romaine rather than iceberg lettuce, and peaches, apricots, or nectarines rather than apples, celery, or cucumbers.

To ensure adequate fiber intake, the pyramid recommends whole grain products. "Many older people have problems with bowel function," says Russell's colleague, Alice H. Lichtenstein. "We want to remind them to get enough fiber—to eat oranges and carrots rather than just drinking the juice, to eat legumes like beans and lentils instead of meat at least twice a week, to select brown rice rather than white, for example. We also want to stress the inclusion of high-fiber foods in every meal because diets high in fiber are also associated with lower cholesterol levels and reduced risk of cardiovascular disease and cancer."

As with the traditional pyramid, the modified food pyramid suggests using fats, oils, and sweets sparingly. "It is particularly important for older people to limit their intake of desserts and snacks like cookies and cake that contribute a lot of calories but have few nutrients," Lichtenstein says.

Necessary Nutrients

As the Tufts researchers point out, eating foods that are high in nutrients is important to seniors, as it is for all age groups (see Table 11.1). Two of the most important components of healthy diets are fruits and vegetables that contain vitamins, minerals, and fiber. When fiber enters the digestive system,

Table 11.1 Sources of Necessary Nutrients

Vitamin B6: eggs, whole grain cereals, liver, herring, salmon, nuts, brown rice

Vitamin B12: meat, poultry, liver, kidney, egg yolk, fish

Folic Acid: liver and kidneys, dark-green leafy vegetables, wheat germ, dried peas and beans

Vitamin C: berries, sweet peppers, broccoli, tomatoes, citrus fruits

Vitamin D: sunshine, milk, liver oils, tuna, salmon, herring, egg yolk, margarine

Vitamin E: nuts, vegetable oils, wheat germ oil, olives, peanut oil

Calcium: milk, cheese, dairy food, sardines

Zinc: meat, eggs, liver, seafood

Magnesium: unrefined cereals, legumes, avocados

Chromium: whole grains, leafy green vegetables

Fiber: whole grains, fruits, vegetables

it "grabs" and absorbs fatty acids, helping to eliminate them from the body. This process reduces bad cholesterol (LDL cholesterol, to be discussed later). Fiber also plays an important role in preventing constipation, a common gastrointestinal complaint of seniors.

HEALTHY EATING CHALLENGES

As mentioned in the beginning of this chapter, a number of challenges may make eating difficult for seniors. The following sections provide details on some of the major limitations.

Difficulty Preparing Meals

Seniors may not have an interest in cooking, may have disabilities that prevent use of cooking equipment, or may be unable to stand for long periods. Despite these limitations, possible options include:

- using a microwave oven to cook frozen meals;
- participating in group meal programs (offered at senior centers);
- having meals delivered to the home;
- obtaining housing that provides meal services.

Appetite Problems

Seniors may lack appetite. They may find mealtimes lonely and simply choose not to eat. Or, if they live alone, they may not wish to prepare meals for themselves. Other commonly cited reasons for decreased interest in food are change in taste buds or medication usage, both of which can dramatically alter the taste of food. To increase interest in eating, your senior clients could consider:

- creating opportunities to eat with others (family, friends);

- taking part in group meal programs through senior centers, faith groups, and related programs;
- talking with physicians about changing medications;
- cooking with spices and herbs to enhance taste.

Inability to Shop

Many seniors find it difficult to shop for necessities. They may no longer drive or find it difficult to walk or stand in lines. Such factors can prevent your senior clients from obtaining nutritious food. Fortunately, they have options, including:

- having groceries delivered (nominal fee or even free for seniors);
- asking a community volunteer to assist with shopping or delivering groceries;
- shopping with family members or friends;
- paying someone to purchase groceries from a prepared list;
- contracting with a home health service to shop for and deliver groceries.

Cost of Groceries

For some seniors, money is an ongoing problem. Sadly, many of them must choose between purchasing medications and buying food. When money is scarce, so too are food choices. Your senior clients who have minimal financial resources can still maintain nutritious diets by following these recommendations:

- Buy low-cost foods, such as dried beans, rice, pasta, soups, and canned vegetables.
- Buy foods on sale and use cost-saving coupons.
- Locate free or low-cost meals through churches or synagogues.
- Participate in Meals on Wheels or in meal programs sponsored through senior centers.
- If eligible, obtain food stamps through local government programs (see below).

AoA's Elderly Nutrition Program

The Administration on Aging promotes senior health and disease prevention through the Elderly Nutrition Program. This program helps seniors build a foundation for health through improved diets, increased physical activity, and improved lifestyle choices. The program strives to provide the following:

- nutritious and satisfying meals in community settings (e.g., senior centers) five days a week, most commonly scheduled at noon

- nutritious and satisfying home-delivered meals (e.g., Meals on Wheels) to homebound seniors five days a week, also at noon
- nutrition and health promotion education to improve health behaviors
- nutrition counseling to help manage nutrition-related chronic diseases
- linkages to other supportive and health-related services, such as physical activity or fitness classes and health screenings

Provided adequate funding exists and the services are not oversubscribed, all adults age 60 and over and their spouses (of any age) may receive services. Priority for receipt of nutrition services is given to those who are in greatest economic or social need (typically low-income and minority adults). In order for your senior clients to receive home-delivered nutrition services, they must be age 60 or older and homebound due to illness, disability, or geographic isolation.

USDA's Food Stamp Program

The Food Stamp Program provides monthly benefits for eligible participants to purchase food at approved food stores. Eligibility and allotments are based on household size, income, assets, and other factors. One out of six recipients is a low-income senior. Seniors can apply for food stamps at local food stamp offices listed in the state or local government pages of telephone books. Local offices will be listed under "Food Stamps," "Social Services," "Human Services," "Public Assistance," or a similar title. Your state may have a toll-free food stamp hotline.

In fiscal year 2002, the food stamp program served an average of 1.5 million households containing seniors each month. The average food stamp benefit for these households was $64 per month. Seniors who received food stamps tended to live alone. In fiscal year 2002, 59 percent of all food stamp households with senior members also received Supplemental Security Income (SSI), and 69 percent received Social Security. Thirty-four percent of all households with senior members received both SSI and Social Security income.

Unfortunately, many seniors who could receive food stamps are going hungry. Only 28 percent of eligible seniors receive food stamps (USDA, 2003a).

Using Food Packaging Labels

All people, regardless of age, should learn to read food-packaging labels to help themselves make healthy choices in grocery stores, at home, and on the road. By law, food manufacturers are required to list all ingredients by weight from greatest to least. The Food and Drug Administration, which oversees truth in labeling, ensures the information on product labels is correct.

Labels are especially useful for people with food sensitivities to see exactly what each product contains. Using this information properly can help your senior clients manage various health problems such as osteoporosis, heart disease, high blood pressure, stroke, obesity, diabetes, and some forms of cancer.

Nutrition labels display five key features: nutritional facts, serving size, percentage of daily value, vitamins and minerals, and recommended daily values. Individual nutrient needs may be more or less than the daily values listed on labels. Seniors with questions might consider speaking with registered dieticians, who can calculate personal daily values. For questions about specific products, seniors can contact food manufacturers directly. Toll-free numbers are located on most product containers.

Food Safety

According to multiple studies, the United States enjoys one of the safest and most healthy food supplies in the world. However, it is cause for concern that science has discovered new and dangerous bacteria in our food supplies. The growth of harmful microorganisms in food, which is preventable, causes millions of illnesses and thousands of deaths each year.

Illness resulting from bacteria is commonly called *food poisoning*, though scientists generally refer to it as *foodborne illness*. Many seniors are knowledgeable about preventing illness and are aware of problems resulting from mishandling food. In fact, federal studies show that seniors do a better job of handling food safely than any other age group. Yet, it can't hurt to continually educate and encourage caution. The following information addresses risk factors and recommendations for preventing foodborne illnesses.

Who Is at Risk?

Although seniors tend to be careful, they are more susceptible to foodborne illnesses than younger adults. This is the result of weakened immune systems and decreases in stomach acid. Stomach acid plays an important role in decreasing the number of bacteria in the intestinal tracts and reducing the risk of illness. Underlying illness such as diabetes, some cancer treatments, and kidney disease may also increase seniors' risk of developing foodborne illnesses.

It is difficult to recognize harmful bacteria in foods because they often can't be seen, smelled, or tasted. Foodborne bacteria usually take one to three days to cause illness. However, people can become ill anytime from 20 minutes to 6 weeks after eating foods with harmful bacteria. Foodborne illnesses can be confused with other types of illnesses because the symptoms are upset stomach, vomiting, diarrhea, or any combination of these. People with foodborne illnesses also experience flu-like symptoms such as fevers, headaches, and body aches. Such symptoms should be reported to a physician. Any acute illness after eating out should be reported to the local health department so an investigation can be made.

Those who do not find time for exercise will have to find time for illness.

Earl of Derby

Exercise and Seniors

The first director of the National Institute on Aging, Robert Butler, says, "If exercise could be packed into a pill, it would be the single most widely prescribed, and beneficial, medicine in the nation." At age 74, Dr. Butler works more than 60 hours a week and exercises daily.

Exercise, if performed properly with the correct frequency and intensity, greatly benefits health. It improves cardiovascular fitness, reduces susceptibility to heart attacks and strokes, enhances carbohydrate metabolism, delays age-related deterioration of some muscles and bones, and improves brain function.

Contrary to what was previously believed, current research indicates that seniors do not need more rest than younger people. In fact, many studies have shown that prolonged bed rest, especially among frail elders, results in physical problems. Inactivity, long known to exacerbate problems, contributes to disease and disability. Some physiological changes commonly attributed to aging are, in reality, caused by reduced activity. As such, physician-guided activity and exercise can dramatically improve seniors' overall health.

Studies show that no group in our population benefits more from exercise than seniors. Physiologically, a senior's muscles are just as responsive to weight lifting as those of younger people. As in a younger body, stretching increases flexibility, coordination, and agility to expand the body's freedom of movement. It also relaxes the body, both mentally and physically.

Unfortunately, many seniors avoid exercise because of mental obstacles. Among those most commonly cited are embarrassment, humiliation, self-deprecation, confusion, self-doubt, and vanity. Some wrestle with unresolved psychological issues involving health and exercise. Medical practice, social customs, and mores were radically different when seniors were born—they often cannot identify with the "exercise revolution."

FACTS ABOUT EXERCISE

- Exercise makes us feel better and enjoy life more.
- Most adults do not get enough exercise.
- Lack of physical activity and poor diet, together, are the second largest underlying cause of death in the United States.
- Regular exercise can lessen the symptoms of certain underlying diseases and disabilities.
- Exercise improves mood and relieves depression.
- Staying physically active on a regular, permanent basis can help prevent or delay certain diseases (cancer, heart disease, diabetes) and disabilities.
- Physical activity reduces incidence of constipation.

According to physicians, physical activity should be part of every senior's daily routine. Norm Bouchard, CSA faculty member and former weight loss counselor, insists that a fitness regimen requires two qualities to help ensure seniors will persist at it:

1. It needs to be attainable.
2. It needs to be pleasurable.

To encourage regular participation in exercise programs, you can suggest that seniors choose activities they find enjoyable. For example, brisk daily walks, bicycle rides, and even dancing are all activities that, while enjoyable, also benefit health. Senior advisors are in a position of identifying what their clients do around the home and in the community. These discussions can be used to encourage seniors to remain active with normal household activities that do not place excess demands on balance, agility, or strength. For example, to prevent falls many seniors must be careful about climbing ladders or walking over uneven terrain.

STEPS TO FEELING FIT FOR LIFE

Almost everyone, regardless of age, should exercise. With few exceptions, nearly everyone can participate in some sort of activity that leads to improvements in health. Your senior clients who are not currently involved in exercise programs should consult with their physicians prior to undertaking new activities. Furthermore, seniors should seek exercise or activity programs that are specifically designed for them and are guided by instructors who are knowledgeable about aging and will protect frail muscles, tendons, and joints and make sure that their senior participants don't fall.

ENDURANCE ACTIVITY

Endurance activity is defined as at least 30 minutes of daily activity that increases breathing and builds stamina, which supports independence and enjoyment of activities. The aerobic activities mentioned earlier—walking, biking, dancing, and the exercycle—are good examples of endurance activities. Using a treadmill in inclement weather and swimming to take pressure off the joints are also popular choices. Endurance activities can not only prevent or delay many age-related diseases, but may help fight chronic diseases and lessen their symptoms.

LIFT WEIGHTS TO LIFT AGING METABOLISM

A study conducted at Tufts University sheds light on why metabolism slows as people age. The findings show that the gradual loss of body cells, especially energy-consuming muscle cells, results in seniors burning fewer calories while at rest, which can lead to weight gain (Roubenoff et al., 2000). The study, published in the *Journal of Gerontology: Medical Sciences,* showed a direct association between metabolic rate and cell mass, also known as lean or fat-free mass. This result means that seniors may regain some of their youthful resting metabolic rate and help avoid obesity with regular muscle-building exercises (Roubenoff et al.).

KEEP MUSCLES MOVING

Remember the old adage "Use it or lose it"? If not used, muscles waste away. Humans lose 20 to 40 percent of their muscle as they age. With this loss comes a loss of strength. Studies show that having sufficient muscle mass may mean the difference between seniors' ability to get up from a chair and having to wait for someone to help them get up. Strong muscles reduce the risk of serious injuries such as falls that cause broken hips and other disabilities. In short, lack of muscle strength can greatly affect seniors' ability to live independently.

DEVELOPING AND MAINTAINING GOOD BALANCE

Balance is critical to seniors' overall safety as they conduct their activities of daily living. Exercise programs geared specifically for seniors typically incorporate exercises to build balance.

STRETCHING

Research shows that gentle stretching preserves flexibility, a vital factor in performing activities such as dressing, bathing, driving, and various household chores.

FUNCTIONAL FITNESS

Functional fitness refers to the ability to successfully carry out specific, fundamental activities of daily living (ADLs). Functional fitness relates to physical independence in terms of:

- mobility (standing, walking, propelling a wheelchair).
- self-care (bathing, dressing, eating, etc.).
- maintaining a living environment (preparing meals, doing necessary housework, driving, reaching and lifting needed objects, etc.).
- pursuing life interests (gardening, caring for pets, playing with grandchildren, and recreational activities).

Beginning a functional fitness program before detectable disabilities set in can help seniors postpone or entirely avoid limitations. Even after functional losses begin, a fitness program can help seniors recover or partially recover certain capabilities. It may even halt or slow further declines. Functional fitness training is invaluable when it succeeds in lowering seniors' risks for accidental falls.

Human balance involves visual, auditory, and other sensory receptors. It also relies upon body alignment (posture), strength, and flexibility. Many seniors have compromised balance, which may reduce their sense of security, comfort, and confidence when using exercise equipment. When choosing equipment to use, your senior clients should consider whether it is likely that they would work beyond their safe range of motion, which is the normal distance and direction through which a joint can move. This is especially important for participants who have arthritis or other joint-related problems. Some machines can be adjusted to accommodate varying ranges. For example, certain types of equipment include minimum-maximum adjustments so the subject's range can be controlled as needed. Some manufacturers offer equipment specifically designed for senior and/or impaired adults.

Biomarkers and Assessment of Health Status

Biomarkers refer to the key physiological factors associated with aging. *Biointerventions* are actions that are designed to retard or reverse the aging process. *Biomarkers of functional age* estimate the rate at which the very fundamental processes of aging occur within individuals. Biomarkers include:

- lean body mass as measured by the Body Mass Index (BMI);
- strength;
- basal metabolic rate (BMR);
- body fat percentage.

These four biomarkers are closely interrelated and are viewed as the primary catalysts for preventing sarcopenia (an age-related loss of muscle).

LEAN BODY MASS

It is a well-established fact that many Americans have too much body fat and too little muscle. Body fat is metabolically inactive—it is energy storage tissue. Everything that is not body fat (e.g., bones, vital organ tissue, central nervous system) is referred to as *lean body mass*—the body's biologically active tissues. Muscle is responsible for the vitality of the whole physiological apparatus. Lean body mass is measured by using the Body Mass Index, which tells us how much of our weight is muscle and how much of our weight is fat. The key to senior rejuvenation is building muscle. Studies show that a high ratio of muscle to body fat on the body offers the following benefits:

- increases in metabolism to help burn body fat and alter body composition
- increases in aerobic capacity—the health of one's cardiovascular system—because more working muscles consume oxygen
- muscle use of more insulin, greatly reducing the chances of developing diabetes
- higher maintained levels of the beneficial HDL cholesterol in the blood

Keeping track of muscle loss is essential in seniors. Not only is it one key to decreased vitality, it is increasingly used by insurance companies as an indicator of overall health. Many studies have shown that as Americans move from young adulthood into middle age, they tend to lose about 6.6 pounds of lean body mass each decade of life. After age 45, the rate of loss accelerates. Studies have also shown that mortality is affected by lack of lean body mass.

STRENGTH

Two factors are responsible for how much muscle people have. The first involves how often muscles are used while the second centers on the level of tissue-maintaining anabolic hormones circulating in the blood. How frequently muscles are used partly determines their size and lifting capacity. A muscle that is frequently used is a muscle that will stay the same. A muscle that is frequently used and is also pushed to the limits of its capacity will grow and gain strength (even in seniors). Regardless of seniors' ages or levels of weakness, they can regain muscle mass and strength.

Isometric exercises, which involve using force applied to resistant objects, build muscle mass. An example of this type of exercise is pushing against a wall with your arms. Tension builds up in your muscles, although your arms do not move.

BASAL METABOLIC RATE

Metabolism refers to the body's chemical processes that build and destroy tissue and release energy, thereby generating heat. *Basal* refers to the rate of the body's metabolic processes at baseline, or at rest. The basal metabolic rate is the rate of your body chemistry when exertion is minimal. The BMR, or caloric expenditure at rest, decreases with age. As noted earlier, reduced muscle mass is primarily responsible for this gradual reduction. Based on estimates of the average loss of lean-body mass with age, a person's BMR drops about 2 percent per decade. To correlate this with caloric need, with each decade from age 20 onward, people need about 100 fewer calories per day to maintain their body's status quo.

BODY FAT

With advancing age, most people gain fat even if their body weight hasn't increased much. The body's ratio of lean body mass to fat decreases with age. Despite this, losing weight should not be the goal. More appropriately, the goal should focus on shedding fat and gaining muscle. The combination of exercise and moderate caloric restriction is the best method yet devised to lose weight and unwanted body fat in a healthful manner.

OTHER BIOMARKERS

Aerobic Capacity

Aerobic capacity is the body's ability to process oxygen within a given time. The process of oxygenation includes the body's ability to perform the following tasks:

- rapidly breathe amounts of air into the lungs to oxygenate blood
- forcefully deliver large volumes of blood via the pumping action of the heart
- effectively transport oxygen to all parts of the body through the bloodstream

By age 65, aerobic capacity is typically 30 to 40 percent smaller than in young adults. However, studies indicate that the decline is less in seniors who exercise regularly.

The *VO2 max* (or maximum oxygen consumption) represents the ability of the heart and cardiovascular system to respond to stress. VO2 max shows how much air the lungs can ventilate. It declines with age and poor physical fitness, reflecting a lower maximal attainable heart rate plus a lower capacity of the tissues to extract oxygen quickly from the blood. To achieve VO2 max levels equivalent to those of young adults, seniors must exercise regularly over a longer period of time.

The amount of air that can be taken in and breathed out rapidly in one very deep breath is the measurement of lung function called forced *vital capacity* (VC). It reflects the integrity of the whole respiratory system: the chest muscles and diaphragm, the central nervous system control mechanisms, and the elasticity of the lungs. VC declines about 40 percent between youth and 70 years of age.

Blood Pressure

When taking blood pressure, the upper number, or *systolic pressure*, is the pressure blood exerts on the arterial walls during the heartbeat. The lower number, or *diastolic pressure*, is the pressure remaining in the arteries between heartbeats. In adults, a blood pressure of 140 systolic and/or 90 diastolic is commonly considered to be at the upper limit of normal blood pressure.

Hypertension refers to abnormally high blood pressure. Although there are usually no notable symptoms in the early stages of hypertension, this certainly does not mean that high blood pressure is not dangerous. It is highly associated with strokes and heart attacks, among other serious problems. The myriad causes of elevated blood pressure include heredity, obesity, high fat intake, excessive salt intake, alcohol, smoking, and too little exercise. Fortunately, most of these lifestyle choices are controllable. Hypertension is serious enough to require medical evaluation, but it can be effectively managed through diet and prescription medications.

Blood Sugar Tolerance

The ability of the body to control blood sugar (glucose) is called *glucose tolerance*. With advancing age, the body gradually loses the ability to take up and productively use sugar from the bloodstream. By age 70, approximately 20 percent of men and 30 percent of women have an abnormal glucose tolerance curve, which increases the risk of developing diabetes. Fortunately, researchers are discovering that this age-related decline is more closely associated with seniors' higher body fat content and lower muscle mass than with the pancreas's diminished ability to secrete insulin.

Dietary sources of glucose are starches (bread, pasta, potatoes) and foods that taste sweet. The process of digestion breaks down carbohydrate starches into individual sugar molecules that enter the bloodstream as glucose—no matter how much starch is consumed, the body tries to maintain blood glucose at relatively constant levels. The more direct causes of insulin insensitivity are two factors associated with aging: increased body fat and inactivity. A third cause is a diet rich in fat.

Fortunately, the combination of a high-fiber diet and exercise can often transform a previously insufficient amount of insulin from the pancreas to an adequate amount. Exercise increases the insulin sensitivity of the tissues and improves carbohydrate metabolism.

Cholesterol/HDL Ratio

Cholesterol, a fatty substance, is a necessary component of the body. Bound to proteins, cholesterol circulates in the bloodstream as *lipoproteins*. Under certain circumstances, cholesterol can collect to form deposits in tissues or create blockages within the arteries of the heart. Blockages within blood vessels, referred to as *atherosclerosis*, contribute to the development of heart disease and other circulatory disorders. Blockage within the arteries of the heart can lead to a heart attack. Deposits built up within the arteries of the brain may cause a stroke.

While rates of death from heart disease have decreased in recent decades, it remains the leading killer of men and women in America. Cholesterol levels, family history, diet, and exercise are all significant factors in heart disease. Research shows that the risk of heart disease is greater in those with a family history of the disease. The good news is that by following a low-fat diet, not smoking, and exercising regularly, the risk can be reduced. Although some high cholesterol foods, such as egg yolks, put cholesterol directly into our system, the liver manufactures most of the body's cholesterol. Cholesterol is not required in the diet, as the body is capable of producing all it needs. But that process is greatly influenced by the amount of fat in the diet. Products labeled "no cholesterol" can still raise blood cholesterol levels if they are not also low in saturated fat.

Cholesterol is commonly divided into two categories: good cholesterol, known as *HDL* (high density lipoprotein), and bad cholesterol, known as *LDL* (low density lipoprotein). The key to managing blood cholesterol is to increase good cholesterol and decrease bad cholesterol. Exercise promotes higher levels of the beneficial HDL and lowers the level of LDL. Adjusting one's eating and nutritional habits also helps lower levels of bad cholesterol.

LDL contributes to the development of heart disease by causing waxy, obstructive plaque buildup within the coronary arteries. HDL does just the opposite. Among other things, HDL appears to act as a kind of scouring agent, cleansing the arteries of plaque. This helps to prevent heart disease. As such, *total* cholesterol count is not the primary issue. The cholesterol/HDL ratio is considered a better predictor of heart disease than the cholesterol level alone. This ratio equals the total cholesterol divided by the HDL. The ratio goal for middle-aged and older men and women should be 4.5 or lower. Harmful LDL can be lowered only by diet change. This, however, will not raise the level of HDL in the blood.

Factors that raise HDL levels include exercise and lowering body fat, as well as quitting smoking. Obesity, especially that found around the abdomen, is a great health risk. This type of obesity correlates with low HDL concentrations. Fat distributed about the abdomen is called *above the belt obesity* and is a serious risk factor for arteriosclerosis and adult-onset diabetes.

The term *fiber* refers to the portions of plants that mammals cannot digest and, therefore, cannot be absorbed through human intestines. Fibers are the substances present in cell walls that give plants their structure and form. Generally speaking, water-soluble fiber helps lower blood cholesterol while insoluble fibers help normalize bowel function and prevent both bowel cancer and diverticulosis. According to studies, the average-size person should consume at least 40 grams of total fiber per day.

Bone Density

Osteoporosis is a disease that causes bones to thin and weaken. Osteoporosis is often called the "silent disease," because it acts unnoticed until the first sign of the disease—often a broken bone. According to the National Osteoporosis Foundation, osteoporosis is a major public health threat for an estimated 44 million Americans (NOF, 2003). In the United States today, 10 million individuals are estimated to already have the disease and almost 34 million more are estimated to have low bone mass, placing them at increased risk for osteoporosis. Of the 10 million Americans estimated to have osteoporosis, 8 million are women and 2 million are men. Thirty-four million

Americans, or 55 percent of the people 50 years of age and older, have low bone mass, which puts them at increased risk of developing osteoporosis and related fractures.

At greatest risk for developing osteoporosis are women who have a family history of the disease, have small body frames, and experienced early menopause. The high incidence of bone loss in women is thought to be associated with hormonal changes that occur during menopause. Lower levels of estrogen are believed to contribute to its development, which prompts many women to choose hormone replacement therapy. In addition to hormonal changes, other causes of bone loss and osteoporosis may include diets low in calcium and insufficient exercise.

The first symptoms of osteoporosis may be a reduction in height or bone breakage. Thanks to medical advances, physicians can accurately test for osteoporosis by using dual energy X-ray absorptiometry (DEXA). This measures bone density in the wrist, hip, and lower spine. Other tests include use of single photon absorptiometry, dual energy absorptiometry, and quantitative computed tomography. Those who believe they are at risk for developing osteoporosis should talk with their physicians about obtaining bone density evaluations.

A lifelong diet high in calcium and vitamin D is critical for developing strong bones. A diet rich in magnesium is also important, as it aids in calcium absorption. Research shows that two weeks of complete bed rest can cause as much calcium loss from bones as one whole year's worth of aging. Today, the medical community agrees that repeated stress placed on a bone causes it to become stronger, rather than weaker. Numerous studies have shown that weight-bearing exercise, such as walking, running, tennis, and cycling, continued over an 8- to 24-month time span, can effectively reduce the rate of bone loss. As stated previously, always check with a physician before advising a senior client to begin any exercise program.

Treatment of osteoporosis is commonly directed toward stopping further bone loss and preventing falls. Hormone replacement therapy is a controversial but common therapy in post-menopausal women.

Body Temperature

Dehydration and heat-related injuries are common among seniors because the body's vital thermoregulatory abilities—including a lower metabolic rate and a decreased ability to shiver—diminish with age. As such, both hot and cold weather pose dangers to seniors.

A reduced sensation of thirst contributes to senior's thermoregulatory problems. It is believed that, as a group, seniors do not drink enough water. Older exercisers also tend to have a lower heart rate response and a smaller heart stroke volume than younger people. This reduced cardiac output impairs blood flow to the skin, where heat build-up in the body would normally find its escape through sweat. This means that heat can remain trapped inside the body, allowing internal temperatures to soar to dangerous, even fatal, levels.

Shivering, the opposite of sweating, is the body's way of generating heat (thermogenesis). Just as an inability to sweat leads to possibly dangerous high temperatures in the body, the inability to shiver can leave internal body temperatures dangerously low.

Alternative Medicine

THE USE OF ALTERNATIVE MEDICINE

To shed light onto the extent, use, and cost of unconventional *alternative medicine* (sometimes called *complementary medicine*) in the United States, researchers Eisenberg and Kessler (Eisenberg et al., 1993) conducted a national survey to determine the prevalence, patterns of use, and costs of healing methods considered "unconventional" by Western medicine standards. Such therapies included acupuncture, acupressure, and various herbal remedies, to name but a few. Of the 1,500 individuals surveyed, 34 percent reported using at least one form of alternative therapy over the previous year. The majority of those surveyed used alternative therapies to treat predominantly chronic illnesses rather than life-threatening problems. The average charge per visit to receive these therapies was $27.60. Most charges were paid out-of-pocket and in full.

Eisenberg and Kessler estimate that Americans made approximately 425 million visits to alternative care physicians. This number exceeded the estimated 388 million visits to primary care physicians. Interestingly, 72 percent of respondents did not tell their primary care physicians that they had used alternative treatments. Roughly half of those who used unconventional therapy had no direct supervision from a medical doctor in the use of such therapies. Of the seniors who responded, 83 percent of those who used unconventional therapies also used conventional medical treatments.

The conditions most frequently treated with unconventional methods were back problems, anxiety, headaches, chronic pain (such as arthritis), and cancer. Unconventional therapies most often used included relaxation techniques, chiropractic care, and massage. Other frequently used treatments were herbal medicine, megavitamin therapy, homeopathy, and acupuncture.

Working with a Certified Alternative Medicine practitioner may provide benefits, especially when treatments are coordinated with seniors' primary physicians. In choosing a Certified Alternative Medicine practitioner, seniors should consider the following factors:

- certification and licensure
- institutional endorsement
- peer endorsement
- patient endorsement
- experience with specific conditions
- cooperation or collaboration with a primary physician
- ability to recognize limitations of the treatment and, as a result, the need to refer to another physician or practitioner
- liability insurance
- projected number of treatments and cost
- time frame for treatment

MASSAGE THERAPY FOR SENIORS

The benefit of touch at any age is too often minimized. For seniors, massage therapy may be extremely beneficial. So often the only touch they encounter is in the doctor's office, when they are being poked with needles or having other tests. In addition to providing noninvasive pain relief or comfort in the wake of chronic illness, massage provides physical and emotional help for those struggling with bodies that just don't work as well as they used to. In addition, research indicates that massage therapy can improve circulation.

Passive range of motion exercises (performed by a therapist) can improve joint mobility by helping joints and tight muscles function properly. Clinical observations and personal journals show that seniors who take advantage of massage therapy become happier and healthier in a very short time. They feel less depressed, have fewer doctor visits, and use fewer stimulants (e.g., caffeinated drinks). For seniors, massage therapy can be performed in a bed or chair. It can even be performed in a wheelchair. Massage therapy designed for seniors is tailored to be gentler than standard massage, thereby preventing damage to fragile skin and tissues.

NUTRITIONAL SUPPLEMENTS AND SENIORS

Nutritional supplements can be extremely beneficial in providing vitamins and minerals to seniors who may not have nutritionally sound diets. However, unsupervised use of nutritional supplements is not recommended. Because of this, seniors should seek advice from qualified professionals regarding the types and amounts of supplements to use. Excessive use of specific nutritional supplements goes beyond their nutritional function and may cause problems (see Table 11.2). For example, taken in excessive dosages, vitamins A, D, and K can be toxic.

Table 11.2 Nutritional Supplement Overdose Symptoms

Vitamin A: fatigue, lethargy, hair loss, headaches, liver damage

Vitamin D: possible kidney failure, heart damage, bone fragility

Vitamin C: gas, diarrhea, dehydration (from diarrhea)

Niacin: flushed skin, impaired liver function

Iodine: enlargement of thyroid gland

Magnesium: diarrhea, possible gastrointestinal and cardiovascular effects

No one should self-medicate large doses of vitamins, minerals, or other nutritional supplements. Use of supplements is best discussed with physicians. This will better ensure that the dosages are safe and that no untoward interactions between the supplements and other prescribed medications will occur.

One thousand Americans stop smoking every day—by dying.

Author Unknown

The Advantages of Quitting Smoking

According to the National Institute on Aging (NIA, 1999), more than a million people break the smoking habit each year. Quitting smoking results in:

- a lower risk of cancer, heart attack, and lung disease;
- better blood circulation;
- healthier family members, particularly children and grandchildren;
- a healthy lifestyle example for children and grandchildren;
- no odor of smoke in your clothes and hair;
- a more sensitive sense of smell.

WHAT SMOKING DOES

Cigarette smoke damages lungs and airways. Air passages swell and, over time, become filled with mucus. This can cause a cough that won't go away. Sometimes this leads to a lung disease called chronic bronchitis. If seniors keep smoking, normal breathing may become harder and harder as emphysema develops. In emphysema, airways become blocked as the tissue of the lungs undergoes changes that make getting enough oxygen difficult.

Smoking shortens life. According to NIA, it brings an early death to more than 400,000 people in the United States each year. And lifelong smokers have a one in two chance of dying from a smoking-related disease. Smoking doesn't just cut a few months off the end of life; it reduces the life of the average smoker by 12 years.

Smoking makes millions of Americans sick by causing:

- heart disease. If you have high blood pressure or high cholesterol (a fatty substance in the blood) and also smoke, you increase your chance of having a heart attack.
- cancer. Smoking causes cancer of the lungs, mouth, larynx (voice box), and esophagus. It plays a role in cancer of the pancreas, kidney, bladder, and maybe the cervix in women. The chance of getting cancer grows as you smoke more cigarettes, smoke more years, or inhale deeply.
- respiratory problems. If you smoke, you are more likely than a nonsmoker to get the flu (influenza), pneumonia, or other infections (such as colds) that can interfere with your breathing. Flu and pneumonia are very dangerous for older people.
- osteoporosis. If you are an older woman who smokes, your chance of developing osteoporosis is greater. Women who are past menopause tend to lose bone strength and sometimes develop this bone-weakening disorder. Bones weakened by osteoporosis fracture more easily. Also, women smokers sometimes begin menopause sooner than the average woman does.

Good News About Quitting

As soon as a person stops smoking, the heart and circulatory system (the arteries and veins that blood flows through) start getting better. The chance of heart attack, stroke, and other circulatory diseases begins to drop. The flow of blood to hands and feet gets stronger. Breathing may be more difficult in the first few weeks, but should become easier a few months after the last cigarette. Quitting smoking can't undo permanent lung damage, but it may help slow further damage to the lungs. The chance of getting cancer from smoking also begins to shrink. According to NIA, within 10 to 15 years after quitting, the risk of cancer and heart disease is almost as low as that of a nonsmoker.

Nicotine Is a Drug

Cigarette smoke contains thousands of chemicals. Some are known to cause cancer. Another, nicotine, is a very addictive drug. When a person first smokes, nicotine feels good and encourages more smoking. Soon, a smoker's body starts to need more nicotine in order to feel good, which leads to smoking even more to keep getting that pleasurable feeling.

The first few weeks after quitting are the hardest. Some people who give up smoking have withdrawal symptoms, becoming grumpy, hungry, or tired. Withdrawal may cause headaches, depression, or problems sleeping or concentrating. Some people, though, have no withdrawal symptoms at all.

People often are worried about gaining weight if they stop smoking. But many people who stop smoking gain little or no weight. Those who do gain usually add less than 10 pounds. But, even with a few extra pounds, quitters will be healthier than if they continued smoking.

Breaking the Habit

Smoking is a strong addiction for both body and mind. That is why it is so hard to stop. But, people do succeed. NIA reported from 1965 to 1999 more than 30 million Americans quit smoking. Advice for quitters includes:

- reading self-help literature;
- taking a quit-smoking class;
- using individual or group counseling;
- joining a support group;
- getting a friend to quit at the same time;
- taking medicine to help with nicotine withdrawal;
- using nicotine replacement therapy.

Each person is different. Sometimes combining several methods is the answer. Many people can stop on their own. Others need help from doctors, clinics, or organized groups. The first step is to make a firm decision to quit, followed by choosing a date to stop smoking and picking one or more methods for quitting. Before stopping, a quitter should try changing smoking habits. For example, someone who smokes a cigarette after each meal should first begin to wait a while after eating. Some people smoke while reading the newspaper and will benefit from trying to replace the smoking behavior while reading with another less harmful habit, like chewing gum. When a person finally decides to completely stop smoking, replacement habits make the addiction easier to break.

People who quit may need special help to cope with their desire for nicotine. Nicotine replacement therapy can help control withdrawal symptoms, but it's not for everyone. Quitters should check with their doctors first. Doctors often recommend one of these four forms:

- nicotine chewing gum, available without a doctor's prescription
- the nicotine patch, also available over the counter
- nicotine nasal spray, which requires a doctor's prescription
- prescription nicotine inhalers

All of these treatments provide nicotine to the body without the harmful substances found in tobacco smoke. They reduce withdrawal symptoms, making it easier for a quitter to learn to fight the physical habit and mental addiction of smoking. Also, this dose of nicotine is less than that from a cigarette and is tapered off during the treatment period. Quitters who use a replacement medication need to know that it is dangerous to smoke while on nicotine replacement therapy.

There is another drug to help handle nicotine cravings. Known as bupropion hydrochloride, it does not contain nicotine and must be prescribed by a doctor. The most common side effects are dry mouth and problems getting to sleep.

CIGARS, CHEWING TOBACCO, AND SNUFF ARE NOT SAFER

Some people think smokeless tobacco (chewing tobacco and snuff), pipes, and cigars are safer than cigarettes. They are not. Using smokeless tobacco can cause cancer of the mouth, a precancerous lesion known as oral leukoplakia, nicotine addiction, and possibly cancer of the larynx and esophagus, as well as tooth and heart problems. Pipe and cigar smokers may develop cancer of the mouth, lip, larynx, pharynx, and esophagus. Those who inhale have the same chance of lung cancer as cigarette smokers have.

BEING AROUND SOMEONE WHO SMOKES

Passive smoking happens when a nonsmoker breathes smoke from someone else's cigarette, pipe, or cigar. It is also called secondhand smoke. We now know that such secondhand smoke is unsafe. People who don't smoke but live or work with smokers are more likely to develop lung cancer than other nonsmokers. In fact, each year an estimated 3,000 people who don't smoke die of lung cancer because of secondhand smoke. It has also been linked to heart disease in nonsmokers.

Passive smoking is very dangerous for someone with asthma, other lung conditions, or heart disease. It may cause bronchitis, pneumonia, an asthma attack, or inner ear infections in babies and young children. It may be associated with SIDS (sudden infant death syndrome). These problems are just some good reasons for a parent or grandparent to think about quitting smoking. Everyone should try not to smoke around young children or infants.

Senior Nutrition, Fitness, and Healthy Lifestyles: Summary

Seniors may face a variety of health-related problems. Uncontrolled, these problems can greatly affect both the quality of seniors' lives and their independence. As studies show, health-related problems are exacerbated not only by age but also by poor nutrition, inactivity, obesity, high cholesterol, failing to control underlying medical disorders, and smoking. By taking an active role in maintaining their health, seniors will be better able to fend off or altogether avoid some of the health-related problems commonly brought on by aging.

You can help improve the lives of your senior clients by assisting them with not only their financial health but also their physical health. For example, to assist with nutritional needs you can gather information about grocery delivery programs offered by local stores and online vendors that your homebound clients can use. Encourage your clients to be active and reject the slowdown myth. You can network with health clubs and senior centers that offer senior safe fitness programs so you can point seniors to local resources. Finally—and perhaps most difficult—you are encouraged to "walk the talk" with healthy diet and exercise in your own life.

References

AoA (Administration on Aging). (2003, August 27). *Nutrition fact sheet*. Retrieved June 17, 2004, from http://www.aoa.dhhs.gov/press/fact/pdf/fs_nutrition.pdf

Eisenberg, D. M., Kessler, R. C., et al. (1993, January 28). Unconventional medicine in the United States. *New England Journal of Medicine*.

Evans, W., Rosenberg, I. H. (1993). *Biomarkers*. New York: Simon & Schuster.

FDA (Food and Drug Administration). (2004). *FDA's plan to confront nation's obesity problem*. Retrieved June 17, 2004, from http://www.fda.gov/oc/initiatives/obesity/

Merck (2004). Obesity. *The Merck Manual of Geriatrics*, chap. 62. Retrieved June 17, 2004, from http://www.merck.com/mrkshared/mm_geriatrics/sec8/ch62.jsp

NIA (National Institute on Aging). (1999). Smoking: It's never too late to stop [Electronic version]. *Age Pages*. Bethesda, MD: National Institutes of Health. Retrieved June 17, 2004, from http://www.niapublications.org/engagepages/smoking.asp

NIA. (2004). *The health ABC study*. Bethesda, MD: National Institutes of Health. Retrieved June 17, 2004, from http://www.nia.nih.gov/research/repository/health%5Fabc%5Fdescription.htm

NOF (National Osteoporosis Foundation). (2003). *Fast Facts*. Washington, DC: NOF. Retrieved June 17, 2004, from http://www.nof.org/osteoporosis/stats.htm

Roubenoff R., Hughes V. A., Dallal, G. E., Nelson. M. F., Morganit, C., Kehayias, J. J., et al. (2000). The effect of gender and body composition method on the apparent decline in lean mass-adjusted resting metabolic rate with age. *Journal of Gerontology: Medical Sciences 2000 55*: M757-M760.

Tufts University (n.d.). *More water, more fiber, fewer calories: Reinventing the food pyramid for older adult.* Retrieved June 25, 2004, from http://nutrition.tufts.edu/magazine/1999fall/pyramid.html

USDA (United States Department of Agriculture). (2000, May). Food insufficiency and the nutritional status of the elderly population. *Nutrition Insights*, No. 18.

USDA. (2002, September). More than one in three older Americans may not drink enough water. *Nutrition Insights*, No. 27.

USDA. (2003a, July) *Trends in Food Stamp Program participation rates: 1999 to 2001.* Retrieved June 25, 2004, from http://www.fns.usda.gov/oane/MENU/Published/FSP/FILES/Participation/trends1999-2001sum.htm

USDA. (2003b, December) Characteristics of food stamp households: Fiscal year 2002. Retrieved June 25, 2004, from http://www.fns.usda.gov/oane/MENU/Published/FSP/FILES/Participation/2002AdvSum.htm

Walford, R. L., & Walford, L. (1995). *The Anti-Aging Plan.* Berkeley, CA: Group West.

Resources

Services

American Cancer Society (ACS). http://www.cancer.org, 1599 Clifton Road NE, Atlanta, GA 30329, 800-ACS-2345. ACS provides extensive resources to help people quit smoking. ACS provides local chapters throughout the country.

American College of Sports Medicine (ACSM). http://www.acsm.org/index.asp, 401 W. Michigan Street, Indianapolis, IN 46202-3233, 317-637-9200. ACSM certifies health and fitness practitioners and provides references to local practitioners.

American Dietetic Association Nutrition & Health for Older Americans. http://www.eatright.com/catalog/older.html. Offers publications specifically designed for seniors, including *Nutrition & Health for Older Americans.*

Fifty-Plus Fitness Association (FPFA). http://www.50plus.org, 1040 Noel Drive, Suite 100, Menlo Park, CA 94025, 650-323-6160. FPFA promotes active lifestyles for older people. FPFA publishes a newsletter, distributes books and videos, and sponsors activities such as "fun runs" for seniors.

Food and Drug Administration's Older Persons Web site. http://www.fda.gov/oc/olderpersons/. This FDA Web site has numerous articles, brochures, and other publications with information for older people on a wide range of health issues, including nutrition and food safety. Selected publications are also in Spanish. Information about safe food handling is available from the FDA hotline, 1-888-SAFEFOOD. The USDA Meat and Poultry hotline, 1-800-535-4555, is also a good resource.

Food and Nutrition Information Center (FNIC) Department of Agriculture. http://www.nalusda.gov/fnic, Agricultural Research Service/National Agriculture Library, 10301 Baltimore Avenue, Room 304, Beltsville, MD 20705-2351. FNIC, part of the federal government, provides information, publications, and audiovisual materials on nutrition. Resource guides on nutrition and older people, heart disease, diabetes, vegetarianism, food safety, and food labeling are available.

Jean Mayer USDA Human Nutrition Research Center on Aging (HNRCA) at Tufts University. http://hnrc.tufts.edu/, 711 Washington Street, Boston, MA 02111-1524, 617-556-3000. HNRCA investigators conduct advanced studies on nutrition and aging. Their research focuses on determining the nutrient requirements necessary to promote well-being for older adults.

National Osteoporosis Foundation. http://store.yahoo.com/nof/membership.html, 202-223-2226. NOF is a key resource for people seeking up-to-date, medically sound information on the causes, prevention, detection, and treatment of osteoporosis. Provides free single copies (up to five different titles) of patient/public education publications.

President's Council on Physical Fitness and Sports (PCPFS). http://www.fitness.gov, Dept. W, 200 Independence Avenue, SW, Room 738-H, Washington, DC 20201-0004, 202-690-9000. PCPFS conducts programs, projects, and campaigns that emphasize the importance of regular physical activity, fitness, and sports participation for children, adults (including seniors), and persons with disabilities.

Chapter 12

Cognitive Aging

One-hundred-and-two-year-old Russell Clark says, "Continuing to work keeps the mind sharp and the body healthy, which aids in maintaining a positive attitude." Clark, of Orem, Utah, works every day as the manager of an industrial park and other real estate developments.

Experience Works, a national nonprofit that specializes in employment training and services for older workers, recognizes the contributions older employees make to workplaces around the country. In September 2003, the organization announced that Russell Clark was "America's Oldest Worker" for that year.

At age 83, Clark retired from his day job as a physician and surgeon. His interest in real estate investment began while he was practicing medicine, and it led him to purchase a clinic and 47-bed hospital.

. . .

Mrs. Blackwell had been living alone in a small community in the two months since her husband passed away suddenly. When her electricity was turned off unexpectedly, she called the electric company and was told that her bill had not been paid in the last two months. Mrs. Blackwell insisted that the bills had been paid and called her daughter to help her resolve the issue.

When Mrs. Blackwell's daughter went through the piles of paper on her mother's desk, she discovered that many bills had not been paid since her father died, while others had been paid twice. She also found her mother's brooch in the freezer and rotten food in the refrigerator, and realized her mother hà not changed her dress since the two of them had gone out to lunch together a week before. Her daughter knew that Mrs. Jones had been having some problems with her memory for a couple of years and hadn't been sleeping well, but didn't think there was any other problem.

When questioned about the situation, Mrs. Blackwell became angry and defensive, stating that she just lost her husband and was grieving.

After calming her mother, Mrs. Blackwell's daughter was able to convince her to see the doctor. Several tests from her general practitioner and a psychiatrist (including assessment of her grief reaction) concluded that Mrs. Blackwell had likely been suffering from dementia for several years. Her husband had compensated for her deficits, a situation that became evident only after he died.

Introduction

While they might not reach the remarkable age that Russell Clark has, most seniors live full, productive lives until well into their seventh decade and beyond. Mrs. Blackwell's story is atypical. Normal aging through the later decades is accompanied by some minimal brain deterioration and slowing, but most mental functioning remains fully intact. Only a small percentage of younger seniors will become, like Mrs. Blackwell, victims of Alzheimer's disease or a related dementia. However, by age 85 nearly half are affected (Alzheimer's Association, n.d.)

Alzheimer's disease is a progressive, age-related, irreversible brain disorder that has become a topic of growing concern in both health care and social policy circles. Not only is the nature of this illness frightening, it has a huge cost to individuals, families, the health care system, and society. The national annual financial cost of caring for people with dementia is $60–120 billion (Ernst & Hay, 1996). Added to that cost are the burden on caregivers and their families, lost family caregiver workdays, and strain on the overburdened health care system. This chapter will provide a foundation for understanding normal aging versus the disease process, and dementia as the syndrome caused by many underlying diseases, with focus on the most prevalent form of dementia, Alzheimer's disease.

Normal Aging Versus the Disease Process

NORMAL AGING

Many people believe that dementia is a normal part of aging—that loss of mental capacity is an inevitable part of late life. This is a fallacy that, unfortunately, contributes to a great deal of negative stereotyping of seniors (*ageism*) in American culture. While some cultures revere the elderly and look to them as the possessors of wisdom, many Americans tend to assume that all seniors become feeble-minded or senile. The reality is that a very small percentage of seniors develop debilitating cognitive disorders.

While dementia is not a normal part of aging, some cognitive changes do occur as a normal part of growing older. The most common cognitive change is a decline in speed of mental processing (Ratcliffe & Saxton, 1998). The speed with which adults are able to take in and process information declines with age. On tests of general mental ability, seniors generally score lower than younger adults. When given extra time to complete tests, however, discrepancies in performance between younger adults and seniors disappear.

Age-related change in speed has a number of practical implications. First, seniors can process information about as well as (or, depending on the activity, better than) younger adults, if given adequate time. Thus, it is important to remember that seniors will be just as likely as younger adults to understand material being presented to them, but they would benefit from more time to absorb the information.

Second, since learning or encoding of new information into memory storage is slower, seniors may be less able to "store" new material that is presented rapidly. This process may also be responsible for a slight decline in ability to learn new information in late life. Similarly, it may take seniors longer to recall information.

Third, reaction time is slowed, which may have implications for performance of activities that require rapid shifts in attention, such as driving a car, for some seniors.

It is important to note that these changes are minimal in normal aging, and do not generally impair the daily functioning of seniors. Further, there is considerable variation among seniors, and all of these changes are relative to the individual's level of functioning. For example, an individual who always remembered every loved one's birthday and sent cards accordingly may need to refer to a calendar (like many younger people do) to recall this information later in life. At the same time, someone who as a young adult was never able to remember anyone's name or face, much less their birthdate, may be more troubled by these slight declines later in life.

Normal aging also is accompanied by declines in vision and hearing, which may be mistaken for cognitive deficits. A senior who cannot hear or see cannot store or recall information accurately. Thus, it is important that seniors maximize the comprehension and retention of information by using any glasses, hearing aids, or other assistive devices they need.

Mild Cognitive Impairment

Mild cognitive impairment (MCI) is a state of progressive memory loss after the age of 50 that is beyond what would be expected as part of normal aging but does not meet the criteria for a diagnosis of dementia (Peterson et al., 1999). People with MCI demonstrate:

- evidence of memory deficits that are abnormal for their age and educational level
- presence of otherwise normal general cognitive functioning
- normal performance of activities of daily living

MCI occurs in between 3 and 19 percent of seniors (Ritchie, Artero, & Tuchon, 2001). Research indicates that 11 to 80 percent of people with MCI will develop Alzheimer's disease within five years (Peterson et al., 2001; Ritchie et al., 2001). These huge variations in estimates are largely due to differences in definitions of the syndrome. Although there is currently no treatment that will stop or reverse MCI, research is currently being conducted to test the effectiveness of medications to minimize memory impairment.

Dementia

The trauma of dementia is not the simple frustration of forgetting. The trauma includes the horror of being separated from one's self, a self made up largely of one's memories. A person without access to their memories—to their essential self—can easily become overwhelmed by the ter-ror of being alone. ... Dementia brings new meaning to the word alone.

Marilyn Mitchell, *Dancing on Quicksand*, 2002

Dementia is a pervasive deterioration of intellectual ability that occurs over an extended period of time. Memory loss is the symptom most common in dementia and is typically the first cognitive change noticed by patients and families. Dementia also affects an individual's: orientation to place and time; language functioning; ability to think abstractly and solve problems; power to evidence good judgment; visual and spatial ability; and personality.

CAUSES OF DEMENTIA

Dementia is often categorized according to the disease that is suspected of causing it. Though the causes of dementia are often difficult to determine, each disease process can result in slightly different symptoms. (Think of this like a pattern of cold symptoms: three people may have the same cold symptoms, but one person's symptoms are caused by a virus, one by a bacterial infection, and one by allergies. These are all different causes of the same *syndrome*, or group of symptoms. Sometimes the treatment will be the same—a decongestant, for example—and sometimes the treatments will be different—antibiotics, for example, used for the bacterial infection only.)

Common types of dementia are noted below. (Details are provided about only the most common causes.)

Treatable Dementias

- *toxic,* from alcohol, drug, or heavy-metal exposure
- *metabolic,* as may be caused by thyroid disease or vitamin B-12 deficiency
- *depression-related pseudodementia* (dementia-like symptoms in the context of a depressive episode; see chapter 4, Psychological Aspects of Aging, for more about this)
- *medication-induced,* the most common cause of reversible dementia in the elderly if detected early

Irreversible Dementias

- *degenerative,* including:

  Alzheimer's disease (AD) is the most common cause of dementia, representing 60 to70 percent of all cases of dementia (Reuben, et al., 2001). The evidence is mixed, but early studies indicate that a specific gene, apolipoprotein E serum lipoprotein (APOE), may account for 10 to 40 percent of all cases of AD (Plassman & Breitner, 1996; Evans, et al., 1997). The gene appears to be responsible for early-onset AD (ages 50-75). Women with the APOE gene are at higher risk of contracting AD than men are (Hendrie, 1998). This gene has not been found to be a risk factor for AD among African Americans (Froehlich, Bogardus, & Inouye, 2001).

Parkinson's disease is associated with the brain's loss of a chemical called *dopamine*. Up to 40 percent of individuals with Parkinson's disease develop dementia, with impairment primarily in executive functioning (planning, problem-solving, abstract thinking) and visual-spatial processing (Emre, 2003).

Dementia with Lewy bodies (DLB) is associated with abnormal structures (*Lewy bodies*) in the brain. It is less well understood than other forms of dementia. DLB is associated with a combination of symptoms of Alzheimer's disease (confusion, attention problems) and Parkinson's disease (motor problems), as well as visual hallucinations. Prevalence of DLB is estimated at between 15 and 35 percent of all cases of dementia, or approximately 0.6 percent of the general population over the age of 65 (Rahkonen, et al., 2003).

- *vascular dementia,* which is caused by small strokes that decrease blood flow to the brain. Vascular dementia is the second most common form of dementia, representing 15 to 20 percent of all cases of dementia. The vascular damage leading to dementia may be categorized as one of the following:

- *infectious,* as may be caused by AIDS

- *other*—for example, conditions such as head injury, brain tumor, or subdural hematoma)

DIAGNOSING DEMENTIA

The diagnosis of dementia is based on criteria defined in the *Diagnostic and Statistical Manual of Mental Disorders* (DSM-IV; APA, 1994), which is the official listing and definition of psychiatric disorders by the American Psychiatric Association (APA). These criteria include:

1. *Deficits in short-term and long-term memory.* Short-term memory is the retention of information over a span of a few minutes to a few hours, such as recalling what one had for breakfast today. Long-term memory is the retention of information over weeks to months, such as the name of the president of the United States, the place an individual was born, and names of children or grandchildren.

2. The individual must have deficits in at least one of the following areas:
   a. *Aphasia* is the inability to understand or use language. A common problem is in identifying the names of familiar objects. Although many seniors complain that it is sometimes difficult to recall the right name or word ("tip-of-the-tongue"), individuals with AD are often unable to produce the "stuck" words, even after a long delay.
   b. *Agnosia* is the inability to recognize and identify objects or persons despite having knowledge of the characteristics of the objects or persons. People with agnosia may have difficulty recognizing the geometric features of an object or face or may be able to perceive the geometric features but not know what the object is used for or whether a face is familiar or not.

c. *Apraxia* refers to difficulty with physical movement despite normal physical functioning. Change in gait (walking) is one common example.

d. *Executive functioning* includes problem solving, abstract thinking (recognizing, for example, that an apple and an orange are both fruit), organization, and judgment. Common examples of these deficits include having problems managing a checkbook or paying bills on time, not knowing what do in an emergency such as a fire, or loss of ability to understand irony, sarcasm, or symbolic stories like parables.

3. The deficits above significantly interfere with daily activities, or represent a significant deterioration from one's previous level of functioning.

4. No other medical condition, such as delirium (see description below) or depression, accounts for the symptoms.

Additionally, in Alzheimer's disease and some other forms of dementia, symptoms appear gradually and get progressively worse over time. In some forms of dementia, such as vascular dementia, symptoms may appear suddenly after a stroke or series of small vascular changes.

Because there are so many possible causes of cognitive problems and different areas of functioning are affected, psychiatrists, psychologists, and others use many different kinds of measures to diagnose the disease. After completing the following evaluations, an accurate diagnosis is likely:

1. *medical history:* A physician should document current mental or physical conditions, onset and progression of memory complaints and behavioral changes, prescription drug intake, and family health history.

2. *mental status evaluation:* A patient should be assessed on his or her orientation to time and place and ability to remember, understand, communicate, and do simple calculations.

3. *neuropsychological evaluation:* This evaluation may consist of tests of memory, concentration, reasoning, visual-motor coordination, and language function.

4. *physical examination:* A patient will be evaluated on nutritional status, blood pressure, pulse, vision, hearing, and motor functioning.

5. *magnetic resonance imaging (MRI) of the brain*

6. *laboratory tests such as blood and urine tests:* [Note that, while genetic research related to Alzheimer's disease is currently being conducted, genetic testing is not appropriate for diagnosis, since many people with Alzheimer's disease do not have the genetic markers (Weiner et al., 1999).]

7. *psychiatric evaluation:* Just as cardiologists are heart specialists, psychiatrists are brain specialists. If one is locally available, seniors should be referred to a geriatric psychiatrist. Otherwise, a referral should be made

to a psychiatrist who is familiar with the diagnosis and treatment of dementia. Psychiatrists can also complete careful assessment of depression or other factors that may be causing the individual's symptoms.

As a CSA, you should make contacts with your local mental health workers who specialize in or are trained to work with people with dementia. You will then be able to make referrals when necessary.

PREVALENCE OF DEMENTIA

The prevalence of dementia among seniors not living in institutions is 6 to 10 percent. At age 65, the prevalence of dementia is 5 to 7 percent, with the risk almost doubling every five years of life until age 90, when rates level off to approximately 40 percent (Ficher, Schroppel, & Meller, 1996; Graves et al., 1996; Sadock & Sadock, 2000). Among nursing home residents, the rates of dementia are as high as 46 to 78 percent (Class et al., 1996; Magaziner et al., 2000). Dementia is the primary reason that many seniors are admitted to nursing homes.

Ethnicity

Rates of Alzheimer's disease are comparable between Caucasians and African Americans, although African Americans have higher rates of vascular dementia. This difference has been attributed to a higher incidence among African Americans of hypertension, diabetes, and stroke (Heyman et al., 1991). Parkinson's dementia is also less common among Caucasians than among African Americans (de la Mente, Hutchins, & Moore, 1989).

Gender

Research has been somewhat mixed, but recent large studies suggest that women and men develop AD at the same rate, although rates are higher for women over the age of 90 (Ruitenberg, Ott, van Swieten, Hofman, & Breteler, 2001). One explanation for this is that women live longer than men, thus they have an increased risk related to their age. Women have lower rates of vascular dementia than men (Ruitenberg et al.).

COURSE OF DEMENTIA

The course of the dementia depends on its cause. However, most dementias get worse over time. Exceptions to this pattern are dementias that, for example, are the result of a traumatic head injury or nonprogressive brain tumor. In these cases, the deficits remain relatively stable over time.

Alzheimer's Disease

Nov. 5, 1994

My Fellow Americans,

I have recently been told that I am one of the millions of Americans who will be afflicted with Alzheimer's disease. Upon learning this news, Nancy and I had to decide whether as private citizens we would keep this a private matter or whether we would make this news known in a public way.

In the past Nancy suffered from breast cancer, and I had my cancer surgeries. We found through our open disclosures we were able to raise public awareness. We were happy that as a result many more people underwent testing. They were treated in early stages and able to return to normal, healthy lives.

So now, we feel it is important to share it with you. In opening our hearts, we hope this might promote greater awareness of this condition. Perhaps it will encourage a clearer understanding of the individuals and families who are affected by it.

At the moment I feel just fine. I intend to live the remainder of the years God gives me on this earth doing the things I have always done. I will continue to share life's journey with my beloved Nancy and my family. I plan to enjoy the great outdoors and stay in touch with my friends and supporters.

Unfortunately, as Alzheimer's disease progresses, the family often bears a heavy burden. I only wish there was some way I could spare Nancy from this painful experience. When the time comes I am confident that with your help she will face it with faith and courage.

In closing let me thank you, the American people, for giving me the great honor of allowing me to serve as your President. When the Lord calls me home, whenever that may be, I will leave with the greatest love for this country of ours and eternal optimism for its future.

I now begin the journey that will lead me into the sunset of my life. I know that for America there will always be a bright dawn ahead.

Thank you, my friends. May God always bless you.

Sincerely,

Ronald Reagan

Alzheimer's disease is an age-expressed, irreversible, progressive disease in which the brain undergoes specific changes. The neurons that transmit information in the brain become tangled and coated in plaque so that information is not accurately processed. The beginning of the disease (sometimes called *insidious onset*) is not apparent. This subtle progression makes it difficult to determine when the condition began. Many people are able to cover the symptoms well in the early stages, particularly if they are highly intelligent or have a spouse or partner to compensate for their losses.

The average survival time following the onset of symptoms ranges from 2 to 16 years. Life expectancy for people with Alzheimer's is lower on average than the general population (Walsh, Welch, & Larson, 1990). Higher rates of mortality in persons with Alzheimer's disease result from loss of muscle control (and, with it, the ability to swallow), dehydration, malnutrition, pneumonia, and other infections. Recent research indicates that artificial nutrition, which refers to various methods of feeding patients when eating orally, does not extend or improve the lives of individuals with late-stage dementia. Therefore, inserting a feeding tube in the late stages of Alzheimer's disease is considered by many to be a futile treatment (Finucane, 2003). Some religious and legal groups contest this conclusion. Nonetheless, many medical patient advocates strongly discourage the surgical insertion of feeding tubes for late-stage dementia patients. This is one issue to consider when discussing advance directives with clients.

Alzheimer's disease is recognizable. There are ways to differentiate early Alzheimer's disease from normal aging. The Alzheimer's Association (2004) has developed a list of 10 warning signs that help identify the disease. Persons who exhibit several of these symptoms should see a physician for a complete examination.

- memory loss that affects job skills
- difficulty performing familiar tasks
- problems with language
- disorientation to time and place (getting lost)
- poor or decreased judgment
- problems with abstract thinking
- changes in mood or behavior
- misplacing things
- changes in personality
- loss of initiative

Symptoms of Alzheimer's disease typically progress through three stages. Staging is somewhat arbitrary, as there is variability within each stage and movement between stages. Alzheimer's disease is not always diagnosed in its early stage. You should recommend a physician's evaluation of any of your clients as soon as early symptoms of Alzheimer's disease are noted.

In the beginning stage, most people with AD maintain the ability to make health care decisions for themselves, but they will lose this capacity over the course of the illness. If a diagnosis of Alzheimer's disease is made, it is very important that the affected individual identify in writing a health care agent to make future health care decisions. (See chapter 14 for further discussion of health care agents.) Designation of a health care agent facilitates optimal health care in later stages of the disease.

EARLY-STAGE ALZHEIMER'S DISEASE

Symptoms of early-stage Alzheimer's disease generally present themselves over a two- to four-year period. People with early-stage AD begin experiencing short-term memory deficits, difficulty in decision-making, problems in performing routine tasks, personality change, and mood changes. Examples of early symptoms of Alzheimer's disease include misplacing jewelry, wallets, and other personal items. Routine paperwork such as writing checks becomes difficult and frustrating. At this early stage, most individuals still function independently, although many benefit from assistance. Many people who have the illness (as well as their family members) may overlook symptoms because the individual speaks fluently and recalls things from the past. Some families believe that if an older relative can remember the name of a first grade teacher, he or she must be fine. They may not realize, however, that she can't remember the name of the person she met just five minutes ago, or whether or not she took her medication that morning.

Common Symptoms of Early Stage Alzheimer's Disease

- progressive memory loss—poor memory for new information; remote memories are generally intact
- mild difficulty finding words with maintenance of rhythm and smoothness of speech
- misplacement of things; disorganization
- mild problems with judgment and abstraction
- sleep difficulty
- loss of spontaneity and initiative
- social withdrawal because of loss of initiative, embarrassment about others witnessing deficits, or other reasons
- delusions—most commonly, these involve belief that others are trying to hurt or steal from the individual
- depressive symptoms—approximately 25 percent of individuals with AD develop depressive symptoms in response to awareness of deficits and decline or brain changes associated with the disease; major depression is rare (Becker, Boller, Lopez, Saton, & McGonigle, 1994; Weiner, Doody, Sairam, Foster, & Liao, 2002)

MIDDLE-STAGE ALZHEIMER'S DISEASE

The middle stage of Alzheimer's disease can last from 2 to 10 years or more after diagnosis. Memory loss often worsens during this stage. Communication skills, reasoning, and attention to personal care needs and hygiene may diminish. During this stage, people with Alzheimer's disease often grow to need full-time care and supervision.

Common Symptoms of Middle Stage of Alzheimer's Disease

- symptoms from early stage continue and worsen
- remote memory declines
- great difficulty finding words, repeating phrases
- visual-spatial problems such as difficulty copying figures and recognizing objects or people
- exacerbation of symptoms when routine or environment is disturbed or there is too much sensory input (e.g., in loud restaurants or shopping malls)
- problems calculating, dealing with money
- problems operating machinery, dressing, and grooming
- agitation, disinhibition (e.g., saying and doing things one wouldn't normally say or do in public)
- sleeping often; waking frequently at night, wandering
- difficulty writing
- verbal and physical aggression—particularly among those who have a troubled relationship with the caregiver before the onset of the illness, as well as for those with significant medical problems
- appetite changes (e.g., huge appetite for sugary, salty, high-fat foods); no memory for when the last meal was eaten; loss of interest in eating
- *sundowning*, a syndrome in which symptoms get worse in the evening
- social and interpersonal skills often look normal until the last stage

The story of Mrs. Blackwell from the beginning of the chapter serves as an illustration of someone who has middle-stage Alzheimer's disease.

LATE-STAGE ALZHEIMER'S DISEASE

Late-stage Alzheimer's disease reflects a further decrease in mental function and communication skills. During this stage, people with AD lose the ability to recognize family members, friends, and caregivers. Activities of daily living require full assistance. People in the final stage cease to speak and eat, lose muscle control and swallow reflexes, slip into a coma, and eventually die. Due to the loss of muscle control and decreased immune functioning, many people with Alzheimer's disease die from sepsis (a severe infection) due to pneumonia or urinary tract infection. This stage lasts from a few months to three years.

Common Symptoms of Late Stage Alzheimer's Disease

- symptoms from middle stage continue and worsen
- remote memory gone
- communication changes; stops speaking or cries out incoherently

- failure to recognize family members, friends, or self in the mirror
- ambulation problems
- assistance required with all activity, including feeding
- incontinence

TREATMENT OF ALZHEIMER'S DISEASE

At this time, there is no treatment that can reverse or cure the effects of Alzheimer's disease. Although many medications have been studied, none has proven to have a lasting effect on the symptoms. Treatment of Alzheimer's disease typically focuses on therapeutic and social interventions that help manage the disease process, with an emphasis on maximizing functional abilities and quality of life. However, establishing a diagnosis as early as possible and providing access to medications that slow cognitive deterioration may delay the onset of disability.

Medications

Pharmaceutical research in recent years has led to the development of several medications that, if prescribed early in the disease process, may help to control symptoms and delay the progression of the illness. The medications do not cure the disease. Approximately 50 percent of patients benefit from these drugs, with effects lasting one to two years. Patients who benefit from the drugs sometimes see an abrupt decline in functioning if the medication is discontinued. Changes in medications should always be coordinated with a physician.

Currently, the Food and Drug Administration has approved two types of medications for treating the cognitive symptoms of dementia.

The first class of drugs was designed to prevent the decomposition of acetylcholine, a brain chemical associated with memory and other cognitive abilities. (Drugs are listed with their trademarked name first, followed by their generic name in parentheses.)

- Aricept (donepezil, approved in 1996)
- Exelon (rivastigmine, approved in 2000)
- Reminyl (galantamine hydrochloride, approved in 2001)
- Cognex (tacrine, approved in 1993, but seldom prescribed today due to side effects, including possible liver damage)

The second type of drug, brand new in the United States, regulates glutamate, a brain chemical involved in learning and memory.

- Namenda (memantine, approved 2003)

Nutritional supplements have also been suggested for the treatment and prevention of dementia. There has been some evidence that vitamin E aids in the prevention of Alzheimer's disease (Zandi et al., 2004) and slows the progression of symptoms of Alzheimer's disease (Sano et al., 1997). Vitamin E is not recommended for people with cardiac illness or blood disorders unless prescribed by a physician. There is mixed evidence for the usefulness of estrogen and nonsteroidal anti-inflammatory drugs (NSAIDS, e.g., ibuprofen or aspirin) for prevention of AD. Because of possible side effects, their use is not currently recommended. Herbal remedies, such as gingko biloba, have no documented effect on dementia.

Medications are often useful in managing the behavioral symptoms of dementia. Selective serotonin re-uptake inhibitors (SSRIs, e.g., Zoloft, Prozac, or Celexa) can be effective in treating the mood-related symptoms of dementia. Benzodiazapines (e.g., Xanax or Ativan) have been used to treat agitation and sleep disorder, but caution must be taken in prescribing these medications due to possible side effects and risk of addiction. Antipsychotic medications (e.g., Risperdal or Haldol) are frequently used to treat psychotic symptoms associated with dementia. Generally these medications have not been found to improve wandering, pacing, or rummaging behavior (Weiner, 2003). All psychiatric medication should be managed for seniors by a geriatric psychiatrist or a psychiatrist experienced in prescribing medication for persons with dementia.

Some research indicates that intellectual activity, such as reading, learning new information, and problem solving, may slow the progression of symptoms and even decrease the risk of getting Alzheimer's disease. People both with and without dementia should be encouraged to engage in as much intellectually stimulating activity as is enjoyable for them.

Psychotherapy and Behavioral Intervention

Psychotherapy may be helpful for individuals coping with the impact of losses associated with Alzheimer's disease. Processing the emotional issues tied to coping with dementia has been shown to be effective in reducing symptoms of depression, improving self-esteem, and preparing for future losses. Both individual and group psychotherapy may be helpful (Cheston, Jones, & Gilliard, 2003; James, Postma, & MacKenzie, 2003).

Many family and professional caregivers become frustrated with inappropriate behaviors sometimes shown by persons with Alzheimer's disease. The inappropriate behavior may be the result of difficulty expressing feelings, controlling impulsive reactions, and solving problems.

Mrs. Jackson had been doing very well during the first six months after she moved into a nursing home. Her family had found a place for her there after her advanced Alzheimer's dementia became too much for them to manage at home. Suddenly, Mrs. Jackson began refusing showers. She became very agitated and screamed when her aide tried to coax her into the bathroom. It wasn't until her daughter came to visit during shower time that the reason for her behavior was discerned. Because of a change in the aide's schedule, she reduced the amount of time she could devote to bathe Mrs. Jackson. To save time, the aide now undressed Mrs. Jackson fully before beginning to wash her, in contrast to her previous procedure, in which she uncovered only the parts she was washing. Her daughter explained that Mrs. Jackson had always been an extremely private, modest person, and sitting naked in the shower chair was terrifying for her. Returning to the prior shower regimen resulted in a significant reduction in Mrs. Jackson's agitated behavior.

MANAGEMENT OF OTHER HEALTH CONCERNS

The unfortunate reality is that medical conditions that could be improved may be overlooked in people with dementia. This is especially true when a cognitively impaired person can no longer communicate that something is wrong. Even a concerned caregiver may inadvertently overlook treatable problems. Proper medical evaluation and treatment can help ensure that an individual with Alzheimer's disease will be able to function at a high level while avoiding pain or other complications that can be caused by a treatable condition.

In addition to treating acute illnesses, it is important for caregivers of persons with dementia to make sure that chronic health conditions, including visual and hearing impairments, are treated. Sensory impairments can exacerbate cognitive problems of individuals with dementia, and simply wearing glasses or hearing aids may greatly enhance functional abilities. Encouraging use of assistive devices such as glasses and hearing aids should start in the earlier stages of dementia. Testing and teaching people with dementia to use new assistive devices becomes more difficult as cognitive abilities deteriorate.

Just as incontinence (loss of bladder or bowel control) is not a normal part of aging, it is not an inevitable part of dementia until the very end of the disease process. When incontinence becomes an issue in the earlier stages, caregivers should look to interventions that can lessen its impact. Incontinence interventions may involve identifying when the incidents happen and what may be triggering them. Possible causes of incontinence include physical conditions (change in bladder or bowel habits, hormonal imbalances, medications), cognitive changes, depression, and chronic or acute disease. One simple strategy is to take a person with dementia to the toilet on a regular schedule. As with all interventions, it is important to maintain the dignity of the individual experiencing the problem. For example, announcing that it is time to go the bathroom to avoid an accident in the middle of a crowded restaurant is inappropriate.

Maintaining good overall health during the course of dementia-related illness is very important but may be very difficult. Seemingly simple factors, such as good nutrition, proper hygiene, and appropriate dental care, can become enormous challenges in caring for cognitively impaired individuals. Proper nutrition is necessary not only to maintain energy and stamina, but to promote resistance to infection and aid in wound healing. As discussed earlier, however, artificial nutrition in late-stage AD does not improve quality of life or extend life (Finucane, 2003).

Delirium

Delirium is a syndrome that is characterized by a significant change in mental functioning that develops over a *very short period of time* (hours to days) and *fluctuates during the day*. Delirium is often mistaken for dementia or depression because they share similar symptoms:

- confusion
- reduced ability to pay attention
- problems with memory, language, or orientation to time, place, or person
  Some people with delirium experience:

- hallucinations (seeing or hearing things that aren't there) or difficulty differentiating dreams from reality
- delusions (false belief that persists in spite of evidence that the belief is untrue, such as the belief that a family member is trying to poison the individual's food)
- agitation or combativeness
- disrupted sleep-wake cycle

Delirium is commonly caused by changes in medication, new strokes, or most often, infection (such as urinary tract infection or pneumonia). People with dementia are four times more likely than those who do not have dementia to experience delirium (LaRue, 1993). It remains unclear why some people develop delirium while others with the same conditions do not.

If the delirium is recognized very soon after symptoms begin, it can often be completely reversed by treating the cause (e.g., resolving an infection with antibiotics). However, many seniors, particularly those with dementia, experience lasting effects of delirium. For some, symptoms never completely resolve. Thus, it is important to recognize and treat delirium very quickly.

Maintaining a Safe and Nurturing Environment

STIMULATION

Creating an environment with adequate amounts of stimulation without overwhelming or confusing an individual with dementia can be very helpful. People with dementia have a limited capacity to process incoming information. Thus, environments with too much stimulation can be overwhelming and lead to agitation and possibly aggressive behavior. Imagine trying to concentrate enough to read this book while your spouse and your sister are each talking to you simultaneously, your children are playing a spirited game next to you, and the radio is on. This is what it might feel like for an individual with dementia to attempt to hold a conversation in a room with the television on.

For persons with middle- and late-stage Alzheimer's disease it is important to avoid very loud or bustling settings with too much stimulation (e.g., busy shopping malls, crowded streets).

WANDERING

People with dementia may wander because they feel lost or are looking for something or someone they believe they have lost. Other reasons for wandering include medication side effects, disorientation, curiosity, boredom, restlessness, or memories triggered by routines or stimuli. Wandering does not have to have dangerous consequences, and does not have to be prevented. In fact, attempts to prevent wandering can result in agitation and conflict. To maintain safety, families can obtain alarms that sound when a door is opened or door stoppers that prevent doors from opening completely. (See Resources section at the end of this chapter.) Locking doors that cannot be opened from the inside can be a fire hazard.

HOUSING

If family members are unable to maintain a safe environment at home, they may consider employing an aide to provide supervision, placement in a specialized adult day program, or relocation to a long-term care facility. When new living arrangements are being considered, families must be sure to choose housing facilities whose resources match the level of disability. In addition to being attentive to physical well-being (e.g., minimizing risk of falling, being alert to wandering) and behavioral disturbance, quality facilities also address emotional, social, and spiritual needs of residents.

Family and professional caregivers face a significant challenge in providing adequate supervision to prevent unsafe activities while maintaining the dignity and freedom of an individual with dementia. There may be a tendency to infantalize the person with dementia by using speech and setting limits as one might with a child. The individual with dementia is an adult, deserving of respect. With creativity and patience it is possible to be respectful and prevent unsafe activities.

Mr. Lopez was a fiercely independent and proud man who enjoyed taking long drives on sunny days. When AD progressed to the point that he was unable to concentrate, he became easily lost. He got into an accident by turning the wrong way down a one-way street. In another accident, he got distracted by a car horn and ran a red light. His children tried to convince him that driving was unsafe, but he was adamant that he was a good driver and refused to give up his driver's license. Mr. Lopez's wife was also reluctant to take away driving privileges because she did not drive and Mr. Lopez was her only source of transportation. His daughter decided to disable the car by removing the spark plugs. Although Mr. Lopez had been an avid amateur mechanic earlier in his life, AD prevented him from figuring out how to fix the car. The family then removed the car from the garage, told Mr. Lopez that repairs were taking longer than expected, and arranged for neighbors to assist with transportation. Mr. Lopez was able to maintain dignity in his belief that he was a good driver who just didn't have a working car to drive, while his family was able to maintain his safety without constant argument.

What to do about seniors with deteriorating ability to drive is an awkward issue for families and service providers. Driving facilitates feelings of independence, competence, and convenience for many seniors. The end to driving can be devastating.

Recall that normal aging includes a decline in the speed of processing information. People with dementia are more compromised and are often unable to judge, observe, or respond quickly enough to stimuli around them. It has been suggested that drivers in the early stages of dementia are impaired at approximately the same level as someone with a blood-alcohol level of .08 (the legal limit in most states).

Warning signs signifying that it may be time to stop driving include the inability to locate or recognize familiar places; poor judgment and slow decision-making in traffic; anger, confusion, or frustration while driving; and failure to observe and follow traffic signs and speed limits. As progression of the disease varies considerably, ability to drive should be assessed individually. If driving skills appear questionable, agencies are available to administer driving tests, including the motor vehicle bureaus in some states.

COMMUNICATION

People with dementia experience increasing difficulty expressing their needs, concerns, and even memories. They may use incorrect or inappropriate words or say the first thing that comes to mind. When inappropriate remarks are made, caregivers should remember that such remarks reflect a disease process.

Caregivers and professionals (including you, as a CSA) must also be attentive to nonverbal signals given by people with dementia. Although people with dementia may not be able to say that they are cold, tired, hungry, or in pain, there are nonverbal ways that they may convey this information. Look for shivers or grimaces of pain, for example.

Nonverbal communication by the caregiver to the persons with dementia is also important. The way an individual with dementia is approached can positively or negatively affect interaction. For example, approaching someone in the late stages of dementia with a smile and a soothing voice increases the likelihood that they will be relaxed and open to communicating. Appearing or sounding angry can be very threatening and lead the individual with dementia to become frightened or agitated. Thus, even if a behavior is frustrating to the caregiver, remain calm and express anger elsewhere. Other helpful techniques include the following:

- Approach the person from the front and maintain eye contact at all times.
- Speak and move slowly.
- Tell the individual who you are and why you are there.
- Particularly in the early stage of dementia when deficits are minimal (and for some, well into the middle stage), speak directly to the individual with dementia rather than directing questions to the caregiver only. This helps to maintain dignity and demonstrates respect for the older adult. Directing questions to the person with dementia in the presence of the caregiver will give the caregiver the opportunity to clarify any misinformation.

- Minimize distractions, particularly when giving instructions.
- Use few words, and words that are familiar to the individual.
- Ask one question at a time or give one step of instruction at a time.
- Ask questions that don't require memory or complicated reasoning.
- Ask yes/no questions when possible.
- Allow adequate time to respond.
- Repeat questions using the same words. If there is still no response, try rephrasing.
- Remain calm, particularly if the individual becomes agitated. Responding to agitation with upset only escalates the situation.
- Use nonverbal communication such as smiles, nods, and gestures. Be careful with touch. Individuals with dementia need touch as much as before the onset of the illness, but cultural traditions and personal preferences, along with fears of strangers, may limit the amount of touch that the individual with dementia can tolerate.
- Use distraction to minimize inappropriate or unwanted behavior.

Ms. Ahmed was in the later stages of AD. She became agitated easily and when frightened called out for her mother, who had long since passed away. This was distressing to staff and other residents of her nursing home. The facility consulted with a psychologist to try to reduce the behavior. Dr. Norris entered Ms. Ahmed's room, and the screaming soon stopped. The psychologist explained to staff that she merely distracted Ms. Ahmed by speaking in a calm voice, asking about the resident's mother, and providing reassurance that Ms. Ahmed appeared to be looking for from her mother. Ms. Ahmed continued to call out for her mother when frightened, but with the help of the psychologist, the staff was able to minimize situations that frightened Ms. Ahmed and distract her when she did become agitated.

Caring for Caregivers

There are many, many, many, many people who are caregivers, and it's very difficult to watch someone you love dealing with illness. You just do it. You just get up and take each day as it comes and put one foot in front of the other. I don't know how. You love. (Nancy Reagan, speaking on C-SPAN, February 2000)

Caring for someone with dementia is stressful. Studies have shown that caregivers of people with dementia have suppressed immune systems and increased rates of infectious illness, and a higher prevalence of major depressive disorder than non-caregivers (Light, Niederehe, & Lebowitz, 1994). Depressed mood, anger, and resentment toward the person with dementia and toward their responsibilities, as well as subjective feelings of burden are also very common. Self-care is imperative to maintain the caregiving role.

Many family caregivers don't get the assistance they may benefit from because they don't identify themselves as caregivers. Family members may feel that they are simply fulfilling responsibilities as daughter, son, or spouse.

While this may be the case, viewing caregiving as solely a family obligation minimizes the enormous amount of work and burden that the role can entail. You can help family members of your clients better define their roles as caregivers and educate them about services, products, and information that are available to make caregiving easier.

There are many resources to help family and professional caregivers. Education about Alzheimer's disease as well as therapeutic regimens can help caregivers be more realistic in expectations of the person for whom they are caring. Local chapters of the Alzheimer's Association and many geriatric clinics offer educational seminars and caregiver support groups to relieve the burden of caregiving and foster better coping skills. Many caregivers also benefit from respite by having someone (e.g., family, friend, church parishioner, neighbor, or professional aide) come to help supervise the individual with dementia, enrolling the individual with dementia in an adult day program specializing in dementia, or taking the individual with dementia to a residential care facility for more extended respite breaks. The latter can be very helpful in allowing caregivers to take vacations or attend to personal business for several days to several weeks at a time. Many nursing homes, especially those with specialized dementia services, offer respite care. Though many caregivers report feeling guilty about wanting to take a break, respite helps to manage stress and prevent caregiver burnout.

Cognitive Aging: Summary

Because there are many misconceptions about dementia, particularly Alzheimer's disease, you should know the myths and realities of the syndrome. For example, just because a senior is forgetful does not mean that he or she has Alzheimer's disease. In fact, the cause of the problem might be side effects of medications, the most common form of reversible dementia.

It is important to know the resources in your community where you can direct your clients for assessment of their physical and cognitive health. You should also know what services and programs are available in your area for your clients with dementia. And you should be able to educate your clients (or their families) who are caregivers about services, products, and information that are available for them.

Perhaps the best service that you can offer your clients who are facing their own or a loved one's diagnosis of dementia is to be an attentive listener. There is perhaps no more difficult journey in the world.

References

Alzheimer's Association. (2004). *10 warning signs of Alzheimer's disease.* Available online at: www.alz.org.

Alzheimer's Association (n.d.). *Statistics about Alzheimer's disease.* Available online at www.alz.org.

APA (American Psychiatric Association). (1994). *Diagnostic and statistical manual of mental disorders, 4th ed.* Washington, DC: American Psychiatric Association.

Becker, J., Boller, F., Lopez, O., Saton, J., & McGonigle, K. (1994). The natural history of Alzheimer's disease: Description of study cohort and accuracy of diagnosis. *Archives of Neurology, 51*, 585–594.

Cheston, R., Jones, K., & Gilliard, J. (2003). Group psychotherapy and people with dementia. *Aging & Mental Health, 7*, 452–461.

Class, C. A., Unverzagt, F. W., Gao, S., Hall, K. S., Baiyewa, O., & Hendrie, H. C. (1996). Psychiatric disorders in African American nursing home residents. *American Journal of Psychiatry, 153*, 677–681.

de la Mente, M., Hutchins, G. M., & Moore, G. W. (1989). Racial differences in the etiology of dementia and frequency of Alzheimer lesions in the brain. *Journal of the National Medical Association, 81*, 644–652.

Emre, M. (2003) What causes mental dysfunction in Parkinson's disease? *Movement Disorders, 18* [Suppl. 6], S63–71.

Ernst, R. I., & Hay, J. W. (1996). The U.S. economic and social costs of Alzheimer's disease revisited. *American Journal of Public Health, 84*, 1261–1264.

Evans, D. A., Beckett, L. A., Field, T. S., Feng, L., Albert, M. S., Bennett, D. A., et al. (1997). Apolipoprotein E epsilon4 and incidence of Alzheimer disease in a community population of older persons. *Journal of the American Medical Association, 277*, 822–824.

Ficher, M. M., Schroppel, H., & Meller, I. (1996). Incidence of dementia in a Munich community sample of the oldest old. *European Archives of Psychiatry in Clinical Neuroscience, 246*, 320–328.

Finucane, T. E. (2003). Artificially giving nutrition and fluids is not one action. *British Medical Journal, 326*, 713.

Froehlich, T. E., Bogardus, S. T., & Inouye, S. K. (2001). Dementia and race: Are there differences between African Americans and Caucasians? *Journal of the American Geriatrics Society, 49*, 477–484.

Graves, A. B., Larson, E. B., Edland, S. D., Bowen, J. D., McCormick, W. C., McCurry, S. M., et al. (1996). Prevalence of dementia and its subtypes in the Japanese American population of Kind County, Washington State: The Kame project. *American Journal of Epidemiology, 144*, 760–771.

Hendrie, H. C. (1998). Epidemiology of dementia and Alzheimer's disease. *The American Journal of Geriatric Psychiatry, 6*, S3–S18.

Heyman, A., Fillenbaum, G., Prosnitz, B., Raiford, K., Burchett, B., & Clark C. (1991). Estimated prevalence of dementia among elderly black and white community residents. *Archives of Neurology, 48*, 594–598.

James, I., Postma, K., & Mackenzie, L. (2003). Using an IPT conceptualization to treat a depressed person with dementia. *Behavioural & Cognitive Psychotherapy, 31*, 451–456.

LaRue, A. (1993). *Aging and neuropsychological assessment.* New York: Plenum Press.

Light, E., Niederehe, G., & Lebowitz, B. D. (Eds.). (1994). Stress effects on family caregivers of Alzheimer's patients: Research and interventions. New York: Springer.

Magaziner, J., German, P., Zimmerman, S. I., Hebel, J. R., Burton, L., Gruber-Baldini, A. L., et al. (2000). The prevalence of dementia in a statewide sample of new nursing home admissions aged 65 and older: Diagnosis by expert panel. *Gerontologist, 40*, 663–672.

Mitchell, M. (2002). *Dancing on quicksand*. Boulder, CO: Johnson Books.

Petersen, R. C., Smith, G. E., Waring, S. C., Ivnik, R. J., Tangalos, E. G., & Kokmen, E. (1999). Mild cognitive impairment: Clinical characterization and outcome. *Archives of Neurology, 56*, 303–308.

Petersen, R. C., Doody, R., Kurz, A., Mohs, R. C., Morris, J. C., Rabins, P. V., et al. (2001). Current concepts in mild cognitive impairment. *Archives of Neurology, 58*, 1982–1985.

Plassman, B. I., & Breitner, J. C. S. (1996). Recent advances in the genetics of Alzheimer's disease and vascular dementia with an emphasis on gene-environment interactions. *Journal of the American Geriatric Society, 44*, 1242–1250.

Rahkonen, T., Eloniemi-Sulkava, U., Rissanen, S., Vatanen, A., Viramo, P., & Sulkava, R. (2003). Dementia with Lewy bodies according to the consensus criteria in a general population aged 75 years or older. *Journal of Neurology, Neurosurgery & Psychiatry, 74*, 720–724.

Ratcliffe, G., & Saxton, J. (1998). Age appropriate memory impairment. In P. J. Snyder & P. D. Nussbaum (Eds.) *Clinical Neuropsychology; A Pocket Handbook for Assessment*. Washington, DC: American Psychological Association.

Reuben, D., Herr, K., Pacala, J., Potter, J., Semla, T., & Small, G. (2001). *Geriatrics at your fingertips*. Philadelphia: Excerpta Medica Publications.

Ritchie, K., Artero, S., & Touchon, J. (2001). Classification criteria for mild cognitive impairment: A population-based validation study. *Neurology, 56*, 37–42.

Ruitenberg, A., Ott, A., van Swieten, J. C., Hofman, A., & Breteler, M. M. (2001). Incidence of dementia: Does gender make a difference? *Neurobiology of Aging, 22*, 575–580.

Sadock, B. J. & Sadock, V. A. (2000). *Kaplan & Sadock's comprehensive textbook of psychiatry, 7th ed.* Philadelphia: Lippincott Williams & Wilkins.

Sano, M., Ernesto, C., Thomas, R. G., Klauber, M. R., Schafer, K., Grundman, M., et al. (1997). A controlled trial of selegiline, alpha-tocopherol, or both as treatment for Alzheimer's disease. *New England Journal of Medicine, 336*, 1216–1222.

Walsh, J. S., Welch, H. G., & Larson, E. G. (1990). Survival of outpatients with Alzheimer-type dementia. *Annals of Internal Medicine, 113*, 429–434.

Weiner, M. F. (2003). Dementia. In A. M. Mellow (Ed.) *Geriatric psychiatry*. Washington, DC: American Psychiatric Publishing.

Weiner, M. F., Doody, R. S. Sairam, R., Foster, B. M., & Liao, T-Y (2002). Prevalence and incidence of major depressive disorder in Alzheimer's disease: Findings from two databases. *Dementia & Geriatric Cognitive Disorders, 13*, 8–12.

Weiner, M. F., Vega, G. Risser, R. C., Honig, L. S., Cullum, C. M., Crumpacker, D., et al. (1999). Apolipoprotein E e4, other risk factors, and course of Alzheimer's disease. *Biological Psychiatry, 45*, 633–638.

Zandi, P. P., Anthony, J. C., Khachaturian, A. S., Stone, S. V., Gustafson, D., Tschanz, J. T., et al. (2004). Reduced risk of Alzheimer disease in users of antioxidant vitamin supplements: The Cache County study. *Archives of Neurology, 61*, 82–88.

Resources

Suggested Reading

The Forgetting. Alzheimer's: Portrait of an Epidemic, by David Shenk. New York: Anchor Publishing, 2003. ISBN 0385498381. This is a biography of Alzheimer's disease written by journalist and NPR commentator David Shenk. Shenk tells the story of the discovery of the disease, the battle of scientists researching it, and the involvement of politicians, caregivers, and victims of AD.

Just the Facts and More Kit. The Alzheimer's Association produces these fact sheets that provide practical strategies for handling common behavior problems in Alzheimer's disease sufferers. Behaviors covered include bathing, combativeness, sundowning, and wandering. Order no. ED 247Z (also available in Spanish, order no. ED 247ZS). Cost: $9.00 per set. Single copies of individual fact sheets are free.

Long Distance Caregiving: A Survival Guide for Far Away Caregivers, by Angela Heath. Denver, CO: American Source Books, 1996. ISBN 1886230005. This handbook covers everything from support groups to care plans to financial issues involved in caring for a loved one across state and national lines.

Losing My Mind—An Intimate Look at Life with Alzheimer's, by Thomas De Baggio. New York: The Free Press, 2002. ISBN 0743205650. This is a first-person account of the daily struggle of living with AD.

The 36-Hour Day: A Family Guide to Caring for Persons with Alzheimer Disease, Related Dementing Illnesses, and Memory Loss in Later Life, by Nancy Mace and Peter Rabins. Baltimore: Johns Hopkins University Press, 2001. ISBN 0446610410. This is the third edition of an invaluable resource that provides the reader with an in-depth understanding of the process of AD and tips on coping with the disease, as well as financial, legal, and housing information.

Suggested Viewing

The Forgetting: A Portrait of Alzheimer's, 2003 video and DVD documentary, narrated by David Hyde Pierce, available from Warner Home Video. ISBN 0780646738. This film originally aired on PBS on January 21, 2004, at 9 p.m. ET/PT, and may be available for viewing through your local PBS station. See also http://www.pbs.org/theforgetting/about/index.html#.

Services

Administration on Aging (AoA). http://www.aoa.dhhs.gov, email: AoAInfo@aoa.gov. National offices located in Washington, DC 20201, 202-619-0724, fax 202-357-3555. Every state and most larger cities have local offices.

Ageless Design—The Alzheimer's Store. http://www.agelessdesign.com or http://www.alzstore.com, 800-752-3238. This online store (paper catalogs are available) offers many products for ensuring the safety and dignity of people with dementia, including door alarms, medication dispensers, incontinence aids, telephone technology, and more. (This resource serves only to alert CSAs to products and services that are available; it is not an endorsement of the company or of any product or service sold by The Alzheimer's Store.)

Alzheimer's Association. http://www.alz.org, email: info@alz.org, 225 North Michigan Ave., Floor 17, Chicago, IL 60601, 24/7 Nationwide Contact Center: 800-272-3900, TTY: 312-335-8882. Contact the national office or the organization's Web site for local chapter information.

Alzheimer's Disease Education and Referral Center (ADEAR-National Institute on Aging), http://www.alzheimers.org, email: adear@alzheimers.org, 800-438-4380, fax: 301-495-3334, P.O. Box 8250, Silver Spring, MD 20907-8250.

Eldercare Locator. http://www.eldercare.gov/Eldercare/Public/Home.asp, 800-677-1116. The Eldercare Locator connects older Americans and their caregivers with sources of information on senior services. The service links those who need assistance with state and local area agencies on aging and community-based organizations that serve seniors and their caregivers.

Mayoclinic.com. http://www.mayoclinic.com. From the Web site, click on "Diseases and Conditions," then choose "Alzheimer's disease."

Chapter 13

Spirituality and Aging

*Said the monk, "All these mountains and rivers and the earth
and stars—Where do they come from?" Said the master:
"Where does your question come from?" Look inside!*

Anthony DeMello (1982)

Look around most congregations at worship and witness the courage and persistence of the aged men and women who arrive with walkers and oxygen tanks, often transported by other older people less encumbered by health problems. Sharing pews with noisy babies, children with crayons, bored teens, and distracted parents, they sing and pray, sit in silence, listen to scripture and sermons, rise and sit as they are able, share the Eucharist if Christian, and exit in friendly conversation with fellow travelers. In the hymns, prayers, scripture readings, and sermons, they hear of love and forgiveness, gratitude and hope, despair and lamentation, anger, fear, and awe. In no other community do persons of so many different backgrounds and ages meet regularly to consider the human condition and turn to the sacred for an enduring sense of meaning and purpose in life.

McFadden, 2003

Introduction

In the last few decades, gerontologists have become increasingly aware of the importance of spirituality to the well-being of seniors. Spirituality is difficult to define and describe. It is a concept that is highly personal, often private, and hard to put into words. For most, spirituality is an inward experience.

Gerontologists often define *spirituality* with a description that came from the 1971 White House Conference on Aging: "the basic value around which all other values are focused, the central philosophy of life—whether religious, antireligious, or nonreligious—which guides a person's conduct, the supernatural and nonmaterial dimensions of human nature" (Moberg, 1971). While this definition mentions familiar terms and concepts that most people would agree relate to spirituality, currently there is no real consensus on a standardized meaning of the term.

Three common components are included in most definitions of spirituality (Bouchard, 1997):

347

- an understanding of self that is defined in the context of relationships to others
- an understanding of a creation story and symbols of faith
- an understanding of a greater power that is outside of the self, yet intimately connected with the sense of self

KEY ELEMENTS OF SPIRITUALITY

- not formal, structured, or organized
- non-denominational, above and beyond denominational
- inclusive, embracing everyone
- the ultimate source and provider of meaning and purpose in life
- the awe we feel in the presence of the transcendent
- the deep feeling of interconnectedness with all that is
- inner peace and calmness
- an inexhaustible source of faith

(Mitroff & Denton, 1999)

Death and the Spiritual Quest

Seniors are always somewhere in the grief process. For most, their experience is dominated by losses such as the deaths of loved ones, decreases in physical functioning, and reductions in income. The accumulation of such losses—and the increasing awareness of their own deaths—can lead seniors to an exploration of spiritual issues.

> *The reason God has engineered the spectacular increase in life expectancy in the last 100 years is because the world is so desperately in need of wisdom that God created elders.*
>
> Emma L. Benignus, 2003

IMPORTANCE OF SPIRITUALITY TO SENIORS

For many, spirituality is key to a vital old age. In fact, aging is often referred to as a spiritual journey (Moberg, 2001). In 2000 Lou Harris and Associates conducted a study of more than 3,000 adults for the National Council on the Aging. The purpose of the study was to examine the experience of aging. Sixty-seven percent of seniors in the study said that having a rich spiritual life contributes meaning to life. The majority of baby boomers in the study also said that, when "thinking about their later years," having a rich spiritual life will be very important (NCOA, 2002).

Many scientists who study spirituality and aging have concluded that spirituality increases with age. However, it is also important to acknowledge that other prominent researchers disagree with this premise (Moberg, 2001).

THE PROCESS OF SPIRITUAL MATURATION

I had an evening of storytelling in my home where I invited some senior women to come and share life stories with some listeners. During the evening I asked a question about how their image of God had changed throughout the years. Herminie, an eighty-year-old woman originally from New York stated, "When I was young, I was scared to death of God. I felt liked I was being watched and was filled with fear. But as I grew older I knew that was a bunch of crap, God is all about love."

I said, "Now wait a minute, Herminie. How did you get from fearing God to finding God as a loving God?"

Herminie responded simply, "That was easy. Every time I loved my husband and children I felt God's presence. When I wasn't loving them God was far from me. It's all about loving ... that is where you will find God." (As retold by Norm Bouchard, CSA Faculty, 2004)

Herminie had experienced a maturation of her faith. She allowed her life experiences to shape her very ideas about God. Her reflections, in turn, permeated her daily life and how she chose to live it. Many seniors experience this kind of maturing as they have more time and interest in addressing the spiritual aspects of their lives.

Finding Meaning and Purpose in Life

As seniors develop spiritually, they often exhibit certain characteristics. They place an emphatic focus on connecting with others, finding meaning and purpose in life, and holding personal power to influence outcomes. They change their relationship to time; become more attentive, patient, and present; and often give themselves permission to speak their truth even when it is unpopular. And perceptions held by others become less important, as does conforming to cultural norms and expectations.

Shift from Doing to Being

For many seniors, the focus on production and accomplishments they held throughout young adulthood and middle age gives way in later years to a concentration on the interior life. Emphasis on making spiritual connections grows.

When seniors perceive aging as a spiritual journey, they raise the priority of enhancing their relationships with God, loved ones, faith communities, and communities of residence (Bianchi, 1997).

As seniors mature spiritually, many experience a shift from *doing* to *being*.

Characteristics of Seniors During the Maturation Process

Older adults who focus on spiritual issues may:

- take more time to reflect on the meaning of events;
- feel despair over the injustices and evils in the world;
- long to make peace with imminent death and their beliefs about death;
- struggle to understand why so many good people suffer;
- seek a comprehensive and more satisfying personal philosophy;
- yearn for solitude and silence;
- seek to communicate unspoken love to others;
- recognize the need for a greater sense of community;
- question beliefs about death and the afterlife.

Spirituality and Religion

For many, religion is a route to spirituality. Both religion and spirituality can bring meaning to life.

Scientists participating in a conference on spirituality and health concluded that both religion and spirituality have a "sacred core" that involves "feelings, thought, experiences, and behaviors that arise from a search for the sacred" (Koenig, McCullough, & Larson, 2001). The conference participants distinguished religion from spirituality by two criteria: People use religion for nonsacred goals such as socialization, and religion employs rituals or prescribed behaviors.

THE MONK AND THE WOMAN

Two Buddhists monks, on their way to the monastery, found an exceedingly beautiful woman at the river bank. Like them, she wished to cross the river, but the water was too high. So one of the monks lifted her onto his back and carried her across.

His fellow monk was thoroughly scandalized. For two full hours he berated him on his negligence in keeping the Holy Rule: Had he forgotten he was a monk? How did he dare touch a woman? And more, actually carry her across the river? And what would people say? Had he not brought their Holy Religion into disrepute?

The offending monk listened to the never-ending sermon. Finally he broke in with, "Brother, I dropped that woman at the river. Are you still carrying her?" (De Mello, 1982)

The monk who helped the woman was more concerned with the spiritual aspects of his faith while the offended monk was clearly more interested in matters of religion.

Other distinctions can be made between spirituality and religion. Religion is organized, formal, prescriptive, and community-related. Spirituality is more personal and not prescriptive. Spirituality is felt. Religion is taught. Religions include doctrines. Spirituality is emotional.

For a list of characteristics further distinguishing religion and spirituality, see Table 13.1.

Table 13.1 Characteristics Distinguishing Religion and Spirituality

RELIGION	SPIRITUALITY
community-focused	individualistic
observable, measurable, objective	less visible and measurable, more subjective
formal, orthodox, organized	less formal, less orthodox, less sympathetic
behavior-oriented, outward practices	emotion-oriented, inward-directed
authoritarian in terms of behaviors	not authoritarian, little accountability
doctrine separating good from evil	unifying, not doctrine-oriented

Source: Koenig et al., 2001.

Spirituality and *religion* are separate but related concepts. Spirituality is the broader of the two. In contrast to spirituality or religious participation, *religiosity* is devoutness or excessive devotion to religion.

For many older adults, spirituality and participation in a religious organization may overlap. For example, sometimes seniors do not participate in organized religious activities due to physical limitations, yet they maintain a rich, private spiritual life through activities such as prayer and personal devotions. This is particularly true of seniors older than age 85.

POSITIVE AND NEGATIVE VIEWS OF RELIGION AND SPIRITUALITY

According to Mitroff and Denton (1999), a person can have four different orientations toward religion and spirituality:

1. *A positive view of religion and spirituality.* Religion and spirituality are essentially the same thing, although spirituality is experienced and deepened only through religion.

2. *A positive view of religion and a negative view of spirituality.* All energies are focused on the religious life, through rituals and practices of a given faith. The principal goal is to be a member of a tightly bound, shared community.

3. *A negative view of religion and a positive view of spirituality.* Religion is perceived as organized, closed-minded, and intolerant, while spirituality is perceived as open-minded, tolerant, and universal.

4. *A negative view of both religion and spirituality.* Religion and spirituality have nothing to do with a modern secular world.

IMPORTANCE OF RELIGION TO SENIORS

Like spirituality, religion plays an important role in the lives of most seniors. In fact, a recent Gallup poll shows that 73 percent of seniors identify religion as being very important to them (Gallup Organization, 2002). Table 13.2 shows a comparison between age groups for this measure. About half of adults ages 18 to 29 say that religion is very important to them, compared to almost three-quarters of seniors.

Table 13.2 How Important Is Religion in Your Life?

	18–29 YEARS	30–49 YEARS	50–64 YEARS	65+ YEARS
Very important	51%	60%	62%	73%
Fairly important	31%	28%	25%	22%
Not very important	17%	12%	13%	4%
Don't know/confused	1%	—	1%	1%

Source: Gallup Organization, 2002. Data purchased by SCSA.

SENIORS' RELIGIOUS AFFILIATION IN THE UNITED STATES

The 2002 survey by the Gallup Group also found that 70 percent of American seniors are Protestant Christians. (See Table 13.3.) Another 20 percent are Catholic, 2 percent are Mormon, and 2 percent are Jewish. There is a dramatic contrast between the percentage of older and younger age groups who are Protestant and Catholic. Thirty-nine percent of adults ages 18 to 29 are Protestant and 29 percent are Catholic. Twenty percent say that they are Christian but not Protestant or Catholic.

Religious Involvement among Seniors

Attendance at a church, synagogue, or other religious venue is the most frequently used measure of religious involvement. Data from the Gallup Group demonstrate that religious attendance is more common among seniors than younger adults. The Gallup poll asked respondents whether they had attended a church or synagogue in the last seven days. Fifty-three percent of seniors responded yes, compared with 30 percent of people ages 18 to 29. (See Table 13.4.) This pattern of higher participation through church attendance for seniors has held true for more than 50 years of data collection (Moberg, 1990).

Table 13.3. Religious Preference of Americans by Age Group

	18–29 YEARS	30–49 YEARS	50–64 YEARS	65+ YEARS
Protestant	39%	50%	60%	70%
Roman Catholic	29%	29%	24%	20%
Orthodox Churches	2%	—	1%	—
Mormon	4%	2%	2%	2%
Other Christian	20%	7%	2%	—
Jewish	2%	1%	1%	2%
Muslim	1%	—	—	—
Other Non-Christian	—	—	—	—
Atheist	—	—	—	—
Agnostic	1%	—	1%	—
Other	1%	1%	2%	—

Note: Percentages may not total 100 due to rounding.

Source: Gallup Organization, 2002. Data purchased by SCSA.

Table 13.4 Attendance at Church or Synagogue in the Last Seven Days

	18–29 YEARS	30–49 YEARS	50–64 YEARS	65+ YEARS
Yes	30%	41%	50%	53%
No	70%	59%	50%	47%

Source: Gallup Organization, 2002. Data purchased by SCSA.

Theories on the Development of Spirituality and Religious Participation in Later Life

Scholars have developed theories about why and how people become spiritual as they grow older. We briefly describe three theories below.

AGE-PERIOD-COHORT ISSUE

David Moberg, a pioneer in age-related religious research, describes the challenge of growing older as the "age-period-cohort issue" (1990). His paradigm includes:

- aging effects—related to the process of growing older
- period effects—related to events of a specific time in history
- cohort effects—related to common characteristics of a specific generation of people born in the same interval of time

Moberg says that the accumulated evidence on period and cohort effects is not enough to explain increased religiosity among seniors. The explanation

353

that stands up best is that "the aging process itself contributes to a deepening of concern in the later years, especially on the private, non-organizational level" (Moberg, 1990).

THEORY OF GEROTRANSCENDENCE

Lars Tornstam offers a theory of "gerotranscendence" that argues for a distinctive path toward age-connected spirituality. Tornstam postulates that seniors are predisposed to consider the spiritual dimension, which includes a preoccupation with the interconnection among generations, the relation between life and death, and the mystery of life (1999). Tornstam's model is similar to James Fowler's 1981 model of the development of faith, which proposes that people progress through developmental stages from simple faith to spirituality.

SPIRITUALITY, AGE, AND NEGATIVE LIFE EVENTS

Paul Wink speculates that there could be an interaction effect among spirituality, age, and negative life events, and that seniors utilize spirituality to cope with life's adversities. Seniors get more involved in spirituality and religion for a wide assortment of practical reasons. With retirement, they have more time to consider their interior lives. For seniors who are uncertain about life after death and the role of salvation, focusing on greater spiritual connection helps them to "hedge their bets." As people age, losses accumulate. Thus, many seniors need the interior strength that comes from spiritual connection to support the death of loved ones, sickness, poverty, isolation, and demoralization (Wink, 1999).

The Role of Faith Communities in Senior Spirituality

A neighbor found Nasruddin on his knees searching for something.

"What are you searching for?"

"My key. I've lost it."

Both men got on their knees to search for the lost key. After a while the neighbor says, "Where did you lose it?"

"At home."

"Good Lord! Then why are you searching for it out here?"

"Because there is more light here."

Of what use is it to search for God in Holy Places if I have lost God in my heart?

(De Mello, 1982)

The "neighbors" we seek out in our faith communities make our spiritual journeys more interesting and sometimes more productive. Seniors gather with other faithful members to connect with themselves and with each other and to nurture a deeper understanding of their God.

MEMBERSHIP IN A RELIGIOUS INSTITUTION

As Table 13.5 shows, among all age groups seniors have the highest rate of memberships in churches, synagogues, and other religious institutions. Seventy-seven percent of seniors are members of such religious organizations, compared to 48 percent of adults ages 18 to 29 (Gallup Organization, 2002). Seniors also are members of faith communities more often than they are members of any other kind of community organization (Palmore, 1995). According to Erdman Palmore, "Churches and synagogues ... are the single most pervasive community institution to which elderly belong. All the other community institutions considered together, including senior citizens centers, clubs for elders, and unions, do not involve as many elders as churches and synagogues."

Table 13.5. Membership in Church or Synagogue

	18–29 YEARS	30–49 YEARS	50–64 YEARS	65+ YEARS
Yes	48%	66%	72%	77%
No	52%	34%	29%	23%

Source: Gallup Organization, 2002. Data purchased by SCSA.

PRINCIPAL FUNCTIONS OF FAITH COMMUNITIES

The principal functions of faith communities are to meet the spiritual needs of their congregations and to provide communal worship of God. For many, membership in a faith community is their route to spirituality.

Neal Krause, writing in *Handbook of Aging and the Sciences* (2001), describes three ways that members of congregations support each other:

- by encouraging each other to devote more time to the practice of their faith, including more frequent prayer or church attendance and more frequent reading of sacred texts
- by helping each other understand their faith better by discussing religious texts or sharing personal religious experiences
- by encouraging each other to use religious coping responses in times of stress

Secondary Functions of Faith Communities

As an important secondary function, faith communities fulfill some social needs of their members. Generally, churches and synagogues do not see themselves as social agencies but rather as caring communities that provide a mixture of programs and services that address the spiritual, social, and survival needs of their members and others in the broader community (Tobin, Ellor, & Anderson-Ray, 1986).

Congregations vary in the extent to which they provide support services. Many offer distinct services for seniors such as day care, transportation services, and help with personal problems. The majority of faith communities offer between two and six distinct services for seniors (Tobin et al., 1986).

Seniors' Contribution to Faith Communities

Seniors provide major support to religious institutions. Nearly half the volunteer work done by seniors is for churches, synagogues, or other church-related organizations (Quadagno, 2002). Sixty-five percent of older volunteers donate time to their church, synagogue, or other religious center (Van Willigen, 2000).

Spiritual Involvement, Longevity, and Health

There is a strong connection between spirituality, health, and longevity. A study of the spiritual practices of almost 4,000 adults ages 64 to 101 by Duke University researchers was one of the first research projects to show an association between private spiritual activities and longevity (Helm, Hays, Flint, Koenig, & Blazer, 2000). Scientists examined the effects of activities like meditation and prayer on survival. The research showed that low levels of meditation, prayer, or other activities significantly predicted death in healthy seniors. Even when the investigators controlled for demographics, health status, depression, and related factors, seniors with little or no spiritual activity were 63 percent more likely to die during a period of six years.

Another Duke University study included patients who have or had blocked coronary arteries (Krucoff et al., 2003). The pilot study integrated spiritual-related therapies (including guided imagery, breath control, touch therapy, and off-site prayer) with traditional treatment. Patients who received spiritual-related therapies in addition to their standard treatment had 30 percent fewer medical complications overall. And those who were treated with off-site prayers from eight prayer groups around the world had 50 percent fewer minor complications and 100 percent fewer major complications.

Religious Involvement, Longevity, and Health

Like spiritual practices, religious involvement is also associated with better health and increased longevity. A study of U.S. adults estimates that religious involvement prolongs life by about seven years (Hummer, Rogers, Nam, & Ellison, 1999). Investigators followed 21,000 adults for nine years. Religious attendance was a strong predictor of survival, even taking into account other factors such as higher incomes and education. People in the study who did not attend religious services were about four times more likely to die from respiratory disease, diabetes, or infectious diseases than those who did attend such services.

In another study of 5,286 people, those who attended religious services weekly or more were 25 percent less likely to die than infrequent attendees (Strawbridge, Cohen, Shema, & Kaplan, 1997). People who attended frequently were also more likely to make healthier choices such as quitting smoking, increasing exercising, and expanding social contacts.

An interesting finding from this study disputes the theory that those in better health are more likely to attend religious services than those who are sick or disabled, which would result in attendees living longer for health reasons, not because of their religious involvement. The study found people with significant impairment in mobility were, in fact, more likely to be frequent attendees.

Even after considering key health and social factors, another recent study found chances of living longer expanded by 28 percent for seniors who attended religious meetings each week (Koenig et al., 1999).

Yet another study surveyed a random sample of nearly 4,000 seniors ages 64 and older living in North Carolina to see if attending religious services had any bearing on living longer. The seniors were interviewed every year for six years. The analysis revealed that the risk of dying for frequent attendees was 46 percent lower than those attending less often. According to the authors of the study, "Religious attendees were physically healthier, had more social support, and lived healthier lifestyles than less-frequent attendees." Women had a 35 percent lower risk of death, compared to a 17 percent lower risk for men.

Mental Health Benefits of Religious Involvement

Fundamental to the positive correlation of spirituality and religion to mental health is their role in helping older people cope with life events. Ninety percent of seniors report that their religion helps them cope with the challenges of aging. Forty-five percent say that religion helps them cope during stressful life events.

Prayer, church attendance, support from a congregation, and related behaviors have been identified as coping mechanisms (Koenig, 1995) suggests the following relationships:

- a positive relationship between religion and self-esteem or self-mastery
- a positive relationship between religion and subjective well-being or life satisfaction.
- an inverse relationship between religion and depression
- an inverse relationship between religion and suicide

Challenges for the Future

FAITH COMMUNITY CHALLENGES

American faith communities are likely to face the same issues as other social institutions with increasing numbers of senior members and aging baby boomers. Estimates are that half of the members of all Protestant and Catholic denominations are over the age of 65. Aging congregations have numerous implications for faith communities. The secondary role of churches and synagogues as service providers is likely to remain important to seniors, especially in the areas of counseling, health care advocacy, and caregiving.

CHALLENGES FOR SENIORS

The following list describes a possible spiritual agenda for seniors:

- Face the realities of life's completion.
- Pay attention to what is happening in the body, mind, spirit, and emotions, giving real attention to the "still small voice within."
- Acknowledge one's own life story:
  —Affirm that life has been meaningful and valuable.
  —Acknowledge life's lessons, mistakes, and accidents of fortune.
  —Identify the threads that connect the events of one's life.
  —Find the pearls in the anxious memories.
- Deal with the loss of pets, friends, children, siblings, and spouses.
  —Examine their dreams, hopes, and expectations for life.
  —Remember their physical prowess and mental functioning.
- Relocate personal dignity, shifting from "doing" to "being."
  —Move away from productivity, possessions, and status.
  —Realize that we are much more than what we own.
- Discover (or rediscover) God.
  —Use meditation, reflection, and prayer to connect the spirit with God or all that is.
  —Acknowledge the gifts of life's struggles.

- Cast off illusions about God and the journey.
  —Repair living relationships.
  —Reach into the past and offer forgiveness and healing to self and others.
- Embrace the role of elder and mentor.
  —Pass on family traditions and the harvest of a lifetime.
  —Become a wisdom keeper.
- Complete practical matters with wills, testaments, and financial plans.
- Demonstrate concern for the common good.
- Support and appreciate the value of diversity in thought and belief.
- Prepare for a serene death and afterlife, making plans that go beyond the grave.

Tools for Bringing Spirituality into the Client Discussion

Each client holds unique spiritual and religious beliefs. If your work with senior clients involves monetary decisions, it is important to remember that such decisions are connected to seniors' personal philosophies, including their spiritual and religious beliefs. Personal philosophies are motivating factors that guide end-of-life plans, insurance plans, and fiscal plans. With knowledge of your senior clients' philosophies, you can think and act responsibly in relation to them.

AUTHENTIC, CONGRUENT OUTCOMES

It is important that as a CSA you engage in genuine dialogues with your clients. To accomplish this, you must listen, reflect, guide, clarify, and affirm the power of thoughtful process. Hold no expectations. Instead, work to obtain outcomes that are authentic and congruent for your clients. *Authentic plans* are those that are genuine and real; they are a truthful reflection of beliefs. *Congruent plans* are consistent, corresponding, and harmonious.

PERSONAL INTROSPECTION

Introspection can help seniors arrive at authentic and congruent outcomes. Introspection enables seniors to explore what matters and why. You can help facilitate the process by using some of the following techniques.

- Conduct values audits with clients. *Values audits* help clients understand what is important to them when setting personal goals.
- Encourage seniors to conduct life reviews. (See the next section in this chapter.)
- Help your clients develop personal mission statements.
- Encourage clients to share values and life priorities with their spouses and significant others so everyone can be "on the same page."

- Work with client couples to create a joint mission statement, which can provide the foundation for planning.
- Conduct *values questionnaires* with clients, which can help them prioritize what matters to them most.
- Conduct *lifelines* with clients, during which participants review key events and life-altering or meaningful experiences that powerfully affected their lives.

The Society of Certified Senior Advisors believes that you should never intrude on seniors' beliefs or attempt to control the planning process in your work as a CSA. You should invite clients to consider options. You should speak with clarity and without judgment. You should "hear from the heart."

It is important that you affirm that the power to choose rests with your clients and not yourself. Therefore, your planning methodology should focus on the potential consequences of each choice. You should invite clients to consider, "What will this produce?" "Do I really want to create that?" "Am I ready to accept all of the consequences of that choice?"

If you are a financial advisor, honor your clients' spiritual journeys by helping them understand that plans for distributing money at the end of life can be integral to their spiritual legacy. Financial advisors have done their jobs well when clients complete their plans and believe that they planned everything themselves. Their plans should confirm their lives and should not conform to other people's expectations.

You should strive to meet the expressed needs of your clients. You should creatively invite options that reflect vital beliefs and priorities. Help clients complete their personal goals and commitments to family, friends, nonprofits, and communities. Help clients feel a sense of completion and self-satisfaction. With thoughtful plans in place, seniors will know they have done the best they could to honorably complete their lives.

Occasionally, you will work with clients who claim to be spiritual, but who are narcissistic, self-indulgent, and insensitive to the needs of others. You may question their veracity. However, it is important not to judge these clients, but to realize that narcissism and self-absorption are often a manifestation of great emotional distress.

REMINISCENCE AND LIFE REVIEW

Many seniors have a need to reminisce. In life reviews, participants hold the prism of their lives into the light of reflection. The process is often a spiritual one. They look at their past with fresh eyes from a different angle. Reviewers savor their experiences, forgive themselves and others, and review what life has taught them. Reviewers revisit opportunities, both lost and embraced. Because life review is often visual, part of the review can occur during sleep, when powerful events replay on an internal screen. Participants watch a play of their lives, in which they are the lead characters in the drama.

Life reviews can be formal or informal, overt or silent. Some reviewers hire professionals who record videotapes or support journal writing. Others do their reviews privately. Sometimes, family members interview reviewers, so that the legacy and the stories of the seniors can be recorded and passed on to future generations. Reviewers can also initiate and participate in an internal life review that is completely private—that is, no one else knows about it.

Reminiscence is about what *really* happened in a senior's life, not what could have happened. Reviewers face reality, sometimes for the first time. A review of choices made at critical junctures can call forth regret, disappointment, or guilt.

When powerful negative emotions are brought to the surface, it is helpful for reviewers to process with others and remind themselves that no one makes it through life without making mistakes. Reviewers focus on lessons and how mistakes often lead to new understanding about self and others. Reviewers bring unresolved conflicts to the surface and explore alternative meanings for mistakes that have previously been conveniently neglected or shoved into the recesses of the mind because they elicited remorse or guilt.

Life reviews touch the mysteries of life: how clients came to be with the people who bore and reared them; the magic of those they met in life, especially their best friends, their spouses, and their children; and how their enemies or people they disliked affected their journey. Reviewers explore the places they lived, how they reared their children, their vacations, physical moves to new locales, and the health concerns they and other loved ones experienced.

Seniors may review their birthdays and holidays and the best gifts they ever received. They revisit the music that touched their souls and made them laugh, as well as those songs that made them cry. Some life reviewers list their top 10 movies and why they loved them and the best television shows they ever saw, which season they remember with the most fondness and which season brought with it the most sadness. They visualize their first pets and the times they shared as they grew up together.

Seniors who successfully complete life reviews may feel that their whole life makes sense. Such seniors may feel surrounded by a peaceful aura of self-satisfaction, fused with completion. They've honored their minutes, their hours, their days, weeks, months, years, and decades. They've connected to their heritage, where they came from, with whom they've come, and who they became.

Spirituality and Aging: Summary

As we have seen, spirituality plays a central role in the lives of most seniors. You can bring this aspect into your client discussions using the tools mentioned in the previous section, such as values audits and life reviews for authentic planning.

The later years of life are often a time of spiritual introspection. Seniors look to churches where they have a personal history for spiritual connections. In doing so, they may pick and choose those elements of faith, spirituality, and religion that elicit their spiritual growth. They are seeking their inner light, which is the key to their journey in the end.

Remember this fable, which Father Anthony de Mello related in his 1982 book *The Song of the Bird*:

> *The Master was asked, "What is Spirituality?"*
>
> *He said, "Spirituality is that which succeeds in bringing man to Inner Transformation."*
>
> *"But if I apply the traditional methods handed down by the Masters, is that not Spirituality?"*
>
> *"It is not Spirituality if it does not perform its function for you. A blanket is no longer a blanket if it does not keep you warm."*
>
> *People change and needs change. So what was Spirituality once is Spirituality no more. What generally goes under the name of Spirituality is merely the record of past methods.*

In other words: Cut the coat to fit the person. Don't cut the person to fit the coat.

What does this mean to you in your work with seniors? First, respect and honor your clients' spiritual journeys and do not impose your beliefs on them.

Second, it is important that you be sensitive to the fact that your senior clients who are not able to attend religious services may feel isolated, frustrated, and depressed. If they are not able to attend services, contact the religious institution of their choice. Ask if they have transportation services or volunteers who would be willing to drive your client or visit periodically. You may even want to consider driving them yourself. For seniors who do not have a church affiliation, help them find one that meets their needs.

Third, consider establishing a resource library. You can work toward meeting client needs by maintaining on-site resource materials. A lending library of spiritual books, articles, motivational handouts, videos, and audios can be very helpful. You'll also increase your reach and your ability to assist clients by maintaining resource lists of professionals who can support spiritual journeys. These resources can be local, county, state, or national, and should include phone numbers, email addresses, or Web pages that might be beneficial.

Finally, and perhaps most important, listen attentively to the stories seniors have to tell. They are an important part of every spiritual journey. As Jean Shinoda Bolen wrote in her book, *Crossing to Avalon* (1994): "The stories people tell have a way of taking care of them."

References

Bianchi, E. (1997). *Aging as a spiritual journey*. New York: Crossroads.

Bolen, J. S. (1994). *Crossing to Avalon: A woman's midlife pilgrimage*. San Francisco, Harper Collins.

Bouchard, N. (1997) Seminar Presentation, Denver: Society of Certified Senior Advisors.

De Mello, A. (1982). *The song of the bird*. Anand, India: Gujarat Sahitya Prakash.

Gallup Organization (2002, December). Gallup Poll Survey. Data purchased from the Gallup Organization by the Society of Certified Senior Advisors. Princeton, NJ: Gallup.

Helm, H., Hays, J. C., Flint, E., Koenig, H. G., & Blazer, D. G. (2000). Effects of private religious activity on mortality of elderly disabled and nondisabled adults. *Journal of Gerontology (Medical Sciences)*, 55A, M400–M405.

Hummer R. A., Rogers, R. G., Nam, C. B., & Ellison, C. G. (1999). Religious involvement and U.S. adult mortality. *Demography* 36(2): 273–285.

Koenig, H. G., Hays, J. C., Larson, D. B., George, L. K., Cohen, H. J., McCullough, M. E., et al. (1999). Does religious attendance prolong survival?: A six-year follow-up study of 3,968 seniors. *Journal of Gerontology: A Biology of Sciences (Medical Sciences)* 54(7), M370–M376.

Koenig, H. (1995). *Research on religion and aging: An annotated bibliography.* New York: Greenwood Press.

Koenig, H. G., McCullough, M. E., & Larson, D. B. (2001). *Handbook of religion and health.* New York: Oxford.

Krause, N. (2001) Social support. In R. H. Binstock (Ed.), *Handbook on aging and the social sciences* (p. 284). San Diego, CA: Academic Press.

Krucoff, M. W., Crater, S. W., Green, C. L., Massa, A. C., Seskevich, J. E., Lane, J. D., Loeffler, et al. (2001). Integrative noetic therapies as adjuncts to percutaneous intervention during unstable coronary syndromes: Monitoring and Actualization of Noetic Training (MANTRA) feasibility pilot. *American Heart Journal, 142*(5).

Larson, D. B., Swyers, J. P., & McCullough, M. E. (1997). *Scientific research on spirituality and health: A consensus report.* Rockville, MD: National Institute for Healthcare Research.

McFadden, S. H. (2003). Older adults' emotions in religious contexts. *Aging, Spirituality, and Religion, Vol. 2.* Minneapolis: Fortress Press.

Mitroff, I., Denton, E.A. (1999). *Spiritual audit of corporate America: A hard look at spirituality, religion, and values in the workplace.* San Francisco: Jossey-Bass.

Moberg, D. O. (1971). *Spiritual well being: Background and issues.* Washington DC: White House Conference on Aging.

Moberg, D. O. (1990). Religion and spirituality. In *Gerontology: Perspectives and Issues* (pp. 179–205). New York: Springer Publishing Company.

Moberg, D. O. (Ed.) (2001). *Aging and spirituality.* New York: Haworth.

NCOA (National Council of the Aging). (2002). *American perspectives of aging in the 21st century.* Washington, DC: NCOA.

Palmore, E. B. (1995). Religious organizations. In *The Encyclopedia of Aging.* New York: Springer Publishing Company.

Quadagno, J. (2002). *Aging and the life course.* New York: McGraw Hill.

Strawbridge, W. J., Cohen, R. D., Shema, S. J., & Kaplan, G. A. (1997). Frequent attendance at religious services and mortality over 28 years. *American Journal of Public Health 87*(6), 957–961.

Tobin, S. S., Ellor, J. W., & Anderson-Ray, S. M. (1986). *Enabling the elderly: Religious institutions within the community service system.* Albany: State University of New York Press.

Tornstam, L. (1999). Late-life transcendence: A new developmental perspective on aging. In L. E. Thomas & S. A. Eisenhandler (Eds.), *Religion, belief, and spirituality in late life.* New York: Springer.

Van Willigen, M. (2000). Differential benefits of volunteering across the life course. *Journal of Gerontology 55B*(5), S308–S318.

Wink, P. (1999). Addressing end-of-life issues: Spirituality and the inner life. *Generations, 23*, 73–80.

Resources

Services

Aging America. http://www.demko.com/aa030301.htm, Dr. David J. Demko, Editor, Age Venture News Service, 19432 Preserve Drive, Boca Raton, FL 33498. The Web site contains three self-help pamphlets on aging and spirituality.

Aish.com. http://www.aish.com/spirituality, One Western Wall Plaza, POB 14149, Old City, Jerusalem 91141, Israel, (972-2) 628-5666 fax: (972-2) 627-3172 email: webmaster@aish.com. One of the world's largest programs that explores the question of why be Jewish, this sponsored site contains articles on spirituality.

All About Aging. http://www.allaboutaging.com, Midwest Spiritual Eldering Project, 9149 Vincent Avenue South, Bloomington, MN 55431, 952-884-1128. From "Age-ing to Sage-ing," this site offers workshops for elder care individuals and professionals.

The Catholic Health Association. http://www.chausa.org, 4455 Woodson Road, St. Louis, MO 63134-3797, 314-427-2500, fax 314-427-0029. The Catholic Health Association sponsors senior spirituality groups in many of its parishes across the country. This site offers slide shows and video presentations of workshops on spirituality and the senior.

The Center on Aging of Union—PSCE. http://www.ttgst.ac.kr, email hsimmons@union-psce.edu. An online annotated bibliography for approaching aging gracefully, the site focuses specifically on religion, aging, and spirituality.

Knowledgism. http://www.knowledgism.com/main/spirit.asp, email: comments@knowledgism.com. A free subscription site containing articles from various authors on spirituality and knowledgism.

Science and Religion Bookstore. http://www.scienceandreligionbooks.org, 203-750-8253. An online bookstore, this site contains publications on spirituality and health.

Spiritual Eldering Institute. http://www.spiritualeldering.org, 970 Aurora Avenue, Boulder, CO 80302, 303-449-7243, fax 303-938-1277. A national, not-for-profit organization, the institute offers resources for seniors to maximize their lives. Tapes, workshops, and books are available.

Torch Trinity Journal. http://www.ttgst.ac.kr. This Web site features "Spirituality and Senior Adults," an article written by Rev. Dr. Glenn A. Jent. Click on the "Publications" link and select "Journal Volume IV-1." Rev. Dr. Jent is academic Dean and Associate Professor of Christian Education at Torch Trinity Graduate School of Theology, Seoul, Korea, and has authored several books on this topic.

Questia. http://www.questia.com. 713-358-2600. Questia is the largest online library containing research on spirituality. It is a subscription site. Over 70,000 books and journals appear here and can be read online.

Chapter 14

End-of-Life Planning

In the early morning hours of January 11, 1983, 25-year-old Nancy Cruzan was driving on a dimly lit road in Carthage, Missouri. No one saw the accident that night but her car was found, flipped over, almost 200 yards from the road. The impact threw Cruzan out of her vehicle some 35 feet, and she lay facedown on the ground.

Nancy Beth Cruzan

Daughter-Sister-Aunt

Born July 20, 1957
Departed Jan. 11, 1983
At Peace Dec. 26, 1990

Inscription on Nancy Cruzan's Headstone

In his book Long Goodbye: The Deaths of Nancy Cruzan *(2002), William Colby relates the progress of events: A passerby called in an emergency, and a highway patrol officer arrived on the scene. In examining Cruzan's body, he found no pulse or respiration and believed she was dead. He advised the Emergency Medical Services (EMS) technicians of this when they arrived. Nonetheless, the paramedics initiated Cardio Pulmonary Resuscitation (CPR) on the apparently lifeless body. EMS protocols and state laws dictate that the technicians resuscitate every patient whose heart or breathing stops, unless there is an out of hospital Do Not Resuscitate (DNR) order. The paramedics therefore, intubated Cruzan's lungs to provide artificial respiration, inserted an IV, connected a heart monitor, suctioned her lungs of mucus and blood, and began chest compressions. Even though she was found lying on the ground, apparently deprived of oxygen for 12 minutes or more, Nancy Cruzan's body responded to the paramedics' efforts, and she began breathing on her own.*

The paramedics felt their efforts were successful and that the victim's rapid recovery was "unusual." Nancy Cruzan's body did recover from her many injuries, but, deprived of oxygen for more than six minutes (considered the point at which permanent brain damage occurs [Colby, 2002]), she never awoke from an unconscious condition called a persistent vegetative state. Her lower brain (the brain stem, which controls breathing and circulation) functioned, but her oxygen-starved upper brain cells (the cerebral cortex, the thinking and awareness part of the brain) had, in her doctor's words, "liquefied." Over time, Nancy Cruzan's body began to deteriorate: her arms and legs drew in, her fingers turned up, and her toes pointed down. She could not swallow or eat, so a feeding tube was inserted in her stomach for food and water, and she was incontinent and had to wear diapers. She did not respond to stimuli or recognize her family, and diagnostic tests, such as electroencephalograms (EEGs), detected no brain waves.

Life-sustaining technology brought Nancy Cruzan back to life and prolonged her marginal existence. However, she lived afterward as a being without recognition, thinking, or feeling. To her family it was not a miracle, but rather a nightmare.

After three traumatic years, they requested the Missouri Rehabilitation Center (a state hospital) to remove her feeding tube. This was not a request for assisted suicide (a procedure recognized only by the state of Oregon). Instead it was a request to withdraw the medical treatment of food and water (nutrition and hydration) via feeding tube. Without hydration, Nancy Cruzan would die, and although it sounds inhumane, a neurologist who treated her testified that, "In a vegetative state, the brain doesn't feel pain" (Colby, 2002). The family believed that if Nancy Cruzan could have decided, she would have rejected her feeding tube. She would not have wanted to live her life as a vegetable.

Often, life and death issues like these are negotiated at the bedside, between the doctor and the family. However, life and law became complicated for the Cruzan family because the state of Missouri objected to their request to remove the feeding tube, leading to a four-year court battle. After years of weekly visits to his hospitalized daughter, Cruzan's anguished father, Joe Cruzan, appealed to the television cameras: "What's the purpose in this?...Our Nancy died that [January] night. We've got her body left, but she has no dignity..." (Frontline, 1992). The Cruzan case went all the way to the U.S. Supreme Court and back to Missouri's courts before a doctor finally removed her feeding tube. In the eyes of her family, almost seven years passed between that January night in 1983—when Nancy Cruzan departed life—and when she was finally at peace in 1990.

Introduction

Nancy Cruzan did not make any end-of-life plans and did not prepare an *advance directive*, a document naming a substitute decision maker and identifying desired medical treatments. Her story illustrates how important it is for every person to preplan and complete such a document, a concept recognized by state laws and supported by most Americans. Survey research indicates that, in the abstract, a majority of Americans prefer death to living hooked up to a machine. Further, they support the concept of an individual's right to die

(Kugiya, 2003). However, only an estimated 18 percent of the adult population has completed one or more elements of an advance directive (Fagerlin, Ditto, Hawkins, Schneider, & Smucker, 2002).

Most people don't want to think about death, much less talk about it, unless the end is near. They may fear a serious illness, but they do not believe they are vulnerable (Fagerlin et al.). Nancy Cruzan, like many other adults, may not have even been aware of advanced directives and their value.

To terminate life support is always a difficult decision, particularly when the patient is a loved spouse, parent, or child. Such decisions become more difficult when the loved one has made no formal indication of their wishes in an advance directive or even simple conversations. It is important for seniors to discuss their treatment wishes with their doctors, family, and friends so that all their loved ones are fully aware of their values, desired treatments, and choices. In addition, it is *equally* important for seniors to discuss the health care wishes with people for whom they may be responsible for making end-of-life decisions.

In some cases, the absence of a written document spelling out an individual's health care desires could pull the family member who decides to "pull the plug" into a spiral of traumatic grief and depression. After Nancy Cruzan was buried, her father entered a deep depression and eventually committed suicide. Dr. Erin Embry, a psychologist practicing in a New York hospital, described a similar situation involving a patient currently in psychotherapy. This patient advocated against intubating her 83-year-old mother, who was afflicted with multiple chronic conditions and had been hospitalized for respiratory failure. There was no advance directive rejecting ventilation, which meant the daughter was compelled to appear before the hospital's ethics committee. The panel eventually agreed, and the tube was removed. While she knows intellectually she did what her mother would have wanted, the daughter feels responsible for her mother's death. With an advance directive, the burden of deciding would not have fallen solely to the daughter.

WHY ARE ADVANCE DIRECTIVES IMPORTANT TO YOUR SENIOR CLIENTS?

This chapter is about advance directives. It is written to help you understand the issues and, in your role as a CSA, to be able to inform your clients about these important documents. It provides background information on medical advances, the aging population, and the different elements of advance directives. It poses some of the soul-searching questions seniors and their families and friends should discuss, and reviews state legislation.

Your position as a CSA situates you appropriately to raise the issue of health care treatment with your clients and encourage them to discuss these matters thoroughly and to complete one or more advance directives. You should become familiar with your state's requirements and be prepared to provide your client with copies of the necessary forms. You can counsel clients that not deciding means someone else—family members, physicians, hospital ethics committees, lawyers, or even state and federal courts—may be forced into the position of determining the outcome.

ELEMENTS OF END-OF-LIFE PLANNING

Be aware that advance directives are but one piece of end-of-life planning. The other elements should include a will or trust document to pass on property, a durable power of attorney for financial affairs, and funeral and burial plans. While each of these is unique and has its own set of issues, these elements are interrelated and should not be completed in isolation. For example, a number of authorities recommend that the same individual who is given power of attorney for financial affairs should also serve as power of attorney for health care under an advance directive. In the absence of a durable power of attorney for health care, some states list who the decision-maker is. (Gay and lesbian couples, in particular, need to know their state's laws in this area.)

Health care decisions may have financial implications and vice versa. Both are important, and some matters may require legal advice.

Background: Impact of Medical Technology

Joe Cruzan described the ethical dilemma faced by an increasing number of Americans when he said, "Medical technology surpassed our society's ability to deal with it" (Colby, 2002). Medical technology has, indeed, brought miraculous advances in treating illness and prolonging life. It also has transformed

Euthanasia, which can take different forms, is the act or practice of terminating the life of a person (Gifis, 1996). There is a difference, however, between terminating or rejecting medical treatments—sometimes called the right to die—and assisted suicide and mercy killing. State laws and court decisions have upheld the right of all persons to refuse medical treatments (as in Nancy Cruzan's case). If a senior is incompetent, an advance directive serves to indicate the individual's wishes for terminating treatment.

Assisted suicide, on the other hand, is a criminal act in most states, and is not, according to the U.S. Supreme Court, constitutionally protected (Vacco v. Quill, 1997). Further, the American Medical Association believes physician-assisted suicide is "fundamentally incompatible with the physician's role as a healer, would be difficult or impossible to control, and would pose serious societal risks" (AMA, 2004).

While there have been efforts to approve such legislation in a number of states, Oregon has approved a law, through a statewide initiative, to permit physician-assisted suicides. Oregon's Death with Dignity Act (1994) permits a licensed physician to issue a prescription for medication to end the life of a state resident (over the age of 18), who is diagnosed with a terminal disease that will lead to death within six months. To date, the law has survived various court challenges and garnered popular support among voters there. It is not widely used, however.

Mercy killing is the intentional act of a health care provider or individual to take the life of a patient. This is a criminal offense, regardless of the motivation.

the nation's demographics, established a new legal standard for death, made chronic diseases the primary cause of death, and introduced a state of uncertainty when treatments for such ailments prolong dying with no hope for a cure.

At the beginning of the last century, 70 percent of those dying were under the age of 65 (Bern-Klug, 2004). Most people did not survive to old age; life expectancy averaged only 47.3 years (CDC, 2003). Both high birth and high mortality rates kept the nation's population young. They died from injuries, childbirth, or a sudden illness that could have been caused by any number of infectious diseases. Bacterial infections such as pneumonia were a major cause of death and remained so until the middle of the 20th century (Dunn, 2001). With a youthful population, dying young meant that chronic diseases were uncommon. A patient normally recovered or passed away quickly.

> *During the past century, we in the United States have seen significant changes in the way we experience illness and death.*
>
> *Means to a Better End: A Report on Dying in America*, Last Acts (2002)

One hundred years later, most people now live to old age. Actuarial charts indicate that a boy child born today will live well past age 70, and a girl child will live until almost age 80 (Census Bureau, n.d.). At this time, the fastest growing segment of the nation's population is the 80-plus group. In 2000, 75 percent of those who died were 65 years or older. One-fourth of those dying were 85 years or older (Bern-Klug, 2004). While life expectancy in this country is several years younger than that in Japan and some European countries, the aging of the population is unprecedented in human history.

Medical advances contributed significantly to the aging of the American population. Pharmacology and public health all but eliminated the longtime scourges of cholera, typhus, and yellow fever. Antibiotics knocked pneumonia off the top of the list of primary causes of death (Dunn, 2001). And lives were saved or prolonged through the arrival of new technologies, equipment, and treatments, including:

- ventilators to provide artificial respiration
- heart and lung machines
- feeding tubes
- defibrillators to restart a heart
- diagnostic tools such magnetic resonance imaging (MRI) and computer-assisted tomography (CAT scans)
- accident scene treatment by EMS technicians

It is interesting to note that Nancy Cruzan's medical condition—a persistent vegetative state—was not even mentioned in medical literature until the 1950s, when heart and lung machines (and later, ventilators) came into widespread use (Linder, 1995).

These same advances have also rewritten the legal definition of what constitutes death. For generations, state laws defined death as the termination of a heartbeat and breathing. If the heart stopped beating, the other organs, including the brain, would quickly stop and the individual would be declared dead. Medical technology changed that. Heart and lung machines, for example, can keep a body alive even without any upper or lower brain activity. Beginning in 1983, states began approving an expanded definition of death to include a new criterion, brain function. The Uniform Determination of Death Act, the model law adopted by many but not all states, now defines death as the "irreversible cessation of circulatory and respiratory functions, or irreversible cessation of all functions of the entire brain, including the brain stem" (Linder, 1995). Some have argued that the whole-brain standard is too expansive. They recommend instead that death be based on the cessation of the higher brain, or the absence of a functioning cerebral cortex (Linder).

These days, instead of accidents and infections, the major causes of the approximate 2.5 million American deaths each year (Census Bureau, n.d.) are heart disease and circulatory problems (accounting for one-third of all deaths) and cancer (one-fourth of all deaths) (Bern-Klug, 2004). Both are chronic diseases, primarily affecting the older population, and with each, it is increasingly difficult to know when the end-of-life stage begins for each patient. For example, with heart disease, a heart attack (infarct) may be an immediate killer, but many individuals who suffer one may slowly decline for years before the heart fails (Lynn & Harrold, 1999). Medical prognoses projecting end of life with heart disease are frequently in error (Bern-Klug, 2004). Cancer is more predictable than heart disease, but with chemotherapy, radiation, and other treatments, medical technology now prolongs the lives of many seniors by months or years. Other common chronic illnesses cited as major causes of death are: lung ailments (emphysema and chronic bronchitis); kidney disease; liver failure; and dementia (Alzheimer's disease and strokes) (Lynn & Harrold, 1999). It is common for many older people to suffer from multiple chronic illnesses, "making them live in a state of vulnerable frailty, somewhere between living and dying" (Bern-Klug).

Widespread Support for End-of-Life Planning

While the majority of Americans do not make end-of-life plans, an estimated 18 percent do preplan and prepare advance directives. For example, in March 1994, former President Nixon died of a stroke at age 81 (Marck, 2004). He was treated at the New York Hospital–Cornell Medical Center, the same institution then caring for the former first lady, Jacqueline Kennedy Onassis, age 64 (McFadden, 1994). She was diagnosed in January 1994 with a form of cancer that attacked her lymphatic system. Both patients completed advance directives indicating that they did not want their lives prolonged with medical treatments if their physicians diagnosed them as terminal. Hospital doctors and health care workers honored those directives (King, 1996). Nixon died in the hospital. Onassis, after chemotherapy and other treatments failed to arrest her cancer, returned home in April to die among family and friends. She died one month later.

There is widespread support for conducting advance planning. AARP, The Robert Wood Johnson Foundation, the Open Society Institute's Project Death in America, Area Agencies on Aging, hospitals, and many others are all promoting end-of-life planning as part of their activities. Professionals—including the American Medical Association and American Bar Association—and many clergy recommend that every adult, and particularly older Americans, complete an advance directive. Finally, federal law (Patient Self Determination Act, 1990) indirectly encourages seniors to complete their own documents by requiring hospitals and nursing homes participating in the Medicare and Medicaid programs (virtually every health care institution) to inform patients of their right to complete an advance directive.

Research indicates that the majority of those completing advance directives tend to be white women with higher levels of education and income. In a study of about 400 older adults in Charlotte County, Florida, researchers concluded that seven factors characterized the older adults living in the county who completed an advance directive (Rosnick & Reynolds, 2003). Those completing an advance directive were likely to:

- be over age 85;
- be more open to different experiences;

- to have a higher income;
- take more prescription medicines;
- have a higher quality of life;
- have lived through a negative life event;
- have a sense of controlling their destiny.

In a separate study of 200 older persons from four ethnic groups, researchers found significant cultural differences regarding end-of-life practices among the different groups. Almost 60 percent of the Korean Americans and 45 percent of the Mexican Americans studied believe that the family, not a proxy, should be the primary decision-maker concerning medical treatments. Only 24 percent of the African Americans surveyed and 20 percent of the whites agreed that the family should be the decision-maker.

The report concluded that important qualities for physicians included cultural sensitivity and cultural competence (Rabow, Hauser, & Adams, 2004).

Cultural sensitivity is important to you as a CSA as well.

THE PHYSICIAN'S INFLUENCE IN END-OF-LIFE PLANNING

Many studies indicate that the physician is a key player in discussing end-of-life planning. The Charlotte County, Florida, study mentioned above concluded that a major factor influencing older adults to complete advance directives is whether physicians discuss advance planning with them.

Unfortunately, seniors commonly wait for physicians to initiate such discussions rather than making the first moves themselves. As a result, the conversation may never occur. General Accounting Office (GAO) research indicates many doctors are reluctant to discuss end-of-life planning with their patients for a number of reasons. These include a lack of training in end-of-life planning, a conviction that death is an inappropriate outcome, or feeling that they are not adequately compensated for conducting such conversations (GAO, 1995). Even if physicians remain silent about advance directives, seniors should initiate such discussions.

According to the GAO, "The American Medical Association and others believe that financial incentives would encourage discussion of advance directives. They would like insurance companies to reimburse physicians for time counseling patients about advance directives" (GAO, 1995). You can encourage your clients to approach their physicians, or if needed, you can act as the point person in arranging the discussion.

GRASSROOTS CAMPAIGNS FOR END-OF-LIFE PLANNING

As mentioned earlier, nationwide the percentage of adults completing an advance directive remains relatively small, but there are cities where the percentage is much higher. For example, a community-wide grassroots advance directive campaign in La Crosse, Wisconsin, called Respecting Choices helped thousands of that city's adults complete their own advance directives (Gunderson Lutheran, 2004). That campaign employed videos and printed materials, together with trained staff in a coordinated approach that appears to be successful. A subsequent study by the group found that 85 percent of those who died during one year (April 1995 to March 1996) had a signed advance directive. Of those dying with an advance directive, 96 percent of their documents were found in the patients' medical records. This Respecting Choices campaign is now being replicated in other communities across the country. For more information, visit the Respecting Choices Web site at http://www.gundluth.org/eolprograms.

Similarly, CRITICAL Conditions is a community-based, educational program designed by Georgia Health Decisions to assist people in understanding and planning for their health care at the end of life. The CRITICAL Conditions program features public awareness materials, a planning guide, family workshops, personal agent workshops, trained community counselors, and training modules for health care providers. CRITICAL Conditions is being introduced throughout the state of Georgia through organizations wishing to sponsor the program and seeks to expand the program across the country. For more information about CRITICAL Conditions, contact Georgia Health Decisions at 800-544-5741, or visit their Web site at http://www.criticalconditions.org.

Aging with Dignity is a private, nonprofit organization based in Florida that is dedicated to affirming and safeguarding human dignity at the end of life. They developed the Five Wishes tool as a user-friendly advance directive that clearly documents individual preferences regarding the type of medical treatment desired as well as providing information about the values and beliefs the individual wants to have guide end-of-life care decisions. Five Wishes provides an excellent vehicle for facilitating family discussion of these issues. Five Wishes will be discussed in more detail later in this chapter. The full document is provided in Appendix A for reference only.

End-of-Life Choices is a 24-year-old nonprofit organization based in Denver, with 32,000 members in 60 chapters. The organization advocates for choice, dignity, and control at the end of life, including the option of legal physician aid in dying under careful safeguards. According to Senior Vice President Faye Girsh, EdD, advance directives are essential but are limited in that they apply only to the refusal or withdrawal of treatment. "People who have completed the forms are not guaranteed a peaceful death since only half of those who die are hooked up to something they can refuse," Girsh says.

Others who are dying and who wish to have more control over their death require other legal choices. Girsh authored a booklet titled *Choices at the End of Life*, which includes information on hospice, refusal of food and hydration, terminal sedation, the Oregon law, and ending one's own life in a humane and dignified way. It also includes post-death options such as what to do with your body, your obituary, and ethical wills. In addition to printed information, End-of-Life Choices provides speakers and workshops. To find out more you can visit them at http://www.endoflifechoices.org, or call 800-247-7421.

Elements of an Advance Directive

An advance directive is made up of two elements: a *durable power of attorney for health care* and a *living will*. Twenty states wrap these two elements into a single comprehensive form, which is preferable (Last Acts, 2002). However, you should determine which forms can be used in your state and whether witness or notary signatures are required. A third element that may be necessary is called a *do not resuscitate* (DNR) order. It alerts emergency medical staff that a patient does not wish to be resuscitated. If a senior does not wish to be resuscitated, this fact should be listed on his or her living will. The patient's physician will then need to complete a DNR and file it with the senior's chart. Each of these elements is discussed in more detail below.

ADVANCE DIRECTIVES MAY BE ORAL OR WRITTEN

The most common and most basic form of an advance directive is the oral communications between a patient and physician or between a patient and family members and friends. Such communications are fundamental to end-of-life planning, because a patient can begin to articulate his or her thoughts about "values, priorities, meaning, and [the] quality of life" (ABA Commission on Law and Aging, 2004). Doctors removed Nancy Cruzan's feeding tube after two former colleagues testified in court about comments she made about not wanting to be kept alive as a vegetable. However, testimony regarding such discussions cannot always be relied upon, as they may not meet the clear and convincing evidentiary requirements of some state laws. (*Clear and convincing* is a legal standard of proof that is "less than what is necessary in criminal cases but more than what is normally required in civil proceedings" [Gifis, 1996].) In some states a written, signed, and witnessed document is required. Further, the recent Terri Schiavo case in Florida has raised additional questions about the validity of oral statements, particularly when there is a family dispute.

In 1990, 26-year-old Terri Schiavo suffered a cardiac arrest that starved her brain of oxygen. Like Nancy Cruzan, doctors diagnosed her condition as a persistent vegetative state. Before her illness, she signed no advance directive, so under Florida law her husband became the *default surrogate* as the next of kin. For eight years, according to her husband, he pursued different experimental and rehabilitative treatments, but Terri Schiavo never improved. In 1998, he petitioned the courts to remove her feeding tube, testifying, along with other relatives, that Terri Schiavo had disclosed a desire to not live in a coma hooked up to life support. Schiavo's parents objected, countering that they too had a right to act as proxies for their daughter's health, and sued to continue her artificial nutrition and hydration. For six years, this dispute was tied up in Florida's legal system and eventually attracted the attention of national news programs. Her parents maintained that Terri Schiavo was not in a vegetative state but was in fact, responsive. When the Court of Appeals ruled in the husband's favor, the feeding tube was removed for a few days. But in an emotional response, the state legislature passed what politicians and the media dubbed Terri's Law, requiring the reinsertion of the feeding tube for this patient who had not signed an advance directive.

Once the legislature approved the law, Florida's governor, Jeb Bush, ordered her feeding tube to be reinserted. However, the Florida Supreme Court later ruled that law was an unconstitutional interference in the judicial system. Schiavo's feeding tube was removed a third and final time and she died 13 days later on March 31, 2005. The pathologic findings of the autopsy report were all consistent with someone in a permanent vegetative state. The possible long-term implications of the Schiavo case are that testimony regarding a patient's wishes may no longer be considered valid. A signed document may be required.

Durable Power of Attorney for Health Care

A *power of attorney* is a legal document naming an agent, called a *proxy* or *surrogate*, to be a substitute decision-maker when a patient is incompetent. To be valid, the proxy or surrogate must meet the state's legal requirements, such as being 18 years of age. Also, the form may need to be witnessed and possibly notarized. The required number and type of signatures vary from state to state. A proxy can be a spouse, adult child, friend, or relative but should live nearby. Most important, this person should know the patient's values and religious beliefs, wishes, and preferences regarding medical treatments, organ donation, nursing home placement, etc., and be willing to speak on behalf of the patient. The proxy must also separate his or her personal views from those of the patient. The power of attorney for health care can be revoked at any time. If the power of attorney is revoked, however, the patient must notify not only the agent, but also the physician, family members, and other persons who may be involved in providing care.

There is a consensus forming that, if people are only going to complete one advance directive, they are best served by appointing a durable power of attorney for health care. If seniors want, they can supplement this with a written health care directive that spells out what interventions they prefer to receive or avoid, and with a living will that states what type of care they want if they are considered terminally ill. Personalized instructions ensure that even if the person named as surrogate is unavailable or unable to carry out the role, the health care team has guidelines and legal documents that will still hold up.

One or all of these documents may be helpful to the proxy decision-maker, but in no way should any of them replace discussions between the patient and the proxy. Paperwork alone is only part of the process of end-of-life planning, and there are many obstacles to the use of health care directives and living wills in specific decision-making circumstances. The health care directive or living will paperwork is by no means a panacea, but can be a helpful part of decision making, especially for people with multiple advanced chronic conditions that will eventually affect the process of dying. These documents are very important in nursing homes. The documents should be part of the ongoing process of advance care planning.

> *Dying is just too complicated. It is individualistic, personalized, sacred, profane, and endlessly nuanced.*
> Morgan & Sabatino, 2001

Naming a Proxy

Naming a proxy is probably the most important task a patient performs when completing an advance directive. Seniors, or their advisors, cannot draft a living will to address every possible medical treatment. If a senior becomes incapacitated, it will be the decision of the proxy (called *substituted judgment*) that matters, or what other authorities determine is in the best *interests* of the patient. Research findings indicate that proxies often lack experience in end-of-life issues and have not always accurately represented the patient's desires, substituting their own values instead (Sabatino, 1999). It is essential that the patient fully communicate with the proxy long before any possible emergency. In addition to naming a proxy, the senior should also designate an alternative proxy or proxies in the event that the primary surrogate is unavailable. In the rare instance when a trustworthy health care proxy cannot be found, it is best not to sign a durable power of attorney for health care.

Role and Responsibilities of a Proxy

In Maryland, state law spells out the role and responsibilities of a proxy. This statute (Maryland Code Annotated, 1998) provides useful guidelines that every surrogate should consider:

In determining the wishes of the patient, a surrogate shall consider the patient's:

(i) Current diagnosis and prognosis with and without the treatment at issue;

(ii) Expressed preferences regarding the provision of, or the withholding of, the specific treatment at issue or of similar treatments;

(iii) Relevant religious and moral beliefs and personal values;

(iv) Behavior, attitudes, and past conduct with respect to the treatment generally;

(v) Reactions to the provision of, or the withholding or withdrawal of, a similar treatment for another individual; and,

(vi) Expressed concerns about the effect on the family or intimate friends of the patient if a treatment were provided, withheld, or withdrawn.

A complete guide to serving as a health care proxy is available on the Web from the Montefiore Medical Center, Albert Einstein College of Medicine, Bronx, NY. (See *Making health care decisions for others* in the Resources section at the end of this chapter.)

LIVING WILL

A living will is distinct from an advance directive in that living wills are generally invoked when a person is considered *terminal*, while a health care directive is not limited to the terminal state.

A living will outlines the type of care a patient would want or would reject in the terminal stage. It can guide both the proxy and health care workers as to the medical treatments provided during that time. Generally, a living will works best when it uses specific terminology such as *do resuscitate* or *do not intubate*. Generic phrases such as *no heroic measures* are simply too vague to provide guidance (Sabatino, 1999).

You should be aware (and inform your senior clients) that one drawback of a living will is that it is not always clear at what point a person with advanced chronic conditions could be or should be considered terminal. Many serious and disabling events, such as stroke, Alzheimer's disease, and coma or "persistent vegetative state," are not considered terminal diseases by many doctors and may not be covered by living wills. Many living wills are never invoked because the person is never formally considered terminal.

Aging with Dignity (mentioned earlier) has produced an advance directive called Five Wishes. That document's Wish 2 addresses medical treatments in a section titled "What 'Life-Support Treatment' Means to Me":

> Life-support treatment means any medical procedure, device or medication to keep me alive. Life-support treatment includes: medical devices put in me to help me breathe; food and water supplied by medical device (tube feeding); cardiopulmonary resuscitation (CPR); major surgery; blood transfusions; dialysis; antibiotics; and anything else meant to keep me alive. If I wish to limit the meaning of life-support treatment [. . .] I write this limitation in the space below. I do this to make very clear what I want and under what conditions.

_____

_____

The same form also lays out four scenarios:

- close to death
- in a coma and not expected to wake up or recover
- permanent and severe brain damage and not expected to recover
- in another condition under which I do not wish to be kept alive

With each of these four, Wish 2 asks the senior to determine if he or she would or would not want life-support, and under what conditions.

A second approach to the issue of medical treatments can be found in the *Consumer's Tool Kit for Health Care Advance Planning*, available on the Web site of the American Bar Association's Commission on Law and Aging. (See the Resources section at the end of this chapter. You may wish to download the entire document and provide copies to your clients as a point of discussion.) In Tools 2 and 3, the guide asks seniors to weigh the trade-off of medical treatments between prolonging life and suffering pain and discomfort.

Tool 2 begins with the question "Are Some Conditions Worse than Death?" and invites seniors to rate, on a five-point scale, whether or not they want treatment.

Tool 2

"WHAT IF YOU...?"	DEFINITELY WANT TREATMENT ←-----→ DEFINITELY DO NOT WANT TREATMENT
No longer can walk but get around in a wheelchair?	
Comments:	1 2 3 4 5
No longer can get outside—you spend all day at home?	
Comments:	1 2 3 4 5
No longer can contribute to your family's well-being?	
Comments:	1 2 3 4 5
Are in severe pain most of the time?	
Comments:	1 2 3 4 5
Are in severe discomfort most of the time (such as nausea, diarrhea)?	
Comments:	1 2 3 4 5
Are on a feeding tube to keep you alive?	
Comments:	1 2 3 4 5
Are on a kidney dialysis machine to keep you alive?	
Comments:	1 2 3 4 5
Are on a breathing machine to keep you alive?	
Comments:	1 2 3 4 5
Need someone to take care of you 24 hours a day?	
Comments:	1 2 3 4 5
Can no longer control your bladder?	
Comments:	1 2 3 4 5
Can no longer control your bowels?	
Comments:	1 2 3 4 5
Live in a nursing home?	
Comments:	1 2 3 4 5
Can no longer think or talk clearly?	
Comments:	1 2 3 4 5
Can no longer recognize family or friends?	
Comments:	1 2 3 4 5
Other?	
Comments:	1 2 3 4 5

Reprinted courtesy of the American Bar Association's Commission on Law and Aging.

Tool 3 from the same publication addresses the trade-offs of pain and discomfort versus possible recovery. It asks: How Do You Weigh Odds of Survival?

Imagine that you are seriously ill. The doctors are recommending treatment for your illness, but the treatments have very severe side effects, such as severe pain, nausea, vomiting, or weakness that could last for months.

Question: Would you be willing to endure such severe side effects if the chance of regaining your current health was:

▪ high (over 80 percent)?	Yes	Not Sure	No
▪ moderate (50 percent)?	Yes	Not Sure	No
▪ low (20 percent)?	Yes	Not Sure	No
▪ very low (less than 2 percent)?	Yes	Not Sure	No"

A related issue to include in a living will might be when hospital treatments should end. Although the number of deaths occurring in hospitals is decreasing, half of all deaths take place there. Of these deaths, half a million people die in Intensive Care Units (ICUs) with an average stay of one week or more (Last Acts, 2002). Death in an ICU is often isolating, painful, and costly.

> *Almost everyone . . . eventually wants to have treatment stopped.*
> *There aren't very many people who prefer to die in an ICU*
> *on a ventilator with multiple system failure.*
>
> Lynn and Harrold (1999)

Palliative Care

Instead of a cure, medical treatment can be focused on *palliative care*, sometimes called comfort care, to preserve the best quality of life by relieving pain, controlling symptoms, and supporting the patient's continuing involvement with life. At the same time, palliative care regards dying as a natural part of life and supports the patient and family in living through this process. The psychological, emotional, and spiritual work involved in the dying process requires energy that can be eroded by severe pain, persistent nausea, or unrelenting shortness of breath. Aggressive management of those symptoms offers patients the opportunity to deal with their anxieties about death, put affairs in order, and attend to the principal relationships that sustain them.

The issue of pain management is an important one to highlight here for there is an increasing body of research that finds pain is not adequately addressed for both the severely ill and elderly patients. In a broadcast titled "The Place of Palliative Medicine," National Public Radio's Patricia Leighton reported, "Without good palliative medicine, studies show 75 percent of all dying patients will suffer pain, 65 percent breathlessness, and half nausea" (Leighton, 1997). Cancer patients and their families in particular report tremendous frustrations over inadequate pain control. Some believe that more aggressive attention to controlling pain, nausea, and shortness of breath offer an alternative to those who are considering physician-assisted suicide because they are hopelessly uncomfortable.

Numerous state legislatures have passed positive initiatives, including approval of the use of medicinal marijuana, expansion of education to medical students and physicians regarding pain management, and elimination of obstacles to ordering adequate amounts of controlled substances (narcotics) for pain control. Other states are expanding laws regarding the criminality of assisted suicide.

Palliative care can be provided by hospices—or less frequently, hospitals—and can be delivered in any setting, including nursing homes. In some cases, nursing home or hospital staff is trained to provide palliative care; in other cases, hospice comes to the hospital or nursing home to help direct and provide palliative care. Some communities have a hospice building, and others have a hospice service that goes wherever the patients are.

The terms *palliative care* and *hospice care* are often used interchangeably, and though related, they are distinct from each other. Palliative care is an approach that seeks to "prevent, relieve, reduce or soothe the symptoms of disease or disorder without effecting a cure. Palliative care in this broad sense is not restricted to those who are dying or those enrolled in hospice programs . . . palliative care, broadly conceived, is also important to those who live with chronic pain or other symptoms" (IOM, 1997). Hospice is a subset of palliative care that focuses on enhancing life during the final stages of a terminal illness.

Medicare will pay for more than six months of hospice care if a physician can document that the patient is still considered terminal with a life expectancy of about six months. Such treatment provides palliative care and supportive services that address the "emotional, social, financial, and legal needs of terminally ill patients and their families" (Last Acts, 2002). (See chapter 9, Home and Community-Based Services, for more information about hospice.)

Do Not Resuscitate Orders

If a senior's heart or breathing stops while in a health care facility, emergency staff is mandated to make every effort to resuscitate that person. However, there are patients for whom resuscitation is inappropriate, and there are patients whose living wills indicate they do not want to be resuscitated. Consequently, the Joint Commission on Accreditation of Healthcare Organizations (JCAOH) requires each accredited institution—almost every hospital and nursing home—to develop a DNR policy to deal with such cases (McGee, Caplan, Spanogle, & Asch, 2001). DNR orders are signed by the patient's physician and placed in the patient's chart if the patient does not wish to be resuscitated. The patient, proxy, or advisor should make sure the physician signed and placed the DNR order in the patient's medical records.

If someone is homebound or in an accident and does not want to be resuscitated, 43 states (Last Acts, 2002) have authorized non-hospital or *out-of-hospital* DNRs. Here the physician submits the DNR to emergency medical services, permitting the technicians not to resuscitate that patient. Without such an order, EMS protocols and state law mandate technicians to attempt to resuscitate any person whose heart or breathing has stopped. Seniors with an *out-of-hospital* DNR often wear a wristband or medallion that reads "Do Not Resuscitate." This is to advise EMS staff of their wishes.

A DNR order will not keep a person from getting other emergency medical treatment or pain relief. Medical attendants, doctors, and others who rely on DNR orders are protected under the law. You or your proxy may revoke a DNR order at any time.

NO UNIVERSAL ADVANCED DIRECTIVE FORM

State-specific advance directive forms and guides to end-of-life planning are widely available on the Internet and in different publications. A partial list of helpful guides and Web sites is available in the Resources section at the end of this chapter. In most instances, the publications can be downloaded from the Internet at no cost or purchased for a nominal fee. You should be aware that there is no universal advance directive form that works in every state. State requirements, as mentioned earlier, vary considerably. However, the widely used and distributed Five Wishes (Appendix A) does substantially meet the requirements of 35 states. (Aging with Dignity's Web site, http://www.aging withdignity.org, has a complete list of these states.)

ADVANCE DIRECTIVES—DISTRIBUTE WIDELY, REVIEW FREQUENTLY

Once completed, an advance directive should not be hidden away in a file drawer or tucked into a safe deposit box. Copies should be made and distributed to the physician, the health care proxy, family members, and others as appropriate. When hospitalized, admitted to a nursing home, or joining an HMO, a patient should make sure the directive is placed in the patient medical chart so that health care workers are advised of the patient's wishes.

Filling out the forms and signing the document is not the end of the process, however. A senior's goals may change over time, along with a revised diagnosis and prognosis. For the physician, end-of-life issues should be considered "an ongoing process, an opportunity to engage with patients and families" (Rabow et al., 2004). The same goes for seniors themselves and their proxies, who should periodically review the advance directive and make changes as necessary. You may need to initiate these reviews for clients who do not recognize the need or may be reluctant to revisit the issues. All that is required to change the document is to complete a new form, making sure all copies of the old directive are destroyed. Of course, the new directive must also meet state legal requirements, such as witnessing the senior's signature. Provide copies of the revised directive to relevant individuals, informing them of the change.

HEALTH CARE PROVIDERS TO HONOR PATIENT WISHES

Health care providers are generally bound to respect a patient's advance directive, although an individual physician may decline to honor a document for reasons of conscience. In that case, however, the physician is required to refer the patient to another doctor. If there is a dispute, either the proxy or the physician can consult with the hospital or nursing home's ethics committee (McGee et al., 2001).

In 1992, following the U.S. Supreme Court's Cruzan decision, the Joint Commission on the Accreditation of Health Care Organizations (JCAHO) began requiring certified institutions to establish a mechanism for dealing with ethical issues. To comply with the JCAHO mandate, more than 90 percent of U.S. hospitals established ethics committees to consult on cases, formulate policy, and educate staff (McGee et al., 2001).

These committees, made up of clinicians, social workers, and private citizens, often provide an administrative mechanism to review ethical issues. For example, a 79-year-old patient with end-stage Parkinson's disease was recently admitted to a New York hospital with respiratory failure (from pneumonia). He completed an advance directive, clearly rejecting ventilation, but his family had a difficult time with the physician, whose religious beliefs were in conflict with the patient's wishes. In this instance, the physician referred the case to the hospital's ethics committee. After assessing the patient's advance directive, the committee overruled the physician, and the ventilator was removed.

Advance directives are grounded in Supreme Court decisions and state laws. The Cruzan decision, for example, upheld the longstanding common law concept of patient autonomy. Writing for the majority, Chief Justice Rehnquist referred to the words of a former justice, who wrote, "Every human being of adult years and sound mind has a right to determine what shall be done to his body." Chief Justice Rehnquist added, "The logical corollary of the doctrine of informed consent is that the patient generally possesses the right not to consent, that is, to refuse treatment" (*Cruzan v. Director, Missouri Dept. of Health,* 1990).

Further, the court also based its Cruzan decision on the 14th Amendment to the U.S. Constitution, which provides that no state "shall deprive any person of life, liberty or property without due process of law." The majority opinion held that citizens do have "a constitutionally protected liberty interest in refusing treatment."

State laws in all 50 states and the District of Columbia authorize and regulate the procedures for advance directives, health care directives, and living wills. These laws also limit a health care worker's liability in following a patient's wishes to reject treatment. In other words, the physician, operating in good faith, can withdraw a feeding tube on the order of an advance directive or living will and not be held liable.

While state laws provide the legal basis for advance directives, health care directives, and living wills, they are by no means consistent, uniform, or user friendly. As already mentioned, there is no advance directive form available to meet 50 frequently disparate standards. Aging with Dignity made an attempt in drafting Five Wishes to produce an advance directive that could be used in every state. However, as mentioned earlier, Five Wishes is applicable in only 35 of the 50 states.

Charles P. Sabatino, of the American Bar Association's Commission on Law and Aging, argued in a recent journal article (Sabatino, 2003) that there are problems with state advance directive laws. You should be aware that such problems may exist in your state and counsel your clients about them. Two such problems that could affect seniors are:

- *Portability.* What happens if a senior completes an advance directive in Wisconsin and then becomes ill in Vermont? Will his or her state-specific advance directive be honored in a state that has its own unique requirements? Most states have reciprocity provisions, but interpretations may vary. Nonetheless, there are 12 states with no such language. On several occasions, federal legislation was introduced, but never passed, to pre-empt state laws to guarantee portability.

- *Multiple Advance Directive Laws.* In the 1970s and 1980s, most states passed their living will statutes; in the 1980s and 1990s, they authorized the durable power of attorney for health care laws. In passing two separate statutes, some states failed to harmonize the different laws and instead left conflicting provisions.

There have also been attempts at the state level to harmonize the sometimes conflicting state laws. In 1993, the Uniform Laws Commission, a national commission drafting model legislation for adoption by the states, approved what is called the Uniform Health-Care Decision Act of 1993 (Last Acts, 2002). This model proposed a single, comprehensive advance directive law with no mandatory state-specific forms or language, authorizing default surrogates (next of kin) when there is no advance directive, and including "close friend" in the list of potential surrogates. However, not every state adopted these reforms. Consequently, the disparities remain.

Beyond the Documents

As a CSA, you are encouraged to participate, along with your clients and families, in advance planning beyond the completion of legal and medical documents. Personal information and inventories of possessions and property are all valuable to you when giving professional advice, as they are valuable to family members who come to you during grieving. Such information can ease the burden of wondering where to locate needed data in a timely manner. In addition to honest, open, and frequent discussions among family members regarding last wishes, professionals experienced in such planning recommend the following:

- List all family members (complete with full names and addresses).
- List prior marriages (with children from each marriage).
- List bank accounts and insurance policies (complete with numbers).
- List all assets, business interests, and credit cards (with numbers).
- Identify the location of any safe deposit boxes and keys.
- List any information that is pertinent to weekly, monthly, or fiscal actions.

This information will provide the groundwork for any family or professionals who deal with probate issues and the estate settlement.

Making a written record of wishes for distribution of possessions will ease decisions and potential conflicts among family members. Some may even wish to share their most sincere remembrances by writing a personal message in the form of a letter to loved ones and friends left behind. Arlene Lowney, RN, MBA, is president of Innovative Health Care Solutions. She encourages you to do your own personal planning as preparation for advising seniors. Taking such a leadership role will enhance your ability to "speak candidly and more comfortably with clients and their families about the importance of advance...planning" (Lowney, 2000).

For information about grief and loss see chapter 4, Mental Health, Grief, and Loss in Later Life.

See chapter 14 for information on funeral planning.

End-of-Life Planning: Summary

Seniors are living longer and, for the most part, healthier lives because of medical technology. But the same technologies that prolong life blur the line between life and death. Increasingly, medical treatments add years to life without providing a cure, sometimes leaving us to ask, "Are some conditions worse than death?" When is the quality of life more important than longevity?

Advance directives can give seniors autonomy and independence in deciding their own fates. While they are legal documents, they are also acts of trust and a form of communication that improves decision making. They can bring medical care in line with the patient's wishes, reducing both over- and under-treatment, and diminish a patient's fears about burdening loved ones. Advance directives can also give voice to patients' wishes about comfort and pain, how they wish to be cared for, and what they want loved ones to know.

End-of-life issues are deeply personal and difficult to discuss. As a CSA you can serve as a catalyst to initiate advance planning. You should be knowledgeable about your state's requirements, and be able to guide your clients to the appropriate forms. You cannot substitute your own judgment and values about medical treatments. You can only encourage the discussions that must take place between a senior and his or her physician and family members. You can encourage the appointment of a health care proxy and the thoughtful execution of a living will, but only the senior can decide what is best for himself or herself. Once the appropriate forms are completed, you can help make sure they are distributed to the right parties and ask, from time to time, if any revisions are needed.

Appendix A: Five Wishes

There are many things in life that are out of our hands. This Five Wishes booklet gives you a way to control something very important - how you are treated if you get seriously ill. It is an easy-to-complete form that lets you say exactly what you want. Once it is filled out and properly signed it is valid under the laws of most states.

WHAT IS FIVE WISHES?

Five Wishes is the first living will that talks about your personal, emotional and spiritual needs as well as your medical wishes. It lets you choose the person you want to make health care decisions for you if you are not able to make them for yourself. Five Wishes lets you say exactly how you wish to be treated if you get seriously ill. It was written with the help of The American Bar Association's Commission on the Legal Problems of the Elderly and the nation's leading experts in end-of-life care. It's also easy to use. All you have to do is check a box, circle a direction or write a few sentences.

HOW FIVE WISHES CAN HELP YOU AND YOUR FAMILY

- It lets you talk with your family, friends and doctor about how you want to be treated if you become seriously ill.
- Your family members will not have to guess what you want. It protects them if you become seriously ill, because they won't have to make hard choices without knowing your wishes.
- You can know what your mom, dad, spouse or friend wants through a Five Wishes living will. You can be there for them when they need you most. You will understand what they really want.

HOW FIVE WISHES BEGAN

For 12 years, a man named Jim Towey worked closely with Mother Teresa and, for one year, he lived in a hospice she ran in Washington, D.C. Inspired by this first-hand experience, Mr. Towey sought a way for patients and their families to plan ahead and to cope with serious illness. The result is Five Wishes and the response to it has been overwhelming. It has been featured on CNN and NBC's Today Show and in the pages of Time and Money magazines. Newspapers have called Five Wishes the first "living will with a heart."

WHO SHOULD USE FIVE WISHES?

Five Wishes is for anyone 18 or older, including lawyers, doctors, hospitals, married or single persons, parents, adult children and hospices, churches, synagogues and friends. Over one million American employers and retiree groups of all ages have already used it.

Five Wishes States

If you live in the District of Columbia or one of the 35 states listed below, you can use the Five Wishes and have the peace of mind to know that it substantially meets your state's requirements under the law:

Arizona	Hawaii	Minnesota	North Dakota
Arkansas	Idaho	Mississippi	Pennsylvania
California	Illinois	Missouri	Rhode Island
Colorado	Iowa	Montana	South Dakota
Connecticut	Louisiana	Nebraska	Tennessee
Delaware	Maine	New Jersey	Virginia
District of Columbia	Maryland	New Mexico	Washington
Florida	Massachusetts	New York	West Virginia
Georgia	Michigan	North Carolina	Wyoming

If your state is not one other 35 states listed here, Five Wishes does not meet the technical requirements in the statutes of your state. So some doctors in your state may be reluctant to honor Five Wishes. However, many people from states not on this list do complete Five Wishes along with their state's legal form. They find that Five Wishes helps them express all that they want and provides a helpful guide to family members, friends, care givers and doctors. Most doctors and health care professionals know they need to listen to your wishes no matter how you express them.

HOW DO I CHANGE TO FIVE WISHES?

You may already have a living will or a durable power of attorney for health care. If you want to use Five Wishes instead, all you need to do is fill out and sign a new Five Wishes as directed. As soon as you sign it, it takes away any advance directive you had before. To make sure the right form is used, please do the following:

- Destroy all copies of your old living will or durable power of attorney for health care. Or you can write "revoked" in large letters across the copy you have. Tell your lawyer if he or she helped prepare those old forms for you.

AND

- Tell your Health Care Agent, family members and doctor that you have filled out the new Five Wishes. Make sure they know about your new wishes.

WISH 1

The Person I Want To Make Health Care Decisions For Me When I Can't Make Them For Myself.

If I am no longer able to make my own health care decisions, this form names the person I choose to make these choices for me. This person will be my Health Care Agent (or other term that may be used in my state, such as proxy, representative or surrogate). This person will make my health care choices if both of these things happen:

- *My attending or treating doctor finds I am no longer able to make health care choices and*
- *Another health care professional agrees that this is true.*

If my state has a different way of finding that I am not able to make health care choices, then my state's way should be followed.

The Person I Choose as My Health Care Agent Is:

_____   _____
First Choice Name   Phone

_____   _____
Address   City/State/Zip

If this person is not able or willing to make these choices for me, OR is divorced or legally separated from me, OR this person has died, then these people are my next choices:

_____   _____
Second Choice Name   Third Choice Name

_____   _____
Address   Address

_____   _____
City/State/Zip   City/State/Zip

_____   _____
Phone   Phone

Picking the Right Person to Be Your Health Care Agent

*Choose someone who knows you very well, cares about you and who can make difficult decisions. Family members or a spouse may not be the best choice because they are too emotionally involved. Sometimes they are the best choice. You know best. Choose someone who is able to stand up for you so that your wishes are followed. Also, choose someone who is likely to be nearby so that he or she can help when needed. Whether you choose a spouse, family member or friend as your Health Care Agent, make sure you talk about these wishes and be sure that this person agrees to respect and follow your wishes. Your Health Care Agent should be **at least 18 years or older** (in Colorado, 21 years or older) and should **not** be:*

- *Your health care provider, including the owner or operator of a health or residential or community care facility serving you.*

- *An employee of your health care provider.*

- *Serving as an agent or proxy for 10 or more people unless he or she is your spouse or close relative.*

I understand that my Health Care Agent can make health care decisions for me, I want my Agent to be able to do the following: **(Please cross out anything you don't want your Agent to do that is listed below.)**

- Make choices for me about my medical care or services, like test, medicine or surgery. This care or service could be to find out what my health problem is or how to treat it. It can also include care to keep me alive. If the treatment or care has already started, my Health Care Agent can keep it going or have it stopped.

- Interpret any instructions I have given in this form or given in other discussions, according to my Health Care Agent's understanding of my wishes and values.

- Arrange for admission to a hospital, hospice or nursing home for me. My Health Care Agent can hire any kind of health care worker I may need to help me or take care of me. My Agent may also fire a health care worker, if needed.

- Make the decision to request, take away or not give medical treatments, including artificially provided food and water and any other treatments to keep me alive.

- See and approve release of my medical records and personal files. If I need to sign my name to get any of these files, my Health Care Agent can sign it for me.

- Move me to another state to get the care I need or to carry out my wishes.

- Authorize or refuse to authorize any medication or procedure needed to help with pain.

- Take any legal action needed to carry out my wishes.

- Donate useable organs or tissues of mine as allowed by law.

- Apply for Medicare, Medicaid or other programs or insurance benefits for me. My Health Care Agent can see my personal files, like bank records, to find out what is needed to fill out these forms.

- Listed below are any changes, additions or limitations on my Health Care Agent's powers.

_____

_____

_____

_____

_____

_____

_____

_____

_____

If I Change My Mind About Having A Health Care Agent, I Will

- Destroy all copies of this part of the Five Wishes form.

OR

- Tell someone, such as my doctor or family, that I want to cancel or change my Health Care Agent.

OR

- Write the word "Revoked" in large letters across the name of each agent whose authority I want to cancel. Sign my name on that page.

WISH 2

My Wish for the Kind Of Medical Treatment I Want Or Don't Want

I believe that my life is precious and I deserve to be treated with dignity. When the time comes that I am very sick and am not able to speak for myself, I want the following wishes, and any other directions I have given to my Health Care Agent, to be respected and followed.

What You Should Keep in Mind as My Caregiver

- I do not want to be in pain. I want my doctor to give me enough medicine to relieve my pain, even if that means that I will be drowsy or sleep more than I would otherwise.
- I do not want anything done or omitted by my doctors or nurses with the intention of taking my life.
- I want to be offered food and fluids by mouth and kept clean and warm.

What "Life-Support Treatment" Means to Me

Life-support treatment means any medical procedure, device or medication to keep me alive. Life-support treatment includes: medical devices put in me to help me breathe; food and water supplied by medical device (tube feeding); cardiopulmonary resuscitation (CPR); major surgery; blood transfusions; dialysis; antibiotics; and anything else meant to keep me alive. If I wish to limit the meaning of life-support treatment because of my religious or personal beliefs, I write this limitation in the space below. I do this to make very clear what I want and under what conditions.

_____

_____

_____

_____

_____

_____

_____

_____

In Case of an Emergency

*If you have a medical emergency and ambulance personnel arrive, they may look to see if you have a **Do Not Resuscitate** form or bracelet. Many states require a person to have a **Do Not Resuscitate** form filled out and signed by a doctor. This form lets ambulance personnel know that you don't want them to use life-support treatment when you are dying. Please check with your doctor to see if you need to have a **Do Not Resuscitate** form filled out.*

Here is the kind of medical treatment that I want or don't want in the four situations listed below. I want my Health Care Agent, my family, my doctors and other health care providers, my friends and all others to know these directions.

Close to Death:

If my doctor and another health care professional both decide that I am likely to die within a short period of time and life-support treatment would only delay the moment of my death (Choose one of the following):

- I want to have life-support treatment.
- I do not want life-support treatment. If it has been started, I want it stopped.
- I want to have life-support treatment if my doctor believes it could help. But I want my doctor to stop giving my life-support treatment if it is not helping my health condition or symptoms.

In A Coma and Not Expected to Wake Up or Recover:

If my doctor and another health care professional both decide that I am in a coma from which I am not expected to wake up or recover and I have brain damage and life-support treatment would only delay the moment of my death (Choose one of the following):

- I want to have life-support treatment.
- I do not want life-support treatment. If it has been started, I want it stopped.
- I want to have life-support treatment if my doctor believes it could help, but I want my doctor to stop giving me life-support treatment if it is not helping my health condition or symptoms.

Permanent and Severe Brain Damage and Not Expected to Recover:

If my doctor and another health care professional both decide that I have permanent and severe brain damage, (for example, I can open my eyes, but I can not speak or understand) and I am not expected to get better and life support treatment would only delay the moment of my death (Choose one of the following):

- I want to have life-support treatment.
- I do not want life-support treatment. If it has been started, I want it stopped.
- I want to have life-support treatment if my doctor believes it could help. But I want my doctor to stop giving me life-support treatment if it is not helping my health condition or symptoms.

In Another Condition under Which I Do Not Wish to Be Kept Alive:

If there is another condition under which I do not wish to have life-support treatment, I describe it below. In this condition, I believe that the costs and burdens of life-support treatment are too much and not worth the benefits to me. Therefore, in this condition, I do not want life-support treatment. (For example, you may write "end-stage condition." That means that your health has gotten worse. You are not able to take care of yourself in any way, mentally or physically. Life-support treatment will not help you recover. Please leave the space blank if you have no other condition to describe.)

_____

_____

_____

_____

The next three wishes deal with my personal, spiritual and emotional wishes. They are important to me. I want to be treated with dignity near the end of my life, so I would like people to do the things written in Wishes 3, 4 and 5 when they can be done. I understand that my family, my doctors and other healthcare providers, my friends and others may not be able to do these things or are not required by law to do these things. I do not expect the following wishes to place new or added legal duties on my doctors or other health care providers. I also do not expect these wishes to excuse my doctor or other health care providers from giving me the proper care asked for by law.

WISH 3

My Wish for How Comfortable I Want To Be.

(Please cross out anything that you don't agree with.)

- I do not want to be in pain. I want my doctor to give me enough medicine to relieve my pain, even if that means I will be drowsy and sleep more than I would otherwise.
- I wish to have my favorite music played when possible until the time of my death.
- I wish to have religious readings and well-loved poems read aloud when I am near death.
- If I show signs of depression, nausea, shortness of breath or hallucinations, I want my caregivers to do whatever they can to help me.

- I wish to have a cool moist cloth put on my head if I have a fever.
- I want my lips and mouth kept moist to stop dryness.
- I wish to be massaged with warm oils as often as I can be.
- I wish to have personal care like shaving, nail clipping, hair brushing and teeth brushing, as long as they do not cause me pain or discomfort.
- I wish to have warm baths often. I wish to be kept fresh and clean at all times.

WISH 4

My Wish for How I Want People to Treat Me.

(Please cross out anything that you don't agree with.)

- I wish to have people with me when possible. I want someone to be with me when it seems that death may come at any time.
- I wish to have my hand held and to be talked to when possible, even if I don't seem to respond to the voice or touch of others.
- I wish to have others by my side praying for me when possible.
- I wish to have the members of my church or synagogue told that I am sick and asked to pray for me and visit me.
- I wish to be cared for with kindness and cheerfulness and not sadness.
- I wish to have pictures of my loved ones in my room, near my bed.
- If I am not able to control my bowel or bladder functions, I wish for my clothes and bed linens to be kept clean and for them to be changed as soon as they can be if they have been soiled.
- I want to die in my home, if that can be done.

WISH 5

My Wish for What I Want My Loved Ones to Know.

(Please cross out anything that you don't agree with.)

- I wish to have my family and friends know that I love them.
- I wish to be forgiven for the times I have hurt my family, friends and others.
- I wish to have my family, friends and others know that I forgive them for when they may have hurt me in my life.
- I wish for my family and friends to know that I do not fear death itself. I think it is not the end, but a new beginning for me.
- I wish for all my family members to make peace with each other before my death, if they can.
- I wish for my family and friends to think about what I was like before I became seriously ill. I want them to remember me in this way after my death.

- I wish for my family and friends to look at my dying as a time of personal growth for everyone, including me. This will help me live a meaningful life in my final days.
- I wish for my family and friends to get counseling if they have trouble with my death. I want memories of my life to give them joy not sorrow.
- After my death, I would like my body to be (circle one): buried or cremated.
- My body or remains should be put in the following location:

  _____

- The following person knows my funeral wishes:_____
- If anyone asks how I want to be remembered, please say the following about me:

  _____

  _____

  _____

  _____

- If there is to be a memorial service for me, I wish for this service to include the following (list music, songs, readings or other specific requests that you have):

  _____

  _____

  _____

  _____

  _____

(Please use the space below for any other wishes. For example, you may want to donate any or all parts of your body when you die. Please attach a separate sheet of paper if you need more space.)

_____

_____

_____

_____

_____

SIGNING THE FIVE WISHES FORM

Please make sure you sign your Five Wishes form in the presence of the two witnesses.

    I,_____, ask that my family, my doctors and other health care providers, my friends and all others, follow my wishes as communicated by my Health Care Agent (if I have one and he or she is available), or as otherwise expressed in this form. This form becomes valid when I am unable to make decisions or speak for myself. If any part of this form cannot be legally followed, I ask that all other parts of this form be followed. I also revoke any health care advance directives I have made before.

393

Signature_____ Social Security #: _____
Address: _____
Phone: _____ Date: _____

WITNESS STATEMENT ___ (2 WITNESSES NEEDED)

I, the witness, declare that the person who signed or acknowledged this form (hereafter "person") is personally known to me, that he/she signed or acknowledged this [Health Care Agent and/or Living Will form(s)] in my presence, and that he/she appears to be of sound mind and under no duress, fraud or undue influence.

I also declare that I am over 18 years of age and am **not**:

- The individual appointed as (agent/proxy/surrogate/patient advocate/representative) by this document or his/her successor,
- Financially responsible for the person's health care,
- An employee of a life or health insurance provider for the person,
- The person's health care provider, including, owner or operator of a health, long-term care or other residential or community care facility serving the person,
- An employee of the person's health care provider,
- Related to the person by blood, marriage or adoption and,
- To the best of my knowledge, a creditor of the person or entitled to any part of his/her estate under a will or codicil, by operation of law.

(Some states may have fewer rules about who may be a witness. Unless you know your state's rules, please follow the above.)

_____ _____
Signature of Witness #1   Signature of Witness #2

_____ _____
Printed Name of Witness   Printed Name of Witness

_____ _____
Address   Address

_____ _____
Phone   Phone

NOTARIZATION—ONLY REQUIRED FOR RESIDENTS OF MISSOURI, NORTH CAROLINA, TENNESSEE AND WEST VIRGINIA

- If you live in Missouri, only your signature should be notarized.
- If you live in North Carolina, Tennessee or West Virginia, you should have your signature and the signatures of your witnesses, notarized.

STATE OF _____ COUNTY OF _____

On this _____ day of _____, 20_____, the

said_____, and _____,

known to me (or satisfactorily proven) to be the person named in the foregoing instrument and witnesses, respectively, personally appeared before me, a Notary Public, within and for the State and County aforesaid, and acknowledged that they freely and voluntarily executed the same for the purposes stated therein.

My Commission Expires: _____

Notary Public

WHAT TO DO AFTER YOU COMPLETE FIVE WISHES

- Make sure you sign and witness the form just the way it says in the directions. Then your Five Wishes will be legal and valid.

- Talk about your wishes with your health care agent, family members and others who care about you. Give them copies of your completed Five Wishes.

- Keep the original copy you signed in a special place in your home. Do NOT put it in a safe deposit box. Keep it nearby so that someone can find it when you need it.

- Fill out the wallet card below. Carry it with you. That way people will know where you keep your Five Wishes.

- Talk to your doctor during your next office visit. Give your doctor a copy of your Five Wishes. Make sure it is put in your medical record. Be sure your doctor understands your wishes and is willing to follow them. Ask him or her to tell other doctors who treat you to honor them.

- If you are admitted to a hospital or nursing home, take a copy of your Five Wishes with you. Ask that it be put in your medical record.

- I have given the following people copies of my completed Five Wishes:

_____

_____

_____

_____

_____

_____

_____

_____

> **Residents of Institutions in CALIFORNIA, CONNECTICUT, DELAWARE, GEORGIA, NEW YORK and NORTH DAKOTA Must Follow Special Witnessing Rules.**
>
> *If you live in certain institutions (a nursing home, other licensed long term care facility, a home for the mentally retarded or developmentally disabled or a mental health institution) in one of the states listed above, you may have to follow special "witnessing requirements" for your Five Wishes to be valid. For further information, please contact a social worker or patient advocate at your institution.*

Five Wishes is meant to help you plan for the future. It is not meant to give you legal advice. It does not try to answer all questions about anything that could come up. Every person is different, and every situation is different. Laws change from time to time. If you have a specific question or problem, talk to a medical or legal professional for advice.

To Order

You can order copies of Five Wishes or the Five Wishes video, a 25-minute educational presentation that explains how to fill out Five Wishes and answers The Five Wishes project frequently asked questions. Simply call, toll-free, 1-888-5WISHES (1-888-594-7437), P.O. Box 1661, Tallahassee, Florida 32302-1661, http://www.agingwithdignity.org. Five Wishes is a trademark of Aging with Dignity.

References

Aging with Dignity. (2001). *Five Wishes.* Retrieved February 10, 2004, from http://wwwagingwithdignity.org

ABA (American Bar Association). Commission on Law and Aging. (2004). *Consumer's tool kit for health care advance planning.* Retrieved February 21, 2004, from http://www.abanet.org/aging/toolkit/home.html

AMA (American Medical Association). (2004). AMA Policy Finder. Retrieved March 17, 2004, from http://www.ama-assn.org

Bern-Klug, M. (2004). The ambiguous dying syndrome. *Health and Social Work, 29*(1) 55–66.

CDC (Centers for Disease Control). (2003). *Vital statistics rates in the United States.* Retrieved February 21, 2004, from http://www.cdc.gov/nchs/about/major/dvs/mortdata.htm

Census Bureau. (n.d.). Available from http://www.census.gov

Colby, W. H. (2002). *Long goodbye: The deaths of Nancy Cruzan.* Carlsbad, CA: Hay House, Inc.

Cruzan v. Director, Missouri Dept. of Health, 497 U.S. 261 (1990).

Death With Dignity Act of 2004, Oregon Revised Statutes, Chapter 127, 127.800-127.995. Retrieved February 15, 2004, from http://www.leg.state.or.us/ors/127.html

Dunn, H. (2001). *Hard choices for loving people*. Herndon, VA: A&A Publishers.

Fagerlin, A., Ditto, P. H., Hawkins, N. A., Schneider, C. E., & Smucker, W. D. (2002). The use of advance directives in end-of-life decision making. *American Behavioral Scientist, 46*(2), 268–283.

Frontline. (1992). *The death of Nancy Cruzan*. Public Broadcasting System, Retrieved February 16, 2004, from http://www.pbs.org/wgbh/pages/frontline/programs/transcripts/1014.html

GAO (General Accounting Office). (1995). *Patient self-determination act: Providers offer information on advance directives but effectiveness uncertain*. Washington, DC: General Accounting Office, GAO/HEHS-95-135.

Gifis, S. (Ed.). (1996). *Law dictionary* (4th ed.). New York: Barron's Educational Series, Inc.

Gunderson Lutheran. (2004). *Respecting Choices: An advance care planning program different than the rest*. Retrieved March 18, 2004, from http://www.gundluth.org/eolprograms

IOM (Institute of Medicine). (1997) *Approaching death: Improving care at the end of life*. Washington DC: Institute of Medicine.

King, N. M. P. (1996). *Making sense of advance directives* (rev. ed.). Washington, DC: Georgetown University Press.

Kugiya, H. (2003, April 13). Series day 1, a life or death issue: Florida woman's fate contested. Available at http://www.newsday.com

Last Acts. (2002). *Means to a better end: A report on dying in America today*. Retrieved February 25, 2004, from http://www.lastacts.org

Leighton, P. (1997, Nov. 7). The place of palliative medicine, *All things considered*. National Public Radio.

Linder, D. O. (1995). The other right-to-life debate: When does Fourteenth Amendment "life" end? *Arizona Law Review, 37*, 1183-1207.

Lowney, A. (2000). Fostering choices—Communicating future health care decisions. *Journal of Society of Certified Senior Advisors*. VI.

Lynn, J., & Harrold, J. (1999). *Handbook for mortals: Guidance for people facing serious illness*. Oxford: Oxford University Press, http:\\www.abcd-caring.org

Marck, J. T. (2004). *Richard Milhous Nixon*. Retrieved April 8, 2004, from http://www.aboutfamouspeople.com/article 1128.html

Maryland Code Annotated. Health-Gen. §§5-601(e), 5-605(c)(2), (3) (1998).

McFadden, R. D. (1994, May 20). Death of a first lady; Jacqueline Kennedy Onassis dies of cancer at 64. *New York Times*.

McGee, G., Caplan, A.L., Spanogle, J. P., & Asch, D. A. (2001). A national study of ethics committee. *The American Journal of Bioethics 1*(4), 60–64.

Morgan, R. C. & Sabatino, C. (2001, July/August). Advance planning and drafting for health care decisions. *Probate and Property 15*(35), 35–38.

Patient Self Determination Act. (1990). 42 U.S.C. 1395cc(f) (Medicare) and 1396a(w) (Medicaid).

Rabow, M. W., Hauser, J. M., & Adams, J. (2004). Supporting family caregivers at the end of life: They don't know what they don't know. *Journal of the American Medical Association, 291*(4), 483–491.

Rosnick, C. B., & Reynolds, S. L. (2003). Thinking ahead: Factors associated with executing advance directives. *Journal of Aging & Health, 15*(2), 409–429.

Sabatino, C. P. (n.d.). *10 Legal myths about advance medical directives.* American Bar Association: Commission on Law and Aging, Retrieved March 18, 2004 from http://www.abanet.org/aging/html.

Sabatino, C. P. (1999). The legal and functional status of the medical proxy: Suggestions for statutory reform. *Journal of Law, Medicine, & Ethics, 27*, 52–68.

Sabatino, C. P. (2003). De-Balkanizing state advance directive law. *Public Policy and Aging Report, 13*(1), 1–11.

Vacco v. Quill, 521 U.S. 793 (1997).

Resources

Suggested Reading

Caring Conversation Workbook is a workbook to help shift the focus of end-of-life planning to include discussions with family and friends and to help families advocate on a patient's behalf. An advance directive form is also included. These publications are available from the Center for Practical Bioethics, http://www.practicalbioethics.org, Town Pavilion, 1100 Walnut St., Suite 2900, Kansas City, MO 64106-2197, 816-221-1100.

Consumer's Tool Kit for Health Care Advance Planning is a helpful guide published by the American Bar Association's Commission on Law and Aging that contains the information needed and questions to ask about completing an advance directive. It can be downloaded at no cost from http://www.abanet.org/aging/toolkit/tool2-lock.pdf

Five Wishes Advance Directive can be ordered from Aging with Dignity, http://www.agingwithdignity.org, P.O. Box 11180, Tallahassee, FL 32302-3180, (toll-free) 888-594-7437.

Handbook for Mortals: Guidance for People Facing Serious Illness by Joanne Lynn, MD, and Joan Harrold, MD (1999, New York: Oxford University Press). This book addresses various end-of-life issues. It provides information on different chronic illnesses, how to plan ahead, how to live with illness, forgoing medical treatments, and other topics. Information about the book and about palliative care are available from Americans for Better Care of the Dying, http://www.abcd-caring.org, 4200 Wisconsin Avenue, NW, Washington, DC 20016, 202-530-9864.

Hard Choices for Loving People: CPR, Artificial Feeding, Comfort Measures Only and the Elderly Patient by Hank Dunn. A readable and helpful 48-page guide to end-of-life decision-making. A&A Publishers, Inc. P.O. Box 1098, Herndon, VA 20172. Available on the Web at http://www.hardchoices.com

Services

Caring Connections, http://www.caringinfo.org, 800-658-8898. Caring Connections is a national program to improve care at the end of life offered by the National Hospice and Palliative Care Organization. Caring Connections provides information and resources related to caregiving and end-of-life issues, as well as a link to and the ability to print state-specific forms for advance directives.

End-of-Life Choices, http://www.endoflifechoices.org, P.O. Box 101810, Denver, CO 80250-1810, 800-247-7421, fax 303-639-1224. End-of-Life Choices is a nonprofit organization that advocates for choice, dignity, and control at the end of life through written materials, speakers, and workshops.

Respecting Choices: An Advance Care Planning Program Different Than the Rest, http://www.gundluth.org/eolprograms. Respecting Choices is a grass-roots campaign to complete advance directives. The campaign's name is now being used in a number of other communities.

Part 4

FINANCIAL LITERACY

If one advances confidently in the direction of his dreams, and endeavors to live the life which he has imagined, he will meet with success unexpected in common hours.

Henry David Thoreau

Part 4 deals with financial literacy: the knowledge that seniors need about estate planning, financial choices and challenges, long-term care insurance, and funeral planning.

Financial literacy in older age begins with a vision of the life that seniors wish to live. For many of you, your clients will enlist you to help them better articulate their vision, to understand financial issues, and to make informed decisions about such issues as purchasing long-term care insurance or planning a funeral. This may involve teaching your clients new concepts and language.

With the knowledge and information provided in this section, you will be better prepared to assist your senior clients with financial issues.

Chapter 15

Estate Planning

Karl and Kathy Webster are retired schoolteachers. They have been investing in real estate since they were married. In addition to their pensions, their rental income has helped them enjoy a comfortable lifestyle. Much to their amazement, Karl and Kathy have acquired a net worth of almost $3.5 million. Karl says, "At this point in my life I want to spend more time with my family, sailing my boat, and traveling with my wife. I would like to sell some or all of our properties." However, the Websters' accountant has told them that the sale of their properties would result in high income taxes because of large capital gains. In addition, their financial advisor has told them that this could result in a tax problem when they die. Karl says, "We want to make sure that our kids and grandchildren inherit as much of our net worth as possible."

. . .

Don and Barbara Wright have not been able to acquire many assets besides their home. They have been married for more than 20 years. They both have two adult children from previous marriages. Don's son, Henry, has been helping them financially, which they greatly appreciate. Barbara's daughter, Verla, visits regularly, helping Don and Barbara with the housekeeping and enlisting her husband when the house needs repair.

When Don and Barbara bought their home, they were told to title it in joint tenancy so the survivor would get it when the first of them died. Barbara says, "What we want, however, is that after our deaths, all our children share in the value of our home. We would also like to give a little more of our estate to Henry and Verla in appreciation of the extra help they have given us."

Death and taxes and childbirth!
There's never any convenient time for any of them.

Margaret Mitchell, *Gone with the Wind*

Introduction

At first glance, the Websters and the Wrights seem to have very different life situations. However, despite the difference in the amount of assets they own, both couples need estate plans. They need to plan both for the possibility they might become incapacitated and for the distribution of their property after they die.

Your clients don't need to own a large amount of property to need estate planning. Because estate plans cover lifetime health and financial needs and the legacies they wish to leave, all adults should have one.

Many people are surprised to learn that lifetime planning is an important part of estate planning. When clients plan for their lifetime needs, the first step should be to address their current health and financial status—and how these might change over the course of their lives. For example, estate plans enable seniors to decide in advance how they want to be cared for and how they want their assets managed if they become incapacitated. And after the clients' deaths, estate plans provide instructions for the orderly distribution of their assets.

Another common misconception is that once an estate plan is in place, the planning process is over. However, almost any plan that deals with fundamental lifetime needs requires periodic review and updating, as discussed in chapter 16, Financial Choices and Challenges for Seniors.

In this chapter, you will gain a basic understanding of fundamental estate planning terms and concepts, as well as common strategies and techniques that apply to the majority of seniors:

- Everyone has an estate plan, whether by choice or default.
- The number of nontraditional families is increasing, and traditional estate planning may affect them differently than traditional, nuclear families.
- A comprehensive estate plan includes key components: non-probate titled property, a will, and several types of trusts and designated beneficiaries. In addition, an estate planning attorney plays an important role.
- Seniors must plan for and manage the possibility of incapacity, a situation that may call for several types of powers of attorney, agent selection, and the use of guardians and conservators.
- Wills and the probate process involve a complicated mix of procedures and documents. You'll need to know what is included or not in the probate process; the importance of personal assets; the roles of the pour-over will and revocable and irrevocable trusts; and steps in selecting a personal representative or executor.
- There are several strategies for managing assets during a senior's lifetime by using trusts, and your clients should understand how trusts can operate as a transfer and management tool or as a tax-saving mechanism for estates. Family limited partnerships and other techniques efficiently transfer ownership of non-liquid assets, such as family businesses.
- Estate taxation and the components of the estate tax system pose another complex challenge. You'll need to understand applicable exclusion

amounts, property that is included in a taxable estate, and use of the unlimited marital deduction and various trusts to manage and reduce estate taxes.

- Seniors can benefit from lifetime gifting, so you'll learn about the types of gifting, gift tax exclusions, the role of charitable contributions in reducing estate taxes, and various ways to make charitable contributions, including foundations, charitable gift annuities, charitable remainder trusts, family limited partnerships, and pooled income trusts.

This information will give you the tools to recognize the issues that have impacts on your senior clients' goals for their estates.

SCSA does not advocate any particular estate planning strategy. If you are not a professional estate planner, you should identify qualified estate attorneys and/or other professionals who can work with you to provide a comprehensive approach to your clients' estate planning needs. You also might consider working with other types of attorneys such as elder law attorneys; financial planners; life, health, and long-term care insurance professionals; home health care and Medicaid/Medicare specialists; and ministers or clergy.

Estate Planning: The Basics

An *estate* is defined as everything a person owns or controls at the time of incapacity or death—money, property, and personal and business assets. An estate includes more than *real property* (the land and the things permanently attached to the land). It also includes a client's interest in jointly owned property, real estate, IRA and investment accounts, promissory notes and money owed to them by others, collectibles, insurance, intellectual property, and personal belongings. In addition, it includes debts such as mortgages, credit card balances, and estate and income taxes. It is easy to see that anyone who owns any sort of property has an estate.

THE IMPORTANCE OF PERSONAL ASSETS

Personal assets are items with no legal documentation to identify who officially owns them. They are also referred to as nontitled property. For example, watches, jewelry, china, silver, books, stamp collections, photo albums, personal mementos, and pets are all personal assets. According to Marlene S. Stum (2004), estate planning attorneys suggest that nontitled personal property, not money or real estate, creates the greatest challenges for families. Planning for the transfer and distribution of such property is just as important—and often more challenging—than making decisions about titled property. Inheritance can symbolize intergenerational transfers of love, trust, power, family rituals and traditions, and family history. Decisions to pass on personal possessions are made within the context of long, complex, and often complicated relationships among siblings, parents, in-laws, and others who consider themselves family. For some family members, deciding who gets what possessions can be the last straw in a long history of conflict and dissension (Stum).

Stum, creator of the program "Who Gets Grandma's Yellow Pie Plate?" (see Appendix A), says that you can be of tremendous service to your senior clients by recommending that seniors think carefully about whom they want to receive their personal belongings after their death. Then clients should make their instructions for transferring their personal possessions *legal* by creating both a will and (named in the will) a separate list identifying the possessions to be distributed. Such a list allows the owner to identify items and recipients and to update and change the list without changing the will.

"Having a legal written list reduces the dilemmas and decisions for estate executors and surviving family members," Stum says. She adds that, when advising your senior clients, you should consult an attorney and review state laws for advice on wills, intestate transfers, and the procedures to formalize decisions about the transfer of personal belongings.

THE PURPOSE OF AN ESTATE PLAN

When estate planning is done well, it considers the lifetime needs of the individual doing the plan and the needs of his or her loved ones. In its fullest sense, an estate plan addresses an individual's desire to:

- provide for personal health care and manage personal affairs and assets if they become incapacitated;
- leave a legacy—of property as well as memories, life experiences, care and support for loved ones and special causes;
- manage and reduce federal and state taxes so the maximum amount of assets is transferred to heirs and beneficiaries.

WHAT IS AN ESTATE PLAN?

An estate plan is a set of legal documents or tools that provide instructions for accomplishing the three main goals of an estate plan described above. These documents include legal and medical powers of attorney, a will, trusts, and beneficiary designations. These topics are covered in detail later in this chapter.

Often the only estate plan individuals make is the instructions they leave in a will. Many people do not even make out wills.

Educate your senior clients that even people who do not formally make out a will or an estate plan have a plan of sorts. Their plan is to let the laws of the state they live in control how they should be cared for, how their assets should be managed if they become incapacitated, and how their assets are distributed after their death.

WHY ADDRESS ESTATE PLANNING?

Your first challenge concerning estate planning may be getting seniors to discuss it at all. Topics such as incapacity and death can raise anxiety and fear, making the issue difficult to discuss. For some seniors, an attempt by their children to broach the topic may cause resentment. If seniors have not previously shared financial matters with their children, the prospect of doing so can raise concerns about independence and mortality.

Encourage seniors to approach estate planning as a favor to themselves and their families. Your CSA education makes you aware that planning for the possible prospect of mental incapacity is preferable to facing it without a plan, and planning for death can provide a great deal of relief to those left behind. It is up to you as a CSA to impart this information to your senior clients with sensitivity. If successful, you can then serve as the catalyst and source of support, information, and advice that can make the estate planning process successful for your senior clients.

NONTRADITIONAL FAMILIES INCREASE THE NEED FOR ESTATE PLANNING

Many seniors live in nontraditional families. Some have one or both parents (or stepparents) who are still alive. Others have adopted children, stepchildren, domestic partners, or lesbian or gay domestic partners. In addition, you may have senior clients who are in their second (or later) marriages or who have been divorced or widowed and are considering remarriage. The prospect of another marriage can create awareness of the "yours, mine, and ours" concept of the blended family. For example, seniors may wish to ensure that children from an earlier relationship are provided for after their deaths—and, at the same time, provide something for the surviving spouse.

Consider the estate planning needs of the following seniors.

Sam and Susan both have children from prior marriages. When they married, Sam moved into Susan's home. If Susan dies first, it is her wish that Sam be allowed to live in her home for as long as he likes. She may even wish that Sam should be able to sell the home and purchase a smaller one for his use. However, once Sam no longer needs the home, Susan wants to leave her home, or the proceeds of its sale, to her children. Susan wants assurance that Sam will leave the home or its sales proceeds to her children—not his, and not to a new wife if Sam remarries.

. . .

Anne and Beth have been domestic partners for 20 years. They own their own home as joint tenants, and all their bank accounts are jointly titled. In addition, they have named each other as beneficiaries on their retirement accounts. However, they have not prepared wills because they incorrectly assume all their personal property will pass to each other when the first of them dies.

Unless seniors such as Sam, Susan, Anne, and Beth have individual estate plans, their assets will be managed if they become incapacitated or distributed after their deaths under their states' default estate plans. While every state's default plan is different, most are based on the concept of a traditional family, where all children share the same parents, and a married couple has children only from that marriage. In some states, the surviving spouse inherits all the decedent's assets; in other states, the surviving spouse receives 50 percent of the decedent's assets, and the remaining half of the assets goes to the children of the decedent and the surviving spouse.

State default plans do not usually fulfill couples' unique desires for how assets should be distributed upon death. For this reason, you should encourage your senior clients who are in nontraditional families to make sure they have an up-to-date estate plan in place.

Estate Planning Tools

You may hear a senior tell a spouse, "If I'm in a coma and there's no hope that I'll recover, pull the plug." Or one of them may tell a child, "After I die, I want you to have my house and for your sister to have my IRA." But expressing these wishes orally and making them legal are two very different things.

For individuals of any age to make legally binding their desires for passing on their legacy, they must use the following legal documents or tools:

- legal and health care directives including powers of attorney
- wills
- property titles, particularly titles with rights of survivorship
- trusts
- named beneficiaries

One of the most common mistakes that people make is that they do not know which legal document controls the management of their assets if they become incapacitated or the distribution of their property after their death. Table 15.1 provides a picture of which legal documents control others. The table underscores the complexity of estate planning.

Table 15.1 Which Legal Documents Control the Management and Distribution of Property?

DOCUMENT	CONTROLS	TAKES LEGAL PRECEDENCE OVER	IS OVERRULED BY
powers of attorney *while alive*	legal, health, and medical decisions on behalf of another person	<ul><li>orally expressed wishes</li><li>personally written notes or letters</li></ul>	<ul><li>instructions in a will (because power of attorney automatically ends at the death of the person signing the document)</li><li>certain property titles</li><li>trusts</li><li>beneficiary designations</li></ul>
will	probate property (property owned solely by an individual for which there is no named beneficiary; joint tenancy property or property owned as tenants in common or jointly and, in some states, as community with rights of survivorship)	<ul><li>orally expressed wishes</li><li>personally written notes or letters</li><li>powers of attorney</li></ul>	non-probate property:<ul><li>certain property titles</li><li>trusts (except for testamentary trusts, which are part of the will)</li><li>beneficiary designations</li></ul>
certain property titles *Trumps!*	non-probate property (property owned by an individual, as tenants in common or jointly and, in some states, as community with rights of survivorship)	<ul><li>powers of attorney</li><li>instructions in a will</li><li>trusts (beneficiary designations)</li></ul>	**These property titles take precedence over all other documents in this chart.**
trusts:<ul><li>testamentary trust</li><li>revocable living trust</li><li>irrevocable living trust</li><li>subtrusts: family, marital, credit shelter, etc.</li></ul>	property placed under the management of a third party for the benefit of individuals or organizations	<ul><li>powers of attorney</li><li>instructions in a will (except for testamentary trusts, which are part of the will)</li></ul>	<ul><li>certain property titles</li><li>beneficiary designations</li></ul>
beneficiary designations	property owned solely by an individual that is designated to be given to another person or organization after death	<ul><li>powers of attorney</li><li>instructions in a will</li><li>trusts</li></ul>	<ul><li>certain property titles</li></ul>

409

Not surprisingly, in many instances an estate attorney must coordinate the use of two or more of these legal documents to ensure the instructions for an estate will be carried out.

In addition to being experts in creating estate plans, estate-planning attorneys have an important role in protecting your clients. Although not licensed mental health professionals, an experienced estate attorney will, within appropriate guidelines, assess the senior client's mental capacity and be alert to potential undue influence by family members or others. The attorney also becomes a witness if there is a dispute over the validity of the estate documents, and the expertise of the attorney is invaluable in preventing or at least reducing problems when these legal documents are implemented.

You should remind your senior clients to periodically review their estate plan documents to ensure they are current. Many seniors will have lifestyle changes of one kind or another that will affect how they wish to provide for themselves and others.

The following sections examine how an estate plan enables individuals to provide for the possibility of incapacity through use of legal and medical powers of attorney, health care directives, and revocable living trusts. As the first step to using these legal documents correctly, it is important to know how incapacity is defined for estate planning purposes, and who is involved in managing it.

AN ESTATE PLAN PROVIDES FOR INCAPACITY

Individuals may be physically disabled but still able to manage and carry out their own legal and medical decisions. Estate planning covers the possibility that an individual's disability results in an inability or incapacity to make or carry out these kinds of decisions. *Incapacity* is typically defined as the lack of physical or mental ability to take action that has legal significance. Incapacity may be obvious, such as a coma, or subtle, such as moderate dementia. An effective estate plan will contain documents that detail one or more options for determining if incapacity exists, for example, a decision by the individual's doctors only, or a joint decision among doctors and selected family members.

SELECTING HELPERS

All seniors, rich and not so rich, face the prospect of having someone else make decisions for them if they are incapacitated. Even if an incapacitated senior has no assets, someone will have to make decisions about his or her health care, housing, and professional assistance. Therefore, it is important for your clients to give serious thought to who will be named to make and carry out important decisions on their behalf if they become incapacitated.

If a court appoints a helper, this individual will have the title of *guardian*, *conservator*, or both. If a trust is involved, the helper is referred to as the *trustee*.

A disinterested or dishonest guardian or trustee can ruin the financial lives of the senior and the senior's family. It is important to help seniors identify a helper who is trustworthy, available, and sufficiently capable of analyzing and making decisions in their best interests. A good guardian or trustee will be able to objectively weigh the options for addressing medical and legal issues, even when family members are at odds with their best interests.

Appointing a helper can cause problems within families. For example:

- Friction may occur when family members question an agent's appointment or actions.

- A particular family member may not have the qualifications to be a guardian or trustee but desire to have the position anyway.

- Chronological or gender-based appointments (such as the oldest child or first male child) do not assure that a particular family member is the best choice.

It is important that seniors appoint both a primary guardian or trustee and at least one contingent (secondary) individual to serve if the primary person is unable or unwilling to fill the role.

Seniors frequently ask about appointing coguardians or cotrustees to prevent resentment among their grown children. Coguardians or cotrustees can be helpful, either to provide additional help waiting in the wings if the preferred person is not up to the task, or to provide some checks and balances, such as when two out of three children are authorized to make a decision for a parent. When naming more than one person to fill the role at the same time, it is important to provide instructions as to how the group is to reach and carry out a decision.

Legal Documents Used to Select Helpers

Powers of Attorney

Powers of attorney are the documents your client uses to name the individuals who may make legal and medical decisions if he or she becomes incapacitated. They may also be called a *durable power of attorney* and *medical power of attorney*. The person who is the helper is named as the *agent* or *attorney in fact*.

Durable powers of attorney get their name from the fact that they "endure beyond incapacity." (Nondurable powers of attorney are impractical because they become legally invalid when the power is needed most—if the senior is incapacitated. Therefore, a power of attorney intended for use during disability should specify that the power is valid even when the senior is incapacitated.)

The documents most commonly used to plan for the possibility of making health care decisions for an incapacitated senior are *medical powers of attorney*, *advance directives*, and *living wills*. You should remember that the technical requirements for each of these documents could be very specific, depending on the state where the document is likely to be used. (Chapter 14, End-of-Life Planning, covers living wills and advance directives.)

Revocable Living Trust

In order to discuss revocable living trusts, you must understand a few key terms. A *grantor*, *settler*, or *trustor* is the person creating a trust, while a *successor trustee* is the individual who oversees the settlement of a trust.

A revocable living trust (a trust that can be changed) can be an excellent tool in planning for the possibility of being incapacitated. If the revocable living trust has comprehensive provisions detailing what happens if the grantor is incapacitated, the successor trustee can take over upon the individual's incapacity and manage all the assets funded in the revocable living trust.

Remember that the grantor or the successor trustee has power over only the assets that are titled in the name of the revocable living trust. For it to be the most effective planning tool possible, your clients must title all assets in the name of the revocable living trust.

Do-It-Yourself Documents

Boilerplate documents are available from many sources, including office supply stores, Internet sites, and from professionals other than lawyers. This do-it-yourself path to estate planning can be fraught with peril. Fixing a sink may be an appropriate do-it-yourself project—because every sink is essentially like every other sink—but no two families, or their assets, are alike.

If your senior clients cannot afford the services of a private estate planning attorney, consult chapter 9, Home and Community-Based Services, to help them find assistance through senior service and legal aid organizations that offer their services at no charge or at reduced fees.

WHEN A PLAN TO MANAGE INCAPACITY IS ABSENT

As a CSA, you may encounter situations in which a sudden illness has left a senior unable to speak, or a cognitive impairment such as Alzheimer's has diminished a senior's ability to understand personal and financial matters. You may discover in such cases that a client has not put a power of attorney or a trust into place to direct their financial affairs or medical treatment. When this is the case, state law takes over.

The court will first assess the individual's level of incapacity and, if it deems it appropriate, will conduct proceedings to appoint a guardian or conservator.

Determining Incapacity

Family, friends, and health care providers may be frustrated with the manner in which a senior carries out daily life. However, most courts operate under the premise that seniors have as much right as anyone else to make bad judgments. Therefore, mere eccentricity and refusal to accept necessary medical care are not reasons for revoking seniors' rights to make their own decisions.

Instead, courts must determine whether or not an individual is incapacitated. Recall that *incapacity* is the lack of physical or mental ability to take action that has legal significance. For example, seniors may be physically incapacitated if they become too frail to read bills, write checks, or express their preferences clearly. And seniors with Alzheimer's disease eventually lose the ability to make sound judgments, remember details, and complete daily tasks.

If a senior shows a persistent and potentially harmful pattern of poor decisions, or a loss of physical capacity, a concerned individual may petition the court to appoint a guardian. When a senior faces imminent danger, the courts may appoint a temporary guardian—sometimes within 24 to 48 hours—to provide protection until the senior's incapacity is fully reviewed and a final determination can be made.

Appointing a Guardian and Conservator

Depending on the state in which an incapacitated person lives, the court will appoint an individual, referred to as a *guardian* or *conservator* to manage the senior's affairs. Most states distinguish between a guardian of the person and a guardian of the assets (a *conservator*). Some states require that separate parties handle personal and financial affairs, while others allow one person to serve in both capacities. The person who is incapacitated may be referred to as the *protected person* or the *ward*.

Guardian

A *guardian* is an individual appointed by the court to manage the personal or medical affairs of a severely impaired individual of any age. (For our purposes, we assume that the person in need of protection is a senior.) The guardian makes decisions regarding the senior's care and housing and sees that his or her daily needs are met. Guardians may also be needed when incapacitated seniors are unable to make or communicate medical decisions on their own behalf.

Guardians are responsible for the well-being of protected seniors. The guardian must make decisions that will provide the appropriate care and treatment of the senior. In some states, the guardian will be required to file an annual report with the court indicating the senior's status and the plans for his or her care.

Conservator

A *conservator* or *guardian of the assets* is an individual appointed by the court to manage the financial and legal affairs of an incapacitated individual. The conservator becomes responsible for all financial decisions relative to the senior's assets. When determined by the court to be in need of a conservator, the senior can no longer legally enter into any contracts.

Once appointed, a conservator prepares an inventory of the protected senior's assets and a financial plan detailing the expected income and expenses. Court approval may be required to buy or sell assets. The conservator must manage the senior's assets with the care of a "reasonable and prudent person." (Check with an attorney in your state for the exact standards that apply.) Ongoing court supervision of the conservator offers some protection against mismanagement of the senior's assets.

If no conservator of the estate has been appointed, a guardian may receive funds on behalf of the senior and use the money for support and care. A conservator, on the other hand, does not have the authority to make health care decisions.

The duty of the guardian and the conservator is undivided loyalty to the senior. They must put the protected person's needs above their own financial gain. When the wishes of the protected senior can be identified, they should be considered when making any decisions. It is usually advisable for the guardian and conservator to have prior court approval before entering into any sort of financial transaction on behalf of the protected person.

HOLDING A COURT HEARING

The individual or agency petitioning the court to appoint a guardian for a senior is required by the court to notify the senior, his or her close family members, and any other interested parties. In most states, the court must hold a hearing. Although not always required to do so by a particular state's laws, the person or agency petitioning the court may elect to engage an attorney because of the complicated nature of the proceedings.

At the hearing, the court considers the stated opinions of medical or mental health professionals regarding the senior's capacity. These opinions may be presented in person, or they may be accepted in the form of an affidavit. The senior is always entitled to have his or her own attorney. In many instances, the court may appoint an attorney to represent the senior.

State law establishes the standard for guardians or conservators who may be appointed. The court will often appoint a family member, unless the senior has a valid reason to object to that individual or there is other evidence that the family member will not carry out the duties effectively. If a family member is not available to serve as a guardian or if family members cannot agree among themselves, the court will appoint a professional. Certain states have public guardianship programs, while others do not.

In today's society many of your clients are unmarried couples. Remember that unmarried partners, whether they are heterosexual, gay, or lesbian, have no priority to serve as guardian or conservator. It may be wise to ask all of your clients who are couples about their legal status. You should also recommend that heterosexual couples who do not want to enter into legal marriages consult with an attorney to ensure they have not unintentionally created a common-law marriage.

Court proceedings can be stressful, expensive, and time-consuming. This is especially true if the senior or family members disagree with the necessity or choice of a guardian by the court. In addition, these proceedings can open a senior's private and sensitive affairs to public scrutiny. Court proceedings also involve court costs, attorney fees, bonds, medical reports, and compensation of guardians and conservators.

Fortunately, such issues and costs can typically be avoided through advance estate planning. You offer a tremendous service to your senior clients and their families by periodically suggesting that they update their estate plans for specific provisions addressing incapacity.

The following sections address the other main purpose of an estate plan: to ensure that assets are distributed after death according to the senior's exact wishes and with minimum taxes to his or her estate, beneficiaries, and heirs.

AN ESTATE PLAN DISTRIBUTES ASSETS AFTER DEATH

In order to ensure that the property of seniors is distributed according to their exact wishes after death, estate plans use a combination of legal documents, including wills, property titles, trusts, and beneficiary designations. These legal documents also determine how much tax the estate, beneficiaries, and heirs will pay.

Before we examine each of these legal documents, however, we'll discuss what happens if a senior dies without an estate plan that contains a trust or, at the very least, a will. In both cases, the state's laws control the distribution of assets—a condition called *intestacy*.

It is a myth that state governments inherit individuals' assets if they die without a will or trust. If seniors die without either document, their probate assets are distributed according to their state's laws of intestacy. Generally, this means that the assets go to family members. However, state laws differ when it comes to intestacy. Certain states distribute some or all assets to the surviving spouse, and, if there are children from another relationship, they may share some of the probate estate with the spouse. If there are no spouse and no children, some states instruct that the assets must be given to other family members, such as parents or siblings.

Even in the most traditional of family circumstances, state plans will rarely match your clients' desires. When making regulations, state governments must be as generic as possible. However, most of us have lives far too complex to fit into a generic mold. It is much more effective for seniors to have wills or estate plans with trusts in place to ensure their assets are distributed in the ways they want, rather than giving control to their states' intestacy laws. This is especially true for unmarried couples, including unmarried heterosexual couples.

THE FUNCTION OF A WILL IN AN ESTATE PLAN

A will is an individual's set of instructions for how to distribute his or her *probate assets* after death. Probate assets are items an individual can legally pass on to others through a will or state intestacy laws because he or she is the sole owner of the property and there is no beneficiary named for the property. Examples of probate property:

- cash in a checking or savings account
- personal possessions such as watches, jewelry, and household furnishings

- for married couples, interest in community-owned property (unless their state allows community property with rights of survivorship; rights of survivorship are exempt from probate)

In their wills, seniors should name a person or company as their *personal representative* or executor to gather probate assets and oversee their distribution according to the will's instructions. (Parents of minor or permanently disabled children may also name a guardian for their children in their wills.)

You should be aware that the technicalities of writing and signing a will differ from state to state. If your senior clients move to another state, counsel them to have their wills reviewed to determine if they are valid in the new state of residence.

Pour-Over Will

As part of their estate plan, some seniors place their assets in a *revocable living trust* to remove them from probate after they die. In this type of plan, it is the revocable living trust rather than the will that provides the details for how the senior's assets are to be distributed at death. However, there may be items in a senior's estate that are not in the revocable living trust at the time of death. To address this situation, any estate plan that uses a revocable living trust must also include a *pour-over will* as a safety net. The pour-over will and revocable living trust together replace a regular will. The pour-over will ensures that all the senior's assets at the time of death that are not already in the revocable living trust are transferred into it, and thus that the instructions included in the revocable living trust will be effective. Thus, the pour-over will may make the probate process simpler and less expensive.

WHAT IS PROBATE?

Probate is the legal process through which a court makes sure that property is distributed to beneficiaries. The court's concerns are to assure that valid creditors are paid and all assets are properly distributed in accordance with the individual's will.

Many people believe that probate is to be avoided at all costs. It is true that some states have antiquated probate statutes, hefty and mandatory fees for executors and lawyers, and probate systems mired in politics. However, many states have adopted probate reforms. In addition, many states allow small estates to be settled without going through the probate process.

As a CSA, you can best serve your senior clients by understanding probate and discussing it with them. To gain this understanding, familiarize yourself with the probate processes in the states where your clients live. Do not assume that probate is to be avoided. Instead, take the time to discuss probate with several experienced estate planning attorneys. There are many valid differences of opinion on how to handle estate planning in each state. You will provide your clients an invaluable service by understanding the approaches of the professionals you work with.

The Probate Process

When a death occurs, most states require that anyone who possesses the decedent's original will must file it with the court of the county in which the decedent resided. After the will is filed, the personal representative (executor), heirs, creditors, or other interested persons may then petition the court to begin the probate process.

Appointment of a Personal Representative

Typically, the county court appoints a personal representative (executor) to settle the senior's estate based either on whom he or she nominated in the will or by statutory priority. The court then issues written documents giving the personal representative the authority to manage the estate, which consists of the right to:

- find and gather the estate assets;
- pay legitimate creditors;
- file and pay estate and income taxes;
- distribute assets to the designated recipients.

To pay creditors of the estate, the personal representative may have to notify them of the time period in which they can submit claims against the estate. States have specific rules about how these notices are to be made and how long the estate must remain open for creditors to file claims. Sometimes this notice may be a classified newspaper advertisement.

Only after all valid debts are resolved is it appropriate for the personal representative to distribute the remaining assets of the estate to the beneficiaries and inheritors. The personal representative will be expected to provide an accounting of how the estate assets were spent.

Settlement Time

A personal representative can complete a small and simple probate in about six months in many states. More complex estates that do not meet their state's definition of "small" may take a year or longer to settle. However, within this time frame:

- estate debts and federal estate taxes must be paid within nine months of the date of death;
- beneficiaries or inheritors who wish to disclaim part or all of an interest in an estate must do so within nine months of the date of death.

The time it takes to settle an estate is affected by the personal representative's experience in business and legal matters and ability to communicate with professionals for help with accounting, financial, tax, or legal issues, as well as the simplicity or complexity of estate assets. For example, if the only assets in the estate are personal property, these will be easy to distribute. However, if the deceased senior is being sued, the personal representative will need to manage the lawsuit, complicating the administration of the estates.

Settlement Costs

The costs of probate include fees to the court, attorneys, accountants, the personal representative, and other agents working to account for and distribute the estate's assets, pay creditors, and file taxes. Probate costs vary widely and depend on each state's probate laws and rules. However, it is not unusual for probate costs to be 2 to 3 percent or more of the estate.

Cost of Settling a Revocable Living Trust

If the senior has a fully funded revocable living trust in his or her estate plan, the estate will not go through probate, but it will still have to pay for the administrative tasks required to settle the trust. These tasks are similar to probate. They include gathering assets, resolving debts, and paying taxes. However, given this, having a revocable living trust may still result in fewer settlement fees when compared to the costs of probate.

Cautions about Serving as a Personal Representative

Many personal representatives take on their duties unaware of the personal liabilities they may incur for extremely complicated financial, legal, and tax matters. Common errors that inexperienced personal representatives make are the premature distribution of estate assets and the failure to provide funds to pay estate taxes.

Bill Bischoff, of SmartMoney, presents an overview of the tax issues that must be addressed at death (Bischoff, 2002). He cautions, "The executor's job is to identify the estate's assets. As executor, you are responsible for paying off all of the estate's liabilities, including taxes, and if you let these obligations slide, the IRS can come after you personally to pay overdue taxes, plus interest and penalties."

Rather than risk errors because of a lack of knowledge and experience, it is wise for personal representatives to hire experienced accountants, attorneys, and other financial services professionals to ensure proper management of the complicated financial, legal, and tax issues involved with estate settlement. This will avoid unnecessary hassles and minimize estate costs.

This is especially true when a personal representative is required to transfer a closely held business that is part of the decedent's estate. When a closely held business is part of an estate, it often restricts the estate's liquidity, which in turn may affect how quickly creditors can be paid and the remainder of the estate settled. Determining the best way to transfer a closely held business is both difficult and extremely important. The personal representative must be prepared to find a qualified manager for the business while the estate is being settled. In addition, finding a buyer for the business may require offering significant discounts on the sale price. These problems become even greater if the business needs to be sold in time to provide the cash to pay estate taxes.

How You Can Help Your Senior Clients

As a CSA, you can help your clients think through who should be their personal representatives. It is very important that seniors select a personal representative in whom they can entrust knowledge about the components of their estate plans and about their personal wishes for the kind of legacy they want to leave. Personal representatives must understand the seniors' wishes in both financial and emotional terms to ensure these are fulfilled.

You should also encourage your senior clients to make sure they have wills that are up to date, including making lists of their personal belongings. Be aware that updating wills involves more than naming heirs and designating who receives personal possessions; it also means reviewing any changes in federal estate or state inheritance tax laws that may affect the seniors' wishes. Remind your senior clients that a will is only one of the documents they should have in their estate plans.

PROPERTY EXCLUDED FROM PROBATE

Property that is *not* included in the estate's probate process, because it is not controlled by a will or state intestacy laws, includes titled property owned as joint tenants with rights of survivorship; tenants by the entirety (a special form of joint tenants with rights of survivorship only available to a husband and wife in some states); revocable living trusts; irrevocable trusts; and property left to a beneficiary—for example, life insurance policies and qualified retirement plan accounts.

THE FUNCTION OF TITLED PROPERTY IN AN ESTATE PLAN

Seniors can use property titles to exclude their property from probate. But they should be sure that they are using this estate planning tool correctly. For example, even though seniors may instruct in their wills that their properties are to be divided equally among their children, if they are not titled correctly, the children will not inherit them.

The property titles that legally supersede the instructions in a will and are therefore not included in probate are: joint tenants with rights of survivorship and tenants by the entirety (a special form of joint tenants with rights of survivorship only available to a husband and wife in some states). These property titles also take legal precedence over the terms of trusts and beneficiary designations. Following is more detail about each type of ownership.

Joint Tenancy with Rights of Survivorship

If the decedent owned property as *joint tenants with rights of survivorship*, the survivor (or survivors) who also owns the property automatically inherits it. Individuals do not have to be married couples to own property jointly with rights of survivorship. Submitting proof of death will place the title in the name of the survivor. For example:

In her will, Mary named all five of her children to receive all her property equally. Mary also named Robert, her middle child, to manage the estate. All of Mary's property was in the form of checking, savings, and investment accounts. For all these accounts, Mary named Robert as a joint tenant with rights of survivorship. When Mary died, Robert inherited all the assets, and Mary's other four children received nothing.

There can be other problems with joint tenancy with rights of survivorship. In this example, creditors of Robert's might be able to garnish Mary's accounts if they can show that a completed gift was made to Robert. This could also create a gift tax liability for Mary. If Robert had died before Mary, half of the joint accounts may have been included in Robert's estate, subjecting his estate to potential estate taxes.

Tenants by Entirety for Married Couples

In some states, married couples may own property as tenants by the entirety. This is a special form of joint tenants with rights of survivorship only available to husband and wife. The survivor automatically inherits the property, and it is excluded from probate.

Community Property with Rights of Survivorship

An interest in community property that a person owns is included in probate unless the state permits community property with rights of survivorship. In such states individuals can title their community property with rights of survivorship. This allows the surviving owners to inherit the property outside the probate process. Individuals do not have to be married to own community property with rights of survivorship.

THE FUNCTION OF TRUSTS IN AN ESTATE PLAN

Trusts can be used alone or in combination with titled property, beneficiary designations, and other estate planning tools to:

- reduce estate taxes;
- manage assets for minors;
- protect assets from income taxes for adult heirs;
- reduce the size of estates to qualify for Medicaid (only for irrevocable trusts).

Trusts supersede the instructions in a will and are excluded from probate. The use of trusts may help reduce the costs and length of time to settle the senior's probate estate.

A *trust* is a legal structure created when an individual *grantor* (also called a settler or trustor) transfers personal assets to the trust and appoints a *trustee* to hold and manage those assets. The person who receives the benefit of the assets in the trust is the *beneficiary*.

As its name implies, a trust creates a relationship between trustee and beneficiary. The trustee has the power over the assets and must use them to the advantage and for the best interests of the beneficiary. A common use of a trust is to provide assets to benefit minor children, with a competent adult or a professional trust company managing the assets that a minor obviously cannot (and typically should not) manage.

Several types of trusts are useful instruments in estate planning: testamentary trusts, revocable living trusts, and irrevocable trusts.

Testamentary Trusts

A *testamentary trust* is established under a will, which describes the terms of the trust, but it is not actually created until the will is probated. This means the testamentary trust is irrevocable when the grantor dies but can be changed while the grantor is alive (and as long as the grantor has the mental capacity to change his or her will). A testamentary trust may provide for asset management for minors, asset protection for adult heirs, or estate tax planning. (Seniors can create a similar after-death trust within a revocable living trust, but this is not called a testamentary trust.)

Revocable Living Trusts

A *revocable trust* must be a living trust, because it can be changed or revoked any time by the grantor who established it. A living trust is also called an *inter vivos trust*.

Revocable living trusts are popular because individuals can establish them to manage their assets during their lives and revoke or change them as their interests and needs change (Esperti, Peterson, & Moser, 1999). For example, the arrival of grandchildren might cause a senior to make a change in his or her revocable living trust.

The grantor (with grantor's spouse as a successor trustee) is typically the initial trustee and beneficiary during the grantor's life. He or she controls the trust's assets and receives its income. When the grantor dies, the terms of a revocable living trust work like the instructions in a will (or state laws of intestacy) to distribute its assets in the manner the grantor has directed. This means a revocable living trust is not included in probate. But assets in the estate that are not titled in the name of the revocable living trust may have to be probated separately or as part of a pour-over will.

Remember that a revocable living trust will contain the distributions normally provided in a will. A pour-over will makes transfers solely to the revocable living trust, which has become irrevocable as of the senior's death. This trust makes the specific distributions intended by the senior.

Make sure your senior clients understand that, by itself, a revocable living trust:

- does not protect their estates against creditors;
- does not remove the assets in the trust from the grantor's estate for the purpose of qualifying for Medicaid;
- may not provide any special estate tax savings.

Irrevocable Trust

A senior cannot revoke or change an irrevocable trust after it is created. Only court action can change the terms of an irrevocable trust.

Irrevocable trusts are most commonly created to reduce estate taxes or remove assets from a grantor's estate for Medicaid-planning purposes. However, the grantor must generally give up all control of the assets in the irrevocable trust to reap its benefits. This may not be a problem for an irrevocable testamentary trust that is created after death, but it can create a significant burden during a senior's lifetime.

There are important issues involved with the transfer of assets from an estate for Medicaid purposes, especially into an irrevocable trust. Your clients can be greatly damaged by an improper transfer. Advise them to obtain the advice of an experienced Medicaid attorney *before* making any transfers of assets from their estates in any form.

Table 15.2 Differences between Revocable and Irrevocable Trusts

Type of Trust	Features of the Trust							
	Gives the Grantor Control Over Assets	Generates Income for Named Beneficiaries	Can Be Modified by the Grantor	When the Trust Can Be Established	Removes Assets for Medicaid-Planning Purposes	Assets Are Included in Probate	Can Reduce Estate Taxes	Protects Estate Against Taxes
revocable trust	yes	yes	yes	during lifetime	no	no	may not	no
irrevocable trust	no	yes	no	during lifetime or after death	yes	no	yes	yes

Naming Beneficiaries

THE FUNCTION OF BENEFICIARY DESIGNATIONS IN AN ESTATE PLAN

If a senior client says to you, "I won't have to pay estate taxes, I've made out my will leaving everything I own to my children and my church," stop them right there and counsel them with this information: Property left to beneficiaries is included in the taxable estate. Therefore, they may still have to pay estate taxes. And, as a result of their inheritance, their children may have to pay more of their own estate taxes; and if they choose to sell part or all of their inheritance, they may have to pay capital gains tax on it.

Or, if a senior says, "I put my retirement plan into a trust so that after I die the money will go to help support my grandkids," ask and advise them: Who is the beneficiary of their retirement plan? If it is not their trust, the trust won't control the money, and the result is that their grandchildren are not guaranteed any money.

Naming beneficiaries is a powerful estate planning tool because it takes legal precedence over a will or trust. It is a very common tool for the majority of seniors who are in the high- and middle-income groups. Many of these seniors own assets such as qualified retirement plans and insurance policies that are legally controlled by a contract that names a beneficiary to receive the assets when they die.

It is wise to name alternate, or successor, beneficiaries. This protects the assets from the probate process and may have other benefits.

Individuals can make serious mistakes unless they get a professional estate attorney to assist them in naming their beneficiaries and completing the beneficiary designation forms correctly. Consider how the use of Amelia and Joseph's assets strayed far from their intentions:

Amelia's will established a testamentary trust to pay for her grandson Eric's education. Eric lives with his mother, but Amelia named Eric's father as trustee of the trust. Amelia wanted her life insurance to fund the trust. However, Amelia named Eric as the beneficiary of her life insurance policy. When Amelia died, Eric was 15 years old. The life insurance proceeds did not go to the trust. Instead, the court appointed Eric's mother as conservator to manage Eric's assets. When Eric turned 16, his mother used the life insurance proceeds to buy Eric a new car, leaving no funding for the testamentary trust that was intended to pay for Eric's education.

. . .

Joseph had a developmentally disabled adult daughter named Sarah. Knowing Sarah would never be independent, Joseph's revocable living trust described an after-death trust to manage assets for Sarah, with special provisions to avoid jeopardizing the government assistance Sarah receives. Joseph also named Sarah as the beneficiary of his individual retirement account. When Joseph died, a conservator was appointed for Sarah to manage her new assets. Because the conservator was obligated to use the

IRA funds for Sarah's support, Sarah received too much money to qualify for her government-funded training and supervised housing. Sarah's conservator had to find new training and housing for her.

These examples illustrate the importance of coordinating all the documents in the entire estate plan. These estate plans would have been effective if Amelia and Joe had named the trust as the beneficiary of the life insurance or IRA.

Remember, seniors may have designated their beneficiaries years earlier. Births, deaths, divorce, remarriage, and other events may create the need to change the original beneficiary selections. Remind your clients to regularly review their named beneficiaries and make any necessary updates. It is also important to name successor beneficiaries.

THE INHERITOR'S DISCLAIMER

Individuals who inherit an interest in an estate may disclaim part or all of their interest in it. The inheritance then passes to the next in line, according to the terms of the will, trust, or state laws of intestacy. Inheritors may want to use disclaimers if doing so would enable them to reduce their own estate taxes. For example:

Ramon's will leaves everything to his wife, Deborah. If Deborah does not outlive Ramon, his will then leaves everything to his sister Ingrid. When Ramon dies, Deborah decides to disclaim her interest in Ramon's property because she already has a sizable taxable estate of her own. As a result, the property goes to Ingrid. Assuming Deborah followed IRS regulations, the property is treated as passing from Ramon to Ingrid, rather than from Deborah. This protects Deborah from suffering estate tax consequences from Ramon's estate and from incurring gift tax problems of her own.

Note that Deborah cannot direct who receives the property as a result of her disclaimer. If Deborah had tried to direct that her son David receive Ramon's property in her place, her disclaimer would not have been effective. A disclaimer operates as if the person disclaiming had died. Because Ramon's will directed that Ingrid receive the property if Deborah died first, Deborah's disclaimer must result in passing the property to Ingrid.

Usually, a disclaimer must occur within nine months of death—and the person who is disclaiming the property cannot receive any interest from the property. For example:

From her husband, Brenda inherited stock, from which she received dividend payments. In the first month after his death, Brenda deposited the dividend payment into her checking account. In the second month, she spent it to help purchase a new car. Because Brenda received the dividend and deposited it into her account, the stock that her husband left her was no longer eligible for the tax benefits of a disclaimer.

Qualified Retirement Plans: A Primary Asset for Many Seniors

For many seniors, their *qualified retirement plan* is the largest single asset and source of retirement income. It is also the primary asset they pass on to their heirs through their estate plan.

This section covers the features of qualified retirement plans that directly affect estate planning, including when minimum distributions must be taken, how distributions can be taken, and *designated*, *nondesignated* and *contingency beneficiaries*. The section also briefly discusses *family limited partnerships*, a vehicle for managing an estate that includes a self-employed senior's business assets.

Qualified retirement plans are widespread today because they receive favorable tax treatment, which promotes saving for the income needs of retired seniors and their spouses. Seniors may have one or more of the following tax-qualified retirement plans:

- individual retirement accounts (IRAs)—traditional, spousal, or Roth
- employer-sponsored plans such as a 401(k), Roth 401(k) or a 403(b), which are provided for employees of not-for-profit organizations, hospitals, and education
- profit-sharing or money-purchase plans

BENEFITS OF QUALIFIED RETIREMENT PLANS

Qualified retirement plans enable individuals to defer income taxes on the pre-tax money they put into the retirement plan (not applicable to Roth IRAs or Roth 401(k)s that are funded with after-tax contributions) and save as a member of a larger investor group, which may result in higher returns on their investments. The benefits of being part of a larger investor group come from having investments managed by financial professionals, as well as receiving matching contributions from an employer, if the plan is employer-sponsored. Individuals can also stretch out the earning power and value of their retirement assets by passing them on to younger beneficiaries.

MINIMUM DISTRIBUTIONS

Once required minimum distributions from qualified retirement plans begin (see following discussion), seniors must take a minimum amount each year. The amount they actually take out is added to all of their other income for income tax purposes. For example, if Dan earns $10,000 of income from rental property and he takes $20,000 from his IRA (assuming no other sources of income), his total income for the year would be $30,000 and he would pay income tax based on that amount of income. If he took a lump sum of $100,000 from his IRA, he would pay income tax on $100,000, creating a significant income tax bill. Most persons want to minimize the amount they have to take from their qualified retirement plans to allow for minimum income taxes each year, and to maximize income tax deferred growth. However, they cannot defer taking their distributions forever. These rules applicable to distributions are discussed below.

How Are Minimum Distributions Calculated?

With a few exceptions, plan owners can determine the amount of their required minimum distribution by looking up their age on the Uniform Distribution Table in IRS Reg. § 1.401(a)(9)-9, then dividing the balance in the qualified retirement plan by the factor on the table that corresponds to their age. An owner whose spouse is more than ten years younger uses a different table called the Joint Life Table. These tables can be found through the Internal Revenue Service.

Beneficiaries Can Take More than a Minimum Distribution

Notice that the previous discussion assumes that it is beneficial to have a longer life expectancy. A longer life expectancy results in a smaller required minimum distribution from the qualified retirement plan, thus allowing the remaining assets in the plan to continue growing tax-deferred or, in the case of a Roth IRA, or Roth 401(k), tax-free.

However, talk of smaller distributions may make some seniors and their beneficiaries nervous. They may worry that they will need larger distributions. You can help alleviate their concerns by reminding them the requirement applies to the minimum that must be taken every year, but there is no limit on the maximum distribution that a beneficiary may take from an inherited qualified retirement plan, even if that beneficiary has not yet reached age 59$\frac{1}{2}$ (Schnepper, n.d.).

Each type of qualified retirement plan has its own income tax rules. These rules affect how seniors will decide to use the assets in their retirement plan: for retirement income or as a legacy for their heirs, or both. Usually, the goal of retirement income will be paramount. But you should take into account the effects of this decision on your client's estate planning. Remember, assets in qualified retirement plans are included in an individual's estate and are taxed after death both under the estate tax and income tax.

When Distributions Can Be Taken

Distributions or withdrawals without penalty from qualified retirement plans:

- may begin at age 59$\frac{1}{2}$;
- are required after the plan owner's death;
- must start by the plan owner's required beginning date—by April 1 of the year following the year the owner turns age 70$\frac{1}{2}$.

Distributions May Start at Age 59$\frac{1}{2}$

Individuals may start taking distributions without penalties from their retirement plans as early as age 59$\frac{1}{2}$. But, as discussed below, if individuals withdraw funds prior to this age, they must pay a 10 percent penalty, plus ordinary income tax on the amount withdrawn (except for after-tax Roth IRA and Roth 401(k) distributions). For more information on early withdrawals, see chapter 16.

Distributions Must Start by Age 70½, the Required Beginning Date

Seniors must begin taking yearly minimum distributions from their qualified retirement plans by their *required beginning date* (RBD) or face a 50 percent penalty tax on the amount that should have been taken. The required beginning date is determined by the age of the plan owner. It is always April 1 of the year following the year in which the senior reaches age 70½. (See Table 15.3.) No distributions are required from Roth IRAs or Roth 401(k)s at age 70½.

It is easier to calculate the required beginning date if you remember that seniors fall into two categories, depending on their birth dates:

- Category 1: Seniors whose birthday falls between January 1 and June 30. Their required beginning date is April 1 of the same year in which they turn 71.

  For example:

  Vivian has a 401(k) from her former employer. Vivian was born on March 4, 1939. Vivian celebrates her 70th birthday on March 4, 2009. Vivian will celebrate her half birthday, turning 70½, on September 4, 2009. Therefore, Vivian's required beginning date is April 1, 2010.

- Category 2: Seniors whose birthday falls between July 1 and December 31. Because they turn 70 in the later half of the year, they won't turn 70½ until the next calendar year, the year they also turn 71. Therefore, their required beginning date is not until April 1 of the year in which they turn 72.

  For example:

  Jim has an IRA from which he has not taken any distributions. Jim's birth date is August 16, 1940. Jim turns 70 in 2010, but won't turn 70½ until 2011. Therefore, Jim's required beginning date is April 1, 2012.

Seniors who are working and contributing to an employer-sponsored plan can delay taking distributions from this plan until they retire. However, they must begin taking distributions on their normal required beginning date from any IRAs they own outside the company plan.

Table 15.3 How to Determine the Required Beginning Date

IF YOU WERE BORN:	YOUR REQUIRED BEGINNING DATE IS:
Between January 1 and June 30	April 1 of the same year you turn age 71
Between July 1 and December 31	April 1 of the same year you turn age 72* *Because the required beginning date is always April 1 of the year following the year in which you turn age 70½

427

DESIGNATED BENEFICIARIES

There is significance to the type of beneficiary named for a qualified retirement account. A designated beneficiary receives special treatment. (Designated beneficiaries are discussed below.) Note that the following examples of distributions assume that the beneficiary qualifies for treatment as a designated beneficiary under the tax rules.

Distributions after Death

What matters most in distributions from qualified plans after death is whether the senior died before or after the plan's required beginning date. This determines the form in which distributions can be paid out (lump sum, rollover, or minimum distributions based on certain life expectancies); how quickly the plans must be paid out; and the tax liability for the beneficiaries. Concerning tax liability, except for Roth IRAs, distributions from qualified retirement plans are subject to income taxes, and distributions from qualified retirement plans are added to the beneficiary's taxable estate, as are any other assets inherited by the beneficiary.

When Death Occurs before the Required Beginning Date

If a senior dies before the required beginning date, his or her qualified retirement plan can be paid out to the designated beneficiaries in one of three ways:

- as a lump sum by December 31 of the first year after the owner's death
- rolled over into an IRA owned by the decedent's spouse who is also the plan's designated beneficiary (an option available only to a legal spouse, not to unmarried heterosexual, gay, or lesbian partners)
- paid out to the designated beneficiary (surviving spouse or other individuals) over the beneficiary's life expectancy in yearly minimum distributions starting no later than December 31 of the first year after the plan owner's death

For example:

> Laura names her only child Matthew as her IRA beneficiary. When Laura dies at age 69, Matthew, age 41, can take a lump sum payment or choose to take yearly minimum distributions based on his life expectancy. If Matthew chooses a lump sum payment, he will have to pay corresponding income taxes and will no longer have retirement assets growing tax-deferred. For example, if the lump sum is $70,000 and Matthew earned $30,000 of other income during that same year, he would be taxed on $100,000 of income at the corresponding (and higher) brackets. However, if Matthew chooses minimum distributions over his life expectancy, he will pay less each year in income taxes, which could help his cash flow as well as build a retirement fund that continues growing tax-deferred.

When Death Occurs after the Required Beginning Date

If a senior dies after the required beginning date, his or her qualified retirement plans can be paid out to the designated beneficiaries in the same three ways as when death occurs before the required beginning date—with a variation on the third option:

- as a lump sum by December 31 of the first year after the owner's death
- rolled over into an IRA owned by the decedent's spouse who is also the plan's designated beneficiary (remember, legal spouses only)
- paid out to the plan's designated beneficiary (surviving spouse or other individuals) in yearly minimum distributions over either the:
  —beneficiary's life expectancy starting no later than December 31 of the first year after the plan owner's death; or
  —decedent's actuarial life expectancy; using the appropriate actuarial tables (The Motley Fool, n.d.)

For example:

> *Luke names his wife Muriel as the beneficiary of his IRA. When Luke dies at age 75, Muriel is 68. If Muriel takes a lump sum distribution, she pays income taxes on the entire amount and the size of her taxable estate is increased. However, Muriel can also roll over Luke's IRA assets into her own IRA or she can choose minimum distributions from Luke's IRA using her own life expectancy or Luke's actuarial life expectancy.*
>
> *If Muriel chooses to take minimum distributions from Luke's IRA and uses her own life expectancy, because she is younger than Luke, the assets in Luke's IRA will keep growing tax-deferred for a longer time. But, if Muriel rolls Luke's IRA into her IRA, she can take even smaller minimum distributions, and her increased IRA assets also grow tax-deferred for a longer time.*

There are two important implications for Muriel and her beneficiaries:

- income taxes—she pays less income tax each year on minimum distributions than she would pay all at once on a lump sum, which could help her cash flow
- estate planning—if Muriel rolls Luke's IRA into her own IRA, she may have more assets to leave to her beneficiaries after she dies, and she can also stretch out her IRA assets (see next section) for as long as possible by naming young beneficiaries such as her nieces and nephews

STRETCH-OUT IRAs

The longer money remains in an IRA, even after an owner's death, the longer it can grow tax-deferred. Naming a beneficiary to keep money in an IRA for as long as possible after the owner's death is referred to as creating a *stretch-out IRA* (Schnepper, n.d.; Merrill Lynch, 2003). Seniors can create a stretch-out IRA using an IRA they already own or by instructing that, at their death, their assets from another qualified retirement plan be rolled over into an IRA.

Before- and After-Death Distributions from Roth IRAs

Use of Roth IRAs and Roth 401(k)s can be an excellent way to stretch out retirement assets and pass them on to heirs free of income taxes. Because Roth accounts are funded with after-tax dollars, once a person has kept a Roth account for the required five-year holding period, he or she can take distributions from it. The distributions are not subject to income tax as long as the 59 1/2 age requirement is met.

Once a Roth owner dies, the minimum distribution rules that apply to traditional IRAs apply to Roths, as though the Roth owner died before his or her required beginning date. The exception is that Roth distributions to the decedent's estate or beneficiaries are not subject to income tax. For this reason, Roths can stretch out retirement assets and pass them on for generations. (Roth accounts are still considered part of the decedent's and beneficiary's estates for estate tax purposes, just like a traditional IRA.)

THE IMPORTANCE OF NAMING BENEFICIARIES

A qualified retirement plan is a unique and potentially large asset. Many people assume that leaving it as an inheritance to others is a simple matter, but it is not. It is one of the most important decisions in estate planning because there are complex tax consequences for the giver's estate and the beneficiaries. Making an uninformed beneficiary selection can:

- generate significant income and estate taxes for the beneficiaries;
- leave loved ones with reduced benefits;
- reduce the long-term value of the retirement account for the beneficiaries.

The identity of the beneficiary determines how quickly minimum distributions must be paid out, in what amount, and how they are taxed.

Who Can Be a Designated Beneficiary?

The *designated beneficiary* of a qualified retirement plan must be an individual or definable group of individuals, or a trust with an individual or group of individuals named as the beneficiary. A designated beneficiary cannot be a company or institution such as a charitable organization. (Individuals can still leave their plan assets to a charity as a nondesignated beneficiary.)

If a plan owner dies before the required beginning date, regardless of how young or old a beneficiary is, his or her life expectancy must be used to determine the minimum distribution. If death occurred after the required beginning date, the beneficiary may choose to use their own life expectancy or the actuarial life expectancy of the owner.

Choosing which life expectancy to use in calculating the amount of the minimum distribution is a very important decision. As we've already seen, the younger the beneficiary, the longer the retirement assets can grow tax-deferred in a traditional IRA or tax-free in a Roth IRA.

Group Beneficiaries

When the designated beneficiary is a group of individuals, there are several options for selecting the life expectancy that will be used to determine the minimum amount that will be distributed to each member of the group.

Beneficiaries can use the age of the oldest in the group. The following example explains this option: Tomas fills out the beneficiary form for his IRA, naming his surviving children equally. When Tomas dies at age 78, he is survived by all three of his children, ages 58, 55, and 51. The yearly minimum distributions from his IRA will be determined based on the life expectancy of the child who is age 58.

They can also use the actuarial life expectancy of the plan owner when the owner died after the required beginning date, or they can create subaccounts that allow each person in the group to use his or her own life expectancy. For example:

Leanna names all three of her children as the beneficiaries of her IRA. When Leanna dies at age 80, her children are 57, 53, and 50. They can keep the IRA in one account and take minimum distributions based on the life expectancy of the oldest, who is age 57. Or they can keep the IRA in one account and take minimum distributions based on Leanna's actuarial life expectancy (because Leanna died after her required beginning date) or split the IRA into three separate subaccounts, one for each child. Then the children can take minimum distributions from their individual subaccounts based on their own life expectancies. (The use of separate subaccounts can be done either before the participant's death or by September 30 of the year following the participant's death. Subaccounts can be used whether the owner died before or after the required beginning date.)

Note that there are specialized rules to qualify for subaccount status. This technique must be put in place by a professional who thoroughly understands the current IRS rules relating to the creation of subaccounts.

A Trust as Beneficiary

Trusts themselves do not have life expectancies. However, a trust can be a designated beneficiary of a qualified retirement plan if it meets certain legal requirements. The trust must be:

- valid under state law;
- irrevocable;
- established for the benefit of identifiable individuals who will clearly receive the distributions from the decedent's qualified retirement plan.

Note that there are specialized rules that apply to naming a trust as a designated beneficiary. This technique must be put in place by a professional who thoroughly understands the current IRS rules relating to the qualification of a trust as a designated beneficiary.

A Charity as Beneficiary

Charities can be beneficiaries of qualified retirement plans. A charity that qualifies for tax-exempt status may receive a lump sum and pay no income taxes on the distribution, no matter how large the distribution is. Note that if both charities and designated beneficiaries are named, special estate planning techniques must be used to ensure the designated beneficiaries can exercise all their payout options. For example:

Bill died at age 79 with a large IRA. He named his church as a beneficiary of 10 per-cent of the IRA and left the remaining 90 percent to his daughter Elizabeth. The church is not a designated beneficiary, so Elizabeth cannot take minimum distributions based on her life expectancy. Instead, she must use Bill's actuarial life expectancy.

In the example above, separate subaccounts could have been used to distribute assets from a retirement plan (Raymond, 2000). If the charity takes its 10 percent of Bill's IRA and puts it into a separate account and Elizabeth does the same with her portion of the IRA prior to September 30 of the first year after Bill's death, then Elizabeth will be the only remaining beneficiary. Because she qualifies as a designated beneficiary, she can then take minimum distributions based on her own life expectancy, if she chooses. The benefit to Elizabeth is that her minimum distributions will be smaller than they would have been using Bill's actuarial life expectancy, and the remaining funds in her subaccount can continue to grow tax-deferred.

Note: If Bill had died before his required beginning date, then it would not have been an option to use his actuarial life expectancy to calculate the minimum distributions. In that case, the use of subaccounts would also work as a solution to allow Elizabeth to use her own life expectancy, which would still reduce her minimum distribution each year.

Naming Contingent Beneficiaries

Seniors should name at least one contingent beneficiary of their qualified retirement plans. In that case, if their primary beneficiary dies, the tax-free growth of the IRAs is still available to someone else (assuming there are assets remaining in the IRA), and the IRA can be stretched out to a younger beneficiary with a longer life expectancy.

Naming a contingent beneficiary also allows the individual, as the original owner of the retirement plan, to pass on the flexibility of some after-death maneuvering to his or her heirs. The owners of retirement plans can use disclaimers to create tax advantages for themselves (see the section "The Inheritor's Disclaimer," earlier in this chapter). For example:

Mark names his wife Linda as the primary beneficiary of his IRA and their son Adam as the contingent beneficiary. At Mark's death, Linda's advisors point out that Linda has sufficient resources that she will likely never need to access Mark's IRA. Also, if Linda inherits Mark's IRA, while there will be no estate taxes on it (because it passes to Linda under the unlimited marital deduction), the IRA would end up being in Linda's estate and could create a higher estate tax burden for her upon her death.

Therefore, Linda decides that she would rather let Adam inherit Mark's IRA. By disclaiming the IRA, Linda allows the IRA to pass to Adam, who will be able to take minimum distributions from the IRA based on his life expectancy, which is longer than Linda's.

This completes our discussion of the key features of qualified retirement plans that affect a large number of middle-income seniors and the success of their estate planning. In addition to qualified retirement plans, many seniors own their own businesses, so you should be aware of family limited partnerships, a vehicle for managing estates that specifically addresses the estate planning needs of business owners.

Family Limited Partnership

Seniors with high net worth often have assets including their own businesses, real estate, and other property. For seniors who have closely held businesses and other assets, the family limited partnership (FLP) and its counterpart, the family limited liability company (FLLC), are useful estate planning tools. (Other business entities can accomplish estate planning goals, including the reduction of estate taxes and protection from creditors. However, space limitations prevent discussion of them in this chapter.)

Simply put, an FLP is an agreement among family members about how to manage and own family wealth. In this agreement, it is common for the owner to maintain control of the business while transferring noncontrolling ownership interests to other family members. An FLP provides the opportunity to transfer assets during the grantor's lifetime with a discounted value for tax purposes. It can be a great vehicle to consolidate assets for management efficiency and for maintaining flexibility in future estate planning. However, an FLP requires significant expertise to establish and maintain. The costs and sophistication of an FLP or other entities make it appropriate only for larger estates, usually those of a million dollars or more.

You will recall that one of the main purposes of an estate plan is to reduce estate and inheritance taxes. In the next section, we discuss several strategies that can be used to manage estate taxes.

Reducing Estate Taxes

What Is Included in an Estate for Tax Purposes?

A taxable estate includes all assets owned or sufficiently controlled by a decedent, including real and probate property; jointly held, tenants-in-common, or community property; household goods; qualified retirement plans; interests in partnerships or businesses; trusts; investments including annuities; promissory notes; and, unless special estate planning techniques have been used, proceeds from life insurance policies.

What most people think of as estate tax is actually a tax system that consists of three distinct taxes on the transfer of assets (in contrast to a tax on income or the sale of consumer goods): estate tax, gift tax, and the generation-skipping transfer tax.

ESTATE TAXES DEFINED

Estate tax was the first transfer tax imposed by the federal government. It is a tax on the transfer of assets resulting from someone's death, such as a mother's transfer of a home to her children.

Estate taxes are separate from and in addition to the final income tax the decedent must pay. In general, they must be paid within nine months of the date of death and are governed by complex federal rules that change often.

Paying estate taxes can be a challenge if the estate does not have enough liquid assets. In planning for estate taxes, seniors should create enough liquidity to pay their estate tax but not, in turn, cause an increase in it.

LIFE INSURANCE POLICIES

Many people mistakenly believe that life insurance proceeds are entirely tax-free. While they may not be subject to income tax, the proceeds are included in the insured's taxable estate, unless another individual or entity such as a trust or charitable organization owns the policy on the insured's life.

Purchasing life insurance to pay for estate taxes requires special planning so the additional life insurance does not increase the size of the estate, and thus estate taxes, in an ever-upward spiral.

To determine the amount of taxes owed on an estate, the personal representative or successor trustee establishes the fair market value of all the estate's assets. Once the fair market value is established, certain items are subtracted from it, such as outstanding debts, settlement expenses, charitable donations, and the applicable exclusion amount for estates and gifts. The remainder is the amount on which the estate pays taxes.

THE APPLICABLE EXCLUSION AMOUNT: ESTATE AND GIFT TAXES COMBINED

After the death of a taxpayer, heirs are allowed to exclude a certain amount of the deceased's assets from taxes on the estate. This amount is called the *applicable exclusion amount*. It is $1.5 million starting in 2004 and increases to $3.5 million in the year 2009 (see Table 15.4).

Table 15.4 Applicable Exclusion Amount and Gift Tax Rate

YEAR	APPLICABLE EXCLUSION AMOUNT*	HIGHEST GIFT TAX RATE**
2004	$1.5 million	48%
2005	$1.5 million	47%
2006	$2 million	46%
2007	$2 million	45%
2008	$2 million	45%
2009	$3.5 million	45%
2010	*Estate tax is repealed*	Gifts above $1 million are taxed at the maximum ordinary individual income tax rate
2011	$1 million	55%

*Includes the $1 million lifetime gift exclusion that does not increase.

**Applied to taxable gift amounts in excess of the $1 million lifetime gift exclusion.

Of this amount, $1 million can be in the form of taxable gifts that the deceased gave to individuals over his or her lifetime prior to death. Although the applicable exclusion amount increases from 2004 through the year 2009, the portion of it that applies to lifetime gifts does not change; it remains at $1 million through the year 2009.

Note that use of the gift tax exclusion during life reduces the estate tax exemption available to heirs at death. Here is an example of how the $1 million lifetime gift exclusion is used in conjunction with the applicable exclusion amount to determine how much estate tax is owed:

> *Every year, Marjorie gives her daughter Jeanette a $25,000 cash gift, and after using the $13,000 annual exclusion every year, Marjorie's applicable exclusion amount is applied to her lifetime gift tax exclusion of $1 million—so every year no gift tax is due on the remaining $12,000. After 10 years of these gifts, Marjorie dies. As a result of these gifts, the applicable exclusion amount on Marjorie's estate has been reduced by $120,000. Assuming Marjorie died in 2009, her estate has a $3.5 million applicable exclusion amount. The remaining applicable exclusion amount is $3.38 million. Marjorie's heirs can deduct $3.38 million from her taxable estate. Because Marjorie's estate is valued at $1 million, her heirs pay no estate tax.*

GIFT TAXES

In the past, people who knew they would die soon could give away their assets before their deaths—removing them from their estates—to avoid the estate tax. Congress perceived this as a loophole in the estate tax system because it gave an unfair advantage to individuals who knew they were dying over those who did not. To close it, Congress created the gift tax.

Individuals can give away as much property as they like during their lifetimes. However, unless the gifts are exempt in some way, they are subject to the gift tax. (The recipient of a gift does not have to pay gift tax unless the donor, that is, the person making the gift, does not pay the tax.)

There are several exemptions to gift tax that are available to individuals or married couples:

- $1 million lifetime gift exclusion
- $13,000 (2009) annual gift tax exclusion, which rises in $1,000 increments based on an inflation index
- unlimited exemptions for gifts paid directly to hospitals, medical providers, and educational institutions on behalf of another individual, but not including health insurance premiums
- gifts between spouses

Annual Gift Tax Exclusion

Taxpayers are allowed to exclude a total of $1 million in gifts in one lifetime prior to death. In addition to this tax exclusion, every year the IRS allows individuals to exclude what it has determined are small gifts. This *annual gift tax exclusion* allows individuals (as of 2009) to give up to $13,000 per calendar year per recipient. The recipient can be any individual, and there is no limit on the number of individuals to whom gifts can be made. Married couples may split or share this annual exclusion, thereby doubling the annual gift tax exclusion amount to $26,000. This strategy is called *gift splitting* and can significantly reduce the taxable value of an estate. The following example illustrates the benefits of the annual exclusion:

> *Tom and Frances have three children, all married. To reduce their taxable estate, Sam writes a check to each child for $26,000, which represents Tom's $13,000 tax-exempt gift as well as his wife's, since she agrees he may use her tax-exempt gift amount too. So each couple receives a total of $26,000. In this way, Tom and Frances remove $78,000 without any gift or estate tax consequences.*

There are special rules to allow the gift splitting, and a qualified tax advisor should be consulted prior to making split gifts.

The annual gift tax exclusion applies to all gifts of any size made during the year, including holiday gifts. The exclusion rises with inflation in increments of $1,000. When a gift exceeds $13,000, the excess amount is applied to reduce the $1 million lifetime gift tax exclusion amount. For example:

> *Jeff buys his daughter, Mary, a new car worth $25,000. Later in the same calendar year, Jeff gives Mary a necklace worth $500. Jeff is unmarried, so he cannot split the gifts. Although the first $13,000 of Jeff's gifts to Mary is exempt, the remaining $12,500 applies against Jeff's lifetime gift exclusion of $1 million.*

If an individual is wealthy enough to have already used the $1 million lifetime gift tax exclusion, the excess amount of the gift is subject to gift tax. For example:

> *As part of his overall estate plan, Craig gives the family business to his daughter Carol. An appraisal values the business at $1.1 million. After applying the $1 million lifetime gift exclusion and the $13,000 annual gift exclusion, Craig must pay gift tax on the remaining $87,000.*

Gifts to Hospital, Medical, and Educational Services Providers

Gifts paid directly to hospital, medical, and educational services providers on behalf of the individual who receives services from them are exempt from gift tax. (If the gift is paid directly to the person who benefits from the gift, it cannot be excluded from gift tax.) These gifts are separate from and do not apply against the $13,000 annual gift tax exclusion or the $1 million lifetime applicable exclusion amount. For example:

> *Kevin pays $25,000 a year for his granddaughter, Suzanne's, college tuition. In addition, he pays the premiums for her health insurance. As long as the tuition is paid directly to the college, the tuition gift won't apply against either the lifetime or the annual gift exclusions. However, because health insurance premiums do not qualify for the medical expenses exclusion from the gift tax, this amount will reduce Kevin's $1 million gift tax exclusion. Therefore, Kevin can use his $13,000 annual gift tax exclusion toward the health insurance premiums for Suzanne.*

Gifts between Spouses

Spouses may use the *unlimited marital deduction* before or after death to give any amount of assets to a spouse who is an American citizen. (If the recipient spouse is not a citizen, the marital deduction is limited to $133,000 for 2009.)

These gifts do not use up any of the other gift tax exclusions. However, when the recipient spouse dies, the gifted assets are included in that spouse's estate and may result in higher estate taxes.

GENERATION-SKIPPING TRANSFER TAX

Congress perceived a second loophole in the estate tax system: By the time wealthy seniors died, their adult children had enough wealth that they didn't need an inheritance. This meant the seniors could more easily afford to make gifts directly to their grandchildren or great-grandchildren, thus skipping a generation. As a result, neither the decedents, nor their adult children, paid estate taxes.

To close this loophole, Congress enacted the generation-skipping transfer tax (GST). It creates an incentive for wealthy seniors to pay the estate tax rather than the generation-skipping tax. The GST tax:

- applies when a taxpayer skips at least one generation in gifting property directly to a will or trust, or within a will or trust;
- may apply to transfers of property to nonfamily members if the recipient is more than $37^1/_2$ years younger than the person making the transfer.

The GST tax has a lifetime exemption equal to the estate tax exemption for the year of the gift, which applies cumulatively to all generation-skipping gifts made during life and at death. You should recommend that your clients who anticipate making a generation-skipping transfer obtain advice from tax- and estate-planning professionals.

Estate Tax Rates in the Future

Table 15.4 shows the increases in the applicable exclusion amount through the year 2009. The exclusion resulted from the Economic Growth and Tax Relief Reconciliation Act of 2001 (EGTRRA). Note that the $1 million life-time gift exclusion does not increase. In 2010, estate taxes are repealed entirely, and during 2010 gifts are taxed at the maximum ordinary individual income tax rate. Congress can vote at any time before 2010 to reinstate the estate tax. In 2011, the estate tax is reinstated with the exemption dropping to $1 million, while the highest gift tax rate changes to 55 percent.

THE UNLIMITED MARITAL DEDUCTION

The simplest but often not the smartest plan for reducing estate taxes is to use the *unlimited marital deduction* to pass all property to a spouse. No tax is due on the transfer of assets to a spouse during life or after death. Thus, when all assets pass to the surviving spouse, the decedent has no taxable estate.

However, using the unlimited marital deduction by itself is not advised because it does not use the decedent's applicable exclusion amount, and it may create or increase a taxable estate for the surviving spouse.

For example:

Brian and Andrea jointly own $4.2 million of property. When Brian dies, his will leaves everything he owns to Andrea—a $2.1 million estate, using the unlimited marital deduction. Therefore, Brian's estate owes no estate tax. But when Andrea dies, her total estate is valued at $4.2 million (her $2.1 million inheritance from Brian, plus the $2.1 million she owned before Brian died). If Andrea dies in 2009, her applicable exclusion amount is $3.5 million. Therefore, her estate must pay estate tax on the $700,000 difference.

The way to resolve this difficulty is by creating one or more trusts that allow Brian and Andrea to each use their individual applicable exclusion amount. This type of estate plan is often referred to as the use of marital deduction trusts, and it must be created by an estate-planning attorney.

USING TRUSTS AND CHARITABLE GIFTS TO REDUCE ESTATE TAXES

In addition to the applicable exclusion amount, gift tax exclusions, and the unlimited marital deduction, several other strategies can be used to reduce the size of a taxable estate:

- donating to charities before or after death
- creating various types of trusts as part of a will or another trust
- purchasing life insurance to pay estate taxes

Charitable Gifts

Seniors who are able to afford it may take generous estate tax deductions by leaving money and other assets to qualified charities. See Table 15.5.

Charitable giving falls into two categories: *traditional* and *planned giving*. Traditional giving includes lifetime gifts, bequeathing funds to a charity through a will, and gifting life insurance to charity. Wealthier individuals may set up charitable foundations during their lifetimes, while those of more modest means may set up a donor-advised account.

The most popular planned-giving vehicles are pooled income funds, charitable gift annuities, and charitable trusts (Raymond, 2000). Other methods include charitable family limited partnerships and pooled-income trusts.

Both traditional and planned giving offer middle- and high-income donors the satisfaction of supporting worthwhile causes while receiving estate and income tax deductions. In addition, planned giving provides additional benefits to the donor and the beneficiaries (see Appendix B: Charitable Giving).

Table 15.5 Common Methods of Charitable Giving

METHOD	DONOR'S WEALTH	CAN REDUCE ESTATE TAXES	CAN REDUCE INCOME TAXES	PAYS INCOME TO DONOR DURING LIFE	BENEFICIARIES AFTER DONOR'S DEATH
Pooled-income funds	Modest	Yes	Possible (see Appendix B)	Yes—varies year to year	Heirs if they are alive when the assets were transferred
Donor-advised funds	Modest to wealthy	Yes	Yes	No	Not applicable
Charitable gift annuities	Modest to wealthy	Yes	Yes	Yes	Charity
Charitable foundation (public and private)	Wealthy	Yes	Yes	No	Not applicable
Charitable remainder trust (created during life or at death)	Modest to wealthy	Yes	Yes	Yes	If created at donor's death, can be named beneficiaries for income; remainder always to charity
Charitable lead trust	Extremely wealthy	Yes	Yes	No—income is given to the charity	Named beneficiaries
Testamentary charitable lead trust	Extremely wealthy	Yes	Not applicable	No—income is given to the charity	Named beneficiaries

Wealth Replacement with ILITs

Donors who wish to participate in charitable contribution plans but don't wish to reduce the assets passed on to heirs may choose to create an *irrevocable life insurance trust* (ILIT) and name their heirs as the beneficiaries. At the donor's death, the proceeds of the trust pass to the heirs free of estate taxes, thus replacing the assets that were given to charity. While living, the owner pays the life insurance policy premiums with the income or tax savings from the charitable plan. The donor must be insurable, and the life insurance must be obtainable at a reasonable cost for an irrevocable life insurance trust to make sense.

This completes our discussion of strategies for reducing estate taxes. Remember that any plan intended to reduce the transfer taxes requires sophisticated techniques that can fail if not properly created and implemented. The following sections briefly address the capital gains tax, which can affect the taxable value of a decedent's estate and have consequences for heirs.

CAPITAL GAINS TAX

We discuss capital gains tax in this chapter only as it applies to estate planning and the tax consequences for a decedent's heirs and beneficiaries. If you have questions about terms such as *cost basis*, please review the explanation of capital gains tax in chapter 16, Financial Choices and Challenges for Seniors.

The Carry-Over Basis

When individuals make gifts, both the asset and its cost basis transfer to the recipient. Therefore, when recipients sell gifts, they must pay capital gains tax on the difference between the sales price and the donor's basis. This is called the *carry-over basis*. For example:

Diane buys a rental home for $100,000. She builds an addition to the home at a cost of $50,000. Therefore, Diane's cost basis in the home is $150,000 (the original cost plus the improvement). Diane gives the rental home to her daughter Sandy. Sandy's basis in the property is the same as Diane's: $150,000. If Sandy sells the property for $200,000, she will be liable for capital gains tax on the $50,000 profit.

The Basis Step-Up

If an asset is transferred as an inheritance rather than as a gift while the owner is alive, the capital gains tax on the asset is calculated differently. The basis is the property's value as of the decedent's date of death. This is called a *basis step-up*. Using the example of Diane and her daughter, Sandy, the following illustrates the basis step-up:

Assume that Diane does not give the rental property to Sandy as a gift. Instead, Diane leaves the property to Sandy through her will. As of the date of Diane's death, the rental property is worth $200,000. Sandy's basis is therefore $200,000. If she sells the property for $200,000, Sandy will not be liable for any capital gains tax.

Remember, the basis step-up applies only to after-death transfer of assets that are part of the decedent's taxable estate. The basis step-up does not apply to gifts that individuals gave before death.

The Step-Up in Basis in 2010

Because estate tax is eliminated in 2010, not all of the appreciated assets in a decedent's estate will receive this favorable step-up in basis. For the year 2010, step-up will be replaced by carry-over basis rules for assets exceeding $1.3 million. The basis step-up can be used to calculate the capital gains tax on the first $1.3 million of the assets in the decedent's taxable estate when left to a nonspousal heir. Furthermore, transfers to a spouse will entitle the spouse to an additional stepped-up basis of $3 million. Assets exceeding $1.3 million carry the decedent's basis or the date of death market value, whichever is smaller. For example:

Shirley has two assets when she dies in 2010: a family farm worth $1.3 million and a commercial office building also worth $1.3 million. Shirley's basis in the farm is $300,000; her basis in the office building is $1 million. Because there is no federal estate tax in 2010, Shirley does not owe estate taxes. Also, the first $1.3 million of her estate receives a basis step-up. Her will leaves the farm to her son Mike. Shirley's personal representative applies the basis step-up to the farm. As a result, Mike does not owe capital gains tax on the farm when he sells it. However, when Mike sells the office building for $1.3 million, he must use Shirley's basis of $1 million, and he is subject to capital gains tax on the $300,000 gain.

Sale of Personal Residence during Life

Individuals who sell a primary residence can exclude up to $250,000 of the sale's capital gains from capital gains tax; married couples can exclude up to $500,000, even if the residence is only titled in one spouse's name. (Note that the couple must file taxes as married, joint.)

STATE INHERITANCE AND GIFT TAXES

Most states have inheritance or estate tax, and most states levy a tax on large gifts. In the past, these state taxes were often linked to the federal tax system. Many states had applicable exclusion amounts equal to the federal applicable exclusion amount. In addition, prior to EGTRRA, federal estate and gift taxes provided a credit to the estate equal to the amount of state inheritance or gift taxes that had been paid. This resulted in a dollar-for-dollar reduction in the federal tax for every dollar paid in state taxes.

EGTRRA reduced the federal credit for state gift and inheritance taxes in 2003 and 2004 and eliminated it in 2005. As a result, a number of states decoupled their inheritance and gift taxes from the federal estate tax. These states often have an applicable exclusion amount that is *lower* than the federal applicable exclusion amount. This change has important implications for seniors like Ross:

Ross dies in 2009 with an estate worth $1.2 million. He owes no federal estate tax because his estate is less than $3.5 million (his applicable exclusion). However, Ross resided in a state that has a $675,000 exclusion amount for inheritance taxes. As a result, Ross' estate will be liable for state inheritance tax on $525,000.

You should find out if your state has decoupled its inheritance taxes from the federal estate tax and advise your clients accordingly.

PROVIDING CASH TO PAY FOR ESTATE TAXES

Some seniors think that life insurance benefits are tax-free, so they purchase them to provide an inheritance for family members or others. But tax-free means only that the beneficiary does not have to pay income taxes on the proceeds that are paid after the insured person dies.

What many individuals do not realize is that life insurance can increase their estate taxes, because the often-substantial value of a life insurance policy is included in a taxable estate. Life insurance can be the asset that pushes an estate's value over the decedent's applicable exclusion amount and into a situation of owing estate taxes.

However, it is possible to exclude a life insurance policy from the taxable value of an estate by making the heirs the owners of the policy, or by creating an *irrevocable life insurance trust* (ILIT) with the heirs as its beneficiaries.

A properly established irrevocable life insurance trust provides an inheritance and funds to pay anticipated estate taxes. For example, it may be distasteful to some individuals to think of being forced to quickly sell a large portion of their assets in a business or real estate to pay federal estate taxes. But if they place these assets in an irrevocable life insurance trust, it allows them to pass on an intact estate to their heirs without liquidating a portion of it to pay estate taxes. Also, if an individual's estate is close to or will exceed the applicable exclusion amount, it makes sense to create an irrevocable life insurance trust to remove assets from the taxable estate, assuming the policy premiums are less than paying the estate taxes.

Seniors who are considering an irrevocable life insurance trust are advised to seek guidance from an estate planning attorney who can ensure this trust is properly crafted to prevent it from being included in the decedent's taxable estate. For example, if the insured senior has any rights of ownership in the policy—such as the ability to borrow against cash value or change beneficiary designations—the life insurance policy will be included in the estate. And, because the senior cannot change an irrevocable trust after it is created, it is important to carefully consider his or her future needs and goals at the time the irrevocable life insurance trust is established.

In addition, married couples can take advantage of a *second-to-die (survivor) life insurance policy*. This policy pays at the second death when estate taxes are due, but usually costs less than buying a separate life insurance policy for each spouse. Second-to-die life insurance policies may be available even when one spouse is uninsurable.

Estate Planning: Summary

Physical assets often represent intangibles—the sum total of an individual's life experiences and values. With this understanding, you will be able to better guide your clients through the estate planning process so they can obtain the satisfaction and relief of appropriately addressing their lifetime needs and goals. Equally important, you can assist your clients in appreciating and passing on their legacies—not just physical property, but also memories, life experiences, care and support for loved ones, and special causes.

If you are proactive in helping your clients address their estate planning needs, it is likely that you will find that they and their families appreciate your services. Specifically, assist your clients in the following areas:

- Determine the locations of important estate planning documents, including wills and trust agreements.
- Determine whether a trust holds any assets. You may be able to help a client find ways to fund the trust when it is appropriate, or you can refer them to the appropriate professionals.
- Review how their assets are titled. Confirm that asset titles address a client's intentions and minimize estate tax when possible.
- Review all beneficiary designations on life insurance, qualified plans, IRAs, annuities, and checking and savings accounts to ensure they are current.
- Review powers of attorney and other documents addressing incapacity to ensure they are up to date.
- Confirm the appropriateness of a client's choice of family members or others who will be responsible for health care decisions, financial issues, or estate matters.
- Determine the likelihood that a client's estate will be subject to federal estate tax or state inheritance tax. Help them to identify ways to minimize this tax liability.

Appendix A: Who Gets Grandma's Yellow Pie Plate?*

Everyone has personal belongings—a pie plate, wedding photographs, a baseball glove—that contain meaning for them and their family members. What happens to those belongings when the owner moves from their lifetime home to an apartment, or when that person dies? It is often assumed that decisions about personal property are unimportant, trivial, or can be handled with an instruction to "divide equally among my children" in a will. Most estate planning resources ignore decisions surrounding the transfer of nontitled property (items without legal documentation, such as a title or deed, to indicate who owns the item officially) as an inheritance issue. The experiences of generations of families and estate planning attorneys suggest a different reality. It is often the nontitled personal property, not the money or real estate, that creates the greatest challenges for families.

Planning ahead for the transfer and distribution of nontitled property is just as important—and often more challenging—than making decisions about titled property. Nontitled property is a decision-making issue that impacts all families regardless of their financial worth, heritage, or cultural background.

Powerful messages are often transferred along with personal property. (Think of how a son might feel when his father leaves to a son-in-law a watch that was passed from father to son for the past three generations.) Inheritance can symbolize intergenerational transfers of love, trust, power, family rituals and traditions, and family history. Decisions to pass on personal possessions are made within the context of long, complex, and often complicated relationships among siblings, parents, in-laws, and others who consider themselves family. For some family members, deciding who gets what possessions can be the last straw in a long history of conflict and dissension.

Consider the consequences . . .

"After Mom died, Dad remarried when he was 69 years of age. My new stepmom moved into the home where my sisters and I grew up. Then my Dad died suddenly a year later. Now my parent's possessions are being passed on to my stepmom's daughters. Do you know how hard it is to see my stepsister wearing my Mom's pearls? There has to be a better way . . ."

You may be in the position to help seniors and their family members communicate, plan in advance, and make more informed decisions about transferring and distributing personal property. Seniors are often searching for ways to plan for property distribution and may want to raise and address the topic with a spouse or adult children—often they simply don't know how to get started. When seniors are planning to move from their home of many

*Authored by Marlene S. Stum, PhD

years to an assisted living facility, they may feel overwhelmed with all the "stuff." Still other seniors may be estate executors and dealing with surviving family members who are facing decisions when there was no advance planning. Planning ahead allows families to have more choices. It provides the opportunity for communication, including the sharing of stories. This may result in fewer misunderstandings and conflicts, and fewer feelings of burden and guilt.

What's Unique about Personal Property?

While there are many similarities in making decisions about titled and non-titled property, there are also some critical differences.

- The sentimental meaning attached to personal possessions can make decisions more emotional.
- Transferring objects can involve the process of grieving and saying good-bye.
- Objects help preserve memories of important people in our lives, family history, and family rituals.
- Decisions may involve objects accumulated over a lifetime and across many generations of family members.
- Since it can be impossible to divide items equally, being fair is more complex than dividing money.
- Personal belongings have different value and meaning to each individual.
- It is difficult to measure the worth or emotional value of personal items.
- Distribution methods and potential consequences are not well known or understood.

Help Avoid Common Obstacles

Our research and work with families and professionals has identified six key decision-making factors that help families make more informed decisions. Understanding these factors is valuable in working with clients, whether they are planning in advance or coping with a crisis. A brief introduction to each follows.

1. Recognize the sensitivity of the issue: Helping family members talk about issues that they normally do not want to address is a first step. There are many reasons that families find it uncomfortable to bring up and make decisions about inheritance-related issues. They may consider it disrespectful and try to avoid the topic. Denial of our own or others' mortality is often at the heart of why conversations about inheritance can be so sensitive. Few people want to suggest that a family member might die or that they would want someone to die.

   Being willing to talk about the issue with family members is an important and huge step for many seniors, spouses, and adult children. Fear of how one's motives may be interpreted can also make inheritance decisions emotionally charged. Adult children often worry about being perceived as greedy or selfish when raising questions about inheritance. In reality, adult children are more likely motivated by the desire to have their parents make decisions while possible. Being clear about one's motives for raising the issue and talking about what you want to have happen and why can help eliminate misconceptions about motives. Issues of power and control, and unresolved conflicts among parents, siblings, in-laws, and other involved family members can heighten the sensitivity of inheritance decisions.

2. Determine what they want to accomplish: Encourage co-owners to identify their individual goals and compare their priorities. Where do they agree or disagree? Identifying and prioritizing what family members are trying to accomplish (their goals) will help them focus and guide their next steps. Families often identify one or more of the following goals regarding personal property distribution:

   - preserving memories, family history, and rituals
   - being fair to all involved
   - improving family relationships (e.g., everyone still talking)
   - maintaining privacy (e.g., keeping decisions in the family, no public auctions)
   - contributing to society (e.g., donating to charities and museums)

3. Decide what's fair for their family situation: Help owners and potential receivers of personal property to understand that different perceptions of what fair means are normal and should be expected. Family members often have unwritten rules and different definitions of what would make fair who gets what, and the decision process. Uncovering and talking about those rules and assumptions is essential.

Identify Unwritten Rules . . .

"In my family everyone knows that you get back gifts you've given when someone dies—except for money and time, that is. I'm the daughter who lives near Mom and Dad and takes them to their doctor appointments, cleans their house, and helps out financially when needed. My sister from back East is always sending expensive gifts for birthdays and holidays. Who do you think will get back the most things when Mom and Dad die?"

Being fair does not always mean being equal, or treating everyone the same. It is often impossible to divide personal belongings—the beloved copy of *Winnie-the-Pooh*—equally among siblings. Being fair may also mean taking into account such differences as informal help, gifts, basic living needs, birth order, gender, or personal interest in an item. Talking about and agreeing on what rules are fair is key to determining who gets what.

Deciding how to decide—identifying the distribution process—is as critical as the end result. This involves agreeing on rules for the process, including:

   - who gets to decide (are in-laws in or out?)
   - how everyone is informed

- how the value of items is measured
- when decisions will be made
- what specific methods will be used

Individuals who have input and agree on how decisions are made are more likely to feel the outcomes of those decisions are fair.

4. Understand what belongings are meaningful: Encourage individuals to avoid making assumptions and find out what items have special meaning to others and why. Accept that not everyone will find the same items meaningful. A prized stamp collection may or may not be of interest to children or grandchildren—or it may be prized for its financial value. Owners and potential receivers can identify special items; they can share why the items are special and discuss feelings about who should receive what and why. Taking time to tell stories and share the meaning of objects can help pass on valuable family history, traditions, and rituals.

5. Consider distribution options and consequences: There is no one perfect method of transfer. Seniors should consider different distribution methods and think through the potential consequences of the various methods given their situation. For example, while pilfering is a method that family members use, hurt feelings, anger, and the need to hide stolen items are potential consequences. Putting labels on items or making verbal promises are other methods frequently used. Each has potential negative consequences. In a majority of states, individuals are encouraged to make their known wishes regarding the transfer of personal possessions legal by creating first a will, and then a separate list identifying personal property to be distributed; this list should be mentioned in the will. Such a list allows the property owner to identify items and recipients; it can be updated and changed without changing the will. Having a legal written list reduces the dilemmas and decisions for estate executors and surviving family members. Consult an attorney and review state laws for advice on wills, intestate transfers, and the procedures to formalize decisions about the transfer of personal possessions. Property owners should also consider the option of gifting while alive; treasured belongings can be given at holidays, birthdays, or other special occasions along with the associated stories.

Happy Endings . . .

"When Emma invited her four children to spend a weekend with her and requested that no spouses or grandchildren come, her children wondered what was up. At the time, their 85-year-old mother was planning to move from her home of 45 years to assisted living. The kids gathered and spent time going through the house and personal possessions with their mom. They talked about memories related to possessions, who wanted what and why, and who should have what and why. A year later when Emma died, the children couldn't help but appreciate the special weekend they had shared together with their mother. What a wonderful celebration of her life and their family history it had been."

SAMPLE: LIST IDENTIFYING TRANSFER WISHES

Page ___ of ___

To: My Family, Heirs, Executor, or Personal Representative

This is the list that I referred to in my last will and testament. Please distribute the items listed below to the persons I have named:

Item:	**To be distributed to:**
Grandfather's woodworking tools in carpenter's box	My brother, George Andersen
My stamp collection	My nephew, Steven Jones
Christening gown used for past two generations	My oldest daughter, Sara

My signature: _____ Date: _____

---

6. Agree to manage conflicts: Help seniors recognize and address potential sources of conflict before they need to be managed. Sources of conflict regarding personal property distribution are most likely to revolve around: (a) lack of communication or miscommunication; (b) differing attitudes, beliefs, or values; (c) differing expectations about who should be doing what; and (d) unresolved prior conflicts among family members. A family history of control and power battles among siblings and other family member conflicts are probably best addressed by family therapists or conflict mediators. Keep in mind that many families have very positive experiences regarding the transfer of property. While conflict may be normal, it is not inevitable.

Various educational resources are available to help seniors and their family members work through the six decision-making factors. A workbook, video, and Web site called "Who Gets Grandma's Yellow Pie Plate?" are being used nationwide to help families make more informed decisions. Details on how to order these resources are listed at the end of this appendix. The project takes its name from a ceramic yellow baking dish in one of the project's participating families that was handed down from a great-grandmother and is still used at family gatherings. The great-granddaughter hopes to carry on the tradition of having apple pie on the table—as a piece of her living history. The title serves as a great metaphor to remind us that we all have pie plates in our families—they just may not be round or yellow.

A core resource is a workbook designed for family members offering a step-by-step guide through the six decision-making factors. It is filled with worksheets to help identify and prioritize goals, talk about and determine what fair means, and identify special items. It also contains practical suggestions, proven strategies, and real-life stories. A 13-minute video complements the workbook and introduces the issues that can arise around personal property transfer. It also provides an overview of the six critical factors to consider. It can be used as a quick tool to get all family members to listen to the same messages as a beginning step. An educational Web site provides background on the issue and quizzes to see if you are prepared as a property owner, adult child, or estate executor. This resource also includes family stories, free conversation starters to use with family members, a description of educational resources and how to order, and more. Web site users can find more in-depth descriptions and view the available educational resources discussed above; these can be ordered on line.

You could directly offer these resources or provide a listing (see end of appendix) for family members to access them on their own. You could also conduct workshops for clients or others in the community. All of the tools needed for teaching about this topic are available in an educator's package (teaching outlines, a disk of PowerPoint documents, the video, and research review). Seniors and adult children have proven eager to attend workshops to learn, listen to others, and have an outlet to tell their own stories.

FINAL THOUGHTS

Few individuals have planned ahead regarding who should get what personal belongings. When the wishes of the property owner are not known, family members are left with many dilemmas and decisions regarding the passing on of personal possessions. There are ways to make more informed decisions about an issue that is not only legal and economic, but also involves complex emotional and family relationship dynamics. You can help your clients understand the importance of addressing personal property decisions, help them work through what can be a challenging and emotional process, and learn how to avoid the common obstacles along the way.

"Who Gets Grandma's Yellow Pie Plate?" resources (workbook: item MI-6686-PP; video: item VH-6692-PP; educator's package: item EP-6636-PP) can be ordered from the University of Minnesota Extension Service Distribution Center, http://www.yellowpieplate.umn.edu, email: order@extension.umn.edu, toll-free 800-876-8636, fax 612-625-6281.

Appendix B: Charitable Giving

POOLED-INCOME FUNDS

Individuals of modest means may transfer cash or other assets to a pooled income fund maintained by a charity. The charity uses this fund to combine the donations of multiple donors. In return, a donor receives a life income from a portion of the fund's annual earnings. Thus, the individual's contributions provide income during life, as well as estate and gift tax relief. The annual income stream will vary from year to year. Although the income is theoretically taxable as ordinary income, a charitable deduction may substantially offset any tax due on the income from the fund. Also, the donor may name other income beneficiaries as long as they are alive when the assets were transferred into the fund. In this way, the donor can provide for a spouse or children even after death.

DONOR-ADVISED FUNDS

With a donor-advised fund, a senior may make an initial donation, choose a name for the fund, and remain active in decisions about how the fund is invested, as well as select the charitable causes to receive grants from the fund. Some financial institutions and many public foundations offer donor-advised funds. The institution or foundation provides administrative support and documentation, manages disbursements, and assures compliance with applicable tax regulations. A small administrative fee is charged to manage donor-advised funds.

Donor-advised funds may be established with a wide range of assets, including cash, securities, closely held stock, life insurance, or real estate. Gifts may be made during life or as after-death bequests that honor the donor's personal interests and values. The donor can also name a successor advisor, which allows the fund's activities to extend across many generations.

CHARITABLE GIFT ANNUITIES

A *charitable gift annuity* is an agreement by a charity to pay a lifetime annuity in exchange for assets received from a donor. The annuity income represents fixed payments over the lifetime of one or two individuals (such as the donor and spouse). The donor receives an immediate income tax deduction and removal of the donated asset from the estate for estate tax purposes. In addition, any capital gains tax that would have been required of the donor is usually deferred. The transaction benefits the issuing charity with few if any costs. A potential disadvantage is that the payments, while fixed, are not adjusted for inflation.

CHARITABLE FOUNDATIONS

Many wealthy seniors wish to support certain charities of their choice and may be looking for reasonable methods to accomplish that. Charitable foundations provide them an opportunity to channel dollars to a particular cause while generating income tax deductions during life and reducing the overall size of their taxable estates.

There are several types of charitable foundations. An individual may set up a private foundation that must incorporate as a nonprofit corporation (a cumbersome process, especially for those with smaller initial donations). As an alternative, a person can give to a large number of community charitable foundations across the country that operate a wide range of nonprofit organizations.

CHARITABLE REMAINDER TRUST

A *charitable remainder trust* (CRT) is an irrevocable trust designed to pay income to living beneficiaries. The donor transfers assets into the CRT, reserving an annuity income interest from the CRT (generally for life), and contributes the remaining assets in the CRT to the charity at the donor's death. The CRT offers income, gift, and estate tax benefits. Although the CRT inherits the donor's basis, the trust generally avoids or minimizes estate, gift, and capital gains tax liability when trust assets are sold because the CRT qualifies for charitable income tax treatment. Upon the death of the annuity beneficiaries or the expiration of a fixed number of years, trust assets pass to one or more designated charities (the donor may reserve the right to change the designated charitable beneficiary). For example:

> Sylvia has owned some vacant land for many years. Although the land has value on the open market, it is not producing income for her. The land has appreciated significantly since Sylvia purchased it, creating a substantial capital gains tax liability for Sylvia if she sells it. Sylvia creates a CRT and transfers the land to the CRT. The CRT provides that Sylvia will receive a set amount of income for life, and when she dies the remainder of the trust goes to her favorite charity.
>
> The CRT sells the land to a third party buyer. (The trustee of the CRT must not be obligated to sell the land when the CRT is created.) The CRT invests the proceeds from the sale to provide Sylvia with the promised income, while minimizing the jeopardy to the principal amount. Sylvia pays income taxes only on the income she receives each year.

The donor may choose to be trustee of the CRT, but the administrative duties of a trustee can be onerous. In addition, there must be meaningful restrictions on a donor trustee for the CRT to qualify for charitable income tax treatment.

As a CSA, you may find some of your clients have highly appreciated assets that are not providing enough income for them. Fearing the capital gains tax, they may be considering holding onto the assets until death so their children can inherit the assets and sell it without incurring capital gains tax. You can advise them to consider a CRT to generate income with the full value of the asset (since it is not reduced by capital gains tax) to create higher returns.

CHARITABLE LEAD TRUST

A *charitable lead trust* (CLT) pays income to one or more charities, and when the CLT is terminated, the remaining assets are distributed to the donor's family members. Generally, CLTs do not reduce a donor's estate for estate tax purposes. Lifetime CLTs can be useful for individuals with discretionary wealth and a philanthropic attitude, but generally CLTs appeal only to extremely wealthy individuals.

However, the use of a *testamentary CLT* can allow a senior whose estate is hovering around the threshold of the applicable exclusion amount to eliminate or reduce estate taxes. A testamentary CLT can be extremely useful for an individual whose estate is worth $3.5 million (the maximum applicable exclusion amount in 2009 under EGTRRA). In 2010, EGTRRA repeals federal estate tax altogether; and in 2011, it establishes the applicable exclusion amount for estate tax at $1 million—unless new federal legislation is passed changing these terms.

The individual can instruct in a will or trust that the CLT be established only if there are estate taxes due and that the CLT last only as long as necessary to bring the estate tax to zero. In essence, the charity is renting the asset and receiving the income. In exchange, the estate receives a charitable deduction sufficient to wipe out the estate tax, and the heirs receive the asset at the end of the trust's term.

References

Bischoff, B. (2002). *Closing down the estate.* Retrieved August 17, 2004, from http://www.smartmoney.com/taxmatters/index.cfm?story=20020830

Esperti, R. A., Peterson, R. L., & Moser, E. G. (1999). *Generations: Planning your legacy.* Denver, CO: Esperti Peterson Institute.

Merrill Lynch. (2003, February 25). *Stretch IRA.* Retrieved June 7, 2004, from http://askmerrill.ml.com/product_details/0,,20398,00.html

The Motley Fool. (n.d.). *Designating IRA beneficiaries.* Retrieved June 7, 2004, from http://www.fool.com/retirement/manageretirement/manageretirement11.htm

Raymond, J. (2000). Charitable estate planning reduces the tax bite. *CSA Journal, 8,* 18.

Schnepper, J. (n.d.) *Stretch your IRA to help your grandkids.* Retrieved June 7, 2004, from http://moneycentral.msn.com/content/Taxes/Taxshelters/P33760.asp

Stum, M. S. (2004). Who gets grandma's yellow pie plate? *CSA Journal, 24,* 1

Resources

Services

Estate Planning Links. http://www.estateplanninglinks.com. A helpful consumer site regarding general estate planning information.

Findlaw. http://www.findlaw.com. This site provides general information on estate planning and the opportunity to locate an attorney who specializes in estate planning.

National Network of Estate Planning Attorneys. http://the.nnepa.com. This site provides general information on estate planning and the opportunity to locate an attorney who specializes in estate planning.

NOLO—Law for All. http://www.nolo.com. This site contains broad information on estate planning, trusts, probate, wills, estate and gift taxes, and incapacity.

SmartMoney, Estate Planning section. http://www.smartmoney.com/estate. This site includes consumer information, articles, and calculators for net worth and estate taxes.

Chapter 16

Financial Choices and Challenges for Seniors

John and Susan Roberts are not sleeping very well these days. Their daughter Chelsea's new baby, George, is the primary reason, and not just because he has yet to learn that nights are for sleeping.

Chelsea, newly single, moved back home to live with her parents. John and Susan recently realized they don't have any idea about how to help Chelsea save for little George's college education, and they are concerned. To add to that, Chelsea has no job and is staying home with George, so her parents are concerned about the extra financial burden. John has been thinking about his income and what will happen to the family if for some reason he no longer receives a regular paycheck.

. . .

Dot Parsons, on the other hand, has been sleeping very well. She just received a sizable inheritance. While she is sad about the underlying event, it excites her to have a not-so-small fortune in the bank. Of course, when Dot has her taxes prepared next year she may not be sleeping quite so well. Every penny of the inheritance is sitting in a taxable certificate of deposit.

. . .

Betty and Bob Barnett are wondering what to do. Betty has been offered an early retirement package she cannot afford to pass up. She will receive a large lump-sum payout and will continue to receive 75 percent of her current salary, indexed for inflation, for the rest of her life. Betty and Bob know they need some help, but whom should they talk to, how do they know who to trust, and what should they do now and in the future?

Introduction

By the time people are seniors, they may have been following a financial plan of some kind for years. They may be living on their current income, hoping their investments will continue generating income for their retirement. Or they may not have enough income to do more than pay for the basic necessities of daily living.

You will be more effective as a CSA if you understand this important fact: It doesn't make much sense for seniors who have not accumulated a large amount of wealth to do traditional long-term financial planning because they no longer have the length of life expectancy necessary to build wealth over the long-term. Instead, it makes more sense to talk about seniors' financial concerns and the strategies they can use to:

- make the best use of their current income, assets, and other resources (regardless of the amount);
- afford as many lifestyle choices as possible throughout their retirement;
- leave a legacy to others after their death.

Today's seniors possess a great diversity of financial needs. Many face new and complex family responsibilities and financial decisions that affect their attitudes about retirement and their ability to save for it. In this chapter we will specifically look at:

- *effects of increased longevity* and inflation on individuals' abilities to save and plan for retirement;
- *key financial concerns of seniors* in three financial groups: high net worth, middle income, and lower income, focusing on the majority of seniors in the middle- and lower-income groups;
- *financial needs at the three stages of retirement:* active, passive, and final;
- *six steps of financial planning* that help individuals estimate and plan for their financial needs through all three phases of retirement;
- *risk-management strategies,* including life and health insurance and tax planning;
- *investment strategies and vehicles:* growth, income, asset allocation; stocks, bonds, and mutual funds;
- *sources of retirement income* commonly used by seniors: IRAs and other qualified retirement plans (including required minimum distributions, early withdrawals, and beneficiary designations), annuities, and reverse mortgages;
- *common investment pitfalls:* what they are and how to protect against them.

Primary Senior Income Groups

It should come as no surprise that seniors occupy the same general income groups as the overall population: high net worth, middle income, and lower income. We characterize the three groups this way:

- *high net worth*: more than enough *assets* to provide for desired lifestyle and to make bequests
- *middle income*: generally enough *income* to provide for a desired lifestyle, but compromises may play a large part
- *lower income*: barely enough *income* to provide for basic needs

Table 16.1 illustrates the differences in financial goals among these three income groups.

Table 16.1 Seniors' Key Financial Concerns by Income Group

SENIOR INCOME GROUP	KEY FINANCIAL CONCERNS
High Net Worth: $1 million-plus in *assets*	■ managing taxes ■ maintaining and growing wealth ■ sharing wealth with heirs, charities, and others
Middle Income: $30,000–$80,000 annual *income* (not assets)	■ outliving assets ■ generating ongoing retirement income ■ financially supporting family members ■ maximizing income from multiple sources
Lower Income: Less than $30,000 annual *income* (not assets)	■ paying for basic necessities of daily living

HIGH NET WORTH

The exact financial point at which an individual is identified as being in the high net worth (HNW) category varies, depending on who is doing the identification. For our purposes, let's place the mark at those with more than $1 million in investable *assets*, not including their primary residence. There are more than 2.9 million HNW individuals in the United States (source: 2006 World Wealth Report by Merrill Lynch and Cap Gemini).

According to Thane Stenner, author of *True Wealth* (2001):

■ Most HNW individuals earned their wealth by owning their own businesses.

■ A large portion of HNW individuals believe that maintaining current wealth and income is more important than building it.

■ HNW individuals face two general challenges:

—ensuring they have a comprehensive financial plan;

—matching sophisticated investments with their unique needs.

Financial Concerns

In addition to maintaining their asset base, HNW individuals tend to have two primary areas of concern. One area of concern is to manage their tax burden, and the other is to maximize growth and income from their assets.

MIDDLE INCOME

It is difficult to identify exactly what qualifies as middle income, but let's say that it is between $30,000 and $80,000 per year. (The median income—that point at which half of seniors have more income than that amount and half have less—for a four-person family in the United States is currently about $70,354 (Source: US Department of Health and Human Services, 2008). Note, too, that we are talking about *income* levels here, rather than *asset* levels as we did with HNW individuals. For both middle- and lower-income individuals, income is usually of greater significance than assets. Also at this level, a senior's most significant asset is typically the primary residence.

Financial Concerns

Seniors in the middle-income group share many of the concerns common to those in the high-income group (especially for those in the upper middle-income category). However, we can also identify a number of concerns specific to the middle-income group: outliving their assets, ongoing retirement income, financially supporting other family members, and maximizing income from multiple sources such as a regular paycheck, Social Security, and Supplemental Security Income.

LOWER INCOME

Definitions of the low-income category for seniors vary. For our purposes, we define it as an annual income below $30,000. This income bracket includes poor seniors, seniors with annual incomes between poverty and 125 percent of poverty, and those with annual incomes between 125 percent of poverty and $30,000. For these seniors, increased expenses of even a few dollars each month have a huge impact.

Poor Seniors

In 2008 the poverty threshold was defined by the Census Bureau as an annual income of $10,400 a year for a single person and $14,000 for two people. The poverty rate in 2007 for seniors 65 and older remained at 9.7 percent, up from 9.4 in 2006; while the number of seniors 65 and older in poverty increased from 3.4 million in 2006 to 3.6 million in 2007.

Seniors with Annual Incomes between Poverty and 125 Percent of Poverty

15.6 percent of the senior population have incomes between poverty and 125 percent of the poverty level (United States Census Bureau, 2006). This means that in 2006 one in six seniors had incomes between $9,800 and $12,250, if they were single, or $13,200 and $16,500, if they were a couple. The Census Bureau is not due to release the 2007 numbers until August 26, 2009.

Seniors with Annual Incomes between 125 Percent of Poverty and $30,000

Many seniors have incomes that are higher than 125 percent of poverty, but are still very low. For example, the overall median income of seniors in 2007 was $17,382. In addition, one fourth of Americans 65 and over had incomes of less than $10,722 in 2007 (Source: Congressional Research Services).

Table 16.2 shows the impact that age has on income. In 2004 the median income of people age 80 or older was barely near the subsistence level and only slightly more than half that of seniors age 65 to 69.

Table 16.2 Median income, by age, 2004

AGE	MEDIAN INCOME (DOLLARS)
65–69	28,969
70–74	22,603
75–79	19,290
80 or older	15,948

Source: *Income of the Aged Chartbook*, Social Security Administration, 2004

Financial Concerns

Low-income seniors face much more fundamental challenges than the middle-income group, including how to pay for housing, food, prescription drugs, and transportation. And they may be people you don't suspect—parents of one of your clients, a next-door neighbor, or a church member. Being prepared to help these economically vulnerable individuals is part of your role as a CSA.

SHIFTING FROM ONE INCOME GROUP TO ANOTHER

Barring a major financial reversal, we can generally assume most HNW individuals will remain HNW individuals. So as HNW individuals solidify their financial position, they are unlikely to shift into a lower income category.

But the same cannot be said for many seniors in the middle-income category. It is all too possible to move from a relatively comfortable lifestyle into one that provides considerably less financial stability. How does this happen? Generally, this results from inadequate financial and retirement planning and by spending too much money, particularly in the five years immediately before and after retirement.

In addition, many, if not most, people underestimate the amount of money they will need to provide for a comfortable retirement (*comfortable* meaning about the same lifestyle to which they have become accustomed). Together, these factors add up to the real possibility that someone who started out solidly at a middle-income level may wind up living at a much lower income level. This does not mean that those in the middle-income category will necessarily move into poverty (although some may). However, it is likely that many of these people will experience a decline in their standard of living during retirement.

Challenges to Retirement Savings and Income

From a financial perspective, the working years prior to retirement are the time for accumulating wealth, so that when seniors retire and enter a *wealth expenditure* period, they will have sufficient income to choose their desired lifestyle for the rest of their lives, and perhaps have remaining property to pass on to their heirs.

Before retirement and to some degree afterwards, financial planners advise *building wealth* through some combination of assets including cash savings, investments, employer-sponsored retirement plans, individual retirement accounts, and real estate—and to *protect wealth* by purchasing insurance and taking other steps to manage tax liabilities and the cost of risks such as possible disability or incapacity.

The amount that seniors have accumulated in personal savings (cash and investments in stocks, bonds, mutual funds, qualified retirement plans, real estate, and other property) determines the quality of lifestyle they can afford during retirement—and for how long.

ADEQUACY OF PERSONAL SAVINGS

If seniors find it challenging to save as much as they would like for retirement, they are not alone. There is significant concern among financial experts that the low personal savings rate in the United States will not create the amount of retirement income needed by today's seniors and baby boomers who will soon retire.

As Figure 16.1 shows, the personal savings rate for the period 2000–2008 in the United States has only once risen above 3 percent of disposable personal income.

Figure 16.1 U.S. Personal Saving Rates

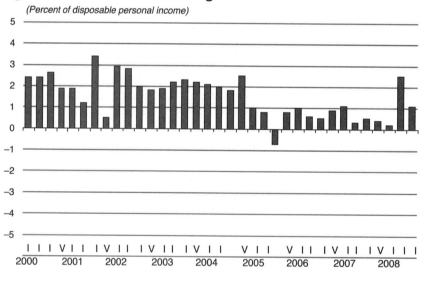

(Percent of disposable personal income)

Source: Bureau of Economic Analysis, United States Department of Commerce

Seniors may hesitate to save and invest when interest rates offer relatively low returns or the stock market performs poorly. But regardless of market conditions or interest rates, *not* saving for retirement is usually a serious mistake.

According to a survey by the Consumer Federation of America and Primerica (Gerencher, 1999), "More Americans believe they have a better chance of making half a million dollars through the lottery than by saving and investing." The survey substantiated the following:

- Most middle- and low-income groups fail to save and have accumulated little wealth other than home equity.
- The average household has a high rate of debt and low level of assets.
- Most respondents overestimated their assets and the assets of others.

This overestimation may contribute to the declining savings rate. The researcher who conducted the survey encourages the education of middle-income earners about savings, mutual funds, and other investment tools. Motivating clients to save before and—if possible—during their retirement years may be among the most valuable services a financial planner may provide.

Interestingly, although attitudes and beliefs certainly play a strong role in how much Americans save, the ability of many individuals to save for retirement is also affected by their increasing longevity.

EFFECTS OF LONGEVITY AND INFLATION ON RETIREMENT SAVINGS

A person born in 1900 could expect to live to about age 47. A person born in 2001 can expect to live to about age 77—a 30-year increase in life expectancy in little more than 100 years. Although we cannot predict what will happen in the next 100 years, it seems safe to say that continued advancements in medical care should cause overall life expectancy to continue to increase (United States Department of Health and Human Services, 2003).

Increasing longevity, combined with inflation, means that middle-class seniors are likely to require retirement nest eggs of $1 million or more to maintain financial independence in their current lifestyles during extended years of retirement. Understanding the impact of inflation and implementing savings and investment strategies to counter its effect are crucial to successful retirement planning. (You should educate your senior clients or refer them to qualified financial professionals who can help them implement strategies to beat inflation's erosion on retirement dollars.)

New Views on Retirement

In addition, increasing longevity has changed our society in two fundamental ways that affect individuals' abilities to save for retirement (Cutler, 2002):

- *balance:* the amount of time for accumulating wealth to fund retirement is shorter
- *complexity*
  —cost of new and expanded family responsibilities
  —shift of responsibility to individual employees to make investment decisions

Balance

In financial planning, the word *balance* means the ratio of time spent accumulating wealth versus the time that wealth is spent. Today we see shorter accumulation and longer expenditure phases because of increasing longevity,

461

prosperity, and early retirements. Individuals are under pressure to create enough financial resources during shorter working years to fund longer and more active retirement years.

Complexity

Personal savings behaviors are significantly affected by:

- increased family responsibilities that may span several generations;
- the shift from defined benefits to defined contribution retirement plans.

In the family structure, increased longevity has created more financial responsibilities for individuals who are sandwiched between children or grandchildren in college and aging parents or grandparents. The expenses of added family responsibilities often affect these individuals' abilities to save for their retirements, and may require them to use portions of their existing retirement assets such as stocks, bonds, and mutual funds to pay for family members' educational, caregiving, health, and medical needs. Also, when retirees do not have enough income to afford their desired lifestyles—including responsibilities such as caregiving or supporting grandchildren—if they are still young enough, they may start a second career or take part-time work.

In the investment area, an employer-sponsored, qualified retirement plan such as a 401(k) or 403(b) is often an individual's largest and most important asset, particularly for middle- and low-income individuals. These plans are *defined contribution* plans, and most employers offer some version of them. They place the responsibility for building adequate retirement assets on individual employees, rather than employers. Individual employees must decide if they want to participate in the employer-sponsored plan, and if so, how much money they want to contribute, and to which type of investments (equities, bonds, mutual funds, etc.).

This is a major change from the days when most employers offered pension (defined benefits) plans to employees that the employer funded, invested, and then, from the profits, paid a guaranteed amount of retirement income to their retired employees.

In addition to a change in the proportion of wealth accumulation and expenditure periods, and the changes in family needs, retirement includes different phases. (For information on those phases, see chapter 2, Aging and Society.) Understanding the phases of retirement can help you understand the changes that your senior clients go through as they adjust to this period in their lives.

Critical Period for Creating Retirement Income

The most critical period for building personal savings for a successful retirement is what Michael Stein refers to as the *Decision Decade*—the five years immediately before and the five years immediately after retirement (Stein, 2000).

5 years	**RETIREMENT**	5 years

Five Years before Retirement

Individuals who are preparing for retirement are more financially comfortable than they've ever been. Salaries are at a peak, college tuitions are generally a thing of the past, often the mortgage is paid, and with children out of the home both spouses may be working. Available funds may increase as much as 5 to 10 times during the five years immediately preceding retirement (Stein, 2000). But instead of using these additional funds to fatten their retirement accounts, couples often expand their lifestyles, consuming additional dollars and increasing their expenses, which must be paid for when they retire.

Five Years after Retirement

In the first five years after retiring, the couple has time on their hands to continue expanding their lifestyles. Because these individuals were at the highest earning level of their lives just prior to retiring, they are used to spending. They've arrived. No more need to save. Run and spend. Numerous ads target the 50-and-older market, urging people to buy luxury automobiles, second homes, time-shares, and vacation properties; to cruise to exotic locales and take luxurious vacations; to trade old furniture for new, higher-quality furniture—the list goes on.

Although there may not be anything wrong with an increased level of spending as retirement approaches, doing so frequently creates real problems after retirement and can compound the problem of not having enough income for later retirement years. It is much easier to get used to luxury living than it is to live on a leaner budget. But once money is spent, it will never be available for future income needs. Also, credit card balances eventually must be repaid.

The Decision Decade could consume tremendous amounts of money and further expand the base of future retirement expenses unless seniors are careful in their spending habits. Stein's comments reinforce the significant differences in financial needs at each phase of retirement. The patterns he describes strongly suggest that you encourage clients to be more aggressive in continuing retirement savings and more realistic in examining the long-term effect of lifestyle decisions on retirement expenses.

Meeting the Financial Challenges of Retirement

Proper financial planning seeks to coordinate a number of interdependent factors in a plan to achieve the individual's financial agenda:

- the most satisfactory mix of cash and debt management
- savings plans

463

- insurance coverage and other risk management techniques
- investment vehicles
- tax strategies
- employment benefits
- retirement plans

The financial planning process provides a structure for identifying and quantifying your client's financial goals and for creating a roadmap to help achieve them. As a CSA, knowing the six steps of this process (Table 16.3) will help you to advise the ones that will most help your clients in their individual situations, based on their individual income levels. If you are not a financial planning professional, knowing these steps will help you recognize when referrals should be made to experts.

Table 16.3 Six Steps of the Financial Planning Process

STEP	PURPOSE
1. The senior and/or the advisor should gather information and data	- clarify data - understand and the senior's financial concerns - establish a relationship with the senior and begin to build trust
2. Analyze data	- identify both current and future financial problems as well as potential solutions
3. Develop goals and planning recommendations	- recommend actions and strategies to address financial concerns, correct problems, and meet the senior's goals
4. Present and review planning recommendations	- solicit the senior's feedback and commitment to implement a coordinated financial plan - have the senior choose, with your guidance, which recommendations to include in the financial plan
5. Implement the plan	- may need to involve other professionals (e.g., attorneys, accountants, investment brokers, etc.) - may include purchasing the risk management and investment vehicles the client has approved
6. Monitor the plan	- adjust the financial plan in response to the client's changing needs, concerns, and goals (this step loops back to step 1)

STEP ONE: GATHER INFORMATION AND DATA

Gather and clarify both relevant qualitative (attitudinal) and quantitative (numbers and names) information; understand the senior's financial concerns and goals, and get to know the senior. Be aware that discussing money

464

may be difficult for many individuals, especially those who were taught that people should keep their financial lives private. You may choose to use a financial questionnaire (see Appendix A) that each senior completes and then reviews in a face-to-face meeting. Seek to fully understand each client's financial and personal goals, attitude toward investment risk, previous investment experience, estate plans, tax exposure, insurance coverage, and available financial resources—as well as assets owned, amounts owed, and family considerations such as age, health, life expectancy, and marriage and divorce expectations.

STEP TWO: ANALYZE DATA

Review and analyze all the information to identify both current and future financial problems, as well as potential solutions. Calculate current cash flow and current net worth. If appropriate, do a retirement income needs analysis.

As analysis progresses, you may need to consult the client's attorney, stockbroker, tax advisor, and others for help in understanding the client's current financial-planning condition. Because a client may be sensitive about confidentiality regarding finances, it is important that you receive express (typically written) permission from the client before contacting other advisors.

STEP THREE: DEVELOP GOALS AND PLANNING RECOMMENDATIONS

Based on the analysis and information gathered from the senior, identify recommended strategies and actions to correct problems and address the senior's financial concerns. Remember that a proper financial plan integrates cash flow, insurance, investments, retirement, taxation, and estate planning.

STEP FOUR: PRESENT AND REVIEW PLANNING RECOMMENDATIONS

Present the recommendations to the senior and solicit the senior's feedback and commitment to implement a coordinated financial plan. Communicate clearly, and exercise caution to ensure that the recommendations make sense to the senior as well as appropriately reflect the senior's needs, values, and concerns. Observe the client's verbal and nonverbal responses to recommendations. Remember that it is up to the client to accept or reject recommendations. Unless a client buys into a plan's recommendations, it will be very difficult—if not impossible—to implement the plan.

STEP FIVE: IMPLEMENT THE PLAN

The better a financial advisor is at explaining the reasons behind recommendations, the more fully the senior is likely to understand and implement them. The implementation stage is likely to involve the client's insurance agent or broker, accountant, stockbroker, financial planner, estate-planning attorney, trust officer, and other advisors.

STEP SIX: MONITOR THE PLAN

Continually monitor and adjust the plan's actual progress, including stock and bond market performance, interest rate fluctuations, and economic and tax law changes. Provide periodic (annual at least) reviews to your client. Ongoing monitoring is beneficial because life changes, such as relocation, the death of a spouse, birth of a grandchild, or deteriorating health may change a client's financial status or goals. Encourage each senior client to share news of such changes as soon as practical.

Retirement Income Needs Analysis

Clients often need help with evaluating the financial impact of a decision to retire early. For instance, many baby boomers wish to retire in their 50s. From a financial perspective, reviewing projected retirement income and expenses should clarify the optimum timing for retirement versus the advantages of continuing to work. Middle-class seniors are likely to require retirement nest eggs of $1 million or more to maintain the financial independence of their current lifestyles during the extended years of their retirement (see Appendix B: Mini-Case Study).

A *retirement income needs analysis* usually starts by preparing a cash flow statement listing cash inflows from employment and investments as well as cash outflows (expenses). Outflows are generally in three categories:

- *Fixed outflows* are difficult to change. Examples include taxes, insurance premiums, loan payments, and housing costs such as rent or mortgage payments.
- *Savings and investments* are deposits made to investment and bank savings accounts. Examples include elective (voluntary) contributions (deferrals) to 401(k) accounts and one-time or periodic deposits into mutual funds, bank accounts, and other investment vehicles.
- *Variable expenses* are those an individual may be able to change. Examples include food (including dining out), clothing, entertainment, and travel.

CASH FLOW

Cash Flow Statement

When it comes to preserving or improving lifestyle during retirement, cash flow is often an issue. A retiree who wishes to travel extensively or enjoy expensive hobbies obviously needs more money than one whose preferences are less costly.

If a client is already retired, completing a cash flow statement reveals his or her approximate cash needs. If the client is still working, the current cash outflows should be adjusted for potential changes in the postretirement years. For example, if a client currently makes mortgage payments but anticipates that the mortgage will be paid off by retirement, the fixed outflow representing the mortgage payment would be eliminated from the postretirement projection. However, expenses for property tax and property insurance would still appear as projected postretirement outflows.

Addressing Cash Flow Problems

Older clients, especially those on fixed incomes, may struggle to find the means to pay their bills. Analysis of current cash outflows may reveal ways to better meet expenses. For example, if a client spends substantial amounts dining out, variable outflow can be reduced if the client goes only to restaurants offering senior discounts and early bird specials.

How Much Income Will Seniors Need in Retirement?

The College for Financial Planning, the insurance industry, and the AARP—institutions that analyze seniors' financial issues—agree that individuals should plan to retire on no less than 80 percent of their preretirement, before tax income. (Few middle-income seniors report they can live on $2,000 per month.)

According to these institutions, when income falls below approximately 80 to 85 percent, retirees may not be able to afford the lifestyles they perceive they have earned. Your clients need to understand how much of a retirement nest egg is required to support a comfortable retirement that statistically could be 30 to 35 years—all without a paycheck.

Seniors should be encouraged to avoid credit card debt because the high interest rates associated with credit card balances can reduce money otherwise available for expenditures. The good news is that many older Americans who lived through the Great Depression avoid debt of any kind. However, retired baby boomers accustomed to carrying credit card debt may struggle with credit card management in the retirement years. Financial planners should encourage clients to pay off credit card balances whenever possible.

Successful advisors learn about local programs that provide cost savings to seniors. Many states sponsor subsidies to help lower- and (sometimes) middle-income seniors pay for prescription drugs. As another example, the city of Chicago provides certificates for reduced-fare cab rides.

Cash Flow Is Only an Estimate

It is not practical to calculate cash inflows and outflows precisely. In practice, planners should expect to encounter significant differences in expense projections. Each client's ultimate postretirement spending pattern may differ significantly from projections. Certain clients will wish to provide college funding for grandchildren or financial help for siblings in their retirement years. Other clients will enjoy dining out more than during their working years.

Recall that spending differs greatly according to lifestyle and the three phases of retirement. Nevertheless, analyzing current and projected or actual postretirement spending is a logical springboard to a retirement income needs analysis at almost any stage of retirement.

USE CONSERVATIVE ASSUMPTIONS TO FORECAST RETIREMENT INCOME

Professional financial planners generally concur that it makes good sense to use conservative assumptions when analyzing retirement income needs, including the following guidelines.

Overestimate Life Expectancy

We cannot presume that clients will live only to their statistical average life expectancy and not longer. Conceptually, average life expectancy indicates that half of the population will outlive this age. Thus, conservative assumptions factor that clients (or spouses) will live 10 or more years beyond the statistical average life expectancy.

Overestimate the Rate of Inflation

In recent years, the rate of inflation has been lower than in most of the years following World War II. This may mislead planners to assume 2 percent inflation rates in retirement income needs analysis. Generally assuming an inflation rate ranging between 3 and 5 percent is considered conservative practice.

Underestimate the Rate of Investment Returns

Although historical studies of the rate of return on stock market investments may show average returns around 10 or 12 percent, the stock market can have extended periods of poor performance. Conservative assumptions about equity (stock) investments often presume an 8 to 9 percent rate of return, reduced by 2 to 3 percent for federal and state taxes. The conservative approach to retirement income needs analysis is likely to use an after-tax compounding rate of 5 to 6 percent on the equity (stock) portion of a moderate risk portfolio. The bond portions of the same portfolio should be expected to earn less.

Again, keep in mind that the objective of financial planning for seniors is financial independence. If assumptions are too aggressive, clients will outlive their money. If assumptions are ultimately too conservative, clients will leave some wealth behind, although that is generally not considered to be as problematic.

Developing a Financial Plan

STRATEGIES TO ADDRESS SENIORS' FINANCIAL CONCERNS

Everyone faces certain issues relative to their lifestyle, health, and finances. So what's the difference among people?

It's *the amount of financial assets and resources* each individual has to address these issues. More assets and resources usually mean more options and possibly less concern. For example, seniors with a high net worth may feel confident they can afford to hire full-time caregivers for themselves or their elderly parents, whereas middle-income seniors may feel the pressure of not being able to afford assisted living care for a disabled spouse, and must therefore provide the care themselves.

Remember that seniors in all income groups want to protect their current level of assets or income and as much as possible and to increase their financial resources to assure a desired quality of lifestyle over their remaining lifetimes. Table 16.4 lists the common strategies and resources available to each income group for achieving these primary financial goals. The overlap of strategies in the categories *Managing Risks to Current Income and Assets* and *Managing the Growth of Assets and Income* underscores the fact that you can provide extremely valuable offerings to your clients by tailoring your services and referrals to seniors' individual needs and financial resources.

Risk-Management Strategies

Unexpected changes in lifestyle and health carry the risk of reducing seniors' assets and income and potentially causing a shift to a lower income group or standard of living.

Table 16.4 Strategies to Address Seniors' Financial Concerns

INCOME GROUP	KEY FINANCIAL CONCERNS	MANAGING RISKS TO CURRENT INCOME AND ASSETS	MANAGING TAXES	MANAGING INVESTMENTS: THE GROWTH OF ASSETS AND INCOME
High Net Worth: $1 million or more in *assets*	▪ managing taxes ▪ maintaining and growing wealth ▪ sharing wealth with heirs, charities, and others	▪ private health insurance ▪ Medicare ▪ Medicaid ▪ Social Security disability benefits ▪ long-term care insurance ▪ personal savings ▪ life insurance: term, permanent (whole)	▪ tax exemptions and deductions	▪ self-owned businesses ▪ qualified retirement plans: IRA, 401(k), 403(b), etc. ▪ annuities ▪ Social Security retirement benefits
Middle income: $30,000–$80,000 annual *income* (not assets)	▪ outliving assets ▪ generating ongoing retirement income ▪ financially supporting family members ▪ maximizing income from multiple sources	*Applies to both high net worth and middle income groups*	*Applies to both high net worth and middle income groups*	▪ self-owned businesses ▪ qualified retirement plans: IRA, 401(k), 403(b), etc. ▪ annuities ▪ pensions (to some degree) ▪ Social Security retirement benefits ▪ delayed retirement ▪ second career or part-time employment ▪ reverse mortgage ▪ alternative sources of income*
Lower income: $30,000 or less annual *income* (not) assets	▪ paying for the basic necessities of daily living	▪ personal savings ▪ Medicare ▪ Medicaid ▪ Social Security disability benefits ▪ life insurance: term, permanent (whole)		▪ Social Security retirement benefits ▪ delayed retirement ▪ second job or part-time employment ▪ reverse mortgage ▪ qualified retirement plans (typically the few who could afford to contribute while working) ▪ pensions (to some degree) ▪ alternative sources of income*

*For example: SSI, Veterans benefits, Medicaid beneficiary, tax credits, etc.

Many baby boomers find themselves part of the sandwich generation, facing the financial burden of caring for elderly parents while financing children through college. Thus, a client's plans to retire, investment strategies, life insurance coverage, and estate plan should be evaluated with family considerations in mind.

Even though modern medicine has made tremendous advances that help to increase longevity and keep seniors in good health, seniors eventually may become unable to maintain their good health. Life insurance is, of course, one tool to help with this area of risk management. (We will discuss life insurance shortly.)

However, the bigger problem for many is one of incapacity rather than death. Without proper planning, an extended period of incapacity will certainly diminish, if not outright deplete, an individual's assets. If your clients are faced with incapacity or reduced ability to perform activities of daily living, they will likely need greater resources to provide income for appropriate postretirement living.

HEALTH INSURANCE

One of the biggest areas of concern for many individuals is health care. This concern is greatly increased among seniors. As people age they have an ever-increasing chance of getting sick or hurt. While medical science is constantly

---

Four Ways to Handle Risk

There are four basic methods of handling risk: avoidance, reduction, retention, and transfer.

Risk Avoidance

Generally, risk avoidance means not taking part in some activities that might be considered risky. For example, if you don't want to get hurt skiing, don't go skiing. However, it may also mean avoiding travel to certain areas or being careful of timing. Given the current state of political unrest in the world, this can be especially important for HNW seniors.

Risk Reduction

Reducing risk relative to wealth preservation can include, for example, installing an alarm system or fencing and gating property. It may involve installing a safe for jewelry or taking similar actions.

Risk Retention

Risk retention simply means accepting a given risk and deciding not to do anything about it. It includes risks such as having high deductibles on insurance policies (i.e., retaining risk in the amount of the deductible).

Risk Transfer

Using insurance is transferring risk. In order to protect the value of your property, you purchase insurance (e.g., homeowners or auto). In order to protect yourself financially against potential lawsuits, you purchase liability insurance (including an umbrella policy). Seniors who want to preserve wealth need to make sure they have adequate insurance coverage. This is especially true of those in the high net worth category.

---

improving health care, the improvements come at a cost. A big cost! In fact, for many people, the fear of not be able to pay medical expenses is one of their biggest financial concerns. Fortunately, health insurance provides some relief from the high cost of medical care.

Medicare

Medicare is a federal health care program for persons ages 65 and older, certain disabled persons, and anyone who has end-stage renal (kidney) disease. Medicare Part A covers hospital charges, such as bed and board, operating room costs, and lab tests. Premiums for Part A are paid by the government. Part B pays for doctor's charges and for other outpatient treatment, and requires a premium payment by the individual. Both Part A and Part B require the individual to pay a deductible, which can be quite large. Some prescription drug coverage is offered. Medicare is covered in greater depth in chapter 19, Medicare.

Medicaid

Medicaid is a combined state and federal program (see chapter 20, Medicaid and Seniors). Although Medicaid operates under general federal guidelines, each state runs its Medicaid program somewhat differently. For example, income and asset levels for eligibility vary from state to state. If you are working in multiple jurisdictions, you need to be aware that different rules may apply.

Medicaid is a form of welfare and has rules (different than Medicare's) that must be followed to qualify for benefits. In addition to medical qualifications required to receive benefits, in general terms, an individual must spend down his or her assets to a low level to be eligible for Medicaid-covered long-term care (LTC). Spending down assets means using up whatever resources are available until there is a very small amount left. Certain assets, such as a home and an automobile, are exempt from the spend-down provisions as long as the patient intends to return home or a spouse remains in the home.

Additionally, there is a limit to the income a person can have and still be eligible for Medicaid. A lien will sometimes be placed on the home of a person who is confined to a long-term care facility. On the sale of the home, the proceeds will be used to repay Medicaid for its expenses in providing the long-term care. When there is a living community spouse, this person can keep the home, some invested assets, and a significant amount of the household income while the confined partner (institutionalized spouse) qualifies for Medicaid.

As mentioned in chapter 20, Medicaid pays for care for nearly 70 percent of nursing home residents of all ages and accounts for 42 percent of overall long-term care spending. When a senior is deciding whether to purchase LTC insurance or to qualify for Medicaid, consider these factors:

- quality of care
- physical qualifications that must be met to receive benefits

- elimination of an inheritance to pass on to children (see chapter 15, Estate Planning)
- possible financial penalties for an improper transfer of assets
- potential loss of a family home and other assets
- availability of Medicaid patient beds

Long-Term Care Coverage

We can identify risk management in the area of incapacity as long-term care. There are a number of levels of care that may be required. These range from skilled care (the most comprehensive and expensive) through intermediate care, custodial care, and finally to home care (requiring the least comprehensive services and having the lowest cost).

Other than using personal assets, two main sources exist to pay for LTC expenses: Medicaid and long-term care insurance (LTCI). LTCI is a much better solution for the many people who want to protect assets, preserve caregiving choices, and maintain a reasonable quality of life.

LIFE INSURANCE

People typically buy life insurance to protect their survivors against the sudden loss of income and ensuing debts or estate taxes that may occur after the death of a breadwinner. Most seniors are past their employment years, so loss of income may not be a factor. However, seniors may wish to consider life insurance when faced with long-term caregiving provided by an informal, unpaid family caregiver, such as a parent with a chronic illness or permanent disability depending on an unemployed adult child for assistance. Costs of replacing the services provided by an unpaid family caregiver may justify the need for life insurance on the caregiver.

There are three main types of life insurance that are useful in protecting income and assets during retirement:

- term life insurance
- permanent life insurance
- life settlements and viaticals

Term Life Insurance

Term policies provide a specified death benefit, presuming the insured dies during the policy term. Terms may range from 1 to 30 years. Several insurers also are currently offering term life insurance with level premiums for the life of the contract. These typically are universal life policies. Term policies build no cash value, although certain policies can be converted at a later date to permanent cash value policies.

Premiums for term policies *start out* lower than for cash value policies, but increase with the insured's age and deteriorating health. Premiums for insured seniors (65 or older) are typically so high that the insurance becomes unaffordable, causing people to drop the policies at the very time they are most likely to be needed. As a result, term policies should primarily be considered for temporary, rather than lifetime, coverage.

Permanent Life Insurance

Permanent life insurance policies provide a death benefit for as long as premiums are paid. Additionally, they usually feature a cash value that accumulates on a tax-deferred basis. Although the purpose of the cash value is to keep the premiums level for the life of the contract, it can also be used for additional purposes. For example, a policy owner may borrow the cash value for any reason, including additional retirement income. Various forms of permanent life insurance policies—including whole life, universal life, and variable universal life—offer different options for premium payment, adjustment of death benefits, and accumulation of cash value. Because a variable life insurance policyholder chooses the investment portfolio used to generate cash value, variable life is considered a security and must be sold by a professional holding a securities license.

Life Settlements and Viaticals

The emotional strain of anticipated death from a terminal illness or the stress of a seriously debilitating chronic illness is worsened by the customary increase in medical bills and the cost of the special care required.

Life settlements and viaticals may offer an option for turning life insurance into cash at a time when a senior most needs it—when the senior is terminally or chronically ill. Using life settlements and viaticals, a percentage of the face value of a permanent life insurance policy is paid by the funding insurance company to the policyholder in exchange for ownership of all or part of the policy. The policyholder and previously designated beneficiaries give up rights to the death benefit when the insured dies, in return for a tax-free settlement (assuming Health Insurance Portability and Accountability Act of 1996 [HIPAA] and other federal guidelines are met) while the insured person is still alive. Third-party companies specializing in viatical and life settlements purchase the policy for less than face value. The investing company that purchases the policy pays future premiums to keep the policy in force and collects the death benefit when the named insured dies.

Viatical settlements may be available to policyholders who are chronically ill and have significantly shortened life expectancy. *Life settlements*, commonly called *senior settlements*, permit seniors who are 65 and older to exchange life insurance benefits for cash. Each insurance or life settlement company establishes its own criteria (which must be available to anyone seeking a settlement) regarding the policyholder's life expectancy and the policy value. The viatical market expanded rapidly among the AIDS/HIV positive population, who experienced notoriously severe disability and financial devastation. Today it is used by individuals with a range of chronic, progressive, and fatal illnesses such as Lou Gehrig's disease, cancer, and heart disease. While certain viatical settlement companies will accept a relatively long life expectancy, most prefer a shorter term.

Money distributed as an accelerated benefit or viatical settlement in conjunction with a terminal illness may be used by the recipient for any purpose. Typical uses for such distributions include the following:

- greater income
- out-of-pocket medical expenses
- alternative treatments not covered by traditional medical expense insurance
- one last dream vacation
- loan payoffs
- cash gifts to loved ones
- charitable gifts
- dignity earned from not dying destitute

Risk management and insurance planning can go a long way toward increasing a senior's financial comfort and provide more of a sense of security. Good planning in this area will also helping seniors hold onto their assets through the proper use of insurance.

Holding onto assets, however, and improving income can create another problem: taxes. The United States has a graduated income tax that, in simplified form, means the more income an individual has, the more opportunity there is to pay more taxes. This can be counterproductive to maintaining a comfortable retirement, so the next area of financial planning to look at is tax management.

Tax Management

Since the inception of this nation, taxes have been a part of everyday life. Congress enacted the first income tax laws in 1862, in part to fund the Civil War. In 1913, the 16th Amendment was added to the Constitution, making income taxes a permanent fixture of the country's taxation system. As a result, tax-related issues can be a big part of the financial planning process. Poor tax management cuts into older Americans' cash flow and ultimately diminishes lifestyle.

Individuals in each of the three income categories can benefit from some amount of good tax planning and management. Even low-income seniors can get some benefit from tax planning. Proper use of available credits, deductions, and exemptions can help reduce income tax. Depending on the income level, IRA or other retirement plan contributions can also help to reduce taxable income, while eventually providing increased retirement income. Enough other possibilities exist to encourage low-income seniors to do at least some tax planning.

The phrase *nontraditional lifestyle* is being heard more and more today. It is important to note that we have a very traditional tax code. This means that some of those with nontraditional lifestyles may not be able to take advantage of all the tax planning opportunities available to people living more traditional lifestyles. For example, the tax code offers some tax filing breaks to couples who are legally married. Most people in common law marriages or in gay and lesbian domestic partnerships will be required to file as single individuals, not as married filing jointly. Depending on the exact financial arrangements, it may also be difficult for those in a nontraditional relationship to take full advantage of certain deductions and credits.

As a CSA, you should realize that nontraditional couples will likely face a different tax situation than those in more traditional relationships. However, whether traditional or nontraditional, most people will have to deal with income taxes, and the first step is usually determining how much income they have.

Income may come from a variety of sources, including compensation, interest, dividend income received from owning an investment (known as *holding period income*), or capital gains (realized on selling an asset at a profit), rent, Social Security, pension, and so forth.

The taxes that affect a majority of seniors are taxes on:

- compensation, which includes wages, salaries, commissions, fees, tips, fringe benefits, and stock options;
- interest and dividends;
- capital gains;
- Social Security retirement and disability benefits.

TAX ON COMPENSATION

Compensation is taxed at ordinary income rates. Deductions and exemptions reduce taxable income. Taxpayers who do not itemize deductions may claim the standard deduction. Of particular importance to seniors who do not itemize is that an additional standard deduction is available to taxpayers over age 65 and for taxpayers who are blind. Two additional standard deductions are allowed for a taxpayer who is both age 65 and blind. In 2009, the standard deduction will be enhanced by real property taxes paid, limited to $500 for a single taxpayer and $1,000 for a married couple filing jointly. (Legislation *may* extend this enhancement in 2009 and beyond.)

DEDUCTIONS

Itemizing Deductions

Some seniors may benefit if the total amount of their itemized deductions exceeds the standard deduction combined with the additional deductions for being age 65 or blind. (These two deductions are not available to seniors who itemize; also, the ability to itemize may be limited for those with substantial incomes.)

Numerous deductions may be itemized (refer to IRS Publication 17) including all real property tax, medical expenses, and charitable gifts.

Medical Expense Deduction

Seniors who itemize deductions may be eligible to deduct medical expenses if the total of medical qualifying deductions exceeds $7\frac{1}{2}$ percent of an individual's or couple's adjusted gross income (for the year 2009). Expenses qualifying for the medical deduction include:

- medical and dental expenses actually paid;
- qualified long-term care insurance premiums;

The Basic Tax Formula

One of the primary goals of good financial planning is to manage tax liability, preferably lowering the amount of taxes owed. To understand the way income tax minimization works, be familiar with the basic formula for computing federal income tax:

Income (broadly defined)

– Exclusions and non-taxable income

= Total income

– Deductions

= Adjusted Gross Income (AGI)

– The greater of:

- *total itemized deductions or*
- *the standard deduction*

– Personal and dependency exemptions

= Taxable income

× Tax rate*

= Total federal income tax due

*Tax rates, which increase progressively for larger amounts of income, are multiplied by taxable income to determine the amount of tax due less any tax credits a taxpayer can apply.

In a sense, this formula mimics IRS Form 1040, which most Americans use to calculate and report their personal income tax. IRS Publication 17 contains instructions for completing Form 1040 and provides accompanying schedules for reporting capital gains, business expenses, and other items.

By understanding common tax consequences and tax-reduction strategies, you can help seniors estimate retirement income, increase spendable income, and leave dollars to heirs rather than to the government (estate taxes are discussed in chapter 15, Estate Planning).

Tax law is constantly changing, so it is important to remain aware of changes to both federal and state laws.

- transportation for medical purposes;
- special medical items and equipment, including installation of wheelchair access ramps, wall railings, and other similar home modifications;
- reasonable home improvements for safety and medical reasons.

Charitable Gift Deduction

Deductions are often available for gifts of cash and other property made to a qualified organization operated exclusively for religious, charitable, scientific, literary, or educational purposes, or for the prevention of cruelty to children or animals. Payments to veterans organizations and certain burial societies may also qualify for the charitable deduction (see IRS Publication 78 or http://www. irs.ustreas.gov). No deduction is available for volunteer activities, but individuals may deduct related personal expenses such as mileage and auto use.

Because there is a ceiling on the amount of deductible charitable contributions that an individual can make, it is critical that seniors obtain expert tax advice before making substantial charitable gifts (see chapter 15, Estate Planning).

EXEMPTIONS

Personal Exemption

Each taxpayer having income under substantial limits, as specified by the IRS, is entitled to claim a personal exemption.

Dependency Exemption

Seniors who take care of siblings, grandchildren, and others should be made aware of the dependency exemption. Additionally, adult children who take care of their elderly or disabled parents or grandparents should be aware of the exemption opportunity. Expert tax advice is critical to determine whether a particular taxpayer may claim an exemption.

Income from Volunteer Organizations

Many seniors are retired and no longer receive taxable compensation, but some will work to advanced ages. Often seniors volunteer their time to organizations. Income paid for supportive services at the following volunteer organizations is generally *excluded* from taxable income:

- Retired Senior Volunteer Program (RSVP)
- Foster Grandparent Program
- Senior Companion Program
- Service Corps of Retired Executives (SCORE)

TAX ON INTEREST AND DIVIDENDS

Many stocks and mutual funds distribute earnings as taxable dividends. Dividends used to be taxed as ordinary income. Qualified dividend income, however, will be taxed at 0 percent in the period 2008–2010 for taxpayers in the 10 and 15 percent tax brackets and at only 15 percent for taxpayers in higher brackets. Nonqualified dividends will continue to be taxed at ordinary rates.

In addition, taxable interest may be generated from bank certificates of deposit (CDs) and passbook accounts, as well as from corporate and Treasury bonds, bills, and notes. While interest on Treasury bonds is always exempt from state taxes, interest on certain bonds issued by states and municipalities may be exempt from federal, state, and local income tax, resulting in a triple tax exemption. Be aware that tax-exempt income derived from some municipal bonds may ultimately become taxable and may be subject to alternative minimum tax (AMT). See Appendix C for the Taxable Equivalent Yield (TEY) formula that can be used to compare the after-tax interest income between two bonds, tax-exempt and taxable.

CAPITAL GAINS TAX

When a capital asset such as an investment, home, or business interest is sold for more than the holder paid to acquire the property, the result is known as a long- or short-term *capital gain*. *Short-term gains* apply to property held less than 12 months and are generally subject to ordinary income tax rates. *Long-term gains* apply to property held longer than 12 months and are subject to lower tax rates, generally 15 percent, or 0 percent through 2012 for lower-bracket taxpayers (15 percent bracket and below).

Cost Basis

With certain exceptions, the after-tax amount the holder paid to acquire the property is considered its *cost basis*. The amount of capital gain that may be taxable is calculated by subtracting the cost basis of the asset from the proceeds received from the sale of the asset.

Example:

Marian sold 100 shares of ABC common stock at $60.00 per share. She originally paid $25.00 per share (cost basis of $2,500 = 100 shares × $25/share). Although Marian received $6,000 from the sale (100 shares × $60/share), her gain is $3,500, because her cost basis was $2,500.

Capital Gains and the Sale of a Personal Residence

Section 121 of the Internal Revenue Code provides a capital gains tax exclusion on a home sale of up to $250,000 for a single taxpayer and up to $500,000 for married taxpayers filing jointly. For sales after 2007, a surviving spouse may exclude $500,000 if the sale occurs within 2 years after the date of the death of the spouse. In order to enjoy the exclusion, however, the following use requirements must be satisfied:

- The taxpayer must have owned and used the home as a principal residence for at least two of the five years (the two years need not be consecutive) before the sale.
- For married joint filers, either spouse may own the home but both must meet the use requirement.
- If a taxpayer fails to meet the requirement above due to a change in health or employment, the taxpayer may be entitled to a partial exclusion.
- If one spouse can take a full exclusion and the other cannot, the exclusion is calculated as if the taxpayers had not been married.
- The Section 121 exclusion can be used once every two years.

Example:

Don and Marge Swenson, who are entering the second stage of retirement, wish to sell their four-bedroom home on Cherry Lane, preferring the lower maintenance of condominium living. The Swensons can claim an exclusion of up to $500,000 in capital gain realized from the sale of their Cherry Lane home. Six years later, the Swensons decide to sell the condominium and move into an assisted living facility. If they realize capital gain on the sale of the condominium, they may again claim the Section 121 exclusion relative to any capital gain realized from selling the condominium.

479

If a rental or vacation property is converted to a personal home, capital gains tax is due on that percentage of the gain equal to the percentage of time the house was used other than as a primary residence since January 1, 2009. Any gain attributable to use as a principal residence will remain excludable, up to the $250,000 and $500,000 limits.

Deferring Capital Gains with Section 1031 Exchanges

Senior clients who own investment property requiring day-to-day management may find they no longer wish to have these daily responsibilities, particularly in their retirement years. But by the same token, seniors may be reluctant to sell their property because it has appreciated and they will owe substantial capital gains tax on the sale. These seniors may wish to take advantage of an IRS Section 1031 tax deferral that allows individuals to exchange commercial property solely for property of like kind for use in business, trade, or for investment (*like kind* does not mean the businesses have to be identical)—without paying capital gains tax on the first property as long as a replacement property is purchased within 180 days. Seniors like Jim in the following example may find a Section 1031 tax deferral appropriate for their lifestyle changes:

Example:

Jim, 70, has owned a commercial warehouse for 20 years. His cost (basis) to acquire it was $300,000. It's now valued at $1 million, but its cash flow has declined and no longer provides Jim with the amount of monthly income he needs. In addition, Jim's arthritis is making visits to the property increasingly difficult, and he wants to move to a warmer climate. But if Jim sells the warehouse outright, he may pay substantial combined federal and state capital gains tax.

Under Section 1031, Jim can exchange his warehouse for a replacement business or investment property such as an apartment building, a farm, or rentable raw land for developed property without paying capital gains tax on his warehouse.

Additional Exemptions to Capital Gains Tax

In addition to a Section 1031 exemption, capital gains tax may be avoided through:

- *Charitable gifts:* Eligible charities generally are not required to pay income tax on capital gains and other income. Outright donations of appreciated property to charities, as well as gifts made through charitable trusts, may effectively eliminate capital gains taxation on certain properties (not to mention provide a charitable income tax or estate tax charitable deduction).

- *Step Up in Basis:* Selling appreciated property during one's life will generate capital gains tax. Seniors may reduce or eliminate capital gains for themselves and heirs when highly appreciated property is transferred at death rather than sold or gifted during life (see Chapter 15, Estate Planning).

TAX ON SOCIAL SECURITY BENEFITS

Senior taxpayers' total income determines if their Social Security retirement and disability benefits are taxed. Most seniors do not pay taxes on these benefits because the current tax code is designed to provide a great deal of tax relief for the average senior. However, individuals with higher incomes above certain limits may have to pay taxes on a portion of their Social Security benefits. The portion that is taxable increases as the amount of income from other sources increases.

Specified income thresholds determine the level of taxation (see Table 16.5). Depending on total income, benefits are taxed at two levels: 50 and 85 percent. No one pays taxes on more than 85 percent of Social Security benefits, and some pay on a smaller portion:

- A taxpayer filing an individual return with a combined income between $25,000 (base amount) and $34,000 may have to pay income tax on 50 percent of Social Security benefits. When combined income exceeds $34,000, up to 85 percent of Social Security benefits is subject to income tax.

- A married couple filing a joint return may have to pay taxes on 50 percent of benefits if their combined income is between $32,000 (base amount) and $44,000. (On the 1040 tax return, combined income is the sum of adjusted gross income, plus nontaxable interest, plus one-half of Social Security benefits.) If combined income is more than $44,000, up to 85 percent of Social Security benefits is subject to income tax.

Table 16.5 Taxes on Social Security Benefits

TAX FILING STATUS	COMBINED INCOME	AMOUNT OF TOTAL SOCIAL SECURITY BENEFITS THAT IS TAXABLE
Individual	$25,000–$34,000	50 percent
	$34,000 and more	85 percent
Joint	$32,000–$44,000	50 percent
	$44,000 and more	85 percent

Income reported for figuring the Social Security tax is defined as all income including wages, salaries, Social Security income, interest (including interest earnings from tax-exempt bonds), dividends, capital gains, rents, and retirement income from IRAs, employer-sponsored plans, Section 457 plans, and tax-sheltered annuities (TSAs). Income from series EE bonds, tax-deferred annuities, and qualified life insurance loan distributions are excluded from these calculations.

See Appendix D for a mini case study that calculates what portion of Social Security benefits are taxable.

ALTERNATIVE MINIMUM TAX

The *alternative minimum tax* (AMT) is a separate tax system established to ensure that wealthier taxpayers pay taxes. Although it targets those with high incomes who make extensive use of tax-reduction strategies, it increasingly affects middle-income taxpayers who have substantial deductions. In its article "The Alternative Minimum Tax," SmartMoney (2004) reported that only 19,000 people owed AMT in 1970, whereas 23 million were paying AMT in 2008, according to the Tax Policy Center. In 2008, legislation provided a temporary "AMT Patch" to decrease the effects on middle income taxpayers. AMT is an ongoing issue and additional legislation may be passed in the future.

AMT uses its own tax rates and rules that are quite different from the familiar rules on Form 1040 regarding itemized deductions and personal and dependency exemptions. SmartMoney recommends that people calculate AMT if their income exceeds $75,000 and they have substantial deductions and exemptions. Taxpayers must pay the higher of the AMT or the regular tax. Taxpayers may owe penalties if they should have paid AMT and did not. AMT is fairly complicated, and seniors who may be subject to it should seek advice from tax professionals.

TAX AVOIDANCE

Americans have always struggled to find ways to reduce or eliminate their taxes. Most Americans dutifully pay their fair share each year, but others attempt to avoid paying any taxes at all. It is understandable and perfectly legal to try to decrease one's tax bill, but there is a distinct difference between *tax avoidance* and *tax evasion*. Tax avoidance is permissible under tax regulations. Tax evasion is not and holds serious legal ramifications for those who are caught. You must help your senior clients differentiate between the two.

- *Tax avoidance* seeks to minimize tax liability by working within the complex scope of tax law found in the Internal Revenue Code (IRC). You may provide valuable guidance to older clients regarding techniques to minimize their taxes. However, both you and your clients should bear in mind that the economic costs of certain tax strategies could outweigh the tax benefits of the transaction. Good business and investment principles should not be abandoned for the sake of lowering tax liability.

- *Tax evasion* is the reduction of tax through illegal means, including tax fraud. Penalties for tax evasion include fines, imprisonment, or both.

Sometimes it can be difficult to differentiate between tax avoidance and tax evasion. Poorly informed senior clients may pursue aggressive strategies that create problems with the IRS. You can assist your senior clients in identifying tax strategies that are economically viable and legally sound.

HOW YOU CAN ASSIST SENIORS

You should be careful when helping seniors with tax planning. This is one area where using a good tax professional can really pay off. So, does this mean that you should not try to help seniors do tax planning? Not at all. You may be able to offer help at even the simplest level. For example, some seniors have trouble identifying all the required papers—receipts, tax forms, etc. Perhaps the senior has some level of mental or physical impairment. You can provide a good service by identifying required tax papers and helping the senior to keep track of them.

You may also want to be alert for the special needs of widows and widowers. Just guiding these seniors through the tax maze can be a huge help and comfort. It may be that all a new widow needs is someone to walk her through the tax calculation and filing process. Perhaps there is time to make adjustments to income, retirement plan contributions, or other adjustments to help reduce this year's taxable income.

As you learn more about tax management, you can help seniors to plan. Also, as you learn more, you will have a better idea of when to involve tax professionals to provide the best service to your clients. Senior taxpayers and their advisors should be aware of the Taxpayer Advocate Service (see Appendix E).

Managing Investments

Today, many Americans over age 65 rely to some extent on investment income to meet their expenses. High net worth seniors have inherited or built their wealth through investments; middle- and lower-income seniors' primary sources of income are often employer-sponsored retirement plans that require them to make investment choices.

- *High net worth* individuals probably have the most potential for investment diversification. Someone in this category might invest in income-producing commercial real estate along with owning a number of individual stocks and bonds. High net worth individuals often also have the opportunity to invest more speculatively in fine arts and other collectibles. Most high net worth individuals are likely to invest with growth as their primary goal.

- *Middle-income* investors may own some rental property, and may also own some nice art, but their primary investment vehicles are going to be stocks and bonds. Many middle-income individuals will do their investing through mutual funds rather than owning the individual stocks and bonds. Middle-income investors will invest for both growth and income, with the balance between the two shifting toward income as retirement lengthens.

- *Lower-income* individuals probably won't do much investing in the true sense of the word—at least outside of company retirement plans. Within those plans, they may invest in a number of mutual funds. Other investments probably will be more in the category of money market funds, passbook savings, and certificates of deposit. Annuities may also offer potential for both growth and income investing.

The purpose of having investments is to increase income and the value of the assets. However, the profitable return on the cost of the investment is subject to the ups and downs of the marketplace, which is influenced by numerous factors, such as the international marketplace, new technologies, and politics.

The best ways for individual investors to manage the market risk to their investments is to choose the right financial advisor and the investment approaches that match their risk tolerance, financial concerns and goals, and available assets.

OBTAINING PROFESSIONAL FINANCIAL ADVICE

Don't assume that just because senior clients may have high net worth that they already have investment advisors and are satisfied with them. Surprisingly, experience has shown that this is not always the case. In the middle- and lower-income groups, seniors can benefit from expert financial advice in many situations—for example, implementing Medicaid spend-downs, choosing the right mix of investments in their employer-sponsored retirement plans, deciding whether to invest in an employee stock ownership or stock purchase plan, determining how to properly use their Social Security retirement benefits, or calculating the best time to retire.

Not only can a qualified financial advisor offer your clients investment strategies and options they may not be aware of to help them beat inflation's erosion on retirement dollars, such an expert can teach your clients the fundamental concepts of investing and guide them through the steps of the financial planning process that are appropriate for their financial resources and goals.

Unfortunately, it's all too easy to make some significant investment mistakes—one of the most significant being the choice of an advisor. Seniors who have a pressing need to supplement income lost from lower interest rates can be susceptible to promises of higher returns without understanding the risks involved and the various sales charges. Senior investors should be especially mindful of common investment problems.

The following sections examine in depth the factors that go into choosing the investment strategies and vehicles that best serve the individual seniors' financial and retirement needs.

SELECTING AN INVESTMENT APPROACH

Deciding which investment is most appropriate depends on your clients' available assets as well as their risk tolerance and time horizon, including their life expectancy and amount of time the investment can grow in value or produce income.

Risk Tolerance

If your clients bought a stock that declined in value by 20 to 25 percent, would they sell it? Do nothing? Buy more?

Often financial advisors ask these kinds of questions to help their clients express their tolerance for investment risk. The client who would sell seems relatively risk averse, whereas the client who would buy more appears to be an above-average risk taker. Risk tolerance is one of the key factors that determine which investment strategies are most appropriate for your senior clients, as Table 16.6 illustrates.

The investment approaches shown in Table 16.6 have the following characteristics:

Table 16.6 Risk Tolerance and Investment Strategies

RISK TOLERANCE LEVEL	INVESTMENT APPROACH	TYPE OF INVESTMENT
High	Aggressive	■ aggressive growth (small cap) ■ high-income bond funds ■ real estate investment trust or real estate limited partnership
Medium	Moderate	■ moderate growth (mid cap) ■ growth and income funds ■ value funds
Low	Conservative	■ conservative growth (large cap) ■ fixed-income (government and high-grade corporate bonds)

Aggressive:

■ best for pre-retirement wealth accumulation due to longer time horizons

■ highest potential for capital appreciation, but also for loss

■ may also be appropriate for early stages of retirement

■ focused almost entirely on growth and capital appreciation

Moderate:

■ best for early and middle stages of retirement

■ decreased potential for gain, but not as much downside either

■ adapting a moderate strategy early (i.e., in pre-retirement) will probably reduce potential gains, but should also produce less volatility

■ look for a balance between growth and income

Conservative:

■ best for later stages of retirement

■ low potential for gain, but also little potential for loss

■ probably focused on income production rather than capital appreciation

As a general rule, the fewer the assets, the more conservative the investor should be. This means that for those individuals who have few assets or low income, aggressive investing is probably inappropriate. High net worth individuals, on the other hand, have the discretionary income and asset base to invest more aggressively. Yes, it is true that the rich get richer, because they have more to work with. However, appropriate investment strategy can help the poor from getting poorer. We will cover investments later in more depth.

Longer retirements and the continuous erosion of inflation on retirement income will likely require investment strategies that go beyond reliance on putting money into certificates of deposit. While safe from market risk, certificates of deposit are vulnerable to other risks, such as inflation. Conversely, when work is no longer a source of income, retirees feel quite protective of their nest eggs and are resistant to exposure to market risk, believing that they cannot make up substantial losses. Wise equity investing (whether in individual stocks or using mutual funds) is one of the most effective ways to create growth in a retirement portfolio. Postretirement investment management seeks to provide individuals with growth and income, along with reasonable preservation of principal and tax advantages. Seniors drawn toward highly conservative investments that focus entirely on safety of principal often find their portfolios eroded by inflation risk (i.e., purchasing power risk). Even seniors with a relatively low (conservative) tolerance for investment risk should consider incorporating a small portion of growth-oriented investments such as common stock.

No one wants to lose money they have invested. Unfortunately, people frequently do just that. There are few guarantees with investing, but there are some ways to minimize potential losses. One of the primary ways to minimize potential losses is to match investments to a client's time horizon.

Time Horizon

A key component of protection against market risk is the *time horizon*. The time horizon is the period of time between making the investment and when that investment needs to be withdrawn to meet goals or other financial needs. Generally, the longer the time horizon, the greater potential for investment growth using investments that would be considered too risky with a shorter time horizon. As a client's investment time lengthens, the average annual compound return that can be earned in a particular investment class (e.g., stocks or bonds) becomes more predictable. The primary goal of investing for retirement is to accumulate as much money as possible in order to meet financial needs during retirement.

The goal of accumulating money actually continues into retirement due to the increased life expectancy most people are experiencing. Poor investment results prior to, or early in, retirement, can have a significant impact on a client's lifestyle as the retirement years increase. Investment results are dependent on many factors, with one of the key factors being matching time horizons with appropriate investment vehicles. For example, it normally would not be wise to invest money that is going to be needed in a year in growth stocks. There is too much possibility of significant market fluctuations during such a short period, without the ability to allow time to even out those fluctuations. A better short-term investment would be a money market fund, or perhaps a high-quality short-term bond mutual fund. Over the long term, a diversified stock portfolio (whether holding individual stocks or in mutual funds) will normally produce the best return.

Look for long-term performance. Poor returns in the stock market during the early 2000s made investors more averse to risk than during the bull market of the 1990s. Poor investment returns cannot be ignored, but investing for retirement over a period of 25 or 30 years or making long-term investments during retirement makes the stock market's return over the short run relatively less important. Historically, performance in exceptionally good years has offset performance in exceptionally bad years for long-term investments. Ernst and Young's retirement planning guide advises that "over any period of 10 years, stock owners can expect to receive a higher average annual rate of return than do lenders who invest in cash and bonds" (Arnone et al., 2002).

MANAGING MARKET RISK: DIVERSIFICATION

Burt, 69, has thousands of dollars in his company's stock that he purchased through its employee stock purchase plan over his 20-year career. Burt counted on the stock appreciating in market value, so he could cash it out in periodic payments for retirement income. But the company suffered severe market losses. Today Burt's stock is essentially worth just pennies. By the time the company might recover and its stock might increase over the price Burt paid for it, Burt could be dead.

What else could Burt have done? Obviously, rather than putting all his eggs in one basket, Burt could have used a number of other investment vehicles to diversify the way he allocated his assets and protect his investments against changes in the market.

Asset allocation should be consistent with an older investor's goals, financial constraints, and time horizon. The goal of asset allocation is to achieve the highest return given an acceptable level of risk or the lowest risk for a needed rate of return

ASSET CLASSES

By combining assets with different characteristics in an investment portfolio, an investor may achieve higher returns with lower risk over the long term. Figure 16.2 illustrates the concept of diversification as a risk-management strategy:

Diversifying funds across a variety of asset classes may be crucial to managing market risk and increasing the return on investments. Assets are classified in broad terms as:

- *Stocks:* large-cap and small-cap, value income and growth, international, and combinations of each; common and preferred
- *Bonds:* Short-, intermediate-, and long-term; tax-free; high-yield; convertible; and international classifications
- *Cash*

Two of the most common types of investments are stocks and bonds. Generally, stocks provide the potential for growth whereas bonds provide income (of course, stocks can also provide income, and bonds may offer some growth potential).

Equity Investing through Common Stock

Common stock belongs in most investment portfolios because, in the past 50 years, it has generally outperformed inflation and has dramatically outperformed other investments. Common stock is a form of equity invest-

Figure 16.2 Pyramid of Financial Independence

ment. In investing, *equity* refers to ownership. The best recognized unit of investment ownership is *common stock*, which implies ownership in a corporation. Such ownership entails limited liability for the shareholder, who can lose no more than the amount paid to acquire the stock (plus costs).

Investing in Debt for Income: Bonds

In investing, debt generally describes bonds, notes, mortgages, and other arrangements involving monies owed and payable. Issuers of debt include federal governments such as the United States Treasury; municipalities, such as states, cities, and counties; and also corporations. An investor who buys a debt instrument is lending money to its issuer with the promise that at some point in time the money must be returned to the lender. Clearly, the investor who holds a debt security has no ownership. Instead, the bond- or noteholder's position is that of the issuer's creditor, because the face amount of the bond or note must be returned to that bondholder.

Not everyone has the resources available to invest directly in stocks or bonds. Prudent investing requires diversification among various types of investments, different industries, and different companies. This helps to reduce market risk. For example, a well-diversified stock portfolio requires at least 12 to 15 different stocks (and perhaps more). Mutual funds were created

Key Terms and Definitions

Investment portfolio: a group of investments, which may include stocks, bonds, real estate, money markets, and/or mutual funds. A portfolio may be managed professionally or by the individual investor.

Capitalization: the market value of a company's stock.

Large-cap stocks: stocks of companies with a market capitalization between $10 billion and $200 billion. Usually large, well-established companies, or blue chips. (Note: Exact dollar amounts may vary. For example, some sources suggest that the upper number should be $300 billion or even more. However, the general guidelines will serve.)

Mid-cap stocks: stocks of companies with a market capitalization between $2 billion and $10 billion. Usually mid-sized companies with some growth potential along with some of the stability of larger companies.

Small-cap stocks: stocks of companies with a market capitalization between $300 million to $2 billion. Usually small, new companies with good growth potential. However, these stocks frequently have high volatility.

Value investing: process of selecting stocks that trade for less than their intrinsic value. A value investor usually looks for stocks of companies that are financially sound but currently undervalued by the market.

Income investing: process of selecting stocks or bonds that produce regular income payments. Payments may be in the form of stock dividends or income (coupon) payments from bonds. Income investors are less concerned with capital appreciation (growth) than with regular income.

Growth investing: process of selecting stocks of companies that seem ready to have strong growth and expansion. These may be established companies, but more often are young companies with a good product and not too much competition (yet). Where income investing looks for periodic income (dividends), growth investing looks for capital appreciation.

Common stock: represents ownership of a company. Owning common stock gives equity in the company, usually along with voting rights, and provides the opportunity to share in the company's growth or income, or both.

Preferred stock: represents ownership of a company, but usually without voting rights. Preferred stock pays a fixed dividend before any common stock dividends are paid. Preferred stock investors are senior to common stock investors and have a greater claim on company assets than common shareholders.

High-yield bonds: typically bonds with a lower credit rating that offer increased returns. While they may offer more income potential, they also have a greater default potential, and conservative investors should be cautious.

Convertible bonds: corporate bond that may be exchanged for a specified number of shares of stock in the same company. Convertible bonds are sold at a premium over the price of the stock. They pay interest and may also offer the opportunity for capital appreciation.

to provide many people with the opportunity to have well-diversified portfolios, even when they might not have the funds to create such an individual portfolio of stocks or bonds.

Mutual Funds

Mutual funds are managed investment companies that offer an investor not only professional management, but also liquidity, diversification, and other important services that would otherwise be unavailable to small or inexperienced investors. There is little wonder that roughly 16,000 managed investment companies operated in the United States in 2007, according to the Investment Company Institute and Strategic Insight Simfund. Despite the popularity of managed mutual funds, the decision as to when an older investor should buy or sell them should take into account the economy; the state of stock and bond market interest rates; and, of course, the client's needs, objectives, and risk tolerances.

Mutual funds invest the pooled money of many small investors in portfolios of securities matching an investment objective stated for that portfolio. Mutual funds charge management or administrative fees for the services they provide, and many impose sales charges upon purchase or sale of the funds. Mutual fund sales charges (commissions) are often referred to as *loads*. There are several different types of commissions for different types of investors.

Open-end mutual funds are among the most liquid of investments because an issuing company must redeem shares on demand. This operates in contrast to nonredeemable securities, where an investor (or a broker) wishing to sell must locate a buyer. Shares are redeemed at net asset value, although back-end loads or redemption fees may be charged.

Mutual funds are available in many varieties. Some invest aggressively in the stock market for growth, while other funds invest more conservatively for income. You need to understand your clients' risk tolerance and total portfolio components before recommending a particular mutual fund. See Appendix F for a brief listing of some popular types of mutual funds.

Computer Modeling to Plan Asset Allocation

Today's financial professionals generally employ sophisticated computer programs that analyze historic returns and risk of asset categories to identify the ideal mix of stocks, bonds, and international investments. These programs are called *optimizers* because they create portfolios that aim for maximum return with the lowest possible volatility. Sample asset allocation models and projected returns should be reviewed with senior clients, who can select the investment strategies that best fit their risk tolerance and financial goals. Exploring various portfolio models allows a senior to consider the impact of different investment strategies.

MARGINAL TAX RATE

Seniors should examine investment vehicles that reduce their exposure to income taxes. The higher a senior's tax bracket (as determined by annual income), the more significant tax-advantaged investments such as public-purpose municipal bonds become. A fully taxable investment must earn a higher rate of return to provide an equivalent rate of return to a tax-free investment. Understanding the impact of marginal tax rate and becoming familiar with tax-advantaged investments could offer significant benefits to seniors.

Primary Sources of Retirement Income

Now we will look at the primary types of investments that the majority of seniors today either have or are using according to their particular financial goals:

- qualified retirement plans (employees choose how to allocate their contributions among the investment choices offered in the plan, such as mutual funds, stocks, and bonds; domestic, international; etc.)
  —individual retirement accounts (IRAs): traditional, Roth, and spousal
  —employer-sponsored plans
  —other business retirement plans
- annuities
- reverse mortgages

TYPES OF QUALIFIED RETIREMENT PLANS

Qualified retirement plans encourage saving for retirement by deferring income taxes on the earnings. These plans are one of the most common and important sources of retirement income for seniors in all three income groups.

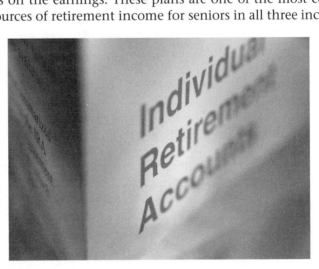

Individual Retirement Accounts (IRAs)

IRAs provide working Americans with tax-advantaged means to save for retirement while self-directing the investments in their accounts. Only those with earned income from working may contribute to IRAs—individuals

491

receiving income only from investments or trusts are ineligible to make IRA contributions.

An American having earned income or reportable alimony may make an annual contribution up to the lesser of 100 percent of compensation or $5,000 to a traditional, spousal, or Roth IRA. Further, an individual age 50 or older may make an annual additional catch-up contribution of $1,000 in 2009 (indexed for inflation, which means the contribution amount may change with inflation). For example, in 2009, a 60-year-old taxpayer could contribute $3,000 to a traditional IRA and an additional $3,000 to a Roth IRA, for a total of $6,000.

Contributions to IRAs may be made up to the tax filing date (typically, but not always, April 15) for the year in which the IRA contribution is intended. Filing extensions do not extend the deadline for making an IRA contribution. Taxpayers can choose among several types of IRAs based on their needs and income: traditional, spousal, and Roth.

Traditional IRAs

Taxpayers who are not active participants in an employer-sponsored retirement plan may deduct an annual contribution up to the full amount they earn, or the maximum contribution amount, whichever is lower, to an IRA.

Alternatively, a taxpayer may wish to make a *nondeductible IRA contribution* to a Roth IRA or a contribution to a nondeductible traditional IRA. If the client qualifies for a Roth IRA (see below), this is generally a preferred investment over a nondeductible traditional IRA because the money in the Roth accumulates tax-free.

For taxpayers who are active participants in an employer-sponsored retirement plan, the IRS determines whether the annual IRA contribution is tax-deductible, and if so, in what amount based on the individual's adjusted gross income (AGI).

The deductibility of traditional IRA contributions for a taxpayer actively participating in a workplace retirement plan is phased out on a pro rata basis over the specified phase-out range of AGI, as shown on Table 16.7.

Table 16.7 Adjusted Gross Income Deductibility Phase-Out Ranges for IRAs

TAX YEAR	JOINT RETURNS	SINGLE RETURNS
2004	$65,000–$ 75,000	$45,000–$55,000
2005	$70,000–$ 80,000	$50,000–$60,000
2006	$75,000–$ 85,000	$50,000–$60,000
2007	$83,000–$103,000	$52,000–$62,000
2008	$85,000–$105,000	$53,000–$63,000
2009	$89,000–$109,000	$55,000–$65,000

As the chart shows, individuals who participate in an *employer-sponsored retirement plan*, and whose income is below the lower limit, may deduct their full contribution to an IRA. However, someone with income above the upper limit will not be allowed to make any deductible contribution. Taxpayers with income between the listed limits can make a partially deductible contribution that decreases as their income increases toward the upper limit.

Spousal IRAs

Married couples who file joint income tax returns may be able to take advantage of spousal IRA contributions even though one spouse earns less than the maximum contribution amount or has no earned income from working.

Presuming the income of the working spouse reaches or exceeds contribution amounts, a working spouse may contribute up to $5,000 ($6,000 if the working spouse is at least age 50) to an IRA established under the name of the nonworking spouse. Contribution amounts are scheduled to be indexed for inflation. This allows the working spouse to make a contribution on behalf of the nonworking spouse, as long as the working spouse's income is sufficient. (Because limits are expected to change every year, you should advise your clients to check with their financial or tax planners when making contributions.)

Roth IRAs

As mentioned above, Roth IRAs permit nondeductible annual contributions up to the lesser of 100 percent of earned income in 2009 or $5,000, with catch-up contributions of up to $1,000 per year available for taxpayers age 50 and over (for a total annual contribution of $6,000). Contribution limits are scheduled to be indexed for inflation. Spousal Roth IRAs may also accept contributions up to $5,000/$6,000 (because limits are expected to change every year, you should advise your clients to check with their financial or tax planners when making contributions).

Annual contribution limits to Roth and traditional IRAs are interrelated: an individual may contribute no more than $5,000/$6,000 per year to the combination of both Roth and traditional accounts (i.e., $3,000 to the Roth and $3,000 to the traditional, for a total of $6,000 annually). No maximum age limits apply to Roth contributions, so seniors of any age (with earned income not exceeding the AGI limits) may contribute.

Income limitations apply to Roth contributions. Only taxpayers whose annual adjusted gross income is within the limits listed in Table 16.8 may contribute to Roth IRAs. The maximum annual Roth contribution is phased out proportionally according to the thresholds shown in the table. This means that someone whose income is below the lower limit may be able to make a full contribution (e.g., $5,000, or $6,000 with the catch-up allowance). Someone with income above the upper limit, however, will not be allowed to make any contribution to a Roth. Taxpayers with income between the listed limits can make a partial contribution that decreases as their income increases toward the upper limit.

Table 16.8 Adjusted Gross Income Contribution Phase-Out Ranges for Roth IRAs in 2009

FILING STATUS	ADJUSTED GROSS INCOME
Single filers	$105,000–$120,000
Joint filers	$166,000–$176,000

As an example of a partial contribution to a Roth IRA, suppose in tax year 2009, your widowed client, age 66, had a modified adjusted gross income (MAGI) of $112,500 (the midpoint of the phase-out range for unmarried individuals). She can contribute $3,000 to a Roth IRA. (Had she been under age 50, she could have contributed only $2,500.)

Employer-Sponsored Retirement Plans

A variety of retirement plans offer tax advantages to employers while potentially increasing employee morale, productivity, and loyalty. These include 401(k)s, defined-benefit pensions, money purchase pensions, and profit-sharing plans. Generally, employers may deduct their contributions to the plan—for example, matching funds up to a certain percentage of the employees' contributions. Employees' contributions are tax-deductible. The newer Roth 401(k) is not deductible by the employee, but qualified withdrawals of the employee's account are tax free.

Retirement Plans for Corporations and Unincorporated Businesses

Tax-deferred retirement plans available to businesses regardless of whether they are corporations or other forms include SEP IRAs, SIMPLE IRAs, and retirement plans for only unincorporated organizations: Keogh (HR-10) plans for the self-employed and 403(b) tax-sheltered annuities for not-for-profit organizations and education employees.

DISTRIBUTIONS FROM QUALIFIED RETIREMENT PLANS

To encourage people to use the assets in their qualified plans plan for retirement income, the IRS established penalties on withdrawals made too early or too late. Withdrawals made between the ages of $59\frac{1}{2}$ and $70\frac{1}{2}$ are subject to ordinary income tax but no penalty.

Early Withdrawals

Early withdrawals are those taken before the taxpayer is age $59\frac{1}{2}$. They are generally subject to a nondeductible 10 percent penalty, along with ordinary income tax at the taxpayer's own bracket.

You may have clients who are not age $59\frac{1}{2}$ but may qualify for and need to use an exception to the 10 percent early withdrawal penalty. For most retirement plans, the exceptions to the early withdrawal penalty are:

- a direct transfer into another similar qualified plan by a worker who changes jobs—for example, from one 401(k) to another 401 (k);
- a rollover (transfer) of funds into a different form of qualified retirement plan—for example, from a 401(k) into a traditional IRA;

494

- purchase of a first home (available for IRAs but not employer-sponsored retirement plans);
- permanent total disability of the plan owner;
- payment of health insurance premiums while the plan owner is unemployed (available for IRAs but not employer-sponsored plans);
- compliance with a court order in conjunction with a divorce (available for employer plans but not IRAs);
- annuitized distributions—distributing substantially equal payments over the plan owner's life expectancy (or the life expectancy of the plan owner and a designated beneficiary) for a continuous period of five years or until the recipient is age 59$\frac{1}{2}$, whichever occurs later.

Roth IRAs and Roth 401(k)s

After a five-year holding period from the date the owner *first* establishes a Roth IRA or Roth 401(k) account, withdrawals of any kind may be taken and not taxed when the owner is at least age 59$\frac{1}{2}$ *or* the distributions are:

- made at or after death (to an estate or a beneficiary);
- generated by the owner's disability;
- used for a qualified first-time homeowner's expenses.

These withdrawals may consist of one or several types of funds: after-tax contributions to the account, earnings, and funds converted from a traditional IRA. (The five-year holding period does not apply to withdrawals that consist of only contributions made by the IRA owner. Also, regular annual contributions are always returned tax-free.)

The five-year period starts with the *first day of the tax year* in which the owner first sets up and contributes to a Roth IRA. For example:

Emily, age 60, made her first contribution to a Roth IRA on October 1, 2003, for the 2003 tax year. The five-year holding period for *all of Emily's succeeding contributions* to this Roth IRA account (that are not converted from a traditional IRA) begins on January 1, 2003.

Even if Emily were to die during this five-year holding period, it still applies to her heirs. They would also have to wait until January 2, 2008 to receive tax-free distributions of earnings from her Roth. A *spouse*, on the other hand, could use the five-year period of the decedent's Roth *or* the five-year period of their own Roth to access the funds in the decedent's Roth on a tax-free basis.

(Taxpayers often mistakenly believe that a separate five-year holding period applies to each year's regular annual contribution.)

The five-year period that applies to a distribution from a conversion of a traditional IRA to a Roth IRA is determined separately for each conversion. It starts the first day of the tax year in which you make the conversion.

No withdrawal is required while the Roth IRA owner lives.

Required Beginning Date

For information on the required beginning dates for qualified retirement plans, see chapter 15, Estate Planning.

Distribution Options after Retirement

Retirees may choose one of four options for taking required minimum distributions from their qualified retirement plans starting on their required beginning date:

- lump-sum payment
- rollover
- direct transfer
- annuitized payments

Lump Sum

The tax consequences of lump-sum distributions differ greatly from those for periodic annuity payments or Roth IRA distributions. Individuals who are considering taking a lump-sum distribution should first have a qualified financial or tax planning expert analyze the tax consequences of a lump-sum payout against other payout options.

Obviously, a potential disadvantage to a substantial lump-sum payout is the temptation to spend too much of it immediately, rather than to invest it to provide future retirement income. However, the advantages of a lump-sum option are that it offers retirees:

- maximum control over investments;
- financial resources for paying unforeseen expenses such as a major illness;
- flexibility for future investment decisions that offer more protection against inflation.

If the employee does not do a custodian-to-custodian transfer, then employers must withhold 20 percent of lump-sum distributions made from employer-sponsored retirement accounts (but not IRAs or Roth 401(k)s) as an advance on income taxes likely to be due on the distributed amount.

Rollover

A retirement account owner who directly receives a lump-sum distribution from his or her employer's retirement plan and rolls it over into an IRA or qualified plan within 60 days may receive a refund of the 20 percent mandatory withholding. This refund occurs when the employee files a tax return. Although the employee only receives 80 percent of the proceeds, and must wait until the next tax year to get the refund, the employee may take money from other personal savings to substitute for the 20 percent, and thus can roll over 100 percent of the distribution amount. This can all be avoided by doing a custodian-to-custodian transfer.

Roth 401(k)s, no matter the holding period or age of the owner, may be rolled over into a Roth IRA.

Direct Transfer

Direct transfer from one qualified plan to another, without passing through the plan owner's hands, is the most effective way to avoid income or penalty taxes. Transfers and rollovers may involve all or only a portion of the distribution.

Annuitized Distributions

An annuity distributes the funds in the plan in fixed monthly amounts that are taxed as ordinary income, with the exception of nondeductible or after-tax contributions, which are tax-free. Payout options must be selected carefully: once one is chosen, it generally cannot be changed. The two payout options that are almost always available are:

- *Single life option:* Pays a set monthly amount to the retiree. Payments stop when the retiree dies. The account balance remains with the financial institution that issued the annuity.

- *Joint and survivor option:* Provides a smaller monthly payment, but a percentage of the payment amount will continue for a surviving spouse after the retiree dies. The survivor benefit may range between 50 and 100 percent of the joint payment.

With either option, a retiree can elect to receive a reduced monthly payment for life, in addition to a guaranteed minimum payment period of 5, 10, or 15 years to a beneficiary (a life income with period certain payout). Monthly payments under period certain or survivor arrangements are smaller than those made under single life options. Note, however, that annuitizing distributions may lock in the money at fixed rates of return, which over time could make them vulnerable to a loss of buying power.

Taxes on Distributions: Owners and Beneficiaries

Distributions from retirement plans have significant financial and tax consequences for the plan owner as well as the beneficiaries These often irreversible decisions can affect whether money lasts through retirement or whether funds are available for a spouse or heirs at the owner's death. Uninformed decisions may leave thousands of dollars in a plan at death and leave nothing for a surviving spouse or heirs.

For many, beneficiary designations on retirement plans were made when the plan was originally established and have not been reviewed since, in spite of inevitable changes in family structure—births, deaths, divorce, or remarriage.

Failure to monitor beneficiary designations may result in unanticipated consequences when a retiree dies. Remaining benefits may go to the IRS in unplanned estate taxes or bypass the current spouse and go to a previous spouse. Further, if beneficiary designations in a retirement plan are in conflict with the retiree's current will, final distribution will be made according to the beneficiary designation—it takes precedence over the will. The estate should generally not be named as a beneficiary since this will subject the proceeds to probate. Specific information about naming beneficiaries and stretching an IRA is discussed in chapter 15, Estate Planning. The tax consequences that follow naming a beneficiary or determining how to receive payments as a beneficiary are significant and demand consultation with a knowledgeable financial and tax professional.

ANNUITIES

Annuities can be used by seniors in each of the three income groups. While many possibilities exist, three uses can be illustrated.

- *High net worth* seniors can make good use of an annuity's tax-deferred growth. When monthly income is not needed, distribution of the annuity can be delayed (unlike many qualified retirement plan distributions). Careful use of beneficiaries can also expand the value of an annuity.

- *Middle-income* seniors, especially those in the lower part of middle, may have several financial assets, but still need to supplement monthly income. Seniors in this situation may also need Medicaid benefits, but have difficulty qualifying due to their financial assets. By purchasing an annuity, it may be possible to reduce financial assets enough to qualify for Medicaid, while also supplementing monthly income. The regulations vary significantly from state-to-state, so it is very important to consult the experts (including elder law attorneys) prior to using this technique.

- *Lower-income* seniors may be in a situation where they need some additional regular, consistent income. A fixed annuity can be ideal for this purpose. Such an annuity can provide guaranteed income payments for life, eliminating at least some concern about having enough money to live on.

Annuities can be a valuable part of retirement planning. In addition to offering some tax benefit, they provide flexible options for both growth and income. In fact, annuities are a major source of income for many seniors, fully retired or working part-time, because:

- seniors receive an income to live on while their investment continues to grow tax-deferred: earnings are taxed only when the money is paid to the annuity owner or the beneficiary;

- unlike any other investment vehicle, the annuity can provide income for the life of the annuity owner or for the life of both the owner and survivor, typically the owner's spouse.

What Is an Annuity?

An *annuity* is as a contract between an insurance company and an individual purchaser. The purchaser makes either one lump-sum single premium payment or a series of periodic premium payments to the insurance company. The value of the annuity grows at a fixed or variable rate and earnings are reinvested. The insurance company promises to distribute the funds, along with accumulated earnings, at a later date in one of several payout options: a lump sum, any number of random withdrawals, or a series of lifetime payments.

The first distribution from an annuitized contract marks the beginning of the liquidation (annuity) period. The contract can be prearranged to self-liquidate at age 65 (or another age) or upon request of the contract owner.

Once lifetime payouts begin, the insurance company calculates the portion of each payment that represents earnings and is subject to taxes. When funds are withdrawn randomly or in a lump sum, earnings (from annuity contracts issued after August 1982) are paid out first and are subject to income tax. After earnings have been distributed, the remainder of the distributed value representing the premiums paid into the contract by the owner is not subject to taxation (because taxes on this money were already paid).

While most annuities are deferred and involve an accumulation period during which no distributions are made, *immediate annuities* begin self-liquidation with virtually no accumulation period—payments begin the month after the single annuity premium is deposited. An immediate annuity may also be purchased with life insurance proceeds or cash values.

Types of Annuities

Broadly speaking, annuities are available in three categories of risk and inflation protection: fixed, variable, or a combination of these. The pros and cons of the different types of annuities are shown in Table 16.9.

Table 16.9 Pros and Cons of Fixed and Variable Annuities

TYPE OF ANNUITY	PROS	CONS
Fixed	Minimum fixed rate of return	Loss of purchasing power due to inflation
Variable	Offers greater growth in value and inflation protection	Rate of growth subject to market—promises no rate of return
Combination	Provides the security of guaranteed payments with the potential for growth and inflation protection	The fixed payments are subject to purchasing power risk and the variable payments are subject to market risk

Fixed Annuities

A *fixed annuity* guarantees a minimum fixed rate of return. The insurance company absorbs the investment risk; if the annuity does not earn the promised rate of return, the insurance company must make it up. However, the annuity owner is exposed to significant risk from loss of buying power (inflation) due to the annuity's fixed rate of return. What may seem an adequate monthly payout on a fixed annuity when it is purchased will have far less purchasing power in 15 to 20 years when the contract is annuitized and payments begin. At that point, the purchaser cannot adjust the monthly payout amount. Once a payout option begins, it cannot be changed.

Variable Annuities

A *variable annuity* is a tax-deferred investment purchased within an insurance contract. The annuity owners assume the investment risk because they select the investment portfolio into which the insurance company invests the annuity premiums. The variable annuity offers potential for greater growth in value. However, the rate of growth will be determined by the market performance of the chosen investment portfolio.

In its purest version, a variable annuity promises no rate of return whatsoever. Annuity premiums are invested into a separate account, where the contract holder may allocate dollars into one or more subaccounts (portfolios). Allocation into diversified common stocks is common. The annuity owner absorbs the investment risk but anticipates (with no guarantee) that long-term performance will outperform inflation.

Combination Annuities

Combination annuities allow an annuity owner, using one contract, to allocate deposits of premium payments between the insurer's fixed and separate accounts. The owner may change allocations at certain intervals (typically annually or quarterly).

Payout Options

Owners can liquidate their annuities using one of several options:

- lump sum
- random withdrawals
- annuitized fixed or variable amounts, paid according to a schedule based on life expectancy and an assumed or actual interest rate for the payout period

The advice of an experienced financial advisor is important in considering the numerous decisions that must be made for the liquidation phase to avoid unanticipated tax consequences for survivors and heirs or the inflation exposure associated with a fixed income stream. Examples of some of the characteristics of these payouts are as follows:

- Once liquidation starts, the option cannot be changed.
- Payments generally continue over the lifetime of the annuitant, although they can be for a fixed period—for example, 5 or 10 years.
- Generally, more payout options are available with individually purchased annuities than with annuities used to distribute qualified retirement plans.

Following are common variations on the main categories of payout options:

- *Straight life (single life):* The annuity stops paying upon the (single) annuity owner's death. This option provides the largest monthly payment per premium dollar among all the options—but provides no value to heirs.
- *Life income with period certain:* The insurance company guarantees a minimum number of payments, regardless of whether the annuity owner is alive. If premium payments have been made on a contract with an annuitized life income with a 10-year period-certain, if the annuitant suddenly dies one year later, the remaining nine years of the 10-year certain period are paid to the named beneficiary. If the original annuity owner does not die within the 10-year period, payments continue as long as the annuitant lives. Thus, under the 10-year period-certain contract, payments continue if the original annuitant lives to an advanced age.

500

- *Refund annuity (cash refund):* If an annuitant dies before receiving an amount that equals the entire premium paid, a beneficiary receives the unpaid balance in a lump sum. Periodic refunds may also be available.

- *Joint life and survivor:* Payments continue to be made as long as one of two or more annuitants remains living. Typically, two annuitants (husband and wife) are named under the contract. Payments to the survivor are typically smaller than with two living annuitants—for example, the so-called joint and two-thirds survivor annuity.

- *Period certain:* A period-certain annuity does not promise lifetime income. Instead, it simply distributes interest and principal in the annuity contract over a given number of years or months. Period certain annuities are typically used to distribute lottery winnings or personal injury awards rather than for providing lifetime retirement income (structured settlements).

In addition to annuities and qualified retirement plans, a third major source of retirement income for seniors is a reverse mortgage—usually in the middle- and lower-income groups.

REVERSE MORTGAGES

> *Marvin, 67, and Yvonne, 65, were devastated when detectives notified them they were one of many investors who had lost money in a large Ponzi investment scam. Marvin and Yvonne lost their entire life savings. But they owned their home, and thanks to a reverse mortgage, now have a new source of income for their retirement.*

Reverse mortgages can provide a source of income for seniors who own their homes but no other significant sources of income.

House-Rich and Cash-Poor

For many seniors their most valuable asset is their home. More than 50 percent of Americans over age 65 own homes free and clear, while an additional 25 percent have considerable equity. Thus, seniors may find themselves house-rich and cash-poor.

Recently, programs have become available that enable retirees to use the equity in their homes to supplement income. *Home equity conversion plans* (reverse mortgages) are relatively new in the United States, although they have been available in Europe for many years. In his article "Reverse Mortgages: A New Source of Income," author Michelle Graves, CSA, writes

> The reverse mortgage has evolved into a sophisticated financial planning tool that enables seniors to stay in their homes, or age in place, and maintain or improve their standard of living without taking on a monthly mortgage payment (Graves, 2000).

Why "Reverse"?

The reverse mortgage allows individuals and couples over age 62 having substantial equity in a home to enter into a type of loan that converts part of their home equity into tax-free income. The amount of money available from

501

a reverse mortgage will depend on the type of reverse mortgage, the age of the borrower, prevailing interest rates, and the condition of the home. The use of projected life expectancies in determining annuity amounts means that older borrowers usually receive larger monthly payments or lines of credit.

With a traditional mortgage, the homeowner makes mortgage payments and builds equity in the home. When the loan is paid off, the borrower owns the home. A reverse mortgage indeed reverses that process: Homeowners give up equity in exchange for payments that are generally used to provide or supplement retirement income. In a reverse mortgage, the senior homeowner receives money from a lender, again with the home as collateral. The money may be received as a lump sum, in a series of monthly payments for life, over a specified period of time, or as a flat or increasing line of credit to be used as needed. The homeowner makes no monthly payments on the reverse mortgage.

Loan Repayment

The reverse mortgage must be repaid when the senior moves, dies, or sells the house. According to Graves:

> One question that often arises is "What happens when the borrower dies?" The lender does not "get" the home when the loan matures. The borrower's estate or family must pay back the loan at that time, with or without a sale of the home. Under many reverse mortgage arrangements, the family virtually has the right of first refusal when it comes to purchasing the home and continuing the family homestead. If the home is sold and the sales proceeds exceed the repayment obligation, the excess funds go to the borrower's estate. If the sales proceeds are less than the amount owed, the shortfall is not the responsibility of the borrower's estate.

> Reverse mortgage lenders generally make loans in amounts less than the full value of the home. In general, the repayment obligation of the borrower's estate can't exceed the value of the property. Borrowers may be able to preserve some equity for heirs by basing the cash advance on only a portion of the home equity. Typically, borrowers can't be forced to sell their homes to repay a reverse mortgage as long as they occupy the home, even if the total of the monthly payments to the borrower exceeds the value of the home.

Qualifying for a Reverse Mortgage

A reverse mortgage is generally available when all the owners of a particular home are at least 62 years old. For the federally insured Home Equity Conversion Mortgage (HECM), the home must be a single-family dwelling or a federally approved condominium. For Fannie Mae's Home Keeper mortgage, the property must be a single-family home or condominium.

Costs of Reverse Mortgages

A number of costs are associated with establishing a reverse mortgage. Many are those typically associated with traditional mortgages and include interest charges, origination fees, title searches, inspections, and the like. Although total costs between the HECM and Home Keeper programs may vary substantially, most cost items do not vary among the specific lending institutions that ultimately provide the reverse mortgage financing. When selecting the appropriate program for a given senior client, a financial planner should compare the total annual loan cost among the various arrangements.

Impact on Taxes and Entitlement Programs

Payments from reverse mortgages generally are not treated as taxable income. Nor do reverse mortgage distributions reduce Social Security or Medicare benefits. However, payments from reverse mortgages may jeopardize a retiree's eligibility for Medicaid benefits or SSI Disability benefits.

Reverse Mortgage Lending Sources

The United States Department of Housing and Urban Development (HUD) and Fannie Mae administer the largest programs in reverse mortgages. HUD's HECM is available through private lenders. It is insured by the Federal Housing Authority (FHA) and is fully described on AARP's Web site. Fannie Mae, the largest investor in reverse mortgages, has two products: Home Keeper Reverse Mortgage and Home Keeper for Home Purchase. HUD's product has been available since 1987, and Fannie Maes were established in 1989.

Most Seniors Are Not Wealthy: Lower-Income Group

William and Helen say they are doing all right in retirement. The mortgage on the house is paid, their car note is paid, and they have food in the pantry. Unfortunately, the rest of the picture is not so rosy. There's no money for gifts to the grandchildren, they cannot travel to see any of the family, and they worry about what will happen when the car finally quits running. William and Helen always meant to save more for retirement, but somehow, they were never able to do so. As a result, if it were not for Supplemental Security Income (SSI), they would have no income. William and Helen say they are doing all right, but when you talk with them for long, you learn that "doing all right" is a far cry from what they envisioned when they were younger.

Some seniors will have more than enough resources with which to have a comfortable retirement. Others will barely be able to make it from month to month. For those who have no other income options, SSI at least can provide some income on which to live (see chapter 21, Social Security and Supplemental Security Income). You should recognize a number of factors that affect the decision regarding when an individual has sufficient resources to maintain lifestyle in retirement.

Whereas middle-income seniors live a very comfortable retirement and face challenges such as selecting the right investment, deciding how to best distribute retirement plan dollars, and planning their next trip, many people in the lower-income category generally depend on government programs such as SSI and Medicaid, and some pension income. Although lower-income seniors worked for companies with employer-sponsored retirement plans, many were not able to afford to contribute to those plans.

We will next take a look at some alternative income sources that may be of special interest to lower-income seniors, and a number of resources that can help them understand what benefits may be available to find solutions to their financial and other concerns.

ALTERNATIVES TO SUPPLEMENT RETIREMENT FUNDS

Some lower-income seniors may rely on Medicaid, charity, and family support to supplement their retirement funds, and others may use the equity in their homes to finance shortfalls in their retirement.

This section offers some resources that may be helpful to lower-income seniors. The resources vary greatly by region, so you will need to do some individual work to find local resources.

Delay Retirement or Consider Part-time Work

Many seniors who do not have adequate financial resources for retirement would be well advised to consider delaying retirement. Working even a few additional years can allow seniors to pay debts down, allow retirement funds to continue their tax-deferred growth, and receive larger Social Security benefits.

Supplemental Security Income

The Supplemental Security Income (SSI) program provides monthly income to people who are age 62 or older (60 in the case of qualified widows), or are blind or disabled, and have limited income and financial resources. Individuals can be eligible for SSI even if they have never worked in employment covered under Social Security.

Qualified Medicare Beneficiary

Medicaid offers a program for beneficiaries with limited income and resources. For those who qualify, the Medicaid program pays Medicare Part B premiums as well as Medicare deductibles and coinsurance amounts for Medicare services. This program is discussed on the Medicare Web site, http://www.medicare.gov.

Veterans Benefits

Veterans and their spouses have access to a variety of benefits including TRICARE for Life supplemental health insurance, low-cost prescription drugs for the veteran, and burial benefits. It is not uncommon for the widow of a veteran to be unaware of important benefits.

Pharmacy Assistance Program

Prescription drugs costs are one of the greatest challenges for low-income seniors. Many seniors fail to take prescribed drugs or they reduce the amount they take because they cannot afford them. Medicare's Web site provides a link to state drug assistance programs. Additionally, many pharmaceutical companies provide assistance with critical drugs for seniors who have low incomes and no other drug coverage. There are a variety of drug discount cards that may offer just the relief needed for some seniors to pay for drugs.

Tax Credits Reduce Taxes Paid

Tax savings represent another potential source of income. Tax credits offer a dollar-for-dollar reduction in taxes owed. Once marginal tax rates are applied to taxable income to calculate the tax due, tax credits are then subtracted directly from the amount of tax due. For an individual in the 28 percent tax bracket, a $1.00 *tax deduction* is worth 28 cents, whereas a $1.00 *tax credit* is worth a full dollar. Every dollar of tax credit represents an additional dollar of spendable income.

Credit for the Elderly and Disabled

Those who are disabled receive a 15 percent credit against tax that is computed on the Schedule R (Form 1040 filers) or Schedule 3 (Form 1040A filers). The credit applies to low-income filers over 65 years of age or other filers who are under 65 and meet special circumstances. In addition to meeting the income limits below, the individual may not receive more than $5,000 ($7,500 for married filing jointly, $3,750 for married filing separately) of nontaxable Social Security or nontaxable pensions. The applicable income limits for 2008 were:

Single, head of household, qualifying widow	$17,500
Married, filing jointly—one spouse eligible	$20,000
Married, filing jointly—both eligible	$25,000
Married, filing separately—live apart all year	$12,500

Earned Income Credit

An earned income credit (EIC) is available to single individuals with eligible lower incomes or those with qualifying children. The credit may apply to older clients who are raising grandchildren. A complex formula is used to calculate this credit. You should track annual increases to income limitations for clients anticipating the EIC.

The Federal Housing Tax Credit Program

The Federal Housing Tax Credit Program is a prefunded stream of tax credits awarded to private developers of affordable housing, including multi-family housing and senior housing. Seniors and others of moderate means rent *affordable housing units* (not to be confused with HUD Section 8 low-income housing). Financial eligibility requires a senior's income to be 60 percent or less of the average income in their county.

Participation in the Federal Housing Tax Credit program may fulfill a senior's wish for socially conscious investing while producing additional income. For a lump-sum investment, a senior may receive predetermined tax credits over 10 to 12 years. If the senior dies before the end of the credit period, the remaining interests are transferable to a beneficiary through the taxpayer's estate.

When properties are sold at the end of the tax credit period, proceeds are distributed and may represent a return in addition to tax credits already received. In many cases, however, tax credits represent the only return. Limited partnerships offering federal housing tax credits are long-term investments with virtually no liquidity. If a senior having unused tax credits dies, credits may be distributed among heirs via probate or according to terms of a trust. Older taxpayers and their advisors should be aware that not all tax implications of investments providing federal housing credits are beneficial.

Tax credits cannot be used to reduce the alternative minimum tax, under which wealthier investors may be forced to pay tax on certain otherwise taxsheltered investments and other income.

When properties are sold, investors may be allocated profits that will generate federal income tax. Limited partnerships offering federal housing tax credits are generally available through larger securities broker dealers. Your client's tax advisor should play a critical role in assessing the suitability of such a partnership for the client.

Retirement Savings Contributions Credit

Effective for taxable years through 2008, lower-income taxpayers may receive a tax credit of up to $2,000 for contributions to qualified retirement savings (elective deferrals and IRA contributions). The amount of the credit is determined on a sliding scale, with the maximum allowable credit being 50 percent of the contribution. This credit is not available for any individual who is a dependent of another taxpayer or when income exceeds established 2008 limits of $26,500 for those filing individually and $53,000 for those filing jointly. This credit may be extended again in 2009 or beyond by legislation; if so, annual limits may also change.

Protecting against Investment Pitfalls

Interestingly, it is not always the frail or uneducated senior who is at most risk from investment scams. Seniors who are active and looking for the goose that lays the golden egg are at highest risk for investment scams.

State securities regulators, the AARP, and the Consumer Federation have identified common investment pitfalls among the senior population. Because many senior citizens are retired, they cannot easily use future wages to replace monies lost in investments. It is critical that older Americans consider investments that are suitable to their needs, especially when their hard-earned savings or lump-sum pension payments are at stake.

The most common pitfalls for seniors who invest are:

- salespeople who misrepresent themselves;
- uninsured products;
- inadequate disclosure about products;

- misleading fund names;
- lack of clarity in account statements.

SALESPEOPLE POSING AS IMPARTIAL ADVISORS

With any investor, but especially older ones, confusion can result from the common use of confidence-inspiring titles such as *investment consultant* and *financial advisor* without the appropriate credentials behind them. Senior citizens may be unaware that investment salespeople typically make their living from commissions. Seniors should also recognize that individuals they speak with may receive referral fees for directing them to financial professionals. Seniors should request that the salespeople disclose their compensations in writing.

UNINSURED PRODUCTS SOLD IN FINANCIAL INSTITUTIONS

Older investors are most likely to place particular trust in banks. It is very important for seniors to remember that investments such as mutual funds, whether purchased on bank premises or at brokerage firms, may lose value and are not insured against loss by the FDIC. If market values decline or interest rates rise, investors may lose money.

INADEQUATE DISCLOSURE ABOUT INVESTMENT PRODUCTS

Older investors must be on guard against unwarranted claims that some financial professionals make in their sales pitches. Prospectuses and other investment disclosure documents that are difficult to understand compound the inadequate or misleading communication about products. Many elderly investors claim they either are not informed of or fail to understand sales charges, up-front fees, or back-end charges. They may not realize that these commissions and fees may also apply to investments purchased at a bank. A good reminder is the old adage: If it sounds too good to be true, it probably is.

MISLEADING FUND NAMES

Often the name given to a mutual fund may not truly reflect its investment objective. Unsophisticated investors may be misled by terms such as *income* or *government* to believe that investments made in such products will not entail risk. In actual fact, the asset value of any mutual fund may fluctuate due to changes in market conditions.

UNCLEAR ACCOUNT STATEMENTS

Most brokerage and mutual fund account statements reveal little about investment performance and fees and commissions. Financial planners can provide valuable assistance to their clients if they can help them to calculate and evaluate these figures and investigate when numbers appearing in statements seem not to make sense or if the statements are not available in writing.

Steps to Wise Investing

To help older investors make proper and informed investment decisions, financial planners should encourage clients to complete the following steps.

DEFINE FINANCIAL OBJECTIVES

The first step in wise investing is to understand current and future financial goals. Before investing, clients should consider the advice of financial professionals in deciding how much investment risk is tolerable. Older investors should be encouraged to provide advisors with written descriptions of their needs and risk preferences. The investors, in turn, may also wish to have financial professionals confirm in writing their understanding of financial goals.

CHECK OUT FINANCIAL PROFESSIONALS

In dealing with an investment professional, investors should check with the National Association of Securities Dealers (NASD). The association maintains records on all stockbrokers and brokerage firms licensed to do business in the United States. Ask if the investment professional is a member of the Financial Planning Association (FPA), which has a code of ethics for its members. In addition, The Certified Financial Planner (CFP) Board of Standards also has an excellent consumer area on its Web site to help seniors find a financial advisor. And, of course, investors will do well to use the services of financial professionals who adhere to the CSA Code of Professional Responsibility. Information for all of these services is available in the Resources section at the end of the chapter.

Seniors should determine exactly the skills, training, and expertise of any people representing themselves as financial services or planning professionals. This will guard against individuals who do not have the appropriate skills and experience to advise them in a fiduciary manner.

BE WARY OF STRANGERS

When strangers call promoting investments, seniors should determine how the caller obtained their name and number, as well as whether the caller would be willing to explain the investment proposal to an attorney, accountant, or another family member. Seniors who receive a challenging reply such as "Can't you make your own decisions?" should hang up the telephone.

RESIST PRESSURE TO ACT

Even more than most investors, older investors need adequate time to check out investments and salespeople. Seniors should not be afraid to ask questions or seek second opinions. Postretirement money is too important to be placed at risk with hasty decisions.

UNDERSTAND THE NATURE OF THE INVESTMENT

Older investors should never assume that investments are federally insured, low-risk, or guaranteed to deliver a certain return. Before buying, any investor should investigate a potential investment by getting and reading the prospectus or similar offering document. Prospectuses can be lengthy and intimidating documents to an elderly person; a financial planner should be able to explain what the various disclosures in a prospectus mean.

INVESTIGATE ANY POTENTIAL INVESTMENT

Almost all investment opportunities must be registered in the states where they are sold. Check out a potential investment by calling a state's securities department. Although state securities departments will not make investment decisions for older investors, they can disclose whether a particular investment is registered in the buyer's state. If a salesperson says, "It isn't an investment that needs registration," then a red flag should go up.

MONITOR ACCOUNT STATEMENTS CLOSELY

An account statement should reflect only an authorized pattern of investing. If there is a discrepancy, a senior should raise the problem immediately with the broker and, if necessary, the branch manager who oversees the broker. With the assistance of a financial planner, a senior should carefully review account statements or other documents that reflect fees and commissions. If such documents do not clearly indicate this information, ask the broker or manager for the figures. If it appears that something is wrong with a client's account and concerns are not promptly being addressed, the NASD or state securities department should be contacted immediately, preferably in writing.

Financial Choices and Challenges for Seniors: Summary

How can you help your clients deal with the change in the wealth accumulation and expenditure periods, with the increased complexities associated with saving for their retirement, and with managing their finances during retirement?

Clearly, the earlier clients can begin saving and investing for retirement, the more likely they will have accumulated sufficient assets to retire according to their timetable and maintain their current or higher standards of living. Encourage your clients to save as aggressively as possible for their retirements (given their individual budgets and circumstances), especially during the Decision Decade. Suggest ways to save. For example:

- One of the easiest ways to save for retirement is through individual retirement accounts (IRAs). Traditional, spousal, Roth, and nondeductible IRAs

509

are generally available to any American with income earned from working (*earned income* or *personal service income*), although there may be limits on how much individuals can contribute each year based on their adjusted gross income.

- In addition to IRAs, employer-sponsored plans are another important savings vehicle available to many Americans. (These plans generally must be offered by employers to employees who are over age 21 following one year of full-time service—defined as 1,000 hours in a year.) You can help your clients find affordable and professional financial assistance in making their investment choices, and support them in being disciplined in making regular contributions.

- It can be an especially good idea to contribute to a 401(k) when an employer provides matching contributions. Many employers will match some or all of an employee's contribution to the company's 401(k) plan. The matching contributions usually are limited, but even so, they can have a great impact on dollars available for retirement.

- Many clients live with too much debt. It can be hard to make contributions to retirement funds when every dollar is being applied to credit card debt payments. One good way to increase available dollars for retirement is to systematically reduce debt. The first step in this process is often a commitment by the individual not to continue to use credit cards. Paying off credit card debt by making just the minimum required payments takes literally years. A better plan is to apply additional amounts of discretionary income to paying down the debt on one credit card. When that debt is paid, the entire monthly payment can be applied to another credit card's debt, reducing the amount of repayment time. In this way debt can be reduced more quickly, freeing dollars to apply to retirement savings.

In addition, many individuals do not have sufficient understanding of their financial and investment account statements, and the pros and cons of the different investment vehicles in their qualified retirement plans from which they can choose. It is important that they make wise choices, particularly because this is the main source of retirement income. As a CSA, you can educate your clients, if you are qualified to do so. Certainly, you should have financial planning and investment professionals in your resource network to whom you can refer your clients for advice; or you can refer your clients to the resources listed at the end of this chapter. Financial planning ties all these strategies together in a coordinated approach to reducing risk and preserving wealth by growing income and asset.

It is especially important when dealing with financial matters to involve other professionals as appropriate. While you may not technically be a fiduciary, the level of care normally required of a fiduciary should be used. Financial issues tend to have implications in almost all areas of life. The more completely you have a grasp on each of these issues, the better you can provide service to seniors, helping them to maintain a high quality of life. To provide senior clients with prudent advice in the financial area or to make appropriate referrals, you must be able to identify important aspects of a client's financial circumstances and be familiar with typical strategies used to accomplish financial goals.

The majority of seniors today occupy the middle-income and lower-income groups. You may find yourself serving as advisor, teacher, and motivator. You may be called upon to:

- recognize financial challenges faced by seniors and have a ready referral network for problem solving;
- educate seniors about matters affecting their finances;
- motivate seniors to act prudently and to avoid investment pitfalls and scams;
- monitor retirement assets;
- help seniors to identify and implement solutions or find help when problems arise.

All income groups in some manner share three main concerns: peace of mind, a sense of security, and a sense of control. Competent use of the information in this textbook will enable you to assist senior clients in experiencing these benefits:

PEACE OF MIND

Taking appropriate financial planning steps may help clients relax about whether they are going to outlive their assets. As a CSA, if you are not trained in financial matters, you must recognize appropriate times for referring clients to financial planners, tax professionals, trust officers, stockbrokers, insurance professionals, and others. CSAs knowledgeable about financial services must enhance their expertise around financial strategies and resources that address issues specific to seniors.

SENSE OF SECURITY

You can help individuals who have not yet retired develop a greater sense of security by encouraging them to do a retirement income needs analysis to estimate how much they anticipate their retirement expenses will be and whether their current income and investment resources will provide enough to cover these expenses.

With this knowledge and appropriate support and referrals, individuals planning for retirement may make more effective decisions about investments, supplemental income, and retirement spending. Those who identify potential income shortfalls may choose to invest more aggressively, cut back on spending, or postpone distributions from qualified retirement plans to better match their expected financial needs during retirement.

You can assist seniors who have already retired and need assistance in maintaining or improving their lifestyles, or you can refer them to professional resources. Either way, your goal is to ensure they are budgeting properly for their income and expenses, and are aware of options and resources for generating more income, such as working part-time, taking advantage of federal and state programs, and using tax credits.

SENSE OF CONTROL

With the knowledge and assistance you offer as a CSA, seniors are better able to make informed choices about their financial matters in light of current market and economic conditions. As an information resource, you create the opportunity for senior clients to participate more fully in financial decision-making, helping them to maintain a sense of some choice and control in their lifestyles.

Appendix A: Financial Information Questionnaire

Family and Financial Information

(The road map for successful retirement)

Family Address: _____

City: _____ State: _____ Zip: _____ Phone: _____

FAMILY MEMBERS

NAME	WORK #	FAX #	D.O.B.	SS #
Client 1				
Client 2				
Children		X		X
		X		X
		X		X
		X		X

Miscellaneous Questions

Are any large expenditure due soon? Explain. _____
_____

What has been your best investment to date and why? _____
_____

Are there any investment areas you wish to avoid? _____

Have you established a contributory savings plan for your children/grandchildren? __Yes __No

What would you expect from your Certified Senior Advisor regarding service, attitude, frequency of communication, systematic mailings, etc.? _____
_____

Last tax year, did you receive a Federal refund? $_____ or owe money? $_____
                                State refund? $_____ or owe money? $_____
Will this tax year be the same? _____

Does either Client 1 or Client 2 have a chronic illness that may affect this plan financially?
Client 1: ____Yes ____No (If yes please give brief details)
_____

Client 2: ____Yes ____No (If yes please give brief details)
_____

Are you a smoker? Client 1: ____Yes ____No   Client 2: ____Yes ____No

Estate Planning

Do you have a current will? ____Yes ____No

Will your estate exceed $1.5 million in 2004–2005 ($2 million in 2006–2008; $3.5 million in 2009)? ____Yes ____No

Do you have a prenuptial agreement or postnuptial agreement in place? ____Yes ____No

Are you actively gifting? ____Yes ____No

Do you have in place a:
Healthcare Power of Attorney?	____Yes ____No
Financial Power of Attorney?	____Yes ____No
Living Will?	____Yes ____No
Funeral Plan?	____Yes ____No

Will you need a referral for an estate-planning attorney? ____Yes ____No

	Client 1	Client 2
When do you plan to retire?		
Up to what age shall we plan your retirement assets to last? (We usually use age 90. Current actuaries run to age 120.)		
What inflation rate do you want applied to your retirement years? (3.5% is long-term average.)		
What realistic percentage do you think your portfolio can average?		
How much capital do you wish remaining after your death?		

	Client 1	Client 2
If your financial partner pre-deceases you:		
Do you want to replace his or her income?	_____	_____
Do you want the mortgage paid off?	_____	_____

Retirement Plans

Type of Plan	Owner	Balance	Monthly Income

Checking & Savings

Where	Current Balance	Purpose	Maturity Date	Client 1	Client 2	Both

Amount of cash reserves you would like to maintain: Client 1 $_____ Client 2 $_____

Real Estate

Property	Orig. Pur. Price	Date of Mort.	Orig. Loan Value	Curr. Mort. Bal.	Interest Rate %	Type	No. of Years	Total Mnthly Pymt	HO Ins. Prem.	Rental Income

Investments

Please give total value of all accounts. Be sure to bring individual statements on each.

Investment	Client 1	Client 2
403(b)		
401(k)		
Roth 401(k)		
Keogh Plans (SEPs, Profit Sharing, etc.)		
Deferred Compensation		
Pension Program (e.g. PERA)		
IRA (Traditional)		
IRA (Roth)		
Brokerage Account (Individual, Stocks, Bonds)		
Mutual Funds		
Savings Bonds (EE, HH)		
Limited Partnerhips		
CDs		
Collectibles		
Real Estate		
Checking		
Savings		
Other		
Other		
TOTAL		

Life Insurance

Company	Type*	Who is the Owner?	Who is Insured?	Who is the Beneficiary?	Death Benefit Payable	Annual Cost	Cash Value Built Up

*Types: WL=Whole Life   T=Term   G=Group   UL = Universal Life   VL = Variable Life

Long-Term Care Insurance

Do you have a long-term care policy on yourself? Client 1 __Yes __No   Client 2 __Yes __No

Are your parents still alive?   Client 1 __Yes __No   Client 2 __Yes __No

Do your parents currently have a long-term care policy on themselves?

Client 1 ____Mother ____Father

Client 2 ____Mother ____Father

Liability

Do you have a personal or professional umbrella liability policy?
Client 1 ____Yes ____No   Amount of coverage $_____
Client 2 ____Yes ____No   Amount of coverage $_____

Homeowner's and automobile insurances are specialties. Consult your insurance carrier.

Debt Payment Schedule

Include Car Payments, Personal Loans, Insurance Loans, TSA Loans, Credit Cards, Home Mortgages and others.

Creditor	Interest Rate	Balance You Owe	Minimum Pymt. Req.	Amount You Pay

Monthly Cash Flow

NOTE: IF YOU USE QUICKEN OR A SIMILAR ACCOUNTING PROGRAM, YOU MAY BRING A PRINTOUT INSTEAD OF COMPLETING THIS PAGE.

INCOME: List all sources of income

Source (Client 1)	Amount	Source (Client 2)	Amount
_____	$_____	_____	$_____
_____	$_____	_____	$_____

FIXED EXPENDITURES		VARIABLE EXPENDITURES	
Retirement Accounts	$_____	Auto: Fuel	$_____
Home Mortgage (1st)	_____	Oil Changes	_____
Home Mortgage (2nd)	_____	Maintenance	_____
Rent for Residence	_____	Food/Groceries	_____
Property Taxes (Auto)	_____	Restaurants	_____
Property Taxes (Other)	_____	Clothes	_____
Utilities: Gas	_____	Cleaners/Laundry	_____
Electricity	_____	Church/Charity Contributions	_____
Telephone	_____	Education Expenses	_____
Water/Sewer/Trash	_____	Lessons (Music/Dance, etc.)	_____
Cable TV	_____	Gifts	_____
Security	_____	Home Repairs/Maintenance	_____
Homeowner Assoc.	_____	Yard/Pool Maintenance	_____
Insurance*: Auto	_____	New Household Purchases/	
Medical	_____	Furnishings	_____
Life-Client	_____	Medical/Dental Care	_____
Life-Spouse	_____	Personal Care	_____
Life-Kids	_____	Subscriptions/Newspapers	_____
Income Protection	_____	Vacations	_____
Child Day Care	_____	Entertainment	_____
Alimony/Child/Elder Sup.	_____	Credit Card Payments	_____
Club Dues/Memberships	_____	Business or School	
Loan Payments	_____	Expenses (unreimb)	_____
Other Installment Loans	_____	Life Insurance Loans	_____
Income Taxes	_____	Pocket Money Client 1	_____
		Client 2	_____
		Children	_____
		Misc.	_____
Total Fixed Expenditures	$_____	Total Variable Expenditures	$_____

*Other than group or not deducted from paycheck

Total Average Monthly Income	$_____
Less Total Average Monthly Expenditures	$_____
Available Dollars to Use for Goals	$_____

This represents the available monthly dollars usable to accomplish your goals.

Appendix B: A Mini Case Study—Projecting Retirement Income

Ken and Louise Hill are both 45. Ken earns $50,000 per year as a junior college instructor. Louise earns $50,000 per year as a computer programmer. We can quantify their current expenses and estimate how much each expense item will change (if at all) after both retire in 20 years at age 65.

EXPENSES	CURRENT (TODAY'S DOLLARS)	PROJECTED (TODAY'S DOLLARS)
Mortgage	10,566	0[1]
Property Tax	2,400	2,880[2]
Income & Social Security Taxes	24,340	14,290[3]
Property Insurance	900	1,200
Health Insurance	0	5,400[4]
Auto Loan	4,773	0
Food	8,400	6,720[5]
Utilities	2,400	3,000[6]
Housekeeper	3,600	900[7]
Clothing	4,800	2,400[8]
Vacation	6,000	9,000[9]
Entertainment	3,600	7,200[10]
Communications	2,400	1,200[11]
Business Expenses	3,600	0[12]
Gifts	4,800	4,800
Donations	3,600	2,400[13]
Roth IRAs	4,000	0[14]
401(k) Elective	5,000	0[15]
Miscellaneous	4,821	6,900[16]
TOTAL	**$100,000**	**$68,290**

Notes:

[1] Mortgage paid off before retirement

[2] Property tax will have increases not specifically pegged to inflation

[3] Income tax and Social Security tax reduced due to elimination of wages

[4] Employer no longer pays premiums. Hills will pay premium for Medicare supplemental insurance and Long Term Care insurance

[5] Eating out less, early bird specials

[6] More time in the house

[7] Housekeeping service reduced but not eliminated

[8] Business clothing no longer necessary

[9] More vacations due to increased leisure time

[10] More hobby-related expenses due to increased leisure time

[11] Reduced cell phone use

[12] Business expenses eliminated

[13] Will donate time rather than money in some circumstances

[14] Roth IRAs will not be funded after retirement

[15] Elective deferrals of $5,000 for Jim will end at retirement

[16] More reading material, etc., with greater leisure time

Note that these numbers, representing the Hills' expenses, are expressed in today's dollars. Presuming they retire in 20 years at age 65, inflation at 4 percent will mean that they need approximately $149,632 in their first year of retirement to support their projected outflow.

Once cash outflow is estimated, financial planners can enter this data into a program (available as software or on the Internet) or into a retirement planning or financial function calculator that analyzes retirement income needs to help clients estimate the amount of money they will need to cover their projected expenses in retirement. Then the amount of *additional* savings they will need to supplement Social Security, employer-provided retirement plans, and personal savings already in place, if any, can be assessed.

Appendix C: Taxable Equivalent Yield (TEY) Formula

When clients are considering whether to buy a tax-exempt or taxable bond, the taxable equivalent yield (TEY) formula can be used to compare the after-tax interest income between the two bonds.

Example:

Martha is in the 28 percent marginal federal income tax bracket. She is considering the purchase of either a municipal bond paying 6 percent annual tax-exempt interest or a corporate bond paying 7.5 percent taxable annual interest. The taxable equivalent yield formula below allows her to compare the yields of these two options.

TEY = yield ÷ (100% – tax bracket)

Tax-exempt municipal bond:	6% ÷ (100% – 28%) =
	.06 ÷ .72 = .0833, or 8.33%
Corporate bond:	7.5%

The taxable equivalent yield formula reveals that Martha receives more income from the tax-exempt municipal bond than from the taxable corporate bond.

Appendix D: Mini Case Study—Calculating What Portion of Social Security Benefits Are Taxable

The taxable portion of benefits is usually not greater than 50 percent. However, when total income (one half of Social Security benefits plus other includable income) exceeds the upper limit ($34,000 for individuals and $44,000 for married couples filing jointly) up to 85 percent of benefits are taxable. Forms 1040 and 1040A include a worksheet to calculate taxable benefits.

Example:

Emily, who is single, has the following income sources:

Social Security retirement benefit	$12,600
Pension distribution	$18,000
Total interest on CDs, money market accounts and municipal bonds	$15,700

Emily is in the 25% tax bracket. Her Social Security tax is calculated below:

Step 1: Calculate income exceeding threshold:

50% of Social Security	$ 6,300
Pensions and interest income	$33,700
Total gross income	$40,000
Base amount (single)	<$25,000>
Excess over base	$15,000

Step 2: Calculate taxable social security:

Income exceeding threshold:

The first $9,000 (difference between Emily's higher level of $34,000 and the threshold of $25,000) is calculated at a 50% rate:

50% × $9,000 =	$ 4,500

The remainder of her excess income (income in excess of $34,000, or $40,000 – $34,000 = $6,000 in Emily's case) is calculated at an 85% tax rate:

85% × $6,000	$ 5,100
Total taxable income	$ 9,600

Taxable Social Security income is the smaller of this calculated amount ($9,600) or 85% of the total Social Security benefit ($12,600 × 85% = $10,710)

Taxable Social Security income =	$ 9,600

Tax to be paid on Social Security income (calculated at Emily's tax bracket of 25%)	$ 2,400

Each January Social Security benefit recipients receive a Social Security Benefit Statement (Form SSA-1099) showing the amount of benefits received in the previous year. This statement is used to complete the federal income tax return and determine whether benefits are subject to tax. There is no requirement to have federal taxes withheld from Social Security benefits, but some may find it easier than paying quarterly estimated tax payments. The IRS Web site contains information on having federal taxes withheld.

IRS publications that are especially helpful in understanding taxation of benefits include IRS Publication 554, Tax Information for Older Americans, and Publication 915, Social Security Benefits and Equivalent Railroad Retirement Benefits. Both publications have worksheets to help determine whether benefits are taxable. Copies are available by calling the IRS at their toll-free number, 1-800-829-3676, or they may be viewed on the IRS Web site, http://www.irs.gov. Viewing these publications online requires Adobe Acrobat Reader software.

Appendix E: Taxpayer Advocate Service

HOW SENIORS CAN USE THE TAXPAYER ADVOCATE SERVICE

Senior taxpayers and their advisors should be aware of the Taxpayer Advocate Service, an IRS program to assure prompt and fair handling of tax problems not resolved through normal channels. The National Taxpayer Advocate heads the program. Each state and service center has at least one local Taxpayer Advocate, who is independent of the local IRS office and reports directly to the National Taxpayer Advocate.

The goals of the Taxpayer Advocate Service are to protect individual taxpayer rights and to reduce taxpayer burden. The Taxpayer Advocate independently represents a client's interests and concerns within the IRS in two ways:

- by ensuring that taxpayer problems not resolved through normal channels are promptly and fairly handled
- by alerting IRS management and developing appropriate legislative proposals in regard to issues that increase burdens or create problems for taxpayers

WHAT A SENIOR CAN EXPECT FROM A TAXPAYER ADVOCATE

An assigned personal advocate will listen to the taxpayer's point of view and work with the taxpayer and the taxpayer's representative to address concerns. A senior can expect the advocate to provide:

- a fresh look at a problem;
- timely acknowledgment;
- the name and phone number of the individual assigned to the case;
- updates on progress;
- time frames for action;
- speedy resolution;
- courteous service.

521

WHO MAY USE THE TAXPAYER ADVOCATE SERVICE

Generally, the Taxpayer Advocate Service is designed to assist taxpayers who:

- are suffering or are about to suffer a significant hardship;
- are facing an immediate threat of adverse action;
- will incur significant cost (including fees for professional representation);
- will suffer irreparable injury or long-term adverse impact;
- have experienced a delay of more than 30 days to resolve the issue;
- have not received a response or resolution by the date promised.

Have your client contact the Taxpayer Advocate Service if he or she has an ongoing issue with the IRS that has not been resolved through normal processes, or has suffered (or is about to suffer) a significant hardship as a result of the application of the tax laws.

Note that the Taxpayer Advocate Service is not a substitute for established IRS procedures or the formal appeals process. The Taxpayer Advocate Service cannot reverse legal or technical tax determinations. Also, the Taxpayer Rights Corner on the IRS Web site contains information about taxpayer rights when dealing with the IRS.

HOW TO REACH THE TAXPAYER ADVOCATE SERVICE

- Call the Taxpayer Advocate Service toll-free telephone number: 1-877-777-4778 or TTY/TTD: 1-800-829-4059.

- Call the general IRS toll-free number: 1-800-829-1040 and request the Taxpayer Advocate Service.

- Call, write, or visit the local Taxpayer Advocate office for your state. A list of Taxpayer Advocate Service offices may be found in Publication 1546, *The Taxpayer Advocate Service of the IRS*, which may be downloaded and printed from http://www.irs.gov.

- Complete and submit Form 911, *Application for Taxpayer Assistance Order*. Form 911 may be obtained by calling the IRS forms-only number, 1-800-829-3676, sending a written request for assistance (if Form 911 is not available), or requesting that an IRS employee complete a Form 911 on the taxpayer's behalf (in person or over the telephone). Form 911 or a written request may be faxed to the local Taxpayer Advocate. An *Application for a Taxpayer Assistance Order* requires an Advocate to determine if significant hardship exists and to review the case to determine what action should be taken to relieve the hardship. In certain situations, enforcement action may be suspended while a case is being reviewed. Taxpayer Advocates resolve the majority of cases administratively. Even when hardship is not a factor, an Advocate is often able to help resolve a taxpayer's problem.

INFORMATION NEEDED BY A TAXPAYER ADVOCATE

The Taxpayer Advocate needs the following information:

- taxpayer's name, address, and Social Security number (or employer identification number)
- taxpayer's telephone number and hours the taxpayer can be reached
- taxpayer's previous attempts to solve the problem and the office contacted
- the type of tax return and year(s) involved
- description of the problem or hardship (if applicable)

A taxpayer who wishes to authorize another person to discuss the matter or to receive information about his or her case may download Form 2848, Power of Attorney and Declaration of Representative, and Form 2848 Instructions from http://www.irs.gov. Or a taxpayer may use Form 8821, Tax Information Authorization, to authorize another person to receive information about a case, but not to represent the taxpayer. If an individual is unable to download and print these documents, hard copies may be obtained at most local IRS offices or by calling the IRS forms-only number, 1-800-829-3676.

CITIZENS ADVOCACY PANELS

The IRS tax districts in Seattle, Brooklyn, Milwaukee, and Ft. Lauderdale were chosen as sites for Citizen Advocacy Panels because of their varied taxpayer populations as well as their ethnic, cultural, and geographic diversity. The IRS has secured and prepared permanent office and meeting space for the panel in each of the host cities. Full-time staffs, including a manager, analysts, and clerical support, are assigned to each panel. A toll-free phone number and voice messaging system allows taxpayers to access panels 24 hours a day, seven days a week. Panels each have a Web site capable of receiving comments from the public.

The panels have endeavored to publicize their existence and produce solid recommendations. Take the time to visit their sites and learn more about the projects they are working on and their accomplishments to date.

Appendix F: Popular Mutual Funds

GROWTH-TYPE FUNDS

- *Growth funds* invest in common stocks for appreciation.
- *Aggressive growth funds* hold common stocks of rapidly growing corporations.
- *Specialized funds*, often called *sector funds*, concentrate in one industry (or one geographic region).

- *Index funds* operate portfolios mirroring those of recognized broad-based indices and averages, such as the Dow Jones Industrial Average or the S&P 500.
- *Growth and income funds* seek appreciation as well as dividend income.

INCOME-TYPE FUNDS

- *Equity income funds* hold high-dividend-paying stocks in industries such as utilities.
- *Corporate bond funds* invest in corporate bonds of many issuers for income.
- *High-grade (investment-grade) bond funds* invest in bonds rated AAA or AA by recognized rating services, such as Moody's and Standard and Poor's.
- *High-yield bond funds*, sometimes called *junk bond funds*, invest in corporate debt with ratings of BB or lower.
- *Municipal bond funds* hold tax-exempt bonds issued by states, cities, and other municipal entities.
- *Intermediate-term municipal bond funds*, called *muni bond funds*, feature bonds with intermediate-term maturities ranging between 5 and 10 years.
- *Long-term municipal bond funds* hold longer-term bonds seeking higher coupons and may hold bonds with maturities between 10 and 30 years.
- *High-yield municipal bond funds* seek higher tax-exempt yields by investing in lower-ranked municipal securities carrying higher yields.
- *Government-guaranteed funds* invest in debt securities, mainly Treasury securities, with no default risk.
- *Government securities funds* invest in both Treasury and agency securities. The return is somewhat higher than that of government-guaranteed funds.
- *Government National Mortgage Association (GNMA) funds* invest in mortgage-backed securities with interest and principal guaranteed by the U.S. government.
- *Money market funds* invest in short-term or soon-to-mature debt. Money market funds are designed to maintain a constant $1-per-share value regardless of interest rate changes.
- *Tax-exempt money market funds* invest in short-term municipal notes and soon-to-mature municipal bonds.

BALANCED-TYPE FUNDS

- *Asset allocation funds* switch portfolio assets among stocks, bonds, and money market securities.
- *Balanced funds* are overseen by managers who buy common and preferred stocks as well as bonds, seeking to blend growth from stocks with a more defensive bond strategy.

GLOBAL FUNDS

- *Global or international funds* invest in stocks or bonds issued throughout the world. Global funds contain both American- and foreign-issued securities.

- *Foreign funds* invest in foreign-issued, non-American securities, seeking profit opportunities in markets currently offering the highest potential return.

Appendix G: Pension Benefits Counseling

PENSION RIGHTS CENTER

Adequate pensions are a key factor in helping older persons maintain financial security and independence, so Congress called for the Administration on Aging (AoA) to establish a demonstration program to assist older Americans in accessing information about their retirement benefits and negotiating with former employers for due compensation, when appropriate. The AoA pension information and counseling projects are designed to reach out, educate, and promote pension awareness and protection among older individuals.

AoA originally funded seven demonstration projects and the Pension Rights Center. Congress provided funding in 1998 to expand the number of projects to 10. Currently the program serves 27 states.

Since the beginning of the Pension Counseling Program, approximately 25,000 people have been served by the projects in one way or another, resulting in a total estimated $50 million recovered for individual claimants. As a result of investigations on their behalf, most of the pension clients have received increases in their pensions in lifetime amounts ranging from $36 to $60 per month—not insignificant for persons living on fixed incomes.

Examples of AoA demonstration projects include:

The University of Alabama School of Law, Tuscaloosa, AL, 205-348-1136. Utilizes law students to provide pension counseling, assistance, and pension outreach to older Americans in both rural and urban communities in Alabama.

The Area Agency on Aging of the City of Chicago, Chicago, IL, 312-744-2676. Operates its Pension Information and Counseling program to assist Chicago seniors to understand and obtain their pension benefits and access retirement income.

The New York Pension Hotline (Legal Services for the Elderly), New York. For New York City residents (and New Yorkers residing outside New York State), 212-997-7714; for New York State residents (outside New York City), 800-355-7714. Operates a hotline that provides telephone guidance and counseling to current and former New Yorkers with pension problems.

The Pima Council Area Agency on Aging, Tucson, AZ, 520-790-1262. Counsels seniors in local area and throughout the state on pension issues.

The Older Women's League, St. Louis, MO, 314-725-1516. Provides innovative, low-cost, user-friendly methods of making pension and retirement support information available to low-income seniors, especially minorities and women.

University of Massachusetts Boston Institute of Gerontology, Boston, MA, 617-287-7311. Serves the entire New England region to educate individuals with information about how to maximize their retirement income.

Minnesota Senior Federation, St. Paul, MN, 651-645-0261. Provides information and counseling services specifically for women, rural residents, and minority populations. The Project also funds similar services in Wisconsin.

Elder Law of Michigan, Lansing, MI, 517-372-5959. The grantee is the recipient organization for the Great Lakes Pension Rights Project, which provides expanded and enhanced pension rights counseling for Michigan, Ohio, and Illinois. Each operates a pension hotline for answering pension and retirement benefit questions, providing in-depth pension counseling services, and conducting an educational outreach campaign.

References

Arnone, W. J., Kavouras, F., Nissenbaum, M., Pape, G. M., Ratner, C. L., Rouse, K. R., et al. (2002). *Ernst & Young's retirement planning guide.* New York: John Wiley and Sons, Inc.

Census Bureau. (2004a). *Median income for 4-person families, by state.* Retrieved July 25, 2004, from http://www.census.gov/hhes/income/4person.html

Census Bureau. (2004b). *Annual demographic survey.* Retrieved September 9, 2004, from http://ferret.bls.census.gov/macro/032004/pov/toc.htm

Census Bureau. (n.d.). *People 65 years and over below 150 percent of poverty, by state.* Retrieved September 9, 2004, fromhttp://www.census.gov/hhes/poverty/150pct 98-00.html

Cutler, N. E. (2002). *Advising mature clients.* New York: John Wiley and Sons, Inc.

Gerencher, K. (1999). Typical American's net assets: $1000. *CBS Market Watch.*

Graves, M. Y. (2000). Reverse mortgages: A new source of income. *CSA Journal, 11,* 28.

SmartMoney. (2004). *Alternative minimum tax.* Retrieved July 27, 2004, from http://www.smartmoney.com/tax/filing/index.cfm?story=amt

Social Security Administration. (n.d.) *Income of the aged chartbook, 2000.* Retrieved September 9, 2004, from http://www.ssa.gov/policy/docs/chartbooks/income_ aged/2000/text_c15.html

Social Security Administration. (n.d.) *Income of the aged chartbook, 2000.* Retrieved September 9, 2004, from http://www.ssa.gov/policy/docs/chartbooks/income_aged/2000/text_c15.html

Stein, M. K. (2000, June). The decision decade: A new focus for retirement planning. *FPA Journal.* Retrieved July 25, 2004, from http://www.fpanet.org/journal/articles/2000_Issues/jfp0600-art3.cfm

Stenner, T. (2001). *True wealth.* Vancouver, BC: True Wealth Enterprises.

United States Department of Health and Human Services. (2003). Life expectancy at birth, at 65 years of age, and at 75 years of age, according to race and sex: United States, selected years 1900–2001 (Table 27). Retrieved September 10, 2004, from http://www.cdc.gov/nchs/data/hus/tables/2003/03hus027.pdf

Resources

Suggested Reading

The Tax Adviser. This magazine published by the American Institute of CPAs offers in-depth discussions of tax strategies and rules. Although written for tax practitioners, even a novice can learn from the information and analysis.

Services

AARP. http://www.aarp.org/money. The Money and Work section of AARP's Web site contains information on financial planning, low-income help, reverse mortgages, and Social Security.

Administration on Aging. http://www.pensionrights.org/. This site is the Administration on Aging's center for assistance on pension issues.

Area Agencies on Aging (AAAs). These agencies, discussed in detail in chapter 9, are available in essentially every community to provide low-income seniors with a variety of services, including home-delivered meals, homemaker services, care management, and caregiver support services.

American Institute of Certified Public Accounts (AICPA). http://www.aicpa.org, 1211 Avenue of the Americas, New York, NY 10036-8775, 212-596-6200, 212-596-6213. This association site for CPAs provides comprehensive information on income tax planning.

Benefits Calculator. http://www.ssa.gov/OACT/quickcalc/calculator.html. This calculator is provided by the Social Security Administration.

Benefits Checkup. http://www.benefitscheckup.org. This site identifies federal and state benefits available to seniors who provide a small amount of demographic information.

CalcCentral.com. http://www.calccentral.com/retirement.html. This page on the CalcCentral site offers retirement planning calculators of many varieties.

The Certified Financial Planner (CFP) Board of Standards. http://www.cfp.net, toll-free 888-237-6275.

Faith communities. Many faith communities fulfill a strong social role in providing services to seniors. Churches may run adult day care programs or provide meals or shelter. Organizations such as Catholic Charities and Jewish Family Services often have some care management and companion services available for seniors.

Financial Engines. http://www.financialengines.com. Financial Engines offers a Web-based calculator, developed by Nobel Prize winner William F. Sharpe, professor emeritus at Stanford University. The calculator analyzes relative portfolio risk and the probability of reaching retirement financial goals with a given portfolio. It also allows the user to modify assumptions about returns, asset class selections, and retirement dates to project the likelihood that certain actions will increase the likelihood of achieving retirement goals.

The Financial Planning Association. http://www.fpanet.org, 3801 E. Florida Ave., Ste. 708, Denver, CO 80210, 800-282-7526. This is the financial planning industry association's Web site. The *Journal of Financial Planning* posts articles on this site.

Internal Revenue Service. http://www.irs.gov, 800-829-1040. This government site contains information about taxation and forms that can be downloaded. Publication 17 (Your Federal Income Tax) provides instructions for completing Form 1040. Publication 554 (Older American's Tax Guide) offers a detailed discussion of taxation issues of special interest to seniors. Publication 915 (Social Security and Equivalent Railroad Retirement Benefits) offers a comprehensive discussion of the taxation of Social Security and railroad retirement benefits.

IRS.com. http://www.irs.com, email: admin@irs.com. This is *not* the IRS government site. (See previous entry for the government site.) It is an independent tax source, providing information, forms, and useful links. It also provides a link to tax professionals at H&R Block and contains filing software.

Medicare. http://www.medicare.gov. Medicare's Web site offers detailed information on its programs, as well as Medicaid enrollment, qualifications, and benefits.

The Motley Fool. http://motleyfool.com. A great site for articles regarding a variety of financial, investment, and tax topics.

mPower Advisors, L.L.C. http://www.mpowercafe.com/. This site is sponsored by mPower Advisors, a registered investment advisor founded in 1995, which provides information on retirement planning. mPower Cafe has been recognized for excellence by *Forbes, U.S. News and World Report*, and *PC World*.

National Association of Securities Dealers. http://www.nasd.com, NASD Public Disclosure Hotline, 800-289-9999.

Pension Rights Center. http://www.pensionrights.org, 202-296-3776. The Pension Rights Center is the country's only consumer organization dedicated solely to protecting and promoting the pension rights of American workers, retirees, and their families.

Schmidt Enterprises. http://www.taxsites.com, email: webmaster@taxsites.com. This site is a tax and accounting site directory and features an extensive list of federal guidelines to help with tax preparation.

SmartMoney.com. http://www.smartmoney.com. A free online service, Smart Money provides a magazine, newsletters, and more on various topics surrounding financial planning, including tax planning. The site is timely and extensive.

Supplemental Security Income. http://www.ssa.gov/notices/supplemental-security-income/. This government site provides a wealth of information on SSI, including a screening tool to determine eligibility for benefits and an online calculator to determine benefits.

TaxNewsletters. http://www.taxnewsletters.com, 1839 S. Alma School Rd., Ste. 260, Mesa, AZ 85210, 800-599-7108, 480-777-1015. Access the site map for an easy search of topics regarding taxes and tax planning.

Today's Seniors. http://www.a-guide-for-seniors.com/index.html. This site contains a variety of information on financial issues for seniors, including retirement calculators.

United States Department of Veterans Affairs. http://www.va.gov

Chapter 17

Long-Term Care Coverage

Jean and Octavio lived on the East Coast. Jean was 86 and Octavio was 93 years old. Jean had Alzheimer's disease, and even though Octavio required regular kidney dialysis he was Jean's full-time caregiver. Octavio promised Jean years before he would never put her in a nursing home. So Octavio, with the help of several local women, provided the supervision and care Jean needed around the clock in her home. The cost for the professional caregivers was $91,000 each year. As long as Octavio was still able to coordinate Jean's care, the system would work as it had for 2 years.

Jean's only son, Stan, age 61, lived in the Midwest. Stan made frequent visits to the East Coast and was in constant contact by phone with Octavio and the shifts of caregivers overseeing Jean's care. Stan's work sometimes required him to travel. On more than one occasion, a business trip of his was called to a sudden halt following yet another crisis with his mother's health.

Jean was at home when the news arrived. Octavio had a heart attack during dialysis and died. Now it was just Jean and the team of caregivers. Jean didn't quite under-stand about Octavio's death. She became depressed, would call out his name at night, and would cry often. Stan sold his home in the Midwest, put his business on hold, and moved in with his mother, taking over Octavio's primary caregiving role. It wasn't many more months before Jean died, still at home and still being cared for 24 hours a day, 7 days a week, by her son and three shifts of caregivers.

. . .

Therese and Hubert were married for more than 60 years and raised seven children. All but one of their children lived more than three hours away from the family home. When Hubert became terminally ill, their daughter Mary—a licensed practical nurse—left her home six hours away and moved in with her parents to help care for her father, allowing him to remain at home until his death.

Four years later at age 84, Therese suffered from bowel control issues from earlier colon cancer, and she began experiencing a series of falls, culminating in a broken wrist. Her son Mike, the only child in the same town, was able to get her to the hos-pital. But with four children of his own as well as full-time and part-time jobs to make ends meet, Mike was not able to provide the help Therese now needed with her daily physical needs, like bathing, dressing, toileting, and eating.

Again, Mary stepped in for a week. Another daughter then came to town for a week, allowing Mary to return home to her job, and another son came to town for a third week. Even though Therese's wrist healed quickly and the immediate crisis had passed, the family realized she could no longer live alone.

As you can see in these examples, long-term care changes everything—family roles, relationship dynamics, careers, and finances. Planning for long-term care can ease stress, allow family members to participate in a discussion before a crisis occurs, and make the outcome much more positive than it would be without a plan.

Introduction

In both of these true-life situations, long-term care services were needed to help the individuals in their day-to-day functioning and to assist their families. What is Long-Term Care (LTC)? According to the National Clearinghouse for Long-Term Care Information (2008), long-term care is a variety of services and supports to meet health or personal care needs over an extended period of time. Most long-term care is non-skilled personal care assistance, such as help performing everyday Activities of Daily Living (ADLs), which are: bathing, dressing, using the toilet, transferring (to or from bed or chair), caring for incontinence, and eating. The goal of long-term care services is to help you maximize your independence and functioning at a time when you are unable to be fully independent.

LTC is not an extension of acute care—it is distinctive in its very nature. Because LTC continues for prolonged periods, it becomes enmeshed in the very fabric of people's lives.

As we live longer with chronic health conditions, the chance that we will need long-term care insurance increases. Few people have saved adequately for the possibility of long-term care, and many people continue to believe the myth that Medicare will pay for their long-term care needs.

LTC can encompass a wide range of services—from skilled nursing care to unskilled assistance or supervision. Most LTC is unskilled, helping care, also known as *custodial care*. Custodial care means physical assistance with ADLs and supervision for people with a cognitive impairment such as Alzheimer's disease or dementia. LTC is intended to maintain and support an individual's existing level of health, to preserve his or her health from further decline, or to manage a deteriorating condition as safely as possible. It is not primarily for the convenience of the insured or the insured's family.

WHO USES LONG-TERM CARE SERVICES?

The good news is that we are living longer, due to healthier lifestyles and advances in medical technology and treatment. The bad news is the longer we live, the more likely we are to need long-term care services. The longer people live, the greater the chance that a chronic condition may develop, resulting in an increased need for help with everyday activities.

The Centers for Medicare and Medicaid Services (2008) estimate that 60 percent of people over the age of 65 will need some form of long-term care. This corresponds with the American Society on Aging estimates that say 60- –70 percent of people over the age of 65 will need some form of long-term care.

For working-age adults, the need for LTC often arises from catastrophic disability caused by a severe illness or accident.

WHO PROVIDES LONG-TERM CARE SERVICES?

Most long-term care is provided by family members, primarily spouses and adult children (see chapter 7). This is typically referred to as *informal care*—care for which there is not normally any payment for services. While there may be no direct cost for care provided by family members, you and your senior clients must recognize that there are costs borne directly by the caregiver. Family caregivers are often subject to a decline in their own physical health when saddled with the responsibility of caregiving. This is especially true for spouses who are also frail. Stress and other psychological factors can affect the physical and mental health of caregivers and even adversely affect family relationships. And informal family caregivers often give up jobs, reduce work hours, or pass up promotions in order to provide care, thereby sacrificing their own financial well-being. Whenever possible, family members should be included in the long-term care planning process—especially those who may directly participate in caregiving duties.

While medical doctors (MDs), licensed therapists, registered nurses (RNs), or licensed practical nurses (LPNs) may provide some skilled services as part of a long-term care plan or when acute, immediate medical problems arise, most professional custodial long-term care services are provided by *paraprofessionals* such as certified nursing assistants (CNAs), home health aides (HHAs), bath aides, homemakers, and companion services. These paid caregivers may work at a nursing home or other facility, they may be found through a home health agency or registry service, or they may be independent contractors.

WHERE ARE LONG-TERM CARE SERVICES RECEIVED?

If asked what first comes to mind when hearing the term *long-term care*, many people will think of a sterile, stark, traditional nursing home or other institutional setting. But long-term care services are received in a variety of settings, including a person's home, adult day care programs, assisted living facilities, continuing care retirement communities, specialized Alzheimer's facilities, hospice facilities for the terminally ill, and skilled nursing facilities or nursing homes. Most long-term care is actually provided at home—either in the home of the person receiving care or at a family member's home. It is estimated that individuals currently turning 65 may need three years of long-term care in their lifetime, with almost two years of that care provided at home. The majority of care given at home—about 80 percent—is provided by unpaid caregivers. (National Clearinghouse for Long-Term Care Information, 2008). The type of housing needs and care services vary according to the individual.

When Dave was diagnosed with early-onset Alzheimer's in his mid-60s, his wife Judy did all she could to maintain as much normalcy as possible in his life. She hired a driver to take Dave to his office at the family business. Though he was no longer very effective at work, it gave Judy a break or respite during the day, and the normal routine helped Dave continue to live at home for nearly two years.

As Dave's disease progressed, it became impractical for Judy to continue as his sole caregiver, and with the input of his physician and a social worker, the family decided he could be cared for better in a residential care/assisted living facility. Dave lived six more years in a private-pay home devoted exclusively to Alzheimer's care with only seven total residents. While the decision to move Dave to a facility was difficult, the family also saw that the care was more practical and the focused attention of the facility staff actually sustained his quality of life at a higher level than his family could have provided as his Alzheimer's progressed through the middle and end stages.

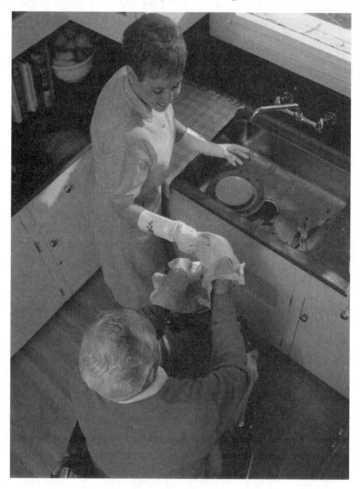

WHAT ARE THE COSTS OF LONG-TERM CARE?

Long-term care is actually the greatest uninsured risk Americans face (U.S. Department of Labor, 2008). Based on the MetLife Mature Market Institute

Survey of Nursing Home & Assisted Living Costs (October 2008) and Adult Day Services & Home Care Costs (September 2008), average costs are:

Home Health Care (2008)

Costs for Home Health Care Aides

Hourly high = $28.00   Hourly low = $12.00

National average hourly rate = $20.00

Average yearly rate (assumes five hours a day, five days per week) = $26,000

Assisted Living—Base Rate (2008)

Monthly high = $4,708   Monthly low = $1,980

National monthly average = $3,031

National average yearly rate = $36,372

Nursing Home Costs for Semiprivate Room (2008)

Daily high = $566   Daily low = $121

National average daily rate = $191

National average yearly rate = $69,715

Note: All costs listed above are subject to change in 2009 and beyond.

You should be familiar with the costs for various types of care and facilities in your area. A local market survey of several home health care agencies, assisted living facilities, and nursing homes should be a prerequisite before engaging any client or prospect in a discussion of long-term care and LTC planning. Help the person consider the costs of where he or she lives now, and where the person may be living in the future.

WHO PAYS FOR LONG-TERM CARE?

The majority of the American public is uninformed about the risks of needing long-term care, the cost of long-term care, and who pays for it. Most people believe Medicare pays for long-term care. It does not. It may pay for a portion of skilled and rehabilitative care needs, but only if a series of strict requirements are met. Most traditional health insurance policies for working-age adults, dealing primarily with acute health care expenses, cover only skilled care, not custodial long-term care costs. While long-term disability insurance addresses lost wages during an illness or injury, it does not provide resources to cover the additional costs of long-term care. In addition, disability coverage ends at retirement.

Medicaid—the health care component of the American welfare system—does cover long-term custodial care costs, but primarily for care in nursing homes, and it is generally available only to those who have nearly exhausted their assets. There are only two other options: paying out of pocket or purchasing long-term care insurance (LTCI) to cover some or all of the costs.

What Is Long-Term Care Insurance?

Long-term care insurance has a relatively short history compared to other types of insurance products. It began in the early 1970s, following the establishment of Medicare and Medicaid in 1965. The first long-term care insurance policies covered care only in nursing homes. They were primitive by today's standards. Such policies were designed using the Medicare model of eligibility for benefits. For example, prior hospital stays were required in order to receive benefits. Over time, policies have evolved to provide easier qualification, payment for more diverse services, and benefits lasting for longer periods of time. The majority of policies today are tax qualified, providing added incentives from the federal government to purchase long-term care insurance.

WHY DO PEOPLE BUY LONG-TERM CARE INSURANCE?

Various surveys of people who purchased long-term care insurance indicate five main reasons why they bought:

1. **Peace of Mind**—The peace of mind offered by quality long-term care insurance is immeasurable. Long-term care insurance offers truly affordable protection and alleviates a large degree of worry for many seniors.

2. **Asset Protection**—Life savings are easily wiped out by rising nursing home costs. Most people would rather their home, life savings, and other assets go to their family or charity, instead of going to a nursing home.

3. **Burden**—Most Americans don't want to be a burden on their spouse or relatives. And because the burden is frequently both financial and emotional, it is incredibly harmful.

4. **Quality Care Access**—The quality of care under Welfare or Medicaid plans is often far substandard to private facilities. As well, high quality nursing homes tend to favor private pay patients for admissions. Private pay coverage can give a family freedom of choice.

5. **Independent Choice**—Americans are used to making choices for themselves. With Medicaid, that freedom of choice is lost, along with personal assets.

WHO SHOULD CONSIDER PURCHASING A LONG-TERM CARE INSURANCE POLICY?

Qualifying for a long-term care insurance policy means being healthy. (Not everyone can qualify medically and, for some, there are other alternatives.) For many people, it is worth the cost and is affordable, but others may not be able to afford a policy with enough benefits to make it worthwhile. Some of the people who should consider buying long-term care insurance are:

- individuals with significant assets and income and those wanting to protect those assets from the cost of long-term care services;

- persons who want to maintain their independence and not have to rely on friends and family for financial or physical support;
- those who want to have the choice about where and by whom they will receive long-term care services;
- people who can afford to pay the premiums every year in the future, including the possibility of premium increases, without experiencing financial hardships in doing so.

Some applicants who apply for long-term care insurance coverage do not qualify for the insurance. In other words, they are *uninsurable*. Applicants must meet certain medical underwriting requirements in order to buy long-term care insurance. Therefore, someone who is in good health should consider applying for and buying long-term care insurance while they are still able to qualify medically. (*Medical underwriting* means that the insurance company uses an applicant's personal health information to predict the likelihood that they will need long-term care and make claims against the policy. Each company has its own underwriting standards, which means one company could reject an application while another would be willing to accept it.)

Anyone who is in poor health, already in a nursing home care facility, or receiving long-term care services would not qualify medically and would not be a candidate for long-term care insurance. Those persons who cannot afford the premiums and those with limited assets are also not considered good candidates for long-term care insurance. The National Association of Insurance Commissioners (NAIC) suggests that long-term care insurance premiums should not consume more than 7 percent of a person's income (NAIC, n.d.). Individuals who often have trouble paying for their utilities, food, medicines, or other important needs or those already receiving Medicaid benefits are unsuitable prospects. Additionally, if a person's only source of income is a Social Security benefit or Supplemental Security Income (SSI), long-term care insurance may not be advised.

You should consider that the family members of some low-income seniors might be willing to pay the premiums in order to provide benefits for the type of care desired by the family.

WHO TYPICALLY BUYS LONG-TERM CARE INSURANCE? WHO DOESN'T?

We know certain traits of individuals who choose to buy long-term care insurance policies and those who don't. The major difference between buyers and non-buyers is that the latter (non-buyers) tend to be somewhat older, are more likely to be male, less likely to live in a household where someone is employed, and less wealthy than are buyers of LTC insurance (HIAA, 2005). Those who didn't buy long-term care insurance cited some of these reasons for their decision: the cost was too great; there was too much confusion over which policy to buy; they were waiting for better policies; they believed they would never need the services; they believed they would be able to pay for the care using their own income and assets.

WHAT FACTORS DETERMINE THE COST OF A LONG-TERM CARE INSURANCE POLICY?

The most significant factor in determining the cost of a long-term care insurance policy is the applicant's age at the time the policy is purchased. Generally, anyone 18 years and older may buy a long-term care insurance policy. While the upper age limit varies by insurance company, people can typically purchase LTCI into their early 80s. Since long-term care insurance is medically underwritten, the younger the applicant, the greater the chance their health will be good and they will be insurable.

An applicant's current health and past health history will also influence the premium cost for long-term care coverage. Life insurance and long-term care insurance are both medically underwritten, but that is where the similarity ends. Life insurance underwriting is concerned with how long someone is expected to live. Long-term care insurance underwriting, on the other hand, isn't concerned with how long the insured is going to live, but rather how long the insured may live in a disabled state.

If you are advising a client to consider long-term care insurance, it is important to be aware of medical conditions that will make your client uninsurable. Underwriting guidelines vary among insurance companies. Consequently, it is important for any CSAs who sell long-term care insurance to become familiar with the medical underwriting requirements of the company or companies they represent. In the past, long-term care insurance underwriting guidelines varied widely from company to company. One company's "decline" may be another carrier's "standard risk." Many insurance companies' applications ask if the applicant has ever been declined for long-term care insurance coverage. Once one insurance carrier declines an applicant for coverage, most other companies will not consider the applicant for coverage. Because of this practice, it is all the more important for CSAs to be familiar with various company underwriting guidelines and encourage applicants to consider coverage where they believe applicants have the best first chance of receiving coverage. There may not be a second chance to apply elsewhere.

The following is a partial list of conditions generally deemed uninsurable for long-term care insurance.

- malignant, inoperable, incurable, recurrent, and metastatic cancers
- Alzheimer's disease or other permanent cognitive impairment
- Parkinson's disease
- HIV or AIDS
- arthritis—rheumatoid and osteoarthritis when degenerative or with functional limitations
- ALS (Lou Gehrig's disease)
- strokes and TIAs (transient ischemic attacks or "mini strokes")
- diabetes with significant insulin use or complications (retinopathy, amputations, etc.)
- multiple sclerosis

- certain eating disorders and severe psychiatric conditions
- current use of assistive devices—canes, walkers, wheelchairs
- already receiving care at home, in assisted living or in a nursing facility

Other factors influencing the insurability of an applicant include pending or recommended surgery, smoking (especially when combined with other questionable health conditions), uncontrolled high blood pressure, and obesity. Most carriers maintain height and weight tables to determine an individual's rate class. An otherwise healthy individual will be charged a higher premium or even declined if their height and weight are not within the guidelines. Insurance companies generally publish detailed underwriting guides for those who sell their products. These guides normally include details of conditions that are insurable and those that are not. Additionally, these publications include lists of medications that will result in an accepted or declined application.

The Cost of Waiting

A primary reason why individuals don't buy long-term care insurance is that they don't understand the need to plan for their long-term care needs. However, waiting to purchase long-term care insurance could result in not being insurable, due to health reasons at the time of application. Some people believe planning for long-term care needs is an "old person's" problem. All we need is the reminder of Michael J. Fox, diagnosed at age 37 with Parkinson's disease, to remind us that the need for LTC can occur at any age.

Since long-term care insurance policies are medically underwritten, and health conditions such as Alzheimer's disease, Parkinson's, or uncontrolled diabetes can prevent insurability, waiting to purchase long-term care insurance can be an expensive mistake. Ideally, consumers would choose to buy long-term care insurance the day before they needed it. Unfortunately, we never know when our health condition will change or if we will be involved in a serious accident or medical situation that will make us uninsurable. Deciding to buy flood insurance the day after the flood is too late; we need to anticipate the risk and insure ourselves ahead of time.

Types of Long-Term Care Insurance Policies

Long-term care insurance is available as a stand alone product or on a group insurance basis through an employer. The majority of long-term care insurance policies are sold by agents or brokers to individuals or couples. However, many employers are offering long-term care insurance to their employees and their families at a group discount.

One significant advantage to buying LTC coverage through an employer is that employees may be able to purchase coverage with little or no underwriting when the insurance is first offered.

The type and plan design of the long-term care insurance policy will also affect the premium charged for the coverage. Long-term care insurance policies come in a variety of packages or configurations. Today's policies can be designed to pay benefits when the insured is in a facility (a facility-only policy—new policies now include both nursing homes and assisted-living facilities) or receiving care at home (a home and community-based care only policy). Comprehensive or integrated policies pay benefits regardless of where the care is provided. Once an applicant has determined where they believe they would most likely receive long-term care services, and who will be taking care of them, they can decide what type of policy would best meet their needs and begin making plan design decisions based on the following questions.

- Where do I plan on spending the final years of my life? Will I move?
- What are the costs of long-term care services in the area where I plan to live? (Costs vary widely across the country; knowing local charges is vital.)
- How much of the cost do I want the policy to pay (benefit amount)? How much am I willing to spend (coinsure) from income or assets for my long-term care service costs?
- With the costs of care rising significantly, how will my benefits keep up with inflation?
- How long or for what period of time do I want the policy to pay (benefit period)?
- How many days of my long-term care services am I willing to pay before the policy begins to pay benefits (elimination or waiting period)?
- What extras do I want the policy to include (benefit riders)?

GENERAL POLICY FEATURES OF LONG-TERM CARE INSURANCE

The Benefit Amount

The first factor to consider in designing long-term care insurance coverage is the benefit amount. This is the amount of money a policy pays—a daily, weekly, or monthly maximum. Some carriers refer to it as the *daily benefit* (DB) or *maximum daily benefit* (MDB).

The DB or MDB is usually based on the amount the policy would pay for a daily benefit in a nursing home or assisted care facility, called the *nursing facility daily benefit*. Home care benefits are then expressed as an equal percentage or a reduced percentage of this base.

Most policies are reimbursement policies, meaning the insurance pays back the actual cost of care up to the maximum daily benefit covered by the policy. A few companies offer an indemnity policy that pays a full benefit amount, even if the actual expenses incurred are less. A policy may also offer a strictly cash benefit (with a higher premium cost) to allow the insured to receive the maximum daily or monthly benefit without proving care occurred on a specific day.

Daily, Weekly, and Monthly Home Care Benefits

Long-term care insurance policies that reimburse actual expenses can pay for home health care using a variety of different formulas. The way a policy covers home care can be of key importance and it may provide valuable flexibility for clients.

Daily benefit policies generally have the lowest premiums but are also the least flexible for covering care at home. Basically, these policies will never reimburse more than the daily limit for care in any day, even if actual caregiving expenses are higher. And a weekly or monthly home care policy can provide additional flexibility when little or no care is received on some days and lots of care is needed on others.

For example, a daily limit policy with a benefit amount of $200 per day will never reimburse more than $200 per day. But using this example, a weekly policy provides a maximum of seven times the daily benefit amount—$1,400 per week, to be used in any fashion during each week. A monthly policy provides a maximum of 30 times the daily benefit amount (in this example, $6,000) to be used for any combination of approved services during each month.

Let's assume a client purchased a policy with a $200 daily benefit amount that includes monthly home care reimbursements. On weekends and two other days a week, he only needs a short bathing assistance visit or brief care to allow his wife or another family caregiver to go shopping or have a respite. But three days a week he needs 10 hours of care so his family caregiver can continue to work. On the three care days, the family is charged more than $200 per day. A daily policy would only reimburse up to $200 for each day. But a monthly policy would reimburse all expenses, including the three care days that cost more than $200 each, until the monthly maximum of $6,000 is reached, thus lowering the potential out-of-pocket costs. These options allow a client to borrow from days when little or no care is needed to help pay for days when a lot of care may be necessary.

The Elimination Period

In long-term care insurance policies, there is an *elimination period*—also called a *waiting period*—similar to a deductible found in auto or homeowners insurance. However, a deductible is generally an amount of money that the insured must pay first before the insurance policy begins to pay benefits to the insured. In contrast, an elimination period in a long-term care insurance policy is determined by the number of days the insured must pay for covered services before the policy begins to pay benefits. The elimination period selected is a key factor in determining the premium cost of a long-term care insurance policy.

Insurance companies offer a wide variety of elimination period choices: from zero-day (*first-day*) benefits, to 30, 60, 90, 100, 180, or 365 days. In most cases, the elimination period must be satisfied only once in a lifetime.

Agents will often advise clients to purchase an elimination period of 60–100 days because applicants will most likely have Medicare or a health plan paying for the first few weeks of skilled care. Medicare will pay for hospitalization but pays for very few long-term care days in a nursing home (see chapter 19). Medicare pays only for skilled care, and long-term care is considered custodial care, not skilled care. Today, most admissions to nursing homes follow hospitalization, especially for Medicare patients. These are typically **short-term** stays for rehabilitation until a patient has recovered enough to be sent home to complete his or her recovery. Medicare benefits cover only 23 days of care in nursing homes, on average (Aging and Eldercare, Nursing Home Checklist 2008).

While a longer elimination period may reduce premium costs, it also increases the total amount of money the insured must pay before the policy begins paying benefits. For example, let's assume today's cost of nursing home care is $7,000 per month. If the applicant selects a 90-day elimination period, he could pay up to $21,000 out-of-pocket (90 days = 3 months × $7,000 per month = $21,000) before the policy begins to pay benefits. Imagine the impact of inflation on a 90-day elimination period over the next 20 years—some experts estimate health care costs will triple in that time. With today's ever-increasing life expectancy, today's $21,000 elimination period dollars might well reach $63,000 in 20 years. CSAs working with seniors would be well advised to consider the long-term financial impact of longer elimination periods. For the more affluent client, however, longer elimination periods can reduce premium costs. Generally, the longer the elimination period—the higher the deductible—the lower the premium.

Benefit Period

Another factor that determines cost is the amount of time the insured receives benefits once a claim begins. While policies are available with an unlimited or lifetime benefit that can never run out, policies with limited benefit periods are also available for lower premiums. The insurance industry calls the limited benefit period a "pool of money." Options range from a benefit period as short as 2 years up to as much as 10 years. While these limited benefit periods are expressed as a period of time, most policies today use the benefit period as a multiplier.

The total amount of benefits in a policy is determined this way: daily benefit amount × 365 days × number of years in the benefit period = total lifetime benefit. For example, $200 per day × 365 days = $73,000 × 5-year benefit period = $365,000 total lifetime benefit (pool of money). If the insured received $200 in long-term care services every day, their policy maximum would be exhausted in five years. However, how long would the policy pay if the insured incurred just $100 in long-term care services per day? Ten years. And what if services weren't provided every day? The policy could last even longer.

Before determining the length of a policy's benefit period, remember that, while most nursing home stays are relatively short in duration, there may be longer periods where long-term care services are provided prior to entering a nursing home, for example at home or in assisted living. Your clients should consider their health, finances, family situation, and the health of their relatives when selecting the appropriate benefit periods in long-term care insurance.

Inflation Protection

The cost of health care and long-term care services will continue to rise. Selecting an inflation rider will raise the policyholder's benefit amount to keep up with the increased costs for long-term care services. There are generally three types of inflation options: simple inflation, automatic compound inflation, and guaranteed purchase option.

Simple Inflation

The annual increase of the daily or monthly benefit maximum and the lifetime benefit maximum (pool of money)—typically 5 percent—is based on the daily benefit amount originally purchased. Using a 5 percent factor, simple inflation will double the daily benefit (and the maximum total benefit) every 20 years.

Compound Inflation

The annual increase starting one year from the effective date of the policy—typically 5 percent—is based on the daily or monthly benefit amount and the pool of money compounded annually. Using a 5 percent factor, compound inflation will double the daily benefit (and the maximum total benefit) every 15 years. Some insurance carriers offer a 3 percent or 5 percent automatic inflation protection option based on the Consumer Price Index (CPI) and as the CPI fluctuates, so will the inflation protection.

Selecting either the automatic simple inflation or the automatic compound inflation options will result in initially higher premiums, but they will also provide an automatic yearly increase in the benefits without a scheduled increase in the premiums. The following table illustrates the impact of 5 percent simple inflation versus 5 percent compound inflation, using a $100 daily benefit.

Daily Benefit Amount Increases at Simple and Compound Rates (5%)

YEAR	SIMPLE	COMPOUND	DIFFERENCE
0	$100	$100	$ 0
10	$150	$163	$ 13
15	$175	$208	$ 33
20	$200	$265	$ 65
25	$225	$339	$114
30	$250	$432	$182

Guaranteed Purchase Option

This option provides a third way to allow a policyholder to keep benefits growing with the rising cost of care. The premium starts much lower than with an automatic inflation option, but the insurance company then offers a guaranteed option to periodically buy more coverage in the future, typically every year or every three years. Premiums increase with each benefit increase purchased, and the new coverage added is priced at the policyholder's current age. Over time this will cost more than an automatic inflation option, and once the insured goes on claim and starts collecting benefits, the options stop just when inflation increases might be needed most.

Inflation protection is so important that it must be offered to LTCI applicants. In most states if an inflation option is not chosen, the applicant must explicitly sign off on the refusal to add an inflation feature. The younger the applicant, the more important the need for inflation protection, because it may be 15, 20, or 40 years before benefits are needed.

There are no hard and fast rules about what type of inflation protection a person should purchase. Generally, compound inflation is most appropriate for applicants under the age of 70 because the benefit grows the fastest over time. Simple inflation should be considered for applicants over the age of 70, especially if their family history includes relatives who have lived very long lives.

Since the enactment of the Deficit Reduction Act of 2005 (DRA05), many states have developed Partnership Programs, which require that specific inflation protections be included in new LTCI policies. These allow the insured to protect an amount of assets from Medicaid spend-down. State programs may be different. Information about Partnership Programs can be found in this AARP report: www.aarp.org/research/**longtermcare**/insurance. (See Partnership Policies below.)

Guaranteed Renewable

Today's long-term care insurance policies must be guaranteed renewable. This means an insurance company cannot cancel the policy or change the benefits as long as premiums are paid. However, this does not mean that the premiums are guaranteed to remain level or fixed. LTC insurers can raise rates if they are needed to pay claims and are approved by regulators. Although long-term care insurance premiums are designed to be level, insurance companies may file a request with state departments of insurance for rate increases on an entire series or class of policies in the future. Unlike car insurance, long-term care insurance companies cannot raise premiums on an individual's policy because of personal claims experience.

There are ways that purchasers can guarantee that premiums will not increase. Some of today's policies allow for the policy to be contractually paid up after a certain period of time, most commonly after 10 years, although a few companies offer a 20-pay option, or for younger applicants a pay-to-age-65 option. While carriers reserve the right to raise rates during the premium pay period, after the period has expired, no more premiums are due. These options cost more in premium—often doubling or tripling the cost of the policy. A few companies offer a rate guarantee for a few years after purchase. This means the insurance company cannot raise the premium rates during that specific period of time. However, after that period of time, the carrier may, once again, raise the premiums on an entire block or series of policies. There are consumer protections included in long-term care insurance policies should the premiums rise too high, based on age and a percentage increase table, which allow the insured to continue with the policy.

PARTNERSHIP POLICIES

Partnership policies are a combined effort among the federal Center for Medicare & Medicaid Services (CMS), state Medicaid programs, and private insurance companies. Individuals who are insured under these special policies do not have to expose all of their assets to the usual spend-down process that is required to qualify for Medicaid. They can protect some or all of their assets and still remain eligible for Medicaid benefits. Since the DRA05, all states can develop their own partnership plans, and many have already done so.

The Federal Long-Term Care Insurance Program

The Federal Long-Term Care Insurance Program, sponsored by the United States Office of Personnel Management and administered by one or more private insurance companies, is a voluntary, group long-term care insurance program. It is offered to federal employees and annuitants (retirees), including the Postal Service and active and retired members of the uniformed services, as well as their spouses and other qualified relatives. It was created by the Long-Term Care Security Act of 2000 to benefit federal employees and their families as well as to provide a model for other employers to provide LTC insurance as an employee benefit.

The creation of this new benefit by the federal government for its personnel sends a strong signal that other programs (e.g., Medicare and Medicaid) will likely not dramatically expand to provide for LTC needs. Therefore, private insurance should be considered a primary funding source for care.

WHAT LONG-TERM CARE SERVICES ARE NOT COVERED

Long-term care insurance policies provide for a wide range of services. However, there are some things that are not covered (*limitations* and *exclusions*). These are very typical of long-term care insurance plans. They generally include:

- intentionally self-inflicted injuries
- care required as a result of alcoholism or drug addiction
- care due to war (declared or undeclared) or service in any of the armed forces or auxiliary units—this exclusion does not exist in the federal employee program, which covers active military personnel
- care due to participation in a felony, riot, or insurrection
- care not normally made in the absence of insurance
- care provided by a member of the insured's immediate family (though under certain circumstances a family member may be able to receive pay to provide care)
- care provided outside the 50 United States and the District of Columbia, unless a provision for international coverage is included

HIPAA AND TAX-QUALIFIED LONG-TERM CARE INSURANCE POLICIES

The Health Insurance Portability and Accountability Act (HIPAA) is legislation that was passed by Congress and signed into law in August 1996. The long-term care provisions became effective January 1, 1997. This new law established tax-qualified long-term care insurance and clarified the tax treatment

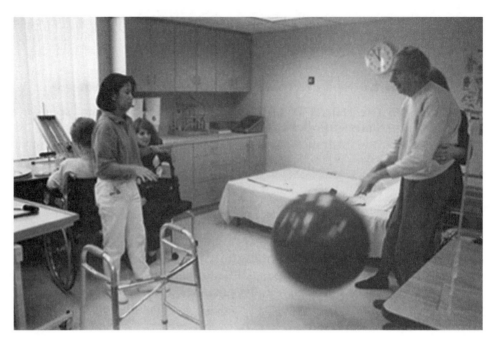

for long-term care insurance premiums, benefits, and out-of-pocket custodial care expenses.

LTC policies issued prior to January 1, 1997, were grandfathered to receive the new tax-qualified benefits as well. As long as policyholders did not materially change these policies, they can deduct an eligible portion of the cost of the policy's premiums and receive benefits tax-free.

Policy changes that can be made but which are not categorized as material changes include:

- exercising a future purchase option
- premium mode changes
- class-wide premium increases or decreases
- benefit reductions requested by the insured
- continuation or conversion of group coverage
- addition of a benefit without a premium change
- reduction in premium when a spouse is insured at a later date and the first spouse then receives his or her marital discount

Tax Incentives for Purchasing Long-Term Care Insurance

With the intent of reducing the growth of Medicare and Medicaid spending, both federal and state governments are supporting the purchase of long-term care insurance as a part of a plan for health care reform and cost containment.

Benefits paid under a HIPAA tax-qualified policy can be excluded from taxable income as long as they do not exceed $280 per day (2009) or the actual reimbursed costs, if greater. This amount goes up each year.

In addition, premiums paid for a tax-qualified policy may be deductible in some cases. You should work with your client's tax advisor to determine the availability of a premium deduction. Generally, the deduction is very limited for individuals, but may be significant for business owners.

For individuals, age appropriate, eligible tax-qualified insurance premiums are a deductible medical expense. But to realize the deduction a taxpayer must itemize their deduction on their tax return's Schedule A. In addition:

- only a limited amount the can be included (the age-based eligible premium noted in the following table); and
- the premium, along with other out-of-pocket, unreimbursed medical expenses, must exceed 7.5 percent of adjusted gross income.

It is important for you to note that many seniors do not itemize on their tax returns because they have a higher standard deduction, and many do not have large mortgage interest payments that justify itemizing. The IRS says only about 4.5 percent of all taxpayers realize any medical expense deduction on their returns. The following table illustrates the amount of premium payments eligible for deductions under 2009 Internal Revenue Code §§7702B & 213(d).

Age Attained Before the Close of Taxable Year	Eligible Tax Deductible Premiums
40 or below	$ 320
41–50	$ 600
51–60	$1,190
61–70	$3,180
71 and above	$3,980

Some states have approved deductibility or a tax credit for some or all of long-term care insurance premiums. In 2008 these states included Alabama, Arkansas, California, Colorado, District of Columbia, Hawaii, Idaho, Indiana, Iowa, Kansas, Kentucky, Maine, Maryland, Minnesota, Mississippi, Missouri, Montana, Nebraska, New Jersey, New Mexico, New York, North Carolina, North Dakota, Ohio, Oklahoma, Oregon, Utah, Virginia, West Virginia, and Wisconsin.

LTC Insurance Benefit Triggers

It is important to understand what must occur before an LTC insurance policy begins to pay benefits. This could be thought of as the *definition of disability* or the *benefit trigger*. New, tax-qualified policies will pay benefits when a person is chronically ill, further defined as:

- A person must be unable to perform, without substantial assistance from another person, at least two ADLs for a period expected to last at least 90 days OR
- A person must require substantial supervision to protect themselves from threats to their own or someone else's health and safety due to severe cognitive impairment.

Not all insurance carriers define ADLs the same way. While the main categories (bathing, continence, dressing, eating, toileting, and transferring) may be the same, it is the definition of each of these terms that determines benefit qualifications.

Also policies may differ in what constitutes *assistance*. Certainly direct, physical, hands-on help with ADLs would qualify in every case, and newer policies consider assistance to simply be standby assistance—that is, the need for another person to be present while the activity is done to ensure the safety of the person needing care. This standby measure is a significantly better definition of an ADL loss.

The HIPAA, tax-qualified LTC policies provide better definitions of benefit triggers, assurances for consumers regarding the tax status of their LTC benefits and at least the potential for a premium tax deduction. Today, very few policies do not meet the federal tax code's criteria to be tax-qualified. These few policies, called non-tax-qualified, generally may offer the consumer more liberal benefit triggers. Non-tax qualified policies do not have to base their ADL trigger on the expectation that the need for care will last at least 90 days, thus potentially being able to pay for short-term care claims where recovery is expected. Such policies also may trigger benefits after a person loses one ADL (versus two with tax-qualified). And non-tax-qualified policies may add a third trigger, called *medical necessity*, allowing for a medical exception to get benefits paid when a person doesn't qualify under a physical ADL or cognitive trigger. (Medical necessity as a separate trigger is not allowed in tax-qualified policies.) However, remember that the majority of LTC policies sold today are tax-qualified.

Many advisors do not have a clear understanding of these very important concepts and their impact on when and how benefits are paid under the terms of a tax-qualified or non-tax-qualified long-term care insurance contract. Talking with a long-term care insurance specialist will help clear up any misunderstanding.

What Constitutes a Good LTCI Policy?

The following questions can help guide your customers through the process of evaluating various long-term care insurance policies:

- What levels of care are covered by this policy? Skilled? Custodial? (Note that some older policies that cover only skilled care would not cover custodial services unless skilled care was received first. New polices must cover all levels without any prerequisite.)
- Which facilities are covered under the policy? Any licensed facilities?

- Does the policy provide home care benefits? At what percent of the daily or monthly benefit maximum?
- Are homemaker services covered? If so, how?
- Can personal care be given by home health aides? Does the aide have to come from an agency, or can I hire an independent contractor?
- Does the policy pay for care in adult day care facilities? Assisted living facilities? Other settings? How are these defined? Do they match what is available in the area and local licensing codes?
- How much will the policy pay per day for home care? Assisted living facility care? Adult day care? Alzheimer's facilities?
- What is the length of the benefit period I should consider?
- What are the benefit triggers of this policy?
- When do benefits start?
- Are the waiting periods for home care cumulative or consecutive? Are the days counted on a service or calendar basis?
- What inflation protection is best for me to keep up with the rising costs of long-term care?
- Am I allowed to buy more coverage? When? How much?
- Do benefits increase automatically?
- Is there a waiver of premium benefit? A waiver of premium for home care?
- When does the waiver of premium go into effect? Is that different for home care?
- Is the policy tax-qualified?
- Is there a discount for couples or domestic partners if both individuals buy policies? What if only one is approved?
- Can the policy for me as an individual be shared with someone in my household or family, and is there a joint policy available (one owner)?
- How much can I afford to pay for my long-term care insurance policy? Can I pay annually? Is monthly automatic bank withdrawal available?
- If I have good health, is there an additional discount?

Long-Term Care Coverage: Summary

The current system for financing the cost of long-term care burdens taxpayers and may bankrupt families. Congress, the Administration, and state governments continue to debate ways to reduce funding for Medicare and Medicaid because currently no new money is heading for these programs. As the baby boomers age and the number of elderly Americans increases, it is imperative to examine whether taxpayers can afford to continue to pay for long-term care costs through public programs. Currently, the cost of paying for long-term care is straining public budgets. At the same time, the government asserts there is insufficient money for any type of long-term care funding. The heat is on and the pressure to address these issues will only increase.

The long-term care financing system should be reformed through public policy to promote the notion that people who *can* pay for their own care *should* either pay for their own care or purchase long-term care insurance that pays for that care. It only makes sense to develop a policy that encourages people to buy long-term care insurance, thereby leaving government assistance for those who are genuinely indigent. The Partnership Programs between insurance carriers (private) and the government (public) have been expanded through DRA05 to encourage private citizens to purchase long-term care insurance.

Many times, couples retire but are reluctant to enjoy their retirement savings because of the *"what if"*: What if one of them becomes ill or disabled and needs long-term care? How will they pay for it? Instead of fully enjoying their golden years, they squander away their precious time in fear of "what if." Planning for long-term care needs is one of the many ways you can help your clients enjoy their retirement. The absence of this type of planning may affect the entire family and generations of the family to come. Long-term care insurance is one way to assist clients in protecting their assets and help provide peace of mind to your customers and their families.

While the average age of purchasers of long-term care insurance is falling, you shouldn't presume people in their 70s and older are too old to apply for long-term care insurance or that the premiums are categorically unaffordable. Long-term care insurance is an affordable strategy for managing the potential financial burden posed by long-term care needs. The wealthy may choose to self-insure and the very poor, will, by necessity, rely on government assistance such as Medicaid. Buying long-term care insurance is the best available option for the vast majority of middle-income Americans. Boomers would be well advised to purchase long-term care insurance early to obtain lower premiums and establish insurance before they experience a change in health.

Should seniors qualify medically for long-term care insurance and have difficulty paying the premium costs, they may decide to involve their adult children in the payment of their premiums. Premiums of $3,000 to $4,000 per year divided among siblings may be a small price to pay for peace of mind and options for our parents, when the time comes when they may need long-term care services. Most families today cannot provide the care for their aging family members, due to career and family responsibilities of their own. Helping pay for insurance that will pay for the care is a wise financial and family decision. Remember, long-term care is a family issue and having a plan to protect the family is one of the best things people can do for each other.

Unfortunately, talking about long-term care is something most people avoid. Most of us do not want to think about it, and we certainly do not think it will happen to us. However, most families today have or will have an experience with caring for a loved one along with the understanding of what it does to their own families. We cannot turn our backs on the importance of planning for quality care in later life. Develop relationships with long-term care specialists, providers, and insurance specialists in your community. Help your clients develop a plan for their long-term care options.

References

U.S. Department of Health and Human Services, National Clearinghouse for Long-Term Care Information, *Own Your Future*, (2008).

Funding Long-Term Care, Senior Market Advisor Magazine (December 2008).

MetLife Mature Market Institute. (2008). MetLife market survey on nursing home, assisted living, adult day services and home care costs. Westport, CT: Metropolitan Life Insurance Company.

NAIC (National Association of Insurance Commissioners). (n.d.) A shopper's guide to long-term care insurance. Kansas City, MO: NAIC.

America's Health Insurance Plans by LifePlans, Inc. (April 2007), Who buys long-term care insurance?

Aging Parents and Elder Care, Nursing Home Checklist (2008), retrieved from www.aging-parents-and-elder-care.com.

Resources

Suggested Reading

Long-Term Care: Your Financial Planning Guide, Phyllis Shelton, LTCI Publishing, 2008, and www.ltcconsultants.com.

The Complete Idiot's Guide to Long-Term Care Planning, by Marilee Driscoll, Alpha Publishing, 2003, and www.LTCmonth.com.

Financing Long-Term Care Needs: Exploring Options and Reaching Solutions. The Health Insurance Association of America, 2002.

In Sickness & In Health, Your Sickness—Your Family's Health, by Harley Gordon, Financial Strategies Press, 2007.

The Long-Term Care Handbook (3rd edition), by Jeff Sadler. The National Underwriter, 2003.

Long-Term Care Insurance: Administration, Claims, and the Impact of HIPAA. The Health Insurance Association of America, 2002.

Long-Term Care Insurance Product: Policy Design, Pricing, and Regulation. The Health Insurance Association of America, 2002.

Long-Term Care: Understanding Needs and Options. The Health Insurance Association of America, 2002.

The Shoppers Guide to Long-Term Care Insurance, National Association of Insurance Commissioners, revised 2006. http://www.naic.org

When Caring Isn't Enough: Meeting the Need for Long-term Care with Long-term Care Insurance, by Samuel Larry Feldman. The National LTC Network Staff, 2000.

Services

AARP. http://www.aarp.org. Searching the site for "long-term care insurance" provides informative articles on long-term care insurance and long-term care insurance programs available to AARP members

American Health Care Association, 1201 L St. NW, Washington, DC 20005. 202-842-4444.

Area Agency on Aging, 800-677-1116.

Center for Long-Term Care Financing. http://www.centerltc.org. The Center for Long-Term Care Financing is a nonprofit advocacy organization dedicated to ensuring quality long-term care for all Americans. The site includes archived and current information on long-term care.

Center for Medicare & Medicaid Services (CMS). http://www.cms.gov. CMS is a federal agency within the U.S. Department of Health and Human Services. Programs for which CMS is responsible include Medicare, Medicaid, State Children's Health Insurance Program (SCHIP), HIPAA, and CLIA.

Citizens for Long-Term Care (CLTC). http://www.citizensforltc.org. An advocate for long-term care, CLTC offers a number of white papers on long-term care, along with other articles of interest.

Elder Life Planning. http://elderlifeplanning.com. In addition to helping caregivers find short- and long-term care options, Elderlifeplanning.com also offers:

- educational articles from respected professionals
- information on government programs
- professional care manager resources
- elder law attorney resources
- online forum to share caregiving experiences with others and receive comments, opinions, and input from other site visitors
- monthly electronic newsletter with articles of interest to caregivers
- bookstore with online resource and book reviews on books pertaining to caregiving and elder issues

Federal Long-Term Care Insurance Program. www.ltcfeds.com This Web site provides all the details (eligibility requirements and consumer information on long-term care) about the Federal Employee's Long-Term Care Insurance Program, as well as an online application or contact information for those interested in applying.

The Kiplinger Retirement Report. http://www.kiplinger.com. This site has an overview of long-term care and some advice on purchasing long-term care insurance policies.

The National Council on Aging (NCOA). http://www.ncoa.org. Articles of interest on long-term care appear on this site. In addition, in the "Publications" section of the site, NCOA offers a paperback book, *Planning for Long-Term Care* ($19.00), that provides alternatives on how to finance long-term care and explores whether long-term care insurance is appropriate for an individual.

National Association of Insurance Commissioners, 120 W. 12th St., Ste. 1100. Kansas City, MO 64105, 816-842-3600.

Office of Personnel Management, Federal Long-Term Care Insurance Program. http://www.opm.gov/insure/ltc, 1900 E St. NW, Washington, DC 20415-1000, 800-LTC-FEDS (800-582-3337). This Web site provides a bulletin board of current information relative to the Federal Long-Term Care Insurance Program and archived bulletin board information.

State insurance departments. Every state has a department of insurance that regulates insurers and assists consumers. For more information, check in the government listings (blue pages) in your local phone book for your state's department of insurance.

United Seniors Health Cooperative, 1331 H St. NW, Ste. 500, Washington, DC 20005, 202-479-6973.

Chapter 18

Funeral Planning

We had gathered, family and friends, to honor the passing of my mother.

I recalled a wicker rocking chair, one that sat in my childhood kitchen. In it, Mom used to rock me and my siblings to sleep and comfort us when we needed it. Many tears were shed in my mom's lap while she rocked back and forth. That rocking chair had not only rocked me, but my mom and her mom as well.

I felt the comfort of that image, and I took the rocking chair and placed it up front by my mother's casket. We started the evening with an opening prayer, and then I sat in the rocking chair and began to tell some of the memories of my mother and the rocking chair, and how she had rocked me to sleep, rocked me to calmness and rocked my fear away. Then I invited people to come forward and sit in the rocking chair and tell a story, memory, or tale about my Mom. Several hours passed as the stories from those sitting in the rocking chair made all of us laugh and cry, ponder and gain insight. It was a powerful tool to tell the story of a powerful woman.

Told by Norm Bouchard, 2004

Introduction

Every funeral service is a ritual to honor the dead and to grieve a loss, whether it is for a head of state, a parent, a spouse, or a child. The ritual acknowledges the reality of the loss, celebrates the life of the deceased, and helps loved ones who are looking for meaning in the passing. While the ritual honors the dead, the funeral serves the living, the survivors.

Most Americans have experienced what is called a traditional funeral in the Western culture, yet religious or spiritual beliefs, ethnic background, family customs, finances, personal preferences, and other factors dictate the characteristics of the funeral ritual and what "normal" or "appropriate" means to different people.

Planning a funeral and burial is an uncomfortable exercise. No one wants to be reminded of their own mortality, whether in planning a funeral—or in creating an advance directive, naming a durable power of attorney, or writing a will or trust. But not to do so can cause problems for survivors, who then struggle in an emotional time.

This chapter highlights the many choices available to seniors in prearranging or arranging a funeral. (Chapters 14 and 18 provide detailed information about other end-of-life issues.) This chapter also provides background information about funeral and cemetery preparations to familiarize you with their associated products and services so you are better prepared to support and advise your clients during the often difficult times that will surround them.

Three Basic Questions

Whether for an elaborate state funeral or a simple memorial service (held without the body of the deceased present), almost all cultures share three basic questions that individuals planning a funeral should answer:

- *What kind of ceremony will it be?* Will it be a traditional funeral for my culture, for example, with an open casket or a memorial service? Will there be a viewing, wake, or rosary? Will it be held in a house of worship or a funeral home? Will there be a graveside ceremony?

- *After death, how will the body be placed in its final resting place?* Will there be an in-ground burial? Entombment? A cremation? Ashes scattered? Will the body be donated to the local medical college?

- *Who will make the arrangements?* Myself, my spouse, my children, my friends? Who will select the funeral home, the casket, flowers, and music? Who will attend to the legal requirements? Who will lead the ritual?

Usually, state statutes designate the next of kin to make funeral arrangements. However, some states also have "freedom-of-choice laws" that allow people to state who will be authorized to make their final arrangements, whether or not they are legally considered next of kin. (This authorization is especially important for gay and lesbian couples.)

Death and funerals are an inevitable part of life and an issue that particularly affects seniors. According to a survey conducted by AARP, one in five Americans ages 50 and older arranged or prearranged a funeral, or both, during an 18-month period between January 1998 and June 1999 (AARP, 1999b).

Demographic trends indicate the number of deaths and related funeral and cemetery arrangements will significantly increase over the next 50 years. From 2000 to 2010, approximately 2.5 million Americans will die each year (Census Bureau, 2004). The overwhelming majority, 80 percent, will be 65 years of age or older (Peres, 2003). The Census Bureau also projects the number of deaths per year will increase to almost 3.5 million by 2030, and 4 million in 2050, as the baby boomers, those born between 1946 and 1964, continue through their cycle of life.

The Funeral

TRADITIONAL FUNERALS

State funerals for famous people and leaders such as Princess Diana, President Kennedy, and former President Reagan exemplify on a grand scale all the elements of what is called a traditional funeral in the Western culture. It is this ritual that most Americans, particularly seniors, recognize. These elements are:

- viewing of the body
- transporting the body from the place of death to a funeral home and, later, in a hearse (sometimes called a funeral coach), from there to a house of worship, and then to a cemetery
- preparing the body—usually including embalming and cosmetology—and placing it in a casket selected by the family
- holding a wake or viewing of the deceased, with an open or closed casket, at the funeral home with family and friends
- conducting a religious or spiritual service at a place of worship or at a funeral home with a religious or spiritual leader directing the ritual, again with an open or closed casket, and with music, flowers, and spoken words
- proceeding from the house of worship to the cemetery, where a committal service is held and the casket is interred in a grave or crypt (a burial space in a mausoleum)

President George W. Bush delivers eulogy at the funeral service for former President Ronald Reagan at the National Cathedral in Washington, DC on June 11, 2004.

- memorialization, or installing a marker or monument and possibly an urn for flowers

While a traditional service may be the most familiar practice to many, there are numerous practical and religious or spiritual alternatives. Even traditional services exhibit vast differences. Some prefer a closed casket for personal reasons (or the condition of the body may require a closed casket) while others welcome viewing by family and friends.

Many families honor the deceased with appropriate music, while others sanctify the service with silence, in which mourners can explore their thoughts. Instead of an in-ground burial, the body can be cremated and the remains scattered, buried, stored in an urn, kept at the family's discretion, or placed in a columbarium (a structure with niches for cremated remains). Families might also arrange a memorial service without the body present—a simple service held graveside or a ritual as the cremated remains are scattered. (You should be aware that, while some religions object to cremation, others expect it.) Memorial services can also be held in other locations such as houses of worship, funeral homes, or the family's home.

In the Jewish and Muslim faiths, embalming is not allowed. Usually the person's body is ritually cleansed, dressed, and placed in a casket. There may also be visitation.

Too often, seniors and other adults do not have enough information about choices and price variations. The next section of this chapter familiarizes you with these alternatives and the typical range of products and services available in many communities, to better prepare you to offer this information to your clients.

ALTERNATIVE ARRANGEMENTS

Jessica Mitford, daughter of an English lord, was a muckraking author (*The American Way of Death, The American Way of Death Revisited*) who satirized excesses in the funeral industry. When she died in 1996, her family could have paid thousands of dollars for a funeral, but instead, she had chosen to be cremated and for her ashes to be scattered at sea for a total cost of $490 (Horowitz, 1999).

Many families cannot afford to spend (as much as $10,000) for a traditional Western funeral, and some prefer not to. Instead, they select from a range of alternative arrangements that include:

- immediate burial
- cremation
- personally burying the remains
- donating the body for medical science

Also, the form of the funeral ritual can be affected by the cause of death and what is available locally. For instance, crematories in rural areas are often hard to come by.

Immediate or Direct Burial

With this alternative, the body is buried directly, without embalming or any funeral service. A funeral home or, in some metropolitan areas, a direct disposal organization (a funeral firm specializing in immediate burials) makes the arrangements. You can find a direct disposal firm or a funeral home listed in the yellow pages under the heading *Funeral Directors*.

The family usually chooses to bury the body in what is called an *alternative container*, although they may choose a casket instead. Alternative containers are constructed of simple pine boards, particleboard, or hard cardboard.

Costs for immediate burial include the services of a funeral director, transportation, an alternative container or casket, and (in some locations) the grave plot. In addition, most cemeteries require the installation of an outer *burial container* of concrete or concrete lined with metal to prevent subsidence (sinking of the ground) over time. Although immediate burial in a minimum casket is available in Kansas City for $900, immediate burial usually ranges from $1,500 to $4,000 and is often sold as a bundle of services by the funeral home, excluding the price of the casket or the alternative container. Cemetery costs include a burial plot, opening and closing of the grave, and any marker.

The price ranges quoted in this chapter are not based on a scientific sampling of the nation's funeral homes and cemeteries. Rather, they are based on a review of 13 Web sites [A Team Master's Caskets; Aldine Funeral Chapel; American Memorial Centers; The Beaver Cemetery & Beaver Mausoleum; Earthman Funeral Directors & Cemeteries; Harrison; Lambert Funeral Home; New Jersey State Funeral Directors Association Survey, 2002; Peabody Funeral Homes, 2004; Peoples Memorial Association; "A Primer on Funerals," 2002; Town of Oxford, 2003; West Laurel Hill Cemetery].

Cremation

Cremation is becoming an increasingly common means of disposing of the body after death, particularly in some parts of the country. It accounted for 27 percent of all final dispositions in 2001 (Cremation Association of North America, 2003). In eight states (Alaska, Arizona, Colorado, Hawaii, Montana, Nevada, Oregon, and Washington), cremations accounted for 50 percent or more of all final dispositions, and the percentage of cremations is expected to continue rising, to 36 percent of the market by 2010. According to an industry survey (Wirthlin Worldwide, 2000), people select cremations because they are less expensive (24 percent); use less land, together with other environmental considerations (17 percent); and are simpler, less emotional, and more convenient (13 percent).

There are various options for funeral services when choosing cremation. It can be accompanied by a traditional Western funeral. The body can be cremated first, and a service held with the *cremains* (cremated remains, commonly referred to as ashes) present. The ashes are returned to the survivors in a cardboard box or other container. Final arrangements may include spreading the ashes, saving them in an urn, placing them in a columbarium, or burying them in a cemetery or other less formal setting.

With a direct cremation, there is no funeral. The body is taken directly to the crematory where it is cremated, and the cremains are returned to the survivors. While some cremation facilities work directly with clients and the survivors, some state laws require that a funeral director be involved.

For a direct cremation, the crematory or the funeral director requires some form of alternative container, a *rigid container*, or a casket to be used to transport and handle the body. It is important for seniors to know that the law does not require a wooden or metal casket for cremation. A funeral director or crematory official who misrepresents this information is in violation of the Federal Trade Commission's Funeral Rule (see Consumer Protections later in this chapter). Direct cremations are usually offered as a package that could cost from $400 to $3,000. Cremations combined with other services, such as a traditional funeral, cost more.

Burial by Family Members

Some consumers choose to bypass the funeral director and *cemeterian* (the cemetery owner or staff) and make their own arrangements for burying the deceased. This may or may not be legal, depending on state laws. Even if it is legal in a particular state, the arranger must make careful plans to comply with all legal requirements. This might include a death certificate, transportation and disposition permits, and other papers. Transporting the deceased to a crematory or burying the body in a private cemetery on family land is legal in most states, but may not always be possible. A helpful book on this subject is *Caring for the Dead: Your Final Act of Love* by Lisa Carlson (1998). It provides useful consumer information and lists the different states' requirements.

Body and Organ Donation

Medical Study

Donating a body or parts of the body to a medical or dental school is a valuable contribution to medical research and education and is the least expensive means of arranging the final disposition of the body. Medical schools rely on these donations for teaching future physicians and dentists and will usually arrange transportation of the body from the place of death to the school. However, some state laws require the services of a funeral director, which will incur a charge.

The school may also return the cremated remains to the family, or it may cremate and bury the remains. Some institutions conduct memorial services to honor the lives of those who donated their bodies. Seniors (and their families or advisors) who choose to donate their bodies for science should contact the nearest medical or dental school for information and recommendations. The National Anatomical Service (see Resources section at the end of this chapter) operates a 24-hour phone service with information about body donations. It is possible that a medical institution will reject a body donation at the time of death because it has no current need, the cause of death precludes study, or the body was autopsied.

Transplants

Medical technology has made organ and tissue transplants less expensive and safer than ever before. Nonetheless, 80,000 names appear on waiting lists for different organs, and in the year 2000, 5,600 people died while waiting for organ transplants (Rehnquist, 2002). Transplants can include any of the following: eye corneas, hearts, livers, kidneys, bone marrow, connective tissues, skin, pancreas, and lungs. Physicians can transplant tissues and corneas acquired from almost anyone, including those over 65. However, there are age limitations with other body parts. Organs and tissues are in high demand.

There are a number of organ and tissue registries, centralized data banks of information on organ donation, where individuals can indicate their willingness to donate. Some are run by state governments while others, such as the National Kidney Foundation (see Resources section at the end of this chapter), are national in scope. Seniors who are interested should contact either agency for information and placement on their databanks. Usually, there is no charge for donating an organ or tissue, but it is important to ask.

You should be aware that some faiths oppose donations, considering it to be a desecration of the body. Most religions, on the other hand, do not disagree with the practice of donating organs and tissues.

To become a donor, a senior can sign a Uniform Donor Card with either a national or state registry (see Figure 18.1). They may also declare a willingness to donate with the state department of motor vehicles when renewing a driver's license or securing an identification card. Even if the deceased did not sign a donor card, the next of kin may authorize a donation at the time of death. Conversely, the next of kin can also veto an organ transplant, even if

Figure 18.1 Sample Uniform Donor Card

Uniform Donor Card of _____
(Print or type name of donor)

In the hope that I may help others, I hereby make this anatomical gift if medically acceptable, to take effect upon my death. The words and marks below indicate my desires.

I give:

(a) any needed organs or parts

(b) only the following organs or parts _____
(Specify the organ(s) or part(s))

for the purpose of transplant, therapy, medical research, or education

(c) my body for anatomical study if needed

Limitations or special wishes, if any _____

_____   _____
Signature of donor   Date of Birth of Donor

_____   _____
Date Signed   City and State

_____   _____
Witness   Witness

This is a legal document under the Anatomical Gift Act or similar laws.

☐ Yes, I have discussed my wishes with my family.

the deceased signed an organ donor card. The best advice is for donors to discuss their wishes with relatives before death.

Unlike whole-body donations, the family of the deceased may still elect to hold a traditional open-casket funeral after the body parts are donated. Normally, such procedures do not disfigure the body.

FUNERAL COSTS

This section respectfully considers the purchase of products and services associated with funerals in more detail. Funerals are one of the most expensive purchases in a lifetime and could cost as much as $10,000 (FuneralWire.com, 2004).

According to an industry accounting firm (Federated Funeral Directors of America, 2004), the average price of an adult funeral in 2003 was $7,115 (based on 225,000 funerals performed by 1,500 different funeral homes). Including burial costs of $2,000 to $3,000, plus $1,000 or more for flowers, family transportation, obituaries, acknowledgment cards, and other costs, the total easily reaches $10,000. However, even though a funeral can be one of the biggest expenses of a lifetime, few arrangers ever obtain comparative prices from two or more funeral homes. An AARP survey found that 7 out of 10 funeral arrangers contacted only one funeral home (AARP, 1999b).

The Funeral Consumers Alliance (FCA) is a national network of mostly volunteer-led, local membership groups, which are independent sources of consumer information about funerals. FCA is organized around the proposition of meaningful, dignified, affordable funerals. The associated groups trace their roots to the Populist Grange Movement that began in the 19th century. Its goal was to lower funeral costs for rural families through group purchasing power.

Many (but not all) funeral information societies continue to offer group purchasing power for a small lifetime membership fee of $25 to $30. For example, in Seattle the Peoples Memorial Association, with 159,000 members, negotiated member prices with a local mortuary and discounts with eight area cemeteries (Peoples Memorial Association, 2003). Some of the funeral plans offered to members include:

- direct cremation for $595, including a cremation container
- immediate burial with a basic casket for $950
- traditional Western funeral with a basic metal casket for $1,525

People's Memorial is also a source of information on funeral homes and cemeteries in the Seattle area. It surveys prices at all funeral homes and cemeteries in the metropolitan area and provides information to the media and its members. Seniors can contact them or affiliates of the Funeral Consumers Alliance in other cities for consumer price information about local funeral homes and cemeteries. All the local groups serve as consumer advocates.

The umbrella organization for these affiliates, FCA, is the leading national source of consumer information on funerals, burials, and alternatives. It also advocates for consumer protections at the national and state levels. To find information on funerals or to locate the address of a local FCA affiliate, check FCA's Web site. (See Resources section at the end of this chapter.)

You should be aware that there may be funeral homes in your area that offer similar funeral services and lower prices for anyone (meaning that people do not have to be a member of FCA to receive them). For example, Kansas City has funeral homes that offer direct cremation for under $500 and immediate burial service with a minimum casket for $900.

ADVANCED PLANNING FOR FUNERALS

Mary Johnson lives alone in Minneapolis and has prepared for everything, including what will happen at her death. She has a will on file with her attorney, along with the deed to her house and title to a cemetery lot. All the details are arranged.

Having lived for almost 80 years, she knows the emotional pressures a sudden death can bring. Just two years ago, her next-door neighbor and friend died of a heart attack. No advance arrangements had been made, and the son, who flew in from California, had only hours to struggle with funeral arrangements.

561

For her peace of mind and to know that her children won't face the same emotional crunch or argue about spending too much or too little to honor her memory, Mary has arranged everything. She phoned and visited several funeral homes, scheduled appointments, and selected her funeral. She also opened a special bank account called *payable-on-death* (POD) to pay for her funeral. Everything is in place for what will come.

Too frequently, a funeral is arranged at the time of a death—a time when survivors are least emotionally prepared to comparison shop. Advance planning, however, has many advantages. Decisions are made at a less stressful and emotional time, and the individual whose service is planned can select his or her own preferences for a casket, burial, music, and other arrangements. You should note, however, that state laws might grant the next of kin the final say with any arrangement. Advise your senior clients that it is best to discuss advance plans with their next of kin.

Seniors can formalize their preplanning arrangements by prepaying and signing a contract for future delivery. Or they can make informal arrangements by simply listing selected goods and services for their funeral and burial and giving the information to a funeral home, the cemetery, and their family. Prearrangements can include some or all of the following:

- traditional funeral, memorial service, or no service
- final disposition
  —in-ground burial
  —cremation
  —mausoleum
- casket
- outer burial container
- transportation of the body
- care of the body (embalming)
- use of the funeral home's facilities
- optional items
- cash advances
- burial plot
  —opening and closing of the grave
  —marker

Preserving Advance Funeral Plans

Seniors should *not* itemize the selections in their funeral plans in a will, and they should *not* place them in a safe-deposit box. (The reading of a will normally takes place well after a funeral, and safe-deposit boxes are frequently sealed, to be opened only as the will is probated.) The best way to preserve advance funeral plans is to file a copy of the plan with the selected funeral home, give a copy to the next of kin, and retain a copy in one's own files with instructions for survivors. Both the funeral home and survivors need immediate access to this information at the time of death. Seniors may want to consider this option: The national FCA sells a plastic kit for $10 that goes in the refrigerator and holds a senior's advance planning documents. The state-specific kit is called, "Before I Go, You Should Know," and can be ordered from FCA's Web site (listed in the Resources section).

Selecting a Funeral Home or Cemetery

There are 22,000 funeral homes (National Funeral Directors Association, 2004) and an estimated 200,000 cemeteries (including small family plots) in the United States (Grassley, 2000). Most people select a funeral home or cemetery based on location, family practice, religion, or reputation. Many funeral homes and burial facilities cater to specific ethnic groups or to specific religions.

A funeral and burial can cost hundreds or thousands of dollars. If seniors limit their choices to only one facility, they may end up paying more than they need to by not comparing prices. In a survey conducted by the Austin Memorial & Burial Information Society, the local FCA affiliate, it was found that the same "full funeral" with a metal casket ranged from $2,545 to $5,520 at different funeral homes in that metropolitan area (Slocum 2004). The bottom line varies according to the goods and services, the geographic area, and the facilities selected. In addition, seniors can purchase caskets on the Internet or from stores listed in the yellow pages of the phone book, and have them shipped to funeral homes.

The FTC's Funeral Rule obliges all funeral homes to disclose their prices in combined or separate price lists for caskets, outer burial containers, and general price listings. Such information is available over the phone, and many funeral homes, even though not required to, will mail a copy of their price list to seniors.

It's probably best to begin searching for a funeral home by asking for recommendations from relatives, friends, religious leaders, and the local FCA affiliate. Ask about prices and reputation and be sure to visit the facility. In addition, contact the local Better Business Bureau (BBB) and the state licensing board for any consumer complaints filed against the facility. You can perform a service for your clients by becoming familiar with the different facilities in your community, the prices for goods and services, and business reputations.

Selecting a cemetery is similar to selecting a funeral home. Ask religious leaders, friends, relatives, and the local FCA affiliate about a cemetery's reputation and pricing, and visit the facility. Burial plots vary considerably depending upon the location. For example, a grave plot overlooking the Pacific Ocean in California will cost hundreds, if not thousands, more dollars than a plot in the valley. Look also at the maintenance of the property. Is the lawn mowed? Are weeds removed? Are the headstones standing upright? Is there a fee charged for maintenance? There's no guarantee that it will be well maintained forever, but if a cemetery is already in disrepair, that's a strong indicator of the future. Seniors should also check with their state's cemetery board (most states regulate cemeteries) and their local BBB.

PRICE LISTS

As previously mentioned, funeral price lists are mandated by the FTC's Funeral Rule, but they are not standardized as to terms or the format of the document. This can make comparison shopping difficult. In each instance, the bottom line—the total sum of the different elements selected—is the most important for comparison. (See Figure 18.2.)

Figure 18.2 Funeral Price List

Item	Cost
Casket	_____
Outer Burial Container	_____
Transportation of Body	_____
Care of the Body	_____
Use of Facilities	_____
Services of the Funeral Director	_____
Cremation	_____
Urn for Cremated Remains	_____
Optional Items (music, flowers, etc.)	_____
Cash Advances (death certificates, permits, etc.)	_____
TOTAL	_____

Caskets

Often the most expensive item for a funeral is the casket. (See Table 18.1.) They vary widely in both price and style and constitute 15 to 30 percent (even higher with the most expensive caskets) of the cost of a funeral. Manufacturers produce literally hundreds of different models made from steel of different gauges, bronze, copper, hardwoods, softwoods, cloth-covered wood products, plastic, and fiberglass. Sixty percent of all caskets sold are made of steel (Casket & Funeral Supply Association of America, 2004). Thicker metal (lower gauge—20, 18, 16, etc.) caskets cost more than thinner ones. For most people, however, the difference between a 20-gauge casket and an 18-gauge casket is unnoticeable. Most metal caskets are *gasketed*, or feature a rubber gasket or other features that retard the entrance of water and protect against rust. Such features increase consumer costs, but seniors should be aware that sealed caskets and other features will not delay the natural decomposition of human remains and they don't always work (FTC, 2000). The Senate Aging Committee found that a gasketed casket leaked the remains of a woman's deceased grandmother onto her above-ground mausoleum (Grassley, 2000). Wooden caskets are not gasketed, and therefore offer no such protective features.

Table 18.1 Typical Variations in Casket Choice

Caskets Type	Price Range
Minimum Casket (cloth-covered wood product with twill or flat crepe interior)	$600–$800
Minimum Steel (20-gauge steel with twill or flat crepe interior)	$850–$1,200
Basic Steel (gasketed, 20-gauge steel with adjustable mattress for viewing and twill or flat crepe interior)	$1,200–$1,500
Premium Steel (gasketed, 18-gauge steel with quality interior and adjustable mattress)	$2,000–$2,500
Stainless Steel (gasketed stainless steel with quality interior and adjustable mattress)	$2,450–$2,900
Premium Metal (gasketed bronze or copper with velvet interior and adjustable mattress)	$3,200–$10,000
Polished Hardwood (pine or poplar with polished finish, crepe interior, and adjustable mattress)	$1,700–$2,300
Oak, Walnut, Cherry, or Mahogany (solid hardwood with polished or semi-dull finish, crepe interior, and adjustable mattress)	$2,400–$12,000

There are several hundred casket manufacturers, most of which are regional or local. Three major national companies—Aurora Casket, Batesville Casket, and the York Group—constitute 70 percent of the market (Schmidt, 2000). In addition, Internet sites allow seniors to order caskets from the United States and abroad. For example, at www.irishfuneral.com, a consumer can order an Irish-made Killarney oak casket with Irish harp end features for $1,965, including shipping costs, and a guaranteed three-day delivery to the funeral home.

Funeral homes traditionally marketed caskets in special rooms, although they may now employ color catalogs. Consumer advocates have long charged that funeral homes exhibit the most expensive caskets in more favorable settings than less expensive caskets, whether on display or in print. (See sidebar.) Renting a casket may be considerably less expensive than purchasing one, and the insert can be used as an alternative container—but not always. For example, in Kansas City, caskets are rented for $1,000, while a person can *buy* an alternative container for $195 or a real casket for as low as $375.

"Simple and Cheap," My Father Said
Josephine Black Pesaresi

My father, Hugo L. Black, died in 1971. At that time, he was 85 years old and the second-longest sitting Associate Justice in the history of the United States Supreme Court, having sat on the Court for nearly 35 years.

He was buried in Arlington National Cemetery, not as a Supreme Court Justice but as a Captain in the Cavalry, next to my mother, who served in the Navy. Their grave markers are standard government issue, noting only the dates of birth, death, and service in the armed forces.

In making the funeral arrangements, we had only three directives from my father: 1) simple, 2) cheap, 3) no open casket. These were not last-minute orders. Our family had heard my father's views about funerals for many years. Appalled by the high costs, he felt that "funeral merchants" often took advantage of grieving families when they were at their most vulnerable. Coming from a humble background, he had seen families spend themselves into debt. He was equally appalled by any person who wished an elaborate and expensive funeral, seeing this as evidence that the person was "puffed up about his own importance in the scheme of things."

With my father's directives firmly in mind, we planned our trip to the funeral parlor to pick out a coffin. We chose a funeral home in Washington, D.C., recommended as a place used by many government officials. Our group included three family members and two Supreme Court Justices—Byron White and William Brennan.

The casket room was elegantly appointed. The carpeting, wall paneling and piped in music set a tone for coffin shopping in undisputed good taste. On entering, one's eye was immediately drawn to the extreme left wall, where a superbly crafted dark wood coffin, softly spotlighted to show the fine wood grain, was perched high on a velvet-draped dais. It looked like a throne coffin. However, we were steered counterclockwise, starting our search at the right. The caskets were arranged head to toe in a semicircle leading up to the throne coffin, and it was obvious that we were going from least to most expensive.

The first coffin we came to—the cheapest—was covered with pink organza, pink satin bows, with a pink ruffled skirt around the bottom. Tasteless and frilly, it seemed totally out of place. The next ones were also cloth-covered, but the cloth looked increasingly more expensive. Our salesman was surprised that we even glanced at these, let alone asked their prices, and indirectly dismissed these as a final resting place for a man of importance. He began to hurry us on until we came to the throne coffin.

We stood in front of this masterpiece of craftsmanship with heads slightly bowed reverently. "This," the coffin salesman said, "is the worthy resting place for a Justice of the United States Supreme Court." When we asked the cost of the throne coffin, he did not immediately give a dollar amount. He noted that while it was the most expensive, he knew that the price was not our main concern when burying a man of my father's stature. Cost considerations would be unworthy. This response was a big mistake and backfired immediately.

Suddenly, almost simultaneously, we looked at each other, smiling as my father's directive hit us full force—cheap. We moved to another emotional dimension—common at wakes—going from a deep grieving sadness to an almost playful mood. Right there, in that elegant room, we knew that together we could do one last thing for my father. No one was going to talk us out of cheap! When pressed, the coffin salesman allowed that the throne coffin cost thousands of dollars. That settled that.

We dispersed, zigzagging around the room, separately appraising the caskets and asking prices down to the penny. All of the polished wood caskets were soon dismissed as too expensive. It had to be a cloth-covered one. To the salesman's horror, Justice White began to scrutinize the first pink organza coffin and then asked what was under the frills. The salesman said it was just a plain, unfinished pine box. Then someone asked about the most expensive cloth-covered casket. That, too, was a plain pine box. When asked the difference between the boxes, the salesman—now completely befuddled—whispered that the more expensive had a "better shape." We looked and thought the shapes were identical.

Huddling for a final conference, someone asked, "Shall we get the pink, the cheapest?" and we all gave a resounding "YES." We said we would buy the pink for $165 with the cloth stripped off. The salesman said that was impossible, it would look terrible. We, however, wanted to see for ourselves since this was our coffin of choice. First, one of us pulled away a little cloth to take a peek, then another ripped more forcefully, and finally we all started ripping off the fabric with careless abandon. Off came the bows, the coffin skirt, and all but a few patches of stubbornly glued pink organza. There stood a perfectly fine plain pine box. The debris littered the elegant carpet, but we were practically euphoric. We had followed my father's directive almost to a T, with the added bonus of deflating pretensions in this very pretentious room (though my father would have felt some compassion for the poor coffin salesman).

When we went into the office to settle the bill, the funeral home director, now understanding our zeal for cheap, asked timidly about filling in the nail holes and sanding down the glue spots. With a closed-casket visitation at the funeral home and a display at the cathedral, they felt their reputation was at stake. We agreed, if nothing was added to the bill, and were assured nothing would be.

Historically, casket retail prices were marked up 200 to 300 percent over wholesale. Most of a funeral home's profits would come from casket sales while they held the line on other items. That may not be as common today, but the practice still exists. For example, *Consumer's Digest*'s March/April 2004 issue reported that caskets sold by an East Coast corporate funeral home were marked up 200 to 300 percent. (The Embassy Cherry casket manufactured by Batesville Casket wholesales for $1,805, while the funeral home sells it for $5,295 [Slocum, 2004].) What has sparked competition among casket prices is that the FTC amended its Funeral Rule to prohibit funeral homes from restricting casket sales to that facility or imposing casket-handling fees.

Currently, Internet sites and independent casket stores advertise and sell these products. They claim to ship their product overnight or within days to the consumer's choice of funeral homes. Prices on the Internet may or may not be lower than at a funeral home; so consumers must price shop—and be aware that quality and shipping have been problems with some casket sales. In Oklahoma, for example, a decorated veteran died in late 2003. He had purchased a $4,000 casket advertised in a veteran's magazine that was to be delivered within 24 to 48 hours of his death, but the casket never arrived. The family purchased another casket from the funeral home and then had difficulty securing a refund for the first one. Their money was returned only after a local consumer reporter contacted the vendor (Edwards, 2004).

Outer Burial Containers

An outer burial container (grave liner or vault) is not required with a crypt in a mausoleum or lawn crypt, but is necessary for most in-ground burials. Two different outer burial containers are available:

- a *grave liner*, made of a rigid material like concrete, which may be porous to water
- a *vault*, steel-reinforced and concrete-lined with metal or asphalt, some with a bronze, copper, or stainless steel lining with protective features such as a gasket to retard the entrance of water

Grave liners cost between $550 and $650, while a standard vault ranges from $800 to $2,400. Both cemeteries and funeral homes compete in the sale of these products.

Transportation Costs

In almost every funeral or alternative arrangement, the body is removed from its place of death and transferred to a funeral home. From there, depending upon the services selected, a funeral director conveys the deceased to a crematory or a cemetery with a possible stop at a house of worship. Transportation charges usually total around $500. If survivors select a family limousine or flower car, the funeral home imposes additional charges.

When death occurs far away from home, survivors may choose to employ a funeral home in the city where the death took place to care for the body, before shipping it to the location for funeral or burial. After embalming the body, the funeral home arranges air transport to another funeral home or burial site. Survivors pay for a casket, air shipment, local transportation costs in both cities, and service fees to both funeral homes. However, you should note that a funeral home can arrange for transportation of the body to another city by using a shipping service. A casket is not required to ship a body.

Care of the Body

Care of the body usually means embalming, but it may also include cosmetology, restoration, or special care with autopsied bodies. State laws do not require embalming, although it may be required with interstate shipping and certain special circumstances (e.g., for a body not buried or cremated within a certain amount of time, for the body of a person who died of infectious disease and for whom an open casket is requested, or for bodies that are not to be refrigerated). Because the body starts to decompose immediately, most funeral homes require embalming to preserve the body in a traditional open- or closed-casket funeral. Sometimes funeral directors levy an additional charge for casketing (placing the body in the casket) or dressing (clothing the body). The cost for embalming ranges from $300 to $600.

Use of Facilities

Visitations, viewings, and wakes are frequently, but not necessarily, conducted at funeral homes. Sometimes families choose to conduct the funeral itself in a chapel at the mortuary instead of a house of worship. Funeral homes charge consumer fees ranging from $100 to $300 for a visitation and $200 to $600 for renting the facility for a funeral. Many funeral homes will discount the cost of the visitation or viewing if it immediately precedes the funeral ceremony.

Services of Funeral Director

With a traditional Western funeral, seniors can pick and choose among all the goods and services listed on funeral price lists, except for the line item concerning the services of a funeral director. This fee pays for a funeral home's overhead, office staff, and salaries.

The consumer receives the following services for this fee: completion of the paperwork for death certificates, obituaries, and permits; arrangement of the interment or cremation; and organization of logistics for transportation, the funeral itself, and graveside ceremonies. Some funeral homes charge an extra fee for arranging the funeral and graveside ceremonies. For the services of a funeral director, mortuary charges range from $500 to $1,000 or more.

Optional and Cash Advance Items

Music and flowers usually form an integral part of a funeral ceremony. They incur an extra charge, however. The family can arrange these items independently, or the funeral home can make the arrangements.

A *cash advance item* is one for which the funeral home pays a third party, such the cost of printing an obituary in the local paper or the fee to file the death certificate with the health department. In turn, the funeral home bills the family for these costs. Prices for both optional and cash advance items vary widely from place to place.

The Bottom Line

To compare prices among different funeral homes, total the charges for the same goods and services on a table. (An example is found in Figure 18.2 in this chapter.) Be sure to compare only the bottom lines, because different facilities charge more or less for the same casket, and more or less for the services of a funeral director. The high price of one item may be offset by a much lower price for another. In some cases, final arrangement costs can decrease over time because of competition and new laws.

CEMETERY ARRANGEMENTS

In-ground burials, the traditional final disposition for Western funerals, remain the most common practice for older adults. But an increasing number of seniors are selecting cremations, which increases the choice of alternatives to in-ground burials, such as columbariums, scattering of cremains, and keeping cremains at home. (Cremains can also be buried in a cemetery.)

Prepurchasing cemetery goods is a common practice with older adults. Some 18 million older adults (one-fourth of people ages 50 and above) have already prepaid their burial plots, mausoleum crypts, or niches in a columbarium, according to a 1998 AARP survey (AARP, 1998).

Increasingly, the two sides of the death care industry are merging (General Accounting Office, 1999). Funeral homes now sell headstones, urns, and other cemetery goods, while cemeteries sell caskets and vaults. The number of combination funeral home-cemetery operations is also increasing, although some state laws prohibit such operations. In the main, however, funeral homes and cemeteries are related but separate businesses, operating under separate statutes and rules. For example, the FTC Funeral Rule requires funeral directors to disclose prices and prohibits certain unfair and deceptive practices. Cemetery sales are not covered by that rule. Price lists may or may not be available from a cemetery, and there is no requirement that cemeteries provide price information over the phone.

While there are many private cemeteries, seniors may also have the choice of a burial in a religious cemetery. The Roman Catholic Church, for example, has thousands of church-related cemeteries in the United States (Norrgard & DeMars, 1992). There are also municipal cemeteries in some areas, and if the deceased was a veteran, the countrywide system of national cemeteries may also be an option.

Purchasing a burial plot is like buying real estate. The purchaser receives a right-of-burial document (like a deed), and the plot can be bought and sold. However, some cemeteries may impose restrictions on the transfer of rights of burial.

Figure 18.3 Cemetery Price List

Item	Cost
Burial Plot (crypt or niche)	_____
Endowment or Perpetual Care	_____
Administrative Fees	_____
Outer Burial Container	_____
Opening and Closing the Grave	_____
Flat Marker	_____
Monument/Headstone	_____
Placement of Marker or Headstone	_____
Urn for Cremated Remains	_____
TOTAL	_____

Cemetery sales can include several items. Figure 18.3 depicts a typical cemetery price list and the available choices.

Cemetery Lots, Crypts, and Niches

There is a wide range of prices for burial plots. Prices vary not only from cemetery to cemetery but within the same facility depending upon the plot's location. It is best to research and visit several cemeteries to view the facilities and available plots. Both casket and urn burial plots (for cremated remains) are available, with the cost of the latter being lower. Some cemeteries offer tandem plots where husbands and wives are buried in the same site.

Because of lawn maintenance costs, many cemeteries are creating sections where only flat markers are permitted. These are called *garden plots* and should cost less than a burial site that allows above-ground headstones or monuments.

Depending upon the cemetery's location and ownership (private, municipal, religious) and the nature and location of the in-ground burial plot, prices could range from $400 to $3,000.

A crypt in a *mausoleum* (a building housing many crypts) or a *lawn crypt* (a below-ground mausoleum) is more expensive than a burial plot because it involves masonry construction. A single crypt may sell for as much as $5,000 to $8,000. Tandem crypts for couples may cost as much as $10,000. Eye-level crypts are more expensive than floor- or ceiling-level sites. An outer burial container is not required with a crypt, which could offset the crypt's higher purchase price.

Increasingly, cemeteries are offering above-ground niches in columbariums for cremated remains. Such sites are less expensive than burial plots. Churches are also building columbariums within their facilities and selling niches to members. The cost of a niche in either location can range from $900 to $2,500.

Endowment or Perpetual Care

States and municipalities are faced with the problem of what to do with abandoned cemeteries, where the grass is never cut, the weeds predominate, and headstones deteriorate. Either these facilities did not set aside adequate funds for perpetual care or their resources were improperly used. To ensure perpetual care, state laws and cemetery practices require setting aside a percentage of each burial plot's purchase price in an investment fund, with the earnings to be used for maintenance.

Cemeteries may wrap perpetual care into the purchase price of a burial plot or add a percentage amount as a separate cost. Seniors should carefully scrutinize the level of care provided by a cemetery and ask about these charges when purchasing a burial plot.

Outer Burial Containers

Both cemeterians and funeral directors sell outer burial containers. Consumers need to know that cemeteries usually require outer burial containers for an in-ground burial with an urn. However, the cost of an urn vault is less than a casket vault. Seniors may even purchase urn vaults, which serve the dual function of being both an urn and a vault.

Opening and Closing

Whether the burial plot is prepaid or purchased at the time of the funeral, there may be an additional charge for opening and closing the grave at the cemetery. Similarly, although less expensive, there is a charge for entombment in a crypt or a niche. Saturday charges are higher than weekday rates, and most cemeteries will not schedule funerals on Sundays and certain holidays. Opening and closing costs may range from $150 for urns to $800 for caskets. You and your senior clients should be aware that some cemetery rules prohibit prepaying for opening and closing costs. This means some survivors may think that the deceased had it all paid for, and then realize they need to pay $850 before the grave will be dug.

Flat Markers

Flat markers to honor the deceased are made of bronze or granite and fit level with the ground, for ease of maintenance (lawn mowing). Costs can range from $150 to $300.

Monuments or Headstones

Monuments or headstones are installed above ground and come in a variety of sizes and shapes. These cost $1,000 or more because they are larger than a flat marker and are often made from more expensive stone. Seniors may purchase a monument from the funeral home, cemetery, or third-party monument dealers. The monument seller usually arranges for engraving the deceased's name and personal details.

Placement of Markers or Headstones

Cemeteries and monument dealers charge seniors an additional fee to install a headstone, monument, or marker. This covers the cost of the equipment and supplies to fit the item. Costs range from $200 to $500.

Urns for Cremated Remains

Urns to hold the cremated remains of the deceased are buried in the ground, placed in niches, or saved by a survivor in some other location. Cemeteries, funeral homes, and crematories all sell these products. Like caskets, there are many styles and models available in showrooms and on the Internet as well as urns handmade by artists. Costs vary from $100 to $1000.

The Bottom Line

As with funeral costs, seniors must compare cemetery costs by looking to the bottom line for the same or similar groupings of goods and services from different sellers. Individual prices for the same or similar items vary from cemetery to cemetery.

PAYING FOR FUNERAL OR CEMETERY GOODS AND SERVICES

For an at-need arrangement, survivors should total the costs of both funeral and cemetery goods and services and determine how to pay that amount, if no prior payments were made. Prearrangers also need to consider today's prices and estimate future increases. According to the Census Bureau, a 65-year-old today can expect to live an additional 18 years on average, and during that time funeral and cemetery costs will increase.

It's difficult to predict what future costs will be, but one yardstick is a review of past increases. Historically, funeral prices have risen at a rate of 4 to 6 percent a year, but during the 1990s, inflationary increases exceeded the Consumer Price Index (General Accounting Office, 1999). Even with annual increases of only 5 percent, today's $10,000 funeral and burial in the Western tradition will cost almost $25,000 in 18 years.

Should you pay $10,000 today or $25,000 in 18 years? Funeral arrangers and prearrangers should consider:

- reducing the bottom line (for example, will a 20-gauge metal casket serve as well as an 18-gauge? could a cremation with no burial be acceptable? does another funeral home have lower prices?)
- reviewing the individual's eligibility for any death benefits
- reviewing existing assets, including life insurance policies, savings, and investments, to determine if a funeral and burial can be paid from existing benefits and assets
- determining whether existing assets and benefits are inadequate (forcing planners to adjust the level of goods and services downward or find alternative sources of funds, such as contributions from the family or loans)

Benefits and Assets

Social Security

A surviving spouse and dependent children are eligible for a $255 one-time death benefit from Social Security. A spouse could use this payment to pay for part of the funeral and burial expenses. However, without an eligible beneficiary—a spouse or young children—Social Security makes no payment. For more information, contact a nearby Social Security office or the agency's Web site (Social Security Administration, 2004). (See Resources section at the end of this chapter.)

Veterans' Burial Benefits

All veterans discharged with honorable conditions are eligible for certain burial benefits. This includes burial in a national cemetery, where space is available to them at no charge. A veteran's spouse and dependent children are also eligible for this burial benefit (National Cemetery Administration, 2004). Some states sponsor veterans' cemeteries and provide burial plots for their resident veterans.

Veterans who were discharged under other than dishonorable conditions are also eligible for a marker or headstone whether they are buried in a national cemetery or not. Spouses and dependent children not buried in a national cemetery are not eligible for this benefit.

For more information, contact the National Cemetery Administration of the Department of Veterans Affairs. (See Resources section at the end of this chapter.)

Other Death Benefits

Death benefits may be available from current or former employers, labor unions, or pension systems. The funeral arranger should check with the deceased's former employers.

Public Benefit Programs

Supplemental Security Income and Medicaid provide seniors no death benefit. However, recipients of those services can set aside a fixed amount of funds in an insurance policy or an irrevocable trust account to provide for a funeral and burial. State and SSI regulations vary, so it is best to check with a state or local social services agency or an Area Agency on Aging.

Existing Assets

Older people often have savings and investment accounts that earn interest or dividends. The question is, are the assets, together with any death benefits, sufficient to pay the funeral and burial expenses? For prearrangers, are the earnings over time adequate to keep pace with price increases?

You and your clients should be aware that access to savings and investment accounts is blocked at the time of death, unless ownership records include the name of someone other than the deceased. Under state probate laws, savings and investment accounts are usually frozen until the estate is settled. While some providers are willing to offer credit or time payments, most prefer to be paid at the time of the funeral or burial.

To avoid any such problems, seniors should add the name of a survivor to any account earmarked for funeral and cemetery expenses.

The asset review should also include any life or burial insurance policies. What is the total amount of insurance benefits? Who is the beneficiary? When can the benefits be paid? Can the benefits be paid directly to the funeral director or cemeterian?

Preneed Arrangements

Seniors can also prearrange a funeral or burial and pay in advance through a personal trust account, a state regulated trust, or a funeral insurance policy. For prearrangers, the advantage to prepaying is that the family's burdens at the time of death are eased, since these details are already settled. With a number of plans, seniors can also lock in a price for delivery at some point in the future.

Personal Trust Accounts

Personal accounts can take two forms:

- *A payable on death (POD) account* requires a consumer to open a savings account with a funeral director or cemeterian as the recipient, payable on death. Seniors might also consider making the POD account payable to a family member or friend, rather than the funeral director, in case they die while on vacation, or the funeral home goes out of business. (This is not available in all states.)

- A *Totten Trust* is a simple agreement that makes the funeral director or cemeterian the beneficiary of a trust. During his or her lifetime, the consumer is the owner, controls the account, and pays taxes on any earnings. At the time of death, the principal and earnings are paid to the funeral home or the cemetery. If the funds are insufficient, survivors need to supplement the trust account. If there is a surplus, that amount is disbursed among the heirs. Such trusts provide the consumer with maximum control, while setting aside funds for end-of-life expenses.

State-Regulated Trusts

Laws in many states (AARP, 1999a) have established a plan whereby a senior pays a specific amount today for the delivery of an itemized list of funeral or burial goods and services at some point in the future. Some states' requirements differ for funeral homes and cemeteries, while some states do not even regulate preneed cemetery sales.

For example, Charles Sommerfield decided to pay $7,500 in advance for his funeral. He visited the Andrew's Funeral Home, selected the elements he wanted for his funeral, signed an agreement for future delivery, and paid the amount in full. State law where Sommerfield lives requires funeral directors to deposit 100 percent of the prepaid funds in an account held in trust until the time of need. Every year the state funeral board audits the funeral director's books to make sure trust funds are where they are supposed to be.

575

Sommerfield also signed a contract for future delivery and prepaid $2,000 to a local cemetery for a vault, opening and closing of the grave, and a marker. (He already held title to a burial plot). With this purchase, the cemeterian, unlike the funeral director, was required to trust only $1,000. (Trust requirements are different for cemeteries and funeral homes in Sommerfield's state.) The other $1,000 remained with the cemetery, but regardless of how it handles that money, it must provide the burial goods and services at the time of need.

Upon Sommerfield's death, the funeral director withdrew the trust funds to pay for the funeral as itemized in the contract. There was no money left over, but if there were, the funds would have been returned to the family or remained with the funeral home, depending on the contract.

Such trusts can be made irrevocable, a requirement for Medicaid and SSI eligibility, but even though consumers may never realize any income, they may be responsible for taxes on the earnings unless they purchased a nontax plan.

Insurance-Funded Plans

A prepaid insurance plan regulates a consumer's funds by placing the prepayment in an insurance policy, with the intent of using the policy's payout at death to cover funeral and cemetery costs. The following is an example of a pre-funded insurance plan.

Edith Helgerson agreed to pay $7,000 in advance for her funeral, but instead of placing these funds in a state-regulated trust account, the funeral director, acting as an insurance agent, sold her a life insurance policy. Helgerson selected the goods and services she wanted, signed a contract for delivery at some point in the future, and purchased an insurance policy with a face amount equal to the funeral cost. The beneficiary of the insurance policy is the funeral home, although Helgerson could appoint a different person at any time, which would void the funeral contract. She paid a single lump-sum premium, although multiple payments (five- or ten-payment plans) were available.

Some insurance companies offer guaranteed-issue policies, meaning that no health questions are asked. However, guaranteed-issue policies can limit the death benefit to the premiums paid for the first few years. Other policies have limited underwriting, and health conditions determine eligibility. If the insurance company determines the consumer to be ineligible for life insurance, an annuity may substitute.

For seniors, the benefit of an insurance-funded product is immediate coverage (unless the policy is guaranteed issue), even if they die before paying all the premiums. With most plans, the sellers offer a price guarantee, and there is no federal or state income tax liability on policy earnings. The principal disadvantage is the historically lower earnings of life insurance policies.

Final Expense Life Insurance

While it is not a preneed product, because no goods and services are tied to these policies, life insurance sales to older persons have become big business. These are small policies, $10,000 or less, marketed on television, in newspaper and magazine ads, through the mails. Final expense life insurance is sold primarily by insurance professionals. It is also sold by the death services industry. The policies' death benefits are used to pay for the costs of a funeral or burial.

Because their risk of death is higher, life insurance for older people is expensive. People 72 and older pay more in annual premiums than the benefits to be paid out, unless they die within a few years of first purchasing one of these policies.

In Washington state, one 74-year-old consumer complained to the insurance commissioner that he paid more than $2,500 in premiums over time but was eligible for only $1,144 in benefits (Norrgard & DeMars). To combat this problem, the Washington state insurance commissioner issued a regulation banning the sale of small, multiple-payment life insurance policies where death benefits are less than premiums paid plus interest (Norrgard & DeMars, 1992). A few other states have taken similar steps, but the abuses continue.

Problems with Preneed

According to an AARP survey conducted in 1998 (the most recent figures available), 40 percent of the adult population age 50 and older had been solicited for a preneed funeral or cemetery purchase. Industry marketing seems to work because approximately one-third of this population prepaid or was in the process of prepaying for a funeral or a burial at that time. Of these, 86 percent had purchased a cemetery plot, crypt, or niche, and 40 percent had prepaid a funeral. Although its products are evolving, preneed continues to be a major segment of the death services industry, with assets in the billions of dollars (General Accounting Office, 1999).

Should a consumer prepay? Both AARP and the Funeral Consumer Alliance caution seniors about this purchase. Other advocates flatly say no. This purchase is unlike any other in that:

- seniors surrender independent control of their funds
- the length of time between signing and fulfillment may be years away, and any mishandling of funds may not be discovered until much later
- the individual signing the agreement will not be present at the time of fulfillment
- earnings may not keep pace with funeral inflation

There have been problems with preneed. Major frauds involving embezzlements and scam investments have been found (Funeral Service Insider, 2004). Major funeral firms have shifted preneed trust funds to life insurance policies or surety bonds without seeking the purchasers' consent (Funeral Service Insider). Also, in bankruptcy proceedings, judges have determined that preneed purchasers are not secured creditors, and are therefore farther down the pecking order for payments if the firm is liquidated (FuneralWire.com, 2003).

In 2000, the Texas Office of Consumers Union issued a report on its review of consumer complaints related to funeral services (Consumers Union, 2000). One-third of the complaints from a two-year period involved preneed funeral contracts. Many were about refunds on canceled or changed preneed policies. According to the report, "Once a preneed policy is written, any changes to the funeral arrangement itself (called a partial cancellation in most contracts) can void the contract or create problems in accessing benefits."

In 2002, AARP's *Bulletin* reported that a 96-year-old Gladys Bohn of Modesto, California, had arranged her own funeral and prepaid in 1989. However, when she died, there was no funeral, only a simple graveside ceremony with no casket or flowers. The family sued the funeral home for breach of contract (AARP, 2002). Similarly, FCA has also received consumer complaints about preneed. For example, Aurelia Rivera of Brownsville, Texas, wrote complaining of the substitution of a casket for her mother worth "$1,000 less than the one we had preselected." FCA recommended she file a complaint with the state funeral board in Texas (FCA, n.d.).

Another concern with preneed plans is the portability of these purchases. Most seniors expect to remain in the communities where they have always lived. Nonetheless, seniors move to be near families or friends even at older ages. If they purchased a plan in New Jersey and move to Chicago, is it portable? If not, is there a penalty for canceling? Is the agreement an irrevocable contract? Setting aside funeral or burial funds in an irrevocable account is required for Medicaid eligibility, but is such an agreement beneficial to seniors not receiving these benefits?

According to industry watchers, preneed complaints are increasing. Nonetheless, funeral directors and cemeterians fulfill most contracts to the satisfaction of seniors. The best preneed guidance you can present to your clients is this: It is certainly good to preplan, and make informed decisions.

Consumer Protections

In 1984, following a lengthy political struggle, the FTC issued a trade rule to regulate the funeral industry. The Funeral Rule, as it is called, is a federal regulation and has the effect of law in all states. It applies to both preneed and at-need funeral arrangements, with one exception: preneed contracts that people entered into *before* the rule went into effect in 1984 *and* have never modified since that year (FTC, 2000).

The Funeral Rule sets out various requirements for funeral directors but not cemeteries, crematories, monument dealers, or third-party sellers. Under this rule, funeral directors must, among other provisions:

- provide funeral price information through price lists available at their place of business and over the phone;
- secure approval before embalming a body;
- not require the sale of a casket for a cremation;
- make no false claims about the preservative value of caskets and outer burial containers.

Industry compliance with the rule varies from city to city. For example, in December 2003, the FTC surveyed 29 funeral homes in the New York City metropolitan area. Of the businesses investigated, 12 facilities were found to be in violation of the rule. According to the General Accounting Office, the "FTC does not have a systematic or structured process for measuring funeral homes' compliance with the Rule." However, the FTC maintains that compliance is improving (General Accounting Office, 1999). Even with its shortcomings of limited coverage and enforcement, the rule is a source of rights for seniors in their end-of-life purchases (FTC, 2003).

States also offer consumer protection through their general consumer protection laws, state licensing boards, and preneed statutes. These provisions, however—including funding, limitations on the investment of proceeds from preneed contracts, and the percentage of preneed sales proceeds to be placed in trust—vary significantly from state to state (General Accounting Office, 1999).

Funeral Planning: Summary

Planning in advance allows seniors to arrange the details of their own funeral and burial. You can assist in this process by:

- learning about the different goods and services, and their costs, that make up a funeral and burial;
- familiarizing yourself with the names, locations, prices, and reputations of different providers in your community;
- learning about state and federal consumer protection laws regarding this approximately $10,000 purchase.

You can also encourage your senior clients to visit different facilities, and even initiate these visits, if appropriate. You should also remind your clients that a funeral and burial is a consumer purchase. There are dozens of choices and alternatives in the goods and services offered by different establishments and over the Internet. Similarly, there is also a wide range of prices for the same or similar goods and services. Shopping around may seem a strange thing to do with funeral and burial products, but it can significantly lower costs. Once a senior has selected a funeral and burial and approved a prepayment plan, you can assist by distributing the prearrangement to all the involved parties.

References

AARP. (1998). Older Americans and preneed funeral and burial arrangements: Findings from a 1998 national telephone survey and comparison with a 1995 survey. Retrieved March 22, 2004, from http://research.aarp.org/consume/d16999_national_1.html

AARP. (1999a). Preneed funeral and burial agreements: A summary of state statutes. Retrieved March 22, 2004, from http://research.aarp.org/consume/d17093_preneed_1.html

AARP. (1999b). Funeral and burial planners survey 1999: Survey findings at a glance, Retrieved March 22, 2004, from http://research.aarp.org/consume/d16998_funeral _1.html

AARP. (2002). Scam alert ... Surprise ending. *Bulletin* (online edition). Retrieved March 22, 2004, from http://aarp.org/bulletin/consumer/Articles/a2003-06-30-advancefunerals.html

Aldine Funeral Chapel. (n.d.). General price list. Retrieved April 15, 2004, from http://home.flash.net/~cdz/aldine/gen.htm

American Memorial Centers. (n.d.). Retrieved April 15, 2004, from http://internet.americanmemorialcenters.com/

The Beaver Cemetery & Beaver Mausoleum. (n.d.). Prices/availability. Retrieved April 15, 2004 from http://www.beaver cemetery.com/prices.htm

Carlson, L. (1998). *Caring for the dead: Your final act of love.* Hinesburg, VT: Upper Access Books.

Casket & Funeral Supply Association of America. (2004). A brief description of the casket industry. Retrieved May 6, 2004, from http://wwwcfsaa.org/Basic InformationCFSAA/habrief.htm

Census Bureau. (2004) Available from http://www.census.gov

Consumers Union. (2000). Final committal: Texas problems with pre-paid funeral services and other tales of mishandled, misrepresented, or overpriced funeral and burial services. Retrieved May 8, 2004, from http://www.consumersunion.org/ other/funeral/final.htm

Cremation Association of North America. (2003). Confirmed 2001 statistics. Retrieved July 23, 2004, from http://www.cremationassociation.org/docs/ Web01Confirmed.pdf

Earthman Funeral Directors & Cemeteries. (n.d.). Earthman funeral homes & cemeteries in Houston. Retrieved May 8, 2004, from http://www.earthmanfunerals. com/Services/CemeteryPkgs.html

Edwards, B. (2004, January 20). Casket company strands family during time of need. *In Your Corner.* Oklahoma City, OK: KFOR. Retrieved July 23, 2004, from http:// www.kfor.com/global/story.asp?s=1608410

FCA (Funeral Consumers Alliance). Casket bait and switch. Retrieved March 28, 2004, from http://www.funerals.org/alert/unavailable.htm

FTC (Federal Trade Commission). (2000). Complying with the Funeral Rule. Retrieved March 28, 2004, from http://www.ftc.gov/bcp/conline/pubs/buspubs/ funeral.htm

FTC. (2003, December 29). FTC announces results of inspection of New York metropolitan area funeral homes for compliance with consumer protection laws [press release]. Retrieved February 11, 2004, from http://www.ftc.gov/opa/2003/ 12/nerofropo3.htm

Federated Funeral Directors of America, Inc. (2004, February 25). Member letter.

Funeral Service Insider. (2004, January 19). *Dear subscriber.* Rockville, MD: United Communications Group.

FuneralWire.com. (2003, August 25) Funeral news: Prime succession bankruptcy update. Retrieved February 23, 2004, from http://www.funeralwire.com/modules.php?name=News&file=article&sid=9869

FuneralWire.com. (2004, February 23) Funeral news: Market changes for funeral businesses. Retrieved February 23, 2004, from http://www.funeralwire.com/modules.php?name=News&sid=11895&file=article

General Accounting Office. (1999). *Funeral-related industries: Complaints and state laws vary, and FTC could better manage the funeral rule* (GAO/GGD-99-156). Washington, DC: General Accounting Office.

Grassley, C. (2000, April 10). Grassley to funeral, burial consumers: Shop carefully (news release). Retrieved May 8, 2004, from http://Grassley.senate.gov/releases/2000/pOr4-10.htm

Harrison, S. (n.d.). The truth about funeral prices. Retrieved May 8, 2004, from http://www.webspawner.com/users/sharrison/

Horowitz, D. (1999, May 25). Queen of the muckrakers' Jessica Mitford had the last laugh [Electronic version]. *The Oakland Tribune*. Retrieved March 3, 2004, from http://www.interment.com/articles/queen.html

Lambert Funeral Home. (n.d.) Service prices. Retrieved May 8, 2004, from http://www.lambertfuneralhome.com/Servicesprices.html

National Cemetery Administration. (2004). Burial & memorial benefits. U.S. Department of Veterans Affairs. Retrieved April 15, 2004, from http://www.cem.va.gov/

National Funeral Directors Association. (2004). NFDA fact sheets. Retrieved February 11, 2004, from http://www.nfda.org/nfdafactsheets.php

New Jersey State Funeral Directors Association. (2002). NJSFDA biennial funeral pricing survey. Retrieved April 15, 2004, from http://www.njsfda.org/fp_survey/index.html

Norrgard, L. & DeMars, J. (1992). *Final choices: Making end-of-life decisions*. Santa Barbara, CA: ABC-CLIO.

Peabody Funeral Homes. (2004, January 1). Service prices. Retrieved May 8, 2004, from http://www.peabodyfuneralhome.com/ServicesPrices.htm

Peoples Memorial Association. (2003). 2002 Survey of funeral home costs. Retrieved March 28, 2004, from http://www.peoples-memorial.org/price.html

Peres, J. R. (2003). End-of-life care: Issues and options. *Public Policy and Aging Report*, 13/1. Washington, DC: National Academy on an Aging Society.

A primer on funerals. (2002, December 15). *Tallahassee Democrat*. Retrieved May 8, 2004, from http://www.tallahassee.com/mld/tallahassee/4742232.htm

Rehnquist, J. (2002). *Organ donor registries: A useful, but limited tool*. Washington, DC: Office of the Inspector General of the Department of Health and Human Services.

Schmidt, J. (2000). It's not Monopoly money. Retrieved May 6, 2004, from http://www.casketstores.org/corgnewspr.html

Slocum, J. (2004). Avoiding funeral home fraud. *Consumers Digest, 42/2*, 53-56.

Social Security Administration. (2004). Survivors benefits. Retrieved April 20, 2004, from http://www.ssa.gov/pubs/10084.html

A Team Master's Caskets. (n.d.). Our steel casket Internet showroom. Retrieved April 15, 2004, from http://burialitems.com/casmetals.html

Town of Oxford. (2003, August 1). Legal notice town of Oxford, cemetery prices. Retrieved May 8, 2004, from http://www.town.oxford.ma.us/Cemetery/CemeteryPrices.htm

West Laurel Hill Cemetery. (2004). Prices. Retrieved May 8, 2004, from http://www.forever-care.com/prices.shtml

Wirthlin Worldwide. (2000). *Funeral and memorial information council, study of American attitudes toward ritualization and memorialization: 1999 update.* Washington, DC: Wirthlin Worldwide.

Resources

Suggested Reading

Carlson, Lisa. *Caring for Your Own Dead.* Hinesburg, VT: Upper Access Publishers, 1987. Carlson offers advice for people who want to take charge of funeral and body disposition arrangements for family members.

Mitford, Jessica. *The American Way of Death*, New York: Macmillan, 1982; *The American Way of Death Revisited*, New York: Knopf, 1998. Muckraker and long-time critic of excess in the funeral industry, Jessica Mitford discusses the technical, financial, and social customs surrounding the American funeral. The second book, a revision of the first, was issued shortly after the author's death in 1998.

Services

AARP, http://www.aarp.org. The Web site of this national membership organization for people over the age of 50 provides information on funerals and burials.

Cremation Association of North America (CANA), http://www.cremationassociation.org. A trade association of crematories.

Department of Veterans Affairs, http://www.va.gov. This federal agency supporting American veterans operates its National Cemetery Administration, a network of national cemeteries that offer plots to military veterans.

Funeral Consumer Alliance (FCA), http://www.funerals.org. 1-800-765-0107. FCA is a consumer organization dedicated to seeking meaningful, dignified, and affordable funerals. This site provides a wealth of information about funeral planning and directs consumers to local memorial societies for local information.

Federal Trade Commission (FTC), http://www.ftc.gov. This federal regulatory agency protects consumers against unfair and deceptive practices and provides consumer information. The FTC promulgated the trade rule governing funeral practices (Funeral Rule) and oversees its implementation.

International Cemetery and Funeral Association (ICFA), http://www.icfa.org. This is the trade association of cemeteries and some funeral homes.

Kavod v'Nichum, http://www.jewish-funeral.org. This site, whose name translates to "honor and comfort," provides information and training about Jewish death practices.

Massachusetts Commission on End of Life Care, http://www.endoflifecommission.org/end_pages/funeral_planning.htm. Consumers can find information here on funeral planning.

Monument Builders of North America, http://www.monumentbuilders.org. This is a trade association of independent monument dealers.

National Anatomical Service, 1-800-727-0700. This service provides information about body donations and can refer consumers to different medical and dental schools.

National Cemetery Administration (see also Department of Veterans Affairs), http://www.cem.va.gov

National Funeral Directors Association, http://www.nfda.org. Run by the national professional membership association of funeral directors, this site also provides funeral planning information and directs consumers to state funeral director associations.

National Kidney Foundation, 30 E. 33rd St., New York, NY 10016, 1-800-622-9010. The National Kidney Foundation manages a national registry for organ donations.

North American Cemetery Regulators Association, http://home.att.net/~ncra/NCRAindex.html. This group is an association of state cemetery regulators.

Social Security Administration, http://www.ssa.gov, 1-800-772-1213. For information on death and survivor benefits, contact your local Social Security office, call the toll-free number, or contact the agency's Web site.

Part 5

MEDICARE, MEDICAID, AND SOCIAL SECURITY

Social Security represents our commitment as a society to the belief that workers should not live in dread that a disability, death, or old age leave them or their families destitute.

Jimmy Carter

Medicare must be made affordable.

Robert N. Butler, Pulitzer Prize winner
and first director of the National Institutes of Health

In Part 5, you will learn about four government programs that form the core of financial security and health care for seniors—Medicare, Medicaid, Social Security, and Supplemental Security Income. It is essential to your success as a CSA to understand these programs, what they provide and don't provide for seniors, how to supplement them, and how to work with them.

Chapter 19

Medicare

Mrs. Adams, who has Medicare and a health insurance plan from her former employer, pays $400 per month for her retiree group coverage. The retiree plan has a few features, like limited prescription drug coverage, that help fill some of Medicare's coverage gaps. But otherwise the plan does not tie in well with Medicare, and it left Mrs. Adams with hefty out-of-pocket costs after a recent hospitalization. She wonders if she's making a mistake by holding on to the employer insurance. She's had it for 10 years.

. . .

Mr. Lewis received a notice from Medicare denying payment for an ambulance trip from his home to a nearby hospital emergency room. His arm was severely broken after he fell from a ladder. He was surprised to learn that Medicare found the ambulance transport to be not medically necessary, and he was disappointed to discover that his supplement insurance policy paid nothing. Mr. Lewis paid the $600 ambulance bill, but now he wonders if there's anything he can do to recoup the money.

Introduction

Medicare plays a dominant role in the lives of seniors. The program covers more than 45 million seniors along with 7 million younger adults who have permanent disabilities. (Kaiser Family Foundation, Medicare Policy Project, Publication Number: 7821, Publish Date: 10-02-2008). Medicare plays a central role in the U.S. health care system, providing health coverage to one in seven Americans. Like Social Security, Medicare is a social insurance program that provides health coverage to individuals, without regard to their income or health status. People pay into Medicare throughout their working lives, so they and their spouses will have Medicare when they turn 65. Medicare funding comes primarily from three sources: payroll tax revenues, general revenues, and premiums paid by beneficiaries. (www.kff.org, 2008)

As a result of Medicare's significant gaps, according to the National Center for Policy Analysis, in 2006, seniors paid for 25 percent of Medicare Part B expenditures and 23 percent of Medicare Part D through monthly premiums. Some also purchased individual Medigap insurance policies. Assuming these factors remain constant, as health spending rises, the proportion of seniors' own incomes spent on their health care will also rise, and they will have to reallocate their incomes to meet their medical needs. (www.ncpa.org/pub/st/st297.html)

This chapter provides basic information about Medicare and Medigap insurance so that, as a CSA, you can help your clients understand the program and the options for filling in its gaps.

President Lyndon Johnson (right), Secretary of HEW John Gardner (second from left), and SSA Commissioner Bob Ball (left) received the first Medicare Part-B application form from a member of the general public, Mr. Tony Palcaorolla, of Baltimore, Maryland (next to President Johnson). Shortly after enactment of the legislation, SSA sent a mass mailing of application forms to all Social Security beneficiaries near or over age 65. Mr. Palcaorolla's completed and returned form was the symbolic first received from this mailing. (September 1, 1965. *SSA History Archives*)

Medicare Basics

The federal government established Medicare in 1965 to provide a system for delivery and payment of medical and hospital care for Americans ages 65 and over. In 1972, the program added coverage for certain individuals with disabilities. The Centers for Medicare & Medicaid Services (CMS, formerly HCFA) is the federal agency that administers Medicare. Through its regulations, policies, and directives, CMS plays an active role in containing the costs of medical services for seniors. It does so at a macro level through elaborate provider payment systems (the Prospective Payment System for hospitals is one example), and at the micro level through medical necessity decisions in individual cases under Medicare's *reasonable and necessary care* rule. CMS contracts with private companies called *fiscal intermediaries* (Medicare Part A) and *carriers* (Medicare Part B) to make coverage determinations and process Medicare claims. The Social Security Administration's role in Medicare is primarily limited to eligibility and enrollment matters.

When seniors reach the age of Medicare eligibility, some may be unpleasantly surprised to learn that the program does not pay for routine physicals, eye and hearing exams, dental care, most long-term care services, and many other excluded medical products and services. Others may be surprised to learn that they face substantial out-of-pocket costs in the form of deductibles, coinsurance charges, or co-payments. This chapter details many of these limitations on Medicare coverage.

Many seniors have a choice between Medicare's two health care delivery systems. The program offers Original Medicare with its Parts A and B, and private insurance, called Medicare Advantage, through Medicare Part C. Original Medicare typifies a traditional fee-for-service delivery model. Medicare Advantage differs from Original Medicare in that private insurance companies offer Medicare coverage through HMOs, PPOs, and Private Fee-for-Service (PFFS) plans under contract with CMS.

The Medicare Prescription Drug, Improvement, and Modernization Act of 2003 (Medicare Modernization Act of 2003, or MMA) added $1.3 billion in funding in 2004 and 2005 for the Medicare Advantage program. As a result, new plans are emerging in markets that until recently had original Medicare as a senior's only option. Thus many more seniors can decide whether to stay in Original Medicare or enroll in a Medicare Advantage plan. In communities with several plan options, this decision can be difficult.

The MMA also created a new prescription drug benefit under Medicare Part D. The Part D program, which adds a voluntary drug benefit to the Medicare program for those who are entitled to Medicare Part A or enrolled in Medicare Part B, started on January 1, 2006.

HOW ARE MEDICARE BENEFITS FUNDED?

The Original Medicare Program has two parts: Part A (Hospital Insurance) and Part B (Supplementary Medical Insurance).

Part A, Hospital Insurance (HI), is financed by a 1.45 percent payroll tax that employees and employers each pay (2.90 percent for the self-employed in 2009). Unlike the Social Security tax, the HI tax is imposed on all annual earnings. Beneficiaries who are entitled to Social Security retirement benefits do not pay a premium for Medicare Part A.

Part B, Supplementary Medical Insurance (SMI), is not to be confused with Medicare Supplement (Medigap) insurance policies. Part B covers physician services and other costs not covered under Part A. Part B is financed with general federal revenues (75 percent of program costs) and monthly premiums deducted from retirees' Social Security retirement benefits (25 percent of program costs). The monthly premium amount for 2009 is $96.40. The Part B premium is income-related. Single seniors with incomes above $85,000, and married couples over $170,000 will pay progressively higher premiums. Still, there are few, if any, circumstances under which insurance acquired through other means is more cost-effective than Medicare.

Part C, Medicare Advantage (MA), is also not to be confused with Medicaid, which in some states is called Medical Assistance and also is abbreviated MA. Part C is financed through a combination of Medicare Part A and Part B funds. Prescription drug coverage in Medicare Advantage plans is funded through Part D.

Part D, the new prescription drug benefit, is financed by general federal revenues (74.5 percent of program costs), premiums, and state payments for some low-income seniors.

MEDICARE ELIGIBILITY

Medicare has three main categories of eligible persons: people age 65 and older generally, certain individuals who have been entitled to Social Security Disability benefits for 24 months, and persons diagnosed with permanent kidney failure requiring dialysis or kidney transplants. Since July 2001, an exception to the disability program's 24-month rule exists for persons with ALS (Lou Gehrig's disease). They are eligible for Medicare in their first month of eligibility for Social Security Disability benefits. In addition, disabled widows and widowers as young as age 50 may be eligible for Medicare coverage.

ENROLLMENT IN MEDICARE

Automatic Enrollment

Seniors who receive Social Security benefits before age 65 are automatically enrolled in Medicare Parts A and B on the first day of the month when they turn 65. Social Security normally mails a Medicare card about three months before a senior's 65th birthday. This mailing also contains a postcard for those who do not want to enroll in Medicare Part B. Those who don't want to enroll in Medicare Part B must return the postcard to Social Security to decline the coverage.

Initial Enrollment Period

Seniors who did not elect to take early retirement benefits may enroll in Medicare during the *initial enrollment period*. They have seven months to enroll, starting three months before the month of their 65th birthday.

The date of enrollment determines the effective date of a senior's Medicare coverage. If a beneficiary enrolls during the three months prior to his or her 65th birthday, coverage begins the first day of the birthday month.

Seniors (or their spouses) who did not pay Medicare taxes may be able to buy Part A coverage. This feature is especially helpful for seniors who immigrated to the United States later in life to be near family members. Medicare can cover them after five years of legal residence. The monthly premiums for Part A coverage, however, are high when compared to Part B. In 2009, the Part A monthly premium is $244.00 for people having 30-39 credits of Medicare-covered employment. The Part A monthly premium is $443 for people who are not otherwise eligible for premium-free hospital insurance and have less than 30 credits of Medicare-covered employment.

Note that the vast majority of seniors, because they paid taxes during their working years through FICA into the Hospital Insurance (Part A) Trust Fund, are entitled to Medicare Part A without paying premiums for the coverage when they reach age 65. They are eligible for Medicare Part A at age 65 even if they wait until later to draw Social Security Retirement benefits. If they do not take Social Security at age 65 or earlier they may still apply for Medicare separately. You should typically recommend that clients seriously consider Medicare coverage when first eligible. It is unlikely that any commercially acquired medical-expense policies for older individuals will be as cost-effective as Medicare Part A coverage. Unlike Social Security, under which the full retirement age (FRA) is gradually increasing, the age of 65 for Medicare eligibility remains in effect and is not scheduled to rise.

General Enrollment Period

Part A: Seniors who do not elect to enroll in Medicare Part A during the initial enrollment period may enroll any month thereafter. Coverage is calculated to begin six months retroactively or during an individual's 65th birthday month, whichever is sooner. There is no penalty for late enrollment for Part A.

Those who are ineligible for automatic Part A coverage may apply and acquire it for a premium as noted above. Otherwise, seniors who apply for Social Security retirement benefits automatically apply for Medicare Part A.

Part B: If a beneficiary does not sign up for Medicare Part B during the initial enrollment period, he or she may only sign up during the *general enrollment period*, which is January 1 through March 31 of each year. The effective date of coverage is the following July 1.

It is not usually a good idea to delay Part B enrollment. A 10 percent penalty is added to the Part B premium for each year that a beneficiary delays enrolling. The exception is for many seniors who continue to work beyond age 65, with health insurance coverage through an employer's health plan. These beneficiaries are exempt from the penalty and may enroll during a *special enrollment period*.

Special Enrollment Period

Seniors who decline Part B at age 65 because they have health insurance coverage through an employer's health plan may later enroll in Part B during an eight-month special enrollment period. The special enrollment period starts when the employer's health plan coverage ceases to be their primary insurance, which is usually at retirement. As noted above, no late enrollment penalty applies.

Retiree medical benefits (COBRA), if offered, are not considered primary insurance by Medicare. Therefore, in most cases, seniors should take Part B coverage during the special enrollment period when they (or their spouse if covered through a spouse's group plan) cease working even if these other options are available. Continuing retiree coverage, when available, essentially acts as a supplement.

The Medicare Card

The senior's Medicare number appears on the Medicare card issued upon a senior's enrollment in the program. It is a nine-digit Social Security number, followed by a letter designation, most commonly A, B, or D. Individuals collecting on their spouses' work records use their spouses' Social Security numbers, not their own. Thus, a senior's Medicare number may or may not simply be the same as his or her Social Security number. The Medicare number for retirees who worked for a United States railroad company is usually the nine-digit Social Security number preceded by a letter, most commonly A, WA, or WD. However, seniors who retired prior to 1967 use a special six-digit number instead of a Social Security number. The card also shows the beneficiary's enrollment status with the effective dates of his or her Hospital (Part A) and Medical (Part B) coverage.

Generally speaking, seniors should be prepared to show their Medicare cards whenever they get health care to ensure that their providers bill Medicare. The one exception, however, is for seniors who belong to a Medicare Advantage plan. That plan issues a membership card that the senior must use to ensure proper claims processing. When doctor office staff sees a Medicare card, they often assume that the claims should go to the Medicare Part B carrier. For Medicare Advantage enrollees, providers must send the bills to the Medicare Advantage plan if they want to be paid.

"Did I Show the Wrong Card?"

Mrs. Church received a notice from a Medicare carrier denying payment for a visit to her physician to treat lesions on her legs. The explanation for the denial noted that Medicare denied payment because the beneficiary is not covered under Medicare Part B. Because Mrs. Church belongs to a Medicare HMO, the doctor's office should resubmit the claim to her Medicare Advantage plan. Note that federal rules permit the Medicare Advantage plans to establish claims filing deadlines stricter than those in Original Medicare, where providers have at least 15 months to submit claims. In Mrs. Church's case, she would not be liable for the bill if the doctor's office failed to meet the Medicare Advantage plan's unique claims filing deadline.

Enrollment by Plan Type

Unless they request otherwise, seniors are automatically enrolled in the original, fee-for-service Medicare program when they sign up for Medicare. Beneficiaries can switch to private plans such as Medicare HMOs or return to Original Medicare on a monthly basis throughout the year.

MEDICARE PART A HOSPITAL INSURANCE (HI) BENEFITS

Benefits are available under Medicare Part A for inpatient hospital care, post-hospitalization skilled nursing facility care (SNF, often pronounced "sniff"), home health care, and hospice care.

MEDICARE PART A BENEFIT PERIODS

Medicare uses *benefit periods* to measure a patient's use of services for inpatient hospital and skilled nursing facility care, and separately for hospice care. In the hospital and skilled nursing facility context, a benefit period begins on the day a beneficiary enters an inpatient hospital and ends when he or she has *not* received inpatient hospital or skilled nursing facility care for 60 days in a row.

If a senior enters an inpatient hospital after one benefit period ends, a new benefit period begins. The practical effect is that a senior owes an inpatient hospital deductible of $1,068 (2009) for the first day of hospitalization in each benefit period (this deductible amount may change in 2010 and beyond); and may owe more than one Part A deductible in any calendar year. It is not an annual deductible. This may surprise some seniors, especially those who've not been hospitalized under the Medicare program. Also, they may not realize that Medicare Parts A and B have separate deductibles.

There is no limit to the number of benefit periods a Medicare patient can have. Benefit periods, along with their sets of Medicare-covered days (see below), renew whenever a patient's discharge from a hospital or SNF is followed by at least 60 days without a subsequent inpatient hospital admission. Conversely, if a patient is hospitalized repeatedly without a 60-day break, the benefit period continues indefinitely and the senior uses up the covered days outlined below.

Inpatient Hospital Coverage

Medicare covers inpatient hospital services, provided the patient needs an inpatient level of care. These services include, among others, semiprivate room and board, regular nursing services, and drugs furnished by the hospital.

In each benefit period, Medicare covers at least 90 days of inpatient care in a participating hospital (including rehabilitation hospitals).

- *For days 1 through 60.* The Medicare beneficiary is responsible for the $1,068 (in 2009) Part A deductible (the amount may change in 2010 and beyond.). The beneficiary owes nothing else for hospitalization until days 61 through 90.

- *For days 61 through 90.* The beneficiary owes a daily coinsurance charge, which is $267 (in 2009; the amount may change in 2010 and beyond). Medicare's payment covers the balance of hospital charges. This out-of-pocket expense could exceed $6,000, even during a fully insured illness.

- *Lifetime reserve days 91 through 150.* In addition to the 90 renewable inpatient hospital days per benefit period, each Medicare beneficiary has 60 *lifetime reserve days*. However, before any lifetime reserve days can be used, a Medicare recipient must have exhausted that benefit period's 90 inpatient days and remain hospitalized. The beneficiary pays a daily coinsurance of $534 (in 2009; the amount may change in 2010 and beyond) for each lifetime reserve day, while Medicare's payment covers the balance of hospital expenses.

- *After 150 days.* Part A coverage ends. Until the benefit period ends (with the required 60-day break between hospitalizations) Medicare does not cover inpatient hospitalization. Note that this happens infrequently. In the vast majority of cases, at least 60 days separate hospitalizations and a new benefit period begins well before a beneficiary uses up all 150 covered days.

Inpatient care in a psychiatric hospital has a lifetime limit of 190 days. (2009)

"Do I Owe the Part A Deductible?"

Assume that Mrs. Flores enters the hospital for a broken hip and is discharged after seven days. If she suffers a stroke and returns to the hospital 20 days later and remains hospitalized for 10 days, the two hospitalizations occur within the same benefit period. She owes only one Part A deductible and has thus far used 17 Medicare-covered inpatient hospital days in the benefit period. If the time between the discharge for the broken hip and the admission for the stroke had been more than 60 days, a new benefit period would start, and Mrs. Flores would owe a second Part A deductible. Observe that benefit periods in Medicare are designated by days, not diagnoses.

. . .

"I Think I Need a Hospital Level of Care!"

Ms. Antonia was hospitalized for a mastectomy. On the day following the surgery, her surgeon announced that he planned to discharge her the next morning despite some instability in her condition. Ms. Antonia had vomited four times already that morning and felt quite weak. She worried that the discharge was premature, and that going home might be dangerous.

To delay the discharge and to avoid financial liability for a noncovered hospital stay, Ms. Antonia could ask the hospital's Utilization Review Committee (URC) to evaluate the medical necessity of a longer hospital stay. If she disagrees with the URC's decision, she could also request an independent review by the Quality Improvement Organization (QIO) in her state. Medicare contracts with QIOs to ensure that Medicare beneficiaries receive high-quality health care services and to investigate beneficiary complaints about poor-quality care. QIOs also rule on the appropriateness of continued hospital stays when patients, like Ms. Antonia, request a review. If Ms. Antonia requests the review quickly, Medicare rules protect her from any financial liability for the hospital stay until the day after the QIO makes its decision.

Skilled Nursing Facility Coverage

Medicare Part A covers up to 100 days of inpatient care in a Medicare participating skilled nursing facility. Medicare covers SNF care if the stay meets the following conditions:

- A physician certifies that the patient needs care in a SNF.
- The patient has been hospitalized for at least three nights in a row preceding transfer to the SNF. (72 hours)

- The patient enters the SNF within 30 days of discharge from the hospital for the same reason he or she was hospitalized (with an exception for medically necessary delays in SNF admission).
- The patient receives skilled nursing or skilled rehabilitation services, or both, on a daily basis.

With respect to the beneficiary's costs:

- *For days 1 through 20.* Medicare covers all costs. The patient owes no deductible or coinsurance charges.
- *For days 21 through 100.* Medicare covers all but a daily coinsurance amount, which is $133.50 (in 2009; the amount may change in 2010 and beyond).
- *Beyond 100 days.* Medicare coverage ends. Medicare provides no SNF coverage until a new benefit period begins.

The Part A deductible and hospital and SNF coinsurance charges typically rise each year. The deductible is based on a national average daily cost of hospitalization. The coinsurance charges are calculated on fixed percentages of the deductible. Consult Medicare in November to learn the amounts of the following year's cost-sharing amounts.

Home Health Care Coverage

Home health care is skilled nursing care, physical therapy, speech therapy, and certain other health care services that patients receive in their homes for the treatment of or recovery from an illness or injury. If a patient receives skilled nursing or rehabilitation services, Medicare also covers home health aide services, in which some custodial needs, such as bathing, are met. Medicare covers *some* home health care if *all* of the following conditions are met:

- A doctor must decide the patient needs medical care in the home and makes a plan for care at home.
- The patient must require at least one of the following skilled services on a part-time or intermittent basis: skilled nursing care, physical therapy or speech language pathology services, or a continued need for occupational therapy.
- The patient must be homebound. (*Homebound* means the patient has a normal inability to leave home and that leaving home is a "considerable and taxing effort." Absences from home must be infrequent or of short duration. A patient may attend religious services, leave the house to get medical treatment—including therapeutic or psychosocial care—and get care in an adult day care programs that is state-licensed or -certified or state-accredited to furnish adult day care services. CMS recently clarified that attendance at family gatherings such as reunions, funerals, and graduations are infrequent absences of short duration for Medicare coverage purposes.)
- Medicare must approve the home health agency caring for the patient.

A common misperception about Medicare's home health benefit is that it does not pay for home health for patients with chronic and stable conditions. The key question, however, is whether the individual continues to need skilled nursing or rehabilitation services on a part-time basis. A federal regulation states, "the determination of whether skilled nursing care is reasonable and necessary must be based solely upon the beneficiary's unique condition and individual needs, without regard to whether the illness or injury is acute, chronic, terminal, or expected to last a long time." In 2001 CMS further clarified that Medicare cannot use a dementia diagnosis to automatically deny therapy and psychiatric claims for Alzheimer's patients (Sohmer Dahlin, 2003).

No Deductible or Coinsurance Charge for Home Health Care Visits

Medicare Parts A and B both cover home health care, with no set limit on the number of nursing or rehabilitation visits a patient receives, provided that the patient continues to meet the coverage rules outlined above. No deductible or coinsurance charges apply. Medicare, however, does not cover around-the-clock nursing or home health aide services, essentially custodial care.

Hospice Coverage

Medicare provides up to 210 days of hospice care without a deductible in situations where a Medicare-insured person is medically certified to have a life expectancy of six months or less. A small fee for drug costs may apply. If a patient survives the 210-day period, Medicare will review the extension of hospice coverage on a case-by-case basis.

Limitations and Exclusions Related to Part A Hospital Insurance

Medicare patients are responsible for 20 percent of reasonable charges for durable medical equipment (DME), such as wheelchairs and oxygen machines, provided by a home health agency following hospital or SNF discharge. DME is covered under Part B.

Medicare does not pay at all for convenience items such as telephones, nor will it cover surcharges for private rooms unless private rooms are medically necessitated. (A recent trend in hospitalization has eliminated many private-room surcharges.)

Medicare does not pay for private duty nursing, the first three pints of blood required in a transfusion, or nursing home care that does not involve skilled care on a daily basis. The program generally excludes coverage for services at a custodial level of care. It does, however, cover some custodial care services provided by home health aides, provided that the patient also receives part-time or intermittent skilled care services. Finally, Medicare generally excludes coverage for care received outside the United States and its territories.

MEDICARE PART B SUPPLEMENTARY MEDICAL INSURANCE (SMI) BENEFITS

Medicare Part B, covers, along with many other services:

- physician and surgeon services
- outpatient services
- medical laboratory fees
- ambulance transportation, when other means of transport are unsafe
- limited outpatient psychiatric care
- screening and prevention services, including breast and prostate cancer screening
- prosthetic devices

Excluded Part B Coverage

Items not covered under Part B include, but are not limited to:

- routine physical examinations (exception is coverage for a one-time, initial physical exam for those newly eligible for Medicare, started in 2005)
- routine eye or hearing exams, eyeglasses or hearing aids
- dental care and dentures (with few exceptions)
- certain immunizations
- chiropractic services, except to treat subluxations of the spine identified by x-ray
- full-time, in-home, private nursing care
- homemaker services provided by a friend or relative
- services not medically necessary

Patient's Financial Responsibilities under Part B

After satisfying a flat $135 annual deduction (in 2009; the amount may change in 2010 and beyond) that represents the first $135 in Medicare's *approved amounts* for covered services, Medicare typically pays 80 percent of its approved amount. Patients are responsible for 20 percent of Medicare's approved amount. Exceptions to the 80/20 rule exist for some prevention and screening services and some outpatient hospital services. Medicare's approved amount for a particular Part B service or item normally is based on a fee schedule, and approved amounts for the same services or items may vary around the country.

The Part B annual deductible increases each year by the same percentage as the Part B premium. The Congressional Budget Office estimates that the deductible will increase to $166 by 2013.

No upper limit or *stop loss* (maximum out-of-pocket amount) applies in the Original Medicare program. This stands in contrast to many Medicare Advantage plans and to most commercial health insurance plans, under which an annual out-of pocket limit protects those insured.

Original Medicare: Assignment

Medicare Part B has a claim filing procedure called *accepting assignment* that that helps control seniors' out-of-pocket costs and expedites payments to physicians and other providers. When seniors choose their physicians or suppliers they should always ask if they accept assignment. Providers who accept assignment agree to charge no more for their services than Medicare's approved amount. Some providers also enter formal agreements with Medicare to accept assignment in all cases. They are called Medicare Participating Providers. Others can accept assignment on a case-by-case, or claim-by-claim, basis.

Physicians who do not accept assignment are allowed to charge up to 15 percent more than Medicare's approved amount. This is often referred to as an *excess charge*. Providers who accept assignment help seniors eliminate this excess charge. Nationally, physicians accept assignment for nearly 90 percent of Part B claims.

Note that durable medical equipment and supply providers are not limited to 15 percent in excess charges. Their excess charges may be even higher, making it even more important to find providers who accept assignment. When seniors use the services of providers who do not accept assignment they must pay for the care and wait for Medicare to reimburse them. Physicians and other Part B providers are required to file all claims with Medicare on behalf of their patients, whether or not the provider accepts assignment.

All Medigap insurance policies sold after 1991 cover the 20 percent coinsurance charge. Some also cover all or part of the excess charge. Assignment applies only to Original Medicare. It does not apply to Medicare Advantage plans, where co-payments are the norm for each physician visit.

When Providers Must Accept Assignment

Some health care providers who are not medical doctors, such as medical social workers, must accept assignment for their services. In addition, doctors, suppliers, and pharmacies must accept assignment:

- for lab tests covered by Medicare;
- for seniors enrolled in Medicaid if the state they live in helps pay their health care costs;
- for Medicare-covered drugs and biologicals (such as serums and vaccines) that are billed to Medicare's claim processor (durable medical equipment regional carriers, known as DMERCs). An example is the medicine used in a nebulizer for a person with asthma;
- for Medicare-covered ambulance services;

- for Medicare-covered drugs and supplies provided by a pharmacy or other supplier.

Some other providers also must agree to always accept the amount that Medicare pays as payment in full. Seniors do not have to ask them if they accept assignment. These providers include:

- hospitals;
- skilled nursing facilities;
- home health agencies and hospices;
- comprehensive outpatient rehabilitation facilities;
- providers of outpatient physical and occupational therapy or speech pathology services.

Seniors who get Medicare-covered prescription drugs or supplies should make sure that the pharmacy or supplier is enrolled in Medicare. If not, Medicare will not pay. All enrolled pharmacies must accept assignment for Medicare-covered prescription drugs or biologicals. Beneficiaries have to pay only their 20 percent coinsurance.

Finding Providers Who Accept Assignment

Seniors should ask their physicians and other health providers whether they accept assignment. In addition, Medicare carriers (companies under contract with Medicare to process Part B claims) can tell beneficiaries which physicians and other medical providers fit this category. DMERCs can tell them which medical equipment suppliers accept assignment.

Seniors can find the phone numbers for their carriers and DMERCs in several ways:

- look on the Medicare Summary Notice issued by a Medicare carrier or DMERC as a record of its coverage decision and payment on a claim
- call 1-800-MEDICARE (1-800-633-4227); TTY users should call 1-877-486-2048
- visit http://www.medicare.gov on the Web
- read "Where to Get your Medicare Questions Answered," a section of the *Medicare & You* handbook that each enrollee receives

The Centers for Medicare & Medicaid Services (CMS) has made information available at http://www.medicare.gov, including helpful directories. The site's Participating Physician Directory locates physicians who accept assignment. This tool contains the names, specialties, and contact information of physicians who agree to accept assignment in all cases. The directory also contains detailed physician information such as board certification, medical school, year graduated, gender, foreign language abilities, and hospital affiliations. The site's Supplier Directory identifies providers of durable medical equipment and covered medical supplies and provides their contact information. You can also go to the CMS website for more information about Medicare: http://cms.gov.

Private Contracts

Assignment does not apply to agreements made between seniors and providers who do not give services through Medicare. Under these *private contracts*:

- Medicare will not pay the doctor or patient for services.
- Seniors have to pay whatever a doctor charges, and there is no limit to what can be billed.
- No claim can be submitted for the service, and Medicare will not pay if a claim is submitted.
- Medicare supplement insurance policies will not pay anything for services under private contracts.
- Most other insurance plans will not pay for the service.

You should be aware that if a senior receives health care that is not eligible for Medicare coverage, the physician must have the patient sign a statement that states that Medicare benefits will not apply. If this does not occur, the senior is not responsible for charges related to the procedure.

MEDICARE PART C: MEDICARE ADVANTAGE

As noted earlier, Medicare Parts A and B are often referred to as Original Medicare. Beginning in 1999, an alternative to Original Medicare became available. In many states Medicare recipients now have the choice of enrolling in Original Medicare or one of several options under Part C. The availability and costs associated with each type of plan depend generally on the area of the country in which a Medicare recipient lives.

MEDICARE MANAGED CARE PLANS

Medicare managed care plans contract with a network of approved doctors, hospitals, and other health care professionals who agree to provide services to Medicare recipients. The network receives a set monthly payment from Medicare covering all enrollees. The health care providers receive the same amount every month, regardless of the services they actually provide. This arrangement encourages health care providers to carefully consider the balance between financial concerns and providing appropriate medical care.

An advantage of the Medicare managed care plans is that older individuals can expect to receive all of their health care through a single source. One disadvantage is that plan enrollees may not be able to select their doctors or hospitals of choice. Another is that the plans offer coverage outside of their service areas for emergency and urgently needed care only. This may present problems accessing nonemergency care for snowbirds and others who are away from their homes for extended periods of time.

Medicare managed care plan sponsors enter agreements with Medicare to provide all covered Part A and Part B services to beneficiaries who enroll. Thus, individuals who select Medicare managed care plans are entitled to all the services provided under Original Medicare, plus additional benefits such as outpatient prescription drugs. You should recognize that those clients who are covered under Medicare managed care plans do not need to acquire Medicare supplement insurance.

Types of Managed Care Plans

Several types of Medicare managed care plans operate today, including HMOs and preferred provider organizations (PPOs). Some HMOs and most PPOs offer point-of-service options, under which members may use providers outside the network in exchange for additional fees or reductions in benefit percentage amounts paid.

Private Fee-for-Service Plans

Private fee-for-service (PFFS) plans are generally more expensive than managed care plans. PFFS plans offer Medicare-approved private insurance coverage. Medicare pays the plans for Medicare-covered services, while each PFFS determines, within limits, how much to charge for the care received. A recipient is then generally responsible for the difference between the amount Medicare pays and the amount the PFFS plan charges.

NOTICES FROM MEDICARE

The Medicare Summary Notice (MSN) is an easy-to-read monthly statement that clearly lists beneficiaries' health insurance claims information. It replaces the Explanation of Your Medicare Part B Benefits (EOMB), the Medicare Benefit Notice (Part A), the Explanation of Medicare Benefits (Part A), and Benefit Denial letters.

The MSN lists all the services or supplies that were billed to Medicare for a 30-day period of time. Beneficiaries should check this notice to be sure they got all the services, medical supplies, or equipment that providers billed to Medicare. Medicare beneficiaries are not expected to pay anything based on this form until and if the provider bills them. The form includes instructions on how to file an appeal.

MEDICARE APPEALS

When Medicare denies payment for a service or item that is otherwise covered by Medicare, an appeal may be in order. Payment denials can result from mistakes, insufficient information to support a claim, or subjective interpretations of Medicare coverage criteria. A *waiver of liability* rule sometimes protects Medicare beneficiaries from financial liability for denied claims. The rule applies when the senior did not know or could not be expected to know that Medicare would deny payment for lack of medical necessity. Normally, this means that unless a provider issues a written notice of noncoverage, they cannot bill the patient for any costs associated with a denied claim.

Even when waiver of liability does not apply, however, beneficiaries can—and probably should—appeal denied claims. Coverage denials are not unusual for home health, ambulance, and durable medical equipment claims. It is important to note, however, that a provider-issued notice of noncoverage or Advance Beneficiary Notice (ABN) does not constitute an official Medicare coverage decision. When asked, providers must submit a bill to Medicare, even if they think that Medicare will not pay for a service. This is called a *demand bill*. After the Medicare fiscal intermediary or carrier issues a denial, the senior can request reconsideration or review of the adverse decision. As noted above, instructions for filing an appeal request appear on the MSN. The MSN also contains notes that describe the reasons for the denial. A senior should read these carefully.

The deadline for requesting review of a coverage denial in the Original Medicare program is 120 days following the issue date of the MSN. The deadline for requesting review of a coverage denial in a Medicare Advantage plan is 60 days from the date that the MA plan issues an *organizational determination*. Medicare Advantage plans must offer an expedited review procedure when the standard time frame would seriously jeopardize the enrollee's life, health, or ability to regain maximum function. In these cases, the MA plan must issue a decision within 72 hours. These plans also must offer a fast-track appeal to review decisions to terminate hospital, SNF, and home health services. In both Original Medicare and Medicare Advantage, additional appeal levels exist, including hearings before administrative law judges (ALJ) when certain amounts of money are at stake (Gottlich, 2002).

"Why Aren't I Considered Homebound?"

Consider the following complaint: "My wife took me to the mall in the winter because my doctor said I should walk to regain my strength after my stroke. I could never have left the house on my own. So how come I'm not considered homebound?" In the home health context, a provider-issued notice of noncoverage or an MSN might state that Medicare coverage is ending because the beneficiary is no longer homebound. If a senior is able to show that she can leave home only with difficulty, a request for reconsideration stands a good chance of succeeding, when accompanied by information about the specific effort involved in leaving home—assistance from a family member or the use of a walker, for example. A letter from a physician that specifically addresses the senior's situation in light of Medicare's coverage rules is also very helpful.

Regardless of whether a senior is enrolled in Original Medicare or a Medicare Advantage plan, the rules that govern coverage decisions are the same.

To file an appeal, send to:

Departmental Appeals Board
Civil Remedies Division, Mail Stop 6132
Cohen Building, Room G-644
330 Independence Avenue, S.W.
Washington, DC 20201

Medicare Supplement (Medigap) Insurance

A disadvantage of the Original Medicare program is that it covers only 57 percent of seniors' medical expenses. Original Medicare is designed with deductibles, coinsurance charges, limits on covered days, and numerous exclusions. You should examine the Medicare Supplement (Medigap) coverage of your clients enrolled in the original Medicare program and recommend purchasing Medigap insurance if none is in place.

The front page of a Medigap policy must clearly identify it as Medicare supplement insurance. Medigap policies are health insurance policies sold by private insurance companies to fill the gaps in Original Medicare Plan coverage.

Insurance companies can only sell you a "standardized" Medigap policy. These Medigap policies must all have specific benefits so you can compare them easily.

You may be able to choose from up to 12 different standardized Medigap policies (Medigap Plans A through L). Medigap policies must follow Federal and State laws designed to protect the senior. A Medigap policy must be clearly identified on the cover as "Medicare Supplement Insurance." Each plan, A through L, has a different set of basic and extra benefits.

It's important to compare Medigap policies because costs can vary. The benefits in any Medigap Plan A through L are the same for any insurance company. Each insurance company decides which Medigap policies it wants to sell.

Generally, when you buy a Medigap policy you must have Medicare Part A and Part B. You will have to pay the monthly Medicare Part B premium. In addition, you will have to pay a premium to the Medigap insurance company.

You and your spouse must each buy separate Medigap policies. **Your Medigap policy won't cover any health care costs for your spouse** (www.medicare.gov, updated March 2008).

A beneficiary who buys a Medigap policy pays premiums to the insurance company selling the plan. As long as a beneficiary pays the premiums, the policy is *guaranteed renewable*, meaning coverage will continue year after year as long as the premium is paid. Medigap policies cover only the health care costs of the purchaser. They do not cover health care costs for spouses or other family members.

In some states, an insurance company may refuse to renew a Medigap policy bought before 1990. At the time these policies were sold, state law was not required to say the Medigap policies had to be renewed automatically each year.

Medigap policies help pay health care costs only if a beneficiary is enrolled in the Original Medicare program. They were not designed to cover the co-payments common to Medicare Advantage plans, such as Medicare HMOs.

Beneficiaries never need more than one Medigap policy. In fact, it is illegal to sell a second Medigap policy to a senior who already has one. It is also illegal in most situations to sell Medigap policies to anyone who has Medicaid. As a CSA you can provide valuable assistance to seniors by making sure they do not have more than one Medigap policy.

A senior generally must have both Medicare Part A and Part B in order to buy a Medigap policy. Most people may not buy a policy until they turn 65, although many states now require insurance companies to sell Medigap insurance to those who are eligible for Medicare through a disability.

Many Medigap policies offer a useful feature called *crossover claims*. The Medicare fiscal intermediary (for Part A claims) or carrier (for Part B claims) electronically shares with the Medigap insurer its claim and payment information. The Medigap insurer then pays the provider for deductibles or coinsurance charges that the beneficiary otherwise would owe. The benefit for seniors is that a crossover claim eliminates paperwork because there are no claim forms to file with the Medigap insurer.

"What If I Need Skilled Nursing Facility Care for More than 100 Days?"

Mr. Reed received daily physical therapy and nursing services in a skilled nursing facility and thus qualified for Medicare coverage for the entire stay. His strength and balance are improving and the doctor expects that he will be ready to return home in three weeks. Mrs. Reed wonders, however, if they will have to pay privately for his continued stay in the SNF. The answer may depend on when Mr. Reed purchased his Medigap insurance. Some of the nonstandardized Medigap policies sold before 1991 (some are still in effect) offered coverage for SNF stays beyond Medicare's 100 days. None of the 10 standard plans sold after 1991 (described below) offer extended SNF coverage.

MEDIGAP PLAN COVERAGE

If you have Original Medicare and already have a Medigap policy without prescription drug coverage, you can join a Medicare Prescription Drug Plan without changing your Medigap policy. New Medigap policies can't include prescription drug coverage. This is because Medicare offers prescription drug coverage to everyone with Medicare. (Choosing a Medigap Policy 2009)

Table 19.1 shows some of the Medicare gaps that Medigap plans cover.

PROVIDERS AND MEDIGAP POLICIES

A beneficiary in Original Medicare who has a Medigap policy can go to any doctor, hospital, or other health care provider who accepts Medicare. However, a senior who has the type of policy called Medicare SELECT must use specific hospitals and, in some cases, specific doctors to get full insurance benefits.

MEDIGAP PLANS A THROUGH L

As mentioned previously, 12 types of Medigap policies are typically available for sale today. Table 19.1 provides you with an overview of these policies. They range from minimal supplemental coverage to policies with increasingly comprehensive coverage and higher cost.

Table 19.1

What Medigap Plans A through L cover

This table gives you a quick look at the standardized Medigap Plans A through L, and their benefits. Every insurance company must make Medigap Plan A available if it offers any other Medigap policy. Not all types of Medigap policies may be available in each state. If you need more information, call the State Insurance Department or State Health Insurance Assistance Program.

If a check mark appears in a column of this table, this means that the Medigap policy covers 100% of the describe benefit. If a column lists a percentage, this means that Medigap policy covers that percentage of the described benefit. If no percentage appears or if a column is blank, this means the Medigap policy doesn't cover that benefit. Note: The Medigap policy covers coinsurance only after you have paid the deductible (unless the Medigap policy also covers the deductible).

Medigap Plans A through L

Medigap Benefits	A	B	C	D	E	F*	G	H	I	J*	K	L
Medicare Part A Coinsurance and all costs after hospital benefits are exhausted	✓	✓	✓	✓	✓	✓	✓	✓	✓	✓	✓	✓
Medicare Part B Coinsurance or Copayment for other than preventive services	✓	✓	✓	✓	✓	✓	✓	✓	✓	✓	50%	75%
Blood (First 3 Pints)	✓	✓	✓	✓	✓	✓	✓	✓	✓	✓	50%	75%
Hospice Care Coinsurance or Copayment										✓	50%	75%
Skilled Nursing Facility Care Coinsurance			✓	✓	✓	✓	✓	✓	✓	✓	50%	75%
Medicare Part A Deductible		✓	✓	✓	✓	✓	✓	✓	✓	✓	50%	75%
Medicare Part B Deductible			✓			✓				✓		
Medicare Part B Excess Charges						✓	80%		✓	✓		
Foreign Travel Emergency (Up to Plan Limits)**			✓	✓	✓	✓	✓	✓	✓	✓		
At-home Recovery (Up to Plan Limits)				✓			✓		✓	✓		
Medicare Preventive Care Part B Coinsurance	✓										✓	✓
Preventive Care not Covered by Medicare (up to $120)					✓					✓		
2009 out-of-pocket limit											$4,620***	$2,310***

* Medigap Plans F and J also offer a high-deductible option. You must pay for Medicare-covered costs up to the high-deductible amount ($2,000 in 2009) before your Medigap policy pays anything.

** You must also pay a separate deductible for foreign travel emergency ($250 per year).

*** After you meet your out-of-pocket yearly limit and your yearly Part B deductible ($135 in 2009), the plan pays 100% of covered services for the rest of the calendar year.

MEDICARE SELECT POLICIES

Medicare SELECT plans offer the benefits of traditional Medicare supplements but cost less. They are a hybrid of regular fee-for-service Medicare, Medigap policies, and managed care. A Select policy must pay the same benefits as any of the standard A through L policies. If beneficiaries use hospitals (and sometimes doctors) inside the network, the policy pays the full benefit. If they use providers outside the network it does not cover the full benefit.

TRICARE

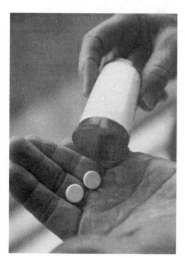

Military retirees, their family members and survivors, and some former spouses are eligible for medical coverage through TRICARE for Life (TFL) and TRICARE Senior Pharmacy Program. TFL, in effect since 2001, operates as a comprehensive wraparound plan for Medicare. It covers both Part A and Part B deductibles, the Part A hospital and skilled nursing facility coinsurance charges, the Part B 20 percent coinsurance charge (except for chiropractic services), the first three pints of blood, and more. TFL covers care outside the United States at 75 percent of an allowable charge (while beneficiaries pay 25 percent). Those who are eligible for TFL pay no premium for the coverage. It is funded by federal payments into the Department of Defense Medicare-Eligible Retiree Health Care Trust Fund. Seniors who are enrolled in TFL have excellent Medicare wraparound coverage and need not purchase additional Medigap insurance (Politi, 2002).

THE PART D PRESCRIPTION DRUG BENEFIT

In December 2003 Congress enacted the MMA of 2003. It added the prescription drug benefit to the Medicare program under Medicare Part D that started on January 1, 2006. The law created a voluntary drug benefit that is delivered through private, stand-alone prescription drug plans (PDP), or through Medicare Advantage (MA) prescription drug plans. The law provides for a government fallback plan for geographic areas without sufficient plan choices.

All Part D plans must offer at least a standard drug coverage benefit or its actuarial equivalent. The monthly premium for the standard benefit is estimated to average $28 in 2009, (which may change in the future) though premiums are likely to vary from plan to plan. The plan sponsors may also offer separate plans with enhanced coverage at an extra cost.

This is the standard Part D drug prescription plan for 2009 required by Medicare:

- If you join a Medicare prescription drug plan, you pay the first $295 of your drug costs. This is known as the deductible.

- During the initial coverage phase, your drug plan pays 75% of the covered prescription drug costs after your deductible is met, and you pay 25% until the total drug costs (including your deductible) reach $2,700.

- Once you reach $2,700 in total drug costs, you will be in the donut hole and you must pay the full cost of prescription drugs until your total out-of-pocket cost reaches $4,350. This annual out-of-pocket spending amount includes your yearly deductible and copay amounts.

- When you spend more than $4,350 out-of-pocket, the coverage gap ends and your drug plan pays most of the costs of your covered drugs for the remainder of the year. You will be responsible for a copay of $2.40 for each generic drug and $6.00 for other drugs. This is known as catastrophic coverage.

The expenses outlined above only include the cost of prescription medications. It does not include the monthly premium that you pay to the prescription drug plan.

It is important to understand that your Part D prescription drug plan may differ from the standard Medicare plan only if the plan offers you a better benefit. For example, your plan can eliminate or lower the amount of the deductible. And, your plan can pay for generic or brand name medications in the coverage gap. In 2009, more than 50% of plans have no deductible and 25% of plans have some drug coverage in the donut hole.

For seniors with prescription drug coverage through employer-sponsored plans, Congress created incentives to encourage employers to continue offering drug coverage to their retirees. The law provides for subsidies of 28 percent of costs to employers if they provide drug coverage that is at least as good as the Part D standard benefit. Seniors who receive drug coverage through a qualified retiree plan may not enroll in a Part D plan.

Exclusions from Part D coverage include drugs for which Medicare Parts A or B already pay (examples include epoetin for severe anemia and cyclosporine to prevent organ rejection), and those dealing with weight loss or gain, cosmetic appearance or hair growth, vitamins and minerals, nonprescription drugs and some others. Part D plans may use formularies, lists of preferred drugs, provided that the formularies meet Medicare standards. The law provides that plan enrollees can appeal for coverage of nonformulary drugs when a prescribing physician determines that formulary drugs would not be as effective, or would create significant adverse effects for the patient, or both.

Medicare: Summary

Medicare is a complex health insurance program. As a result, many of the questions seniors ask you about Medicare and its related programs do not have simple answers. Yet the two scenarios at the beginning of this chapter illustrate two common threads that tie together many of the questions you will encounter as a CSA. The first involves Medicare's coverage and cost gaps and the challenges they create for seniors who are trying to decide which supplemental option or combination of options is best for them and their pocketbooks. Options include an employer group plan, a Medicare supplement policy, Medicare managed care plan, veterans' benefits, drug discount cards, or Medicaid.

The second thread involves a fundamental Medicare principle. Generally the program pays only for reasonable and necessary care in the diagnosis or treatment of an illness or injury. But the line between covered, reasonable, necessary care and noncovered, unnecessary care is not always clear, and those who draw the line sometimes make mistakes. As a CSA, the guidance you offer will be invaluable in helping seniors make sense of the Medicare questions that perplex them.

References

Unless noted below, all facts in this chapter are from the Centers for Medicare and Medicaid Services, contact information in the Resources section.

Gottlich, V. (2002). *Medicare appeals process.* Center for Medicare Education Issue Brief Vol. 3, No. 4. Retrieved July 17, 2004, from http://www.medicareed.org/Publications.cfm?Detail=81

Kaiser Family Foundation. (2008). *Medicare Policy Project*, Publication number: 7821, Publish date 10-02-08.

National Center for Policy Analysis. (2007). *The Rising Burden of Health Spending on Seniors*, Publication number: 297, February 2007.

Politi, E. (2002). *Medicare and TRICARE*, Center for Medicare Education Issue Brief Vol. 3, No. 2. Retrieved July 17, 2004, from http://www.medicareed.org/Publications.cfm?Detail=76

Sohmer Dahlin, H. (2003, Dec.). *Staying at home: A guide to the Medicare Home Health Benefit*, Health Assistance Partnership Issue Brief No. MC2003-1. Retrieved July 17, 2004, from http://www.healthassistancepartnership.org/site/DocServer/Staying_at_home_final.pdf?docID=1161

Resources

Services

Center for Medicare Education, http://www.medicareed.org, 202-508-1210. The Center for Medicare Education publishes monthly issue briefs on topics of interest to those involved in educating Medicare beneficiaries. Their full set of issue briefs is posted on the Web site.

Centers for Medicare and Medicaid Services (CMS), http://www.medicare.gov and http://www.cms.hhs.gov, 800-MEDICARE.

The first CMS site listed is geared to the general public. It offers many helpful informational tools, including "Personal Plan Finder" with community-specific Medicare plan option descriptions and comparisons; "Nursing Home Compare," "Home Health Compare," and "Dialysis Facility Compare," with provider-specif-

Centers for Medicare and Medicaid Services (CMS), http://www.medicare.gov and http://www.cms.hhs.gov, 800-MEDICARE.

The first CMS site listed is geared to the general public. It offers many helpful informational tools, including "Personal Plan Finder" with community-specific Medicare plan option descriptions and comparisons; "Nursing Home Compare," "Home Health Compare," and "Dialysis Facility Compare," with provider-specific quality information; "Prescription Drug and other Assistance Program" (PDAP) that contains Medicare discount drug card and drug price information at local pharmacies; "Helpful Contacts," a roster with the contact information for Medicare's fiscal intermediaries, carriers, DMERCs, and other state agencies; and "Participating Physician Directory" and "Supplier Directory." The site offers most of Medicare's beneficiary-oriented publications, including FAQs on eligibility and enrollment along with many coverage topics.

The second listed CMS Web site contains Medicare's coverage manuals, national health care determinations, and program memoranda, along with a wealth of policy and statistical information about Medicare and the other programs that CMS administers. CMS has regional offices in ten major American cities, in addition to their central office in Baltimore. CMS regional offices are often the first point of contact for beneficiaries, health care providers, state and local governments, and the general public. To find the nearest office, call the CMS toll-free number or check their Web site.

Beneficiaries with questions about Medicare cards and related issues, including card replacement, should contact the Social Security Administration (800-772-1213).

Each year, Medicare publishes an informative handbook titled *Medicare & You*. You can order it, and any of Medicare's many other free publications, by calling Medicare's toll-free number, 800-633-4227 (800-MEDICARE); 866-226-1819 TTY for the hearing- and speech-impaired. Customer service representatives are available at this number 24 hours a day, seven days a week.

State Health Insurance Programs (SHIPs) are good starting points for acquiring state-specific information. Among other information and assistance services, these programs help seniors and their caregivers compare price information for Medigap policies and other insurance options. Their services are free of charge, and volunteers staff many of the local SHIP programs. The contact numbers for these agencies, which all receive CMS funding, may be found in the *Medicare & You* handbook, on the Medicare Web site under "Helpful Contacts," or by calling 1-800-MEDICARE.

Health Assistance Partnership, http://www.healthassistancepartnership.org, 202-737-7340. The Health Assistance Partnership, a grant-funded program of Families USA designed to support the SHIPs (mentioned above), has several useful "Resource Centers" on its Web site, including one that fully describes the appeal systems for both the Original Medicare and Medicare Advantage programs.

Kaiser Family Foundation, http://www.kff.org, 650-854-9400. The Kaiser Family Foundation has an outstanding Web site with hundreds of fact sheets, issue papers, and program summaries related to Medicare and Medicaid. They also offer periodic webcasts on Medicare-related topics.

TRICARE for Life, http://www.tricare.osd.mil/tfl, 1-888-DOD-LIFE and 1-877-DOD-MEDS, separate phone numbers for the insurance and pharmacy plans, respectively.

Chapter 20

Medicaid and Seniors

Sammy moved into a nursing home three years ago at the age of 88. At that time, after six years of paying for around-the-clock home health aids, his original port- folio of $500,000 had dwindled to $20,000. The monthly fee for the nursing home was $4,745, so it took only four months until he reached his state's asset limit of $2,000 and could apply for Medicaid.

Sammy's diabetes has gotten better since he moved into the home, where he eats a healthy diet, takes his medications regularly, and enjoys daily walks. Sammy, who worked for the same printing company for over 40 years says, " I never expected to outlive my money. Where would I be without Medicaid?"

. . .

Evy is part of a new trend in long-term care provided through Medicaid, called home and community-based services. She receives home-based service instead of nursing home care because the state she lives in, Florida, has a "Medicaid waiver." The waiver allows Evy to live with her son, daughter-in-law, and eight-year-old granddaughter and receive personal care from them. Without the waiver program, she would have to live in a nursing home.

Medicaid also covers Evy's Medicare premiums and pays for her walker and prescription drugs. At age 85, she says the greatest gift is being able to live with her granddaughter, who plays Chinese checkers with her many evenings.

Introduction

Medicaid is the United States health care safety net. It is health insurance for people who cannot pay for their healthcare themselves. Medicare is health insurance for seniors and some disabled individuals under age 65; Medicaid is health insurance for young people, families and seniors. It is important for you to know about Medicaid for a number of reasons:

- Today, many seniors live to age 80 or 90, and some, like Sammy, outlive their assets. Medicaid can provide them with the health care they would otherwise not receive.

- Qualifying for Medicaid through gifts or other "medical planning" techniques is a controversial and complicated issue important to the financial well-being of many seniors. Failure to understand how the system works can have financially devastating consequences.

- Medicaid can help pay for Medicare premiums and other costs not covered by Medicare.

- Differing from Medicare, Medicaid is the biggest financer of long-term care (LTC) services in the United States. Today, Medicaid covers a broad low-income population, including working families, individuals with diverse physical and mental disabilities, and seniors. Medicaid's beneficiaries include many of the poorest and sickest people in the nation.

- The Medicaid system is changing dramatically and rapidly. Failure to keep up with these changes could mean that some senior clients will lose out on benefits and services.

This chapter covers the major issues that you should know about Medicaid and its coverage. The chapter includes: a brief history of the Medicaid program, an explanation of the differences between Medicaid and Medicare, a breakdown of Medicaid services, details on Medicaid's coverage of institutional and community-based services, and the importance of Medicaid in planning for long-term care.

History of the Medicaid Program

Title XIX of the Social Security Act, known as *Medicaid*, became law in 1965 as a program to provide medical assistance for certain individuals and families with low incomes and resources. It is a jointly funded cooperative program between the federal and state governments.

Within broad national guidelines provided by the federal government, each state Medicaid program must:

- establish its own eligibility standards;

- determine the type, amount, duration and scope of services;

- set the rate of payment for services;

- administer its own program.

Medicaid programs vary greatly from state to state, and even within a particular state, Medicaid requirements are quite complex and frequently subject to case law interpretations. They often require consultation with professional elder law attorneys and financial planners familiar with their state's requirements. Failure to obtain qualified advice before taking action could be one of the most financially devastating omissions seniors make. Your knowledge of Medicaid and resources for seniors might prevent unwise choices.

Medicaid Defined

MEDICAID VS. MEDICARE

Many people confuse Medicaid and Medicare. Medicaid is a *means-tested program*, meaning it is available to those who, regardless of age, meet their state's medical and financial eligibility requirements. The federal and state governments finance Medicaid jointly, and the states administer it. The program pays medical costs when individuals cannot.

Medicare, on the other hand, is a federally funded health care insurance program. The federal government runs the program through the Centers for Medicare and Medicaid Services (CMS). Specific information regarding Medicare eligibility and benefits is covered in detail in chapter 19.

MEDICAID'S BENEFICIARIES AND COSTS

According to the The Kaiser Family Foundation, Kaiser Commission on Medicaid and the Uninsured, *Medicaid Primer 2009* (January 2009), in 2005, Medicaid covered 59 million people, including one-quarter of U.S. children. In the absence of Medicaid, the vast majority of its beneficiaries would join the ranks of the nearly 46 million uninsured. Medicaid is a major source of health care financing as well as coverage. It funds almost one-sixth of total national spending on personal health care It is the main source of financing for long-term care, paying 40 percent of the national bill for both nursing home care and long-term care overall. It is also the largest source of public funding for mental health care. Hospitals and health centers that care for the uninsured and many in the low-income population depend heavily on Medicaid revenues.

Many states are struggling with decreased revenues, budget deficits, and spiraling health care costs. Their financial woes often push them to cut their Medicaid budgets, which results in a loss of federal matching funds. Nearly 10 million Americans, including 6 million elderly and about 4 million children and working-age adults, need long-term care. Medicaid covers more than 6 of every 10 nursing home residents and finances 40 percent of all long-term care spending in the nation, including 43 percent of nursing home spending. More than half of Medicaid long-term care spending is for institutional care, but an increasing share is attributable to home- and community-based services (Kaiser, 2009).

The federal Deficit Reduction Act of 2005 (DRA) was passed to help reduce the growth of Medicaid expenditures over several years. It tightens eligibility rules in regard to assets of applicants. DRA also allows the state more flexibility in providing Medicaid services. DRA changes will be noted throughout this chapter.

MEDICAID SERVICES

States are continually designing and launching Medicaid health care reform programs. All states cover a minimum set of services, including hospital, physician, and nursing home services. States have the option of covering 31 additional services, including prescription drugs, hospice care, and personal care services.

Ultimately, state and federal Medicaid dollars come from the same taxpayer's pocket. Between 2007 and 2017 our total health care bill will double, from $2.2 trillion to an estimated $4.3 trillion. By 2017 we'll be spending almost $1 of every $5 of our gross domestic product on health care. If we aren't able to control health spending, it will eat into important priorities at every level [remarks to the National Conference of State Legislatures Spring Forum, April 24-25, 2008, according to Kerry Weems, Acting Administrator for the Centers for Medicare and Medicaid Services (www.cms.gov)].

DRA will also allow states to offer alternative, reduced Medicaid benefits packages to certain individuals, primarily adults who are not disabled or pregnant and whose incomes exceed specific limits. The restricted packages still must meet minimum benefit standards.

Medicaid is the largest source of funding for long-term care among all Americans, including the middle class. Although two-thirds of Medicaid spending is for institutional care, Medicaid has made great strides in shifting the delivery of services from institutional settings to home and community settings.

WHAT DOES MEDICAID COST?

In 2006, combined federal and state Medicaid spending on services was $304 billion. Almost 60 percent of Medicaid spending on services is attributable to acute care, including payments to managed care plans. Over a third (36 percent) of spending goes toward long-term care. Administrative costs are less than 4 percent.

More than 45% of Medicaid spending for medical services is attributable to dual eligibles, the low-income Medicare beneficiaries who also qualify for Medicaid (Kaiser 2009).

SENIORS, MEDICAID, AND MEDICARE

Virtually all seniors who receive Medicaid also receive Medicare. However, they may not receive full Medicaid benefits. For seniors who are enrolled in both programs, Medicare is the primary source of payment for those services that it insures.

Long-Term Care Services

Medicaid is a significant source of financing for long-term care. The elderly and disabled make up one-quarter of the Medicaid population but account for about 70 percent of program spending. While more than two-thirds of Medicaid spending for long-term care is on institutional services, home and community-based services (HCBS) waivers enable states to deliver community-based care. (See chapter 9, Home and Community-Based Services). In fact, more Medicaid beneficiaries now receive community-based services than institutional services.

All state Medicaid programs are required to cover either nursing facility care or home health care for people who qualify for nursing facility care. Medicaid's qualifications for home health care are far less strict than Medicare's—beneficiaries do not have to qualify for nursing facility care or to have been discharged from a hospital or nursing home to receive care. (This is an important contrast between

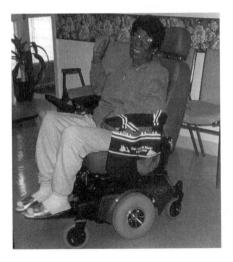

the two programs of which you should be aware.) State Medicaid programs also have the option of covering other services, including case management services, personal care services, prescription drugs, respiratory care services, private duty nursing services, hospice care, PACE services (addressed below), and home and community-based services provided through waivers (see next section).

HOME AND COMMUNITY-BASED SERVICES

Although most long-term care spending is for institutional care, Medicaid is shifting the delivery of services to HCBS. Beginning in 2007, the DRA allowed states to provide certain home- and community-based services without first getting a waiver.

Medicaid's payments for HCBS are often referred to as *section 1915 waivers*, after the section of the Social Security law that approves them. States who employ section 1915 waivers widen the options for applicants who qualify for institutionalized care. Section 1915 allows funds for such care to be applied to services provided in a home setting, rather than in an institution.

Another Medicaid waiver program also offers flexibility to states with respect to Medicaid long-term care services. They are called *section 1115 demonstration waivers*, after the section of the Social Security Act that authorizes them. Section 1115 allows applicants who are disabled to receive money directly from Medicaid to purchase long-term health services themselves. The waiver offers an option from the traditional method of Medicaid administration, where money passed directly to a care provider or institution and patients had fewer service options.

States provide consumer-directed services through section 1115 or 1915 waivers. The section 1115 waiver gives states more flexibility than section 1915. Under section 1115, states can provide services even to individuals who do not need institutional care, and they can give beneficiaries cash payments with which they can purchase services directly. In contrast, under section 1915, states can enroll only individuals who require institutional care, and they cannot give cash directly to beneficiaries.

Program of All-Inclusive Care for the Elderly

The *Program of All-Inclusive Care for the Elderly* (PACE) is a popular option for delivering HCBS to frail seniors. PACE permits participants to live at home and receive services. PACE programs are not available in every state, so check with your state Medicaid office.

To qualify for PACE, a person must be 55 years of age or older, live in a PACE service area, and be certified by the state to need nursing home-level care.

The typical PACE participant is very similar to the average nursing home resident. On average, the participant is 80 years old, has 7.9 medical conditions and is limited in approximately three activities of daily living. Forty-nine percent of PACE participants have been diagnosed with dementia. Despite a high level of care needs, more than 90 percent of PACE participants are able to continue to live in the community. (2008; National PACE Association, www.npaonline.org).

PACE programs are not limited to services reimbursable under Medicare and Medicaid. They have the flexibility to deliver all services participants need, including social services. Here are some testimonials given to the National PACE Association by family members of PACE enrollees:

> *PACE takes care of all my husband's medical needs. In or out of the hospital, they step up to the plate when they are needed.*

> *When we enrolled in PACE, the staff came into my mother's home, putting in grab bars where they needed to and outfitting the bathroom for her. PACE provided the physical things that she needed to keep living on her own.*

> *Before we found PACE, our family was really struggling with how to best honor our mother's wishes while at the same time meeting her needs. It was a real challenge. PACE has made a huge difference in our being able to do that.*

PACE is able to provide the entire continuum of care and services to seniors with chronic care needs, while they live independently in their homes for as long as possible. Care and services include:

- adult day care that offers nursing; physical, occupational, and recreational therapies; meals; nutritional counseling; social work and personal care;
- medical care provided by a PACE physician familiar with the history, needs, and preferences of each participant;
- home health and personal care visits (but not hourly work shifts);
- all necessary prescription drugs;
- social services;
- medical specialists in areas such as audiology, dentistry, optometry, podiatry, and speech therapy;
- respite care;
- hospital and nursing home care when necessary.

Medicaid Planning for Long-Term Care

Many people believe that Medicare will cover long-term care costs. This is a widespread and dangerous misperception. In truth, Medicare benefits for long-term care are very limited. Medicare pays only for skilled care that is deemed "medically necessary." It does not cover personal care required by most seniors with chronic, custodial care needs. In fact, most typical nursing home admissions either do not require the level of skilled care demanded by Medicare or exceed the time limits for Medicare coverage, leaving seniors and their families searching for other funding sources for ongoing coverage of long-term care costs.

USING MEDICAID TO PAY FOR LONG-TERM CARE

Projections of the percentage of our population that will require nursing home use during their lifetime vary from 39 to 49 percent (www.cms.gov). For those needing nursing home care, it is highly likely that they will eventually have to rely on Medicaid.

MEDICAID PLANNING—A CONTROVERSIAL DEBATE

Seniors should have a plan for how they are going to pay for long-term care if the need occurs. Your senior clients may have questions about applying for Medicaid benefits to cover LTC costs. To do so requires reducing their assets and income to the poverty level.

Seniors forced to take such measures may have no other option—they have neither the income nor the assets to purchase long-term care insurance or pay the costs of long-term care on their own. Or, they may be uninsurable. Others wish to avoid accumulating massive medical bills that will impoverish a spouse or consume an estate they hope to pass on to their heirs.

You have probably heard the term *Medicaid planning*. This strategy helps seniors manage their assets and income at the same time that they are able to qualify for Medicaid if needed. However, Medicaid "planning" is actually a misnomer, as most seniors do not plan to go on Medicaid, but are faced with an imminent care need and have no other choice. Medicaid planning is most often reactive, initiated in a crisis mode after care has already begun or following the diagnosis of a serious, progressive disease.

Medicaid planning is a controversial topic. Federal and state governments have made it increasingly difficult to transfer assets in order to qualify for Medicaid. The 2005 DRA specifically addressed handling of assets. Many believe that this tightening of the purse strings is insensitive to seniors. Their contention is that the government must address the financial devastation that faces seniors who need long-term care but lack necessary resources. To support their argument, they point to the wealthy, who easily pay their own long-term care costs in the environment of their choice, and to the poor, who easily qualify for state assistance.

Those who believe that the government is insensitive say that the hard-working middle class must endure impoverishment before they can receive federal assistance with their long-term care costs. The argument is that the small "nest egg" that these middle-class seniors saved to provide for a spouse or to help their adult children can be consumed by long-term costs in a matter of months.

The other side of the argument is that Medicaid is a means-tested program designed as a safety net for individuals with low income and limited resources and should be used when no other resources exist. Those who support this position would point out that persons with $500,000 in home equity have a significant asset to use for their care and therefore are not impoverished.

MEDICAID ELIGIBILITY—FINANCIAL CRITERIA

The most challenging aspect of Medicaid eligibility involves meeting state-specific financial qualifications regarding income and assets. With regard to income, the federal government requires states to provide Medicaid coverage to most individuals who receive federally assisted income maintenance payments such as Aid to Families with Dependent Children (AFDC) or Supplemental Security Income (SSI). As a whole, these beneficiaries are termed *categorically needy*. States may also set eligibility guidelines referred to as *medically needy* provisions. Seniors who qualify for Medicaid benefits through a medically needy determination are those who face medical bills—including long-term care expenses—in excess of their ability to pay. In determining eligibility for medically needy benefits, Medicaid looks at both assets and income, although assets are the key determinant in most states.

Medicaid Eligibility—Assets

Medicaid does not count all assets when determining eligibility. Seniors may keep some assets (*noncountable assets* or *inaccessible assets*) and not others (*countable assets*). For example, Medicaid counts investments but does not count an irrevocable burial fund trust.

Noncountable Assets

A primary residence is not counted as long as the applicant, a spouse, or other member of a protected class resides there. Home equity is discussed further in the section "The Family Home."

Other noncountable assets include: basic household furnishings, a car, wedding ring, burial plots, an allowance for funeral expenses, life insurance of limited value or property, and income-producing businesses. These are sometimes called *exempt assets*. It is important for you to recognize that these assets are not necessarily protected (from potential probate law or recovery by the state, as discussed later), but simply are not counted for eligibility for Medicaid.

Countable Assets

All other cash, stocks, bonds, investments, and retirement plan assets are counted by Medicaid to determine eligibility for benefits. Generally, if an applicant has access to the principal of an asset—even if the principal has never been touched or if it is subject to taxes or penalties—it is a countable asset.

According to federal law, an unmarried applicant to Medicaid may retain noncountable assets plus no more than $2,000 to $4,000 in countable assets (in 2009; this amount may change in the future). Each state determines its own criteria within these limits. Before Medicaid benefits will begin, an applicant must consume or eliminate the amount of countable assets (*spend-down assets*) above this limit. (Spend-down assets are expected to be spent on health care.)

Spousal Resource Allowance

Medicaid laws protect a healthy spouse when the unhealthy spouse applies for Medicaid. In order to understand Medicaid's regulations about spousal protection, you need to become familiar with two terms commonly used in written Medicaid material: *community spouse* (CS) and *institutionalized spouse* (IS). *Community spouse* refers to a healthy spouse who continues to live in the community, while *institutionalized spouse* refers to a spouse who requires care in a nursing home and is applying for Medicaid benefits.

When a married couple applies for Medicaid, a snapshot is taken of the couple's total assets. All of the assets of the husband and wife, whether held jointly or separately, are pooled together. Medicaid disregards prenuptial agreements, which may imperil financial plans that were set up to protect separate assets and prevent their use for the other spouse.

For 2009, the community spouse may keep between $21,912 and $109,560 (indexed annually) or half of the couple's combined assets, whichever is less. This is known as the *community spouse resource allowance* (CSRA). Some states disregard the one-half limitation and permit a community spouse to keep all of the countable assets up to the CSRA maximum, even if that exceeds one-half the countable assets.

Jointly Owned Assets

Seniors applying for Medicaid cannot protect their assets by creating joint accounts. Medicaid will count assets jointly held by the applicant and another individual other than a spouse as belonging entirely to the applicant if the title is such that any single owner of the resource can control it without the cosignature of another owner. As an estate planning technique many seniors put an adult child's name on their accounts as a joint owner. (Chapter 15 goes into more detail on this issue.) While this may allow an asset to be transferred at death without being subject to probate, it does not provide asset protection from Medicaid.

Transfer of Jointly Held Assets

The transfer of a jointly owned asset can trigger a Medicaid penalty. In the case of an asset held jointly, Medicaid considers the asset to be transferred if the joint owner (not the Medicaid applicant) withdraws any money. If a transfer occurs during a look-back period (discussed below), it will create a period of Medicaid ineligibility. This rule is one of many reasons why it is important that seniors seek advice from professionals who are knowledgeable about Medicaid's regulations. Seniors can easily make a costly error when approving this type of transfer without understanding the consequences.

Assets held jointly by spouses are not usually problematic under this rule. It is problematic, however, for seniors who create joint ownership arrangements with adult children. Again, it is important to have the advice of a professional who is knowledgeable about Medicaid.

The Family Home

Until the Deficit Reduction Act (DRA) of 2005, an applicant's home was not included in determining eligibility for Medicaid. Under the DRA, an individual with more than $500,000 in home equity is ineligible for Medicaid. States can increase the home equity limit up to $750,000. This rule does not apply if the applicant's spouse, minor child, or disabled child resides in the house. The spouse, minor, or disabled child is referred to as a *member of a protected class*. According to current guidelines, members of the protected class include:

- the applicant's spouse;
- any child under 21;
- any child of any age who is blind or permanently and totally disabled;
- a brother or sister who owns equity interest in the home and resided in the home for at least one year preceding the Medicaid application;

- any child who resided in the home for two years prior to admission to the nursing home *and* provided care that permitted the applicant to stay in the home.

The fact that a senior's home may be a noncountable resource at the time of application for Medicaid benefits does not mean the home is protected from estate recovery by Medicaid after the applicant's death. When a Medicaid beneficiary with an interest in a personal home dies and the home is no longer occupied by a member of the protected class, the state may seek to recover the amount of benefits paid by placing a claim against the value of the home.

Since the most valuable asset for most seniors is a home that is owned outright, it is extremely important to obtain competent advice about options for handling the home's ownership from an elder law attorney or other professional knowledgeable about Medicaid.

The "Look-Back Period" and Ineligibility Penalties

Applicants risk a penalty by attempting to qualify for Medicaid by transferring assets during a period of time called the *look-back period*. Transfers of assets for less than fair market value (by the applicant or spouse) within this time will result in a period of ineligibility for Medicaid.

The Balanced Budget Act of 1997 sought to make it a federal crime to advise a person to transfer assets for the sole purpose of becoming eligible for Medicaid. A subsequent court ruling held this law to be unconstitutional, and it is currently not being enforced. Regardless, you should advise your senior clients to seek legal counsel when considering action in this area.

Since February 8, 2006, the look-back period during which Medicaid can review any financial transactions begins on the date of the Medicaid application and "looks back" 60 months for all transfers. Medicaid reviews any assets that have been transferred for less than full value during the look-back period. The uncompensated value of any assets transferred during this period is then divided by the state-established monthly nursing home cost to determine a period of Medicaid ineligibility. For example, transferring an asset valued at $100,000 in a state with a monthly nursing home cost of $5,000 for a semi-private room would result in a 20-month ineligibility/penalty period ($100,000 divided by $5,000), starting when the individual becomes eligible for Medicaid.

Naturally, the larger the transfer within the look-back period, the longer the ineligibility. For example, a $500,000 transfer within the look-back period against a state-established nursing home cost of $5,000 would result in 100 months of ineligibility. Note that the penalty period is longer than the look-back period. If multiple transfers occur within the look-back period, the ineligibility penalty is determined based upon the combined value of the transfers and begins on the date of the Medicaid application. States no longer round down on the penalty. States can impose partial months of ineligibility. For example, if a transfer created a penalty period of 4.25 months, the ineligibility period would be four months and eight days. Transfers occurring prior to the look-back period are not considered by Medicaid.

Permissible Transfers

There are several circumstances under which assets may be transferred without creating a period of ineligibility:

- transfer of a home to a member of the protected class
- non-home transfers to a spouse or to another for the sole benefit of the spouse (limited to the CSRA maximum on countable assets)
- non-home transfers to a blind or disabled child or for the sole benefit of the blind or disabled child
- transfers in which a satisfactory showing is made to the state that:
  —the asset was intended to have been disposed of at fair market value
  —the transfer occurred exclusively for some reason other than to qualify for Medicaid
  —applying a penalty period of ineligibility will create undue hardship
  —all assets transferred have since been returned to the individual

Estate Recovery

Federal law requires states to seek recovery for Medicaid benefits by placing a claim against the probate (taxable) estate of the deceased beneficiary. Medicaid applicants with annuities are now required to name the state as remainder beneficiary to facilitate recovery of the Medicaid expenditures for that individual. Federal law also authorizes, but does not require, states to recover nonprobate assets such as jointly owned property and living trusts. Even assets not counted during eligibility such as a home may be included in these recovery actions. Thus, while exempt assets may preserve some portions of an estate during the life of the applicant, they may not pass on to heirs according to the preferences of the deceased.

Liens against the property of a Medicaid recipient prior to death are prohibited except in very limited circumstances. Seniors who have had a lien placed by the state should seek legal advice. In Colorado, for example, liens are often placed before death. As a CSA you should contact the agency that oversees Medicaid in your state to learn more about the process.

Medicaid Eligibility—Income

After assets, the second criteria that state Medicaid programs use to determine eligibility is income. Medicaid counts Social Security income, defined benefit pensions, alimony, and income from immediate or *annuitized* annuities as income. If the principal of an income-producing asset is available, even if it is not accessed, it is not considered income but is counted as an asset.

Most income counted by Medicaid will be applied toward nursing home and other care costs. Medicaid makes up the difference between the total cost and available income. It is extremely important to recognize that Medicaid benefits, even once qualified, are not truly free. The requirement that beneficiaries contribute most of their income toward care is essentially a huge copayment for services.

Income decisions are complicated for married individuals. When a Medicaid applicant is married, a determination must be made regarding the allocation of income to each spouse. Income of the CS is not counted. In most states, the income is credited to the individual whose name is on the income check. Income in both names is split evenly, as is income in community property states.

Income Allowance for the Community Spouse (CS)

Congress established a very complicated formula to determine the basic income allowance for the CS. Currently, the CS is entitled to a *minimum monthly maintenance needs allowance* (MMMNA) that in 2009 is between $1,750 and $2,739 per month (legislation may change MMMNA).

When the CS has less personal income than the minimums set by the state, it may be possible for the CS to retain some of the IS's income, up to the amount allowed by the MMMNA. DRA requires states to follow the "Income First" rule. That means that the income of the IS must be used first to bring the CS's income up to the MMMNA before using assets to provide that additional income.

CSAs should understand not only the importance of protecting the assets of a client who is applying for Medicaid, but also the income and lifestyle needs of the community spouse.

Income Allowances for the Applicant

Each state establishes amounts of countable income (at least $30 per month in 2009) that may be held back by the Medicaid applicant for a small personal needs allowance. Some states also allow the applicant to retain an allowance (typically $150 to $500) for home maintenance in the event the applicant returns to the community and for expenses related to health insurance or other medical needs. All other income must be contributed toward the cost of care.

Income Cap States

Income cap states are states that set an income threshold for Medicaid eligibility and deny applications when the applicant's income exceeds the threshold. According to federal law, these states can set their income level anywhere between the one-person standard for Supplemental Security Income ($647 in 2009) and 300 percent of that amount ($1,941 in 2009). Income cap states do not have to allow a spend-down to meet Medicaid eligibility requirements.

The income cap states are:

Alabama	Idaho	Oklahoma
Alaska	Iowa	Oregon
Arizona	Louisiana	South Carolina
Arkansas	Mississippi	South Dakota
Colorado	Nevada	Texas
Delaware	New Mexico	Wyoming
Florida		

Note: States could change their Medicaid legislation regarding eligibility.

Miller Trust

The Omnibus Budget Reconciliation Act of 1993 established an exemption for certain trusts that may be set up to help an applicant qualify for Medicaid. One of these, the Miller Trust, is frequently used for individuals who live in income cap states and have too much income to qualify for Medicaid.

The specific requirement for a Miller Trust is that all of the applicant's income goes into the trust. The trustee distributes the income within the trust only to:

- the institutionalized individual's personal needs allowance;
- the nursing home for the patient payment amount; and
- the community spouse, if applicable, to increase the MMMNA.

Upon the beneficiary's death, any remaining assets within the trust are paid directly to the state to repay their share of Medicaid's costs.

Medically Needy States

States other than those listed above are medically needy, spend-down states. Applicants in these states who fall into the medically needy category must comply with the state's asset limits. Again, they must spend all income on medical care, less a small personal needs allowance and an allowance for spousal support. Medicaid then pays the difference between the nursing home costs and the applicant's income.

You should determine the current status of your state's income rules and whether it is an income cap or medically needy, spend-down state.

Annuities and Medicaid Planning

Elder law attorneys and other professionals sometimes use immediate annuities to convert a client's countable assets into an income stream to help qualify the client for Medicaid's long-term care benefits. To accomplish this, countable assets are paid to an insurance company as a single premium for an immediate annuity that provides income, eligible for inclusion in the Medicaid recipient's income.

As previously mentioned, DRA requires states to be listed as remainder beneficiaries for annuities. The state can be the secondary beneficiary after a spouse or a minor or disabled child.

Preserving Assets

Irrevocable trusts and annuities are very common measures used to preserve assets. Effective and safe use of these financial tools requires a knowledgeable professional. Medicaid looks at assets in a revocable trust as available to the applicant and, therefore, as a countable resource. For Medicaid purposes, annuities must be immediate and irrevocable and meet other requirements determined by Centers for Medicare and Medicaid Services (CMS).

There are numerous other steps that may help seniors preserve portions of an estate or protect the standard of living of a spouse. For example, since the senior's home is a noncountable resource, cash assets may be used to make substantial improvements and repairs to the home that will either be occupied by the spouse or returned to the applicant in the future. Seniors can purchase family burial plots or prepay funeral expenses to convert non-exempt cash assets into an exempt asset. This can also provide peace of mind to families that may not have readily available assets for meeting funeral expenses. Seniors might also consider paying off debts or prepaying certain annual expenses.

Management of Assets

It is important that seniors who plan to rely on Medicaid assistance for long-term care weigh their sources of income and the value of their countable assets against the requirements of their state. Fortunately, there are a variety of financial options (e.g., receiving retirement annuities in lump sum rather than monthly income, using cash to pay off a mortgage) and tools (e.g., creation of special trusts, annuities, or gifting) that can reduce income and protect countable assets. However, simply transferring countable assets into noncountable assets or property can help with eligibility but may not protect assets for heirs.

In short, most Medicaid planning boils down to one proposition: transferring countable assets so they are inaccessible to both the Medicaid applicant and Medicaid by either giving them away or placing them in a trust. This is generally the practice of elder law attorneys. Again, you and your clients are strongly encouraged to seek the advice of a qualified elder law attorney who specializes in Medicaid.

Partnership Plans—Long-Term Care Insurance

Under DRA, all states have the option to create their own relationships with private insurance carriers to offer new long-term care insurance plans. These new plans allow purchasers to protect some or a majority of their assets from Medicaid spend-down rules. The goal is to reduce the dependence on Medicaid.

Successful Partnership Plans increase the percentage of Americans who can purchase private long-term care insurance to protect them against impoverishment due to the cost of long-term care.

When a resident of a partnership state purchases a tax-qualified long-term care insurance policy, the policy must meet all state-specific requirements. When the insured person needs long-term care, the policy pays benefits. When the individual has exhausted his or her assets, the person can apply for Medicaid and is allowed to protect assets that would have otherwise been spent on his or her care. This is called "dollar-for-dollar" asset protection or asset disregard. The policyholder is allowed to protect from spend down the amount of assets equal to the benefits received under the partnership policy. What is important is that those protected assets are not included in estate recovery following the policyholder's death.

The main difference between Partnership and non-Partnership policies is that Partnership policies must have an appropriate inflation protection option based on the applicant's age. According to the National Association of Insurance Commissioners (NAIC), individuals age 60 or younger must have "annual compound inflation protection" included in their long-term care insurance policy. Individuals at least 61 but younger than 76 must have some type of inflation protection. This need not be automatic annual compounded increases; it could be simple rate increases, a guaranteed purchase option, or some other form of inflation protection. Individuals age 76 or older must be offered an inflation protection option, but they are not required to purchase that option. Each state offering Partnership Plans can set the inflation protection limitations based on NAIC guidelines. Inflation protection is important so that policyholders have adequate coverage when needed.

The DRA intended to promote reciprocity, which is the recognition of Partnership Policies issued under one state's program by other states. Policyholders may not receive Medicaid asset protection if they move to another state that has not adopted reciprocity. Additionally, some states may not implement Partnership programs. As a CSA, you should be familiar with your state's program.

DEALING WITH INCAPACITY

Establishing and executing powers of attorney (financial and medical) is critical to the success of Medicaid planning. (Durable powers of attorney for financial matters and health care decisions are discussed in other chapters. They are particularly important if a senior suddenly becomes incapacitated, in which case he or she is not able to make transfers of assets and changes in their ownership.)

In the absence of established powers of attorney, the family or nursing home would have to approach the court to establish a guardian to manage the applicant's affairs. The guardian would then act under the supervision of the court and would not necessarily make the same decisions the senior or the senior's family would make.

Medicaid Provides a Safety Net

While Medicaid clearly provides a critical safety net for many seniors, the decision to rely on Medicaid entails inherent risks. Careful selection of an appropriate long-term care insurance policy is a good option for many seniors and can provide peace of mind while permitting the person to pass on an estate to designated heirs. In other cases, good financial planning can help the senior self-fund long-term care without eroding the principal of estate assets.

RISKS OF MEDICAID PLANNING

The decision to transfer and retitle assets can limit seniors' options. For example:

625

- Those who receive the transfer may not manage the assets well or support the senior in accordance with his or her wishes.
- Required care may not be long-term, in which case the senior will be impoverished to no avail.
- Medicaid regulations may change.
- Transfers may trigger substantial income, gift, or capital gains taxes that would otherwise be avoided with prudent financial and estate planning.
- If institutionalization is required, nursing home beds may not be available for Medicaid beneficiaries. (Medicaid beds are often limited because the amount paid by the state for Medicaid patients is substantially less than the rates paid by private-pay or insurance-funded patients. And some nursing homes and assisted living facilities do not accept Medicaid patients at all.)
- The senior and his or her family may face long waiting periods for admission to a particular facility.
- The nursing homes that accept Medicaid patients in your client's area may not be desirable.
- There may be a long waiting list for home and community-based programs available through Medicaid waivers, or Medicaid waiver programs may not be available in the area where the senior lives.

Medicaid and Seniors: Summary

Medicaid is an important program that can provide benefits to a range of senior clients, including those who outlive their assets.

It is important for you to understand the Medicaid services that are available to seniors in your state. For example, if you live in Florida, seniors in your state have a range of home and community-based services available to them. These programs will enable your clients to receive the long-term care they may need without having to enter a nursing home. Other states may have limited home services.

As a CSA, it is also important for you to understand how Medicaid can work with Medicare to pay for services that seniors would otherwise not receive. For example, Medicaid's requirements for home health care—where available—are less stringent than Medicare's. Medicaid picks up the cost of prescription drugs, and, it will pay Medicare premiums and related expenses for those who qualify.

You should also keep up with the Medicaid changes in your state. The best way to stay on top of Medicaid changes is to professionally network with elder law attorneys and others who specialize in Medicaid. Budget constraints may force your state to limit services, tighten eligibility requirements, change penalty periods, or increase state recovery efforts, which in turn may make Medicaid an unattractive option for clients who have other resources. Alternatively, there may be new and innovative programs, such as the PACE program, coming to your area.

You should also be aware of the controversial technique of artificially spending down assets through gifts and transfers to qualify for Medicaid and the pros and cons of such actions. In the case of Sammy, whose story opened this chapter, spending down assets enabled him to qualify for Medicaid and to receive the care he needed. For others, spending down may not be appropriate, particularly if adequate services are not available in their areas.

References

Begley, T. D., & Jeffreys, J. H. (2000). Using Medicaid to pay for nursing home care. *Journal of Society of Certified Senior Advisors, 6.*

Kaiser Foundation. Medicaid Primer 2009 (2008). Retrieved from http://foundationcenter.org.

National PACE Association (2008). Who does PACE serve? Retrieved from www.npaonline.org.

Resources

Suggested Reading

Fossett, J. W. (Ed.) (2004, May). *Managing Medicaid Managed Care.* New York: Rockefeller Institute Press.

Web Sites

Medicaid information must be constantly updated to ensure that it reflects the most current federal and state regulations. In addition to written information from your local Medicaid agency, information on laws and state-specific requirements is available from the Web sites listed below.

Families USA, http://www.familiesusa.org. Families USA is a national, nonprofit organization dedicated to the achievement of high-quality affordable health and long-term care for all Americans. The organization produces health policy reports, manages advocacy groups including the Medicaid Advocacy Group, produces public information campaigns, and maintains information clearinghouses, including the Medicaid Clearinghouse.

Centers for Medicare and Medicaid Services, http://www.cms.gov. CMS is the federal agency that administers the Medicare, Medicaid, and Child Health Insurance Programs. This site contains statistics, laws, regulations, and informative articles on Medicaid from the perspective of the government.

Center for Long-Term Care Financing, http://www.centerltc.com is a nonprofit organization dedicated to ensuring quality long-term care for all Americans by promoting public policy that targets scarce public resources to the neediest. The center publishes a newsletter and publishes reports on long-term care.

Kaiser Family Foundation, Kaiser Commission on Medicaid and the Uninsured, http://www.kff.org. The commission provides policy papers and frequent updates and analysis of Medicaid issues.

Chapter 21

Social Security

Earl and Jane Clark had their first child in 1955, at which time Jane quit her job as a clerical worker in an insurance company. The Clarks went on to raise a family of four children. When Earl retired from teaching in public schools, he did not qualify for Social Security, but received a pension from the Ohio State Retired Teacher's Association. It never occurred to the Clarks to check Jane's Social Security record— they just assumed that she had not worked long enough to qualify for benefits.

In 1995, a few weeks after their 46th wedding anniversary, Earl died. In 1997 Jane decided that she needed to "get into the world again," and she applied for a part-time job. Her new employer's human resources department helped her check her Social Security record and found that she had 34 credits from her early working years. After a year and a half of part-time employment, Jane qualified for Social Security benefits, which she now receives in addition to her survivor's benefit from the Ohio state plan.

. . .

Upon retirement Harold Grant was disappointed to find out that the pension plan he earned from the private company where he had worked for many years had a "small print" clause that allowed them to reduce his monthly pension plan by the amount of his monthly Social Security check, which he qualified for from prior work. This resulted in a loss of income of about $500 a month. Harold says, "I am a pretty smart guy, but I feel stupid that I did not realize this little 'catch' in my retirement plan. It makes me feel sour about all the years I gave my company."

. . .

Dottie, age 66, is homebound with diabetes. With the help of a counselor, she found out about a year ago that, even though she receives Social Security survivor benefits, she was eligible for Supplemental Security Income (SSI). Dottie was also happy to find out that the state she lives in, Vermont, pays a supplement to SSI. Dottie says that she is "still just barely getting by. I still can't afford vitamins, much less ice cream, but my check from SSI has helped me stay in my little apartment, which has been my home for over twenty years."

Introduction

As a CSA, you need to know about Social Security for a number of reasons:

- It is the *major* source of income for most seniors and the *entire* source of income for one in five.

- Social Security is a federal agency that provides those who qualify with a number of related programs—retirement, disability, dependent, and survivor benefits. It is important to know the differences between these programs and how they can help your senior clients.

- Social Security has its limitations, and its rules are complicated, which can lead to disappointment for retirees.

- Like most seniors, your clients will have many fears about the security of the Social Security program.

- Many of your senior clients will be facing important decisions about Social Security that will have permanent consequences for them—such as whether to take early, full, or late retirement to receive benefits.

It is also important for you to understand when Supplemental Security Income (SSI) can pick up some of the gaps in Social Security benefits and, in some situations, provide the only monthly check a senior receives.

President Franklin Roosevelt signed the Social Security Act into law on August 14, 1935, considering it to be the cornerstone of his presidency. He believed the program would eliminate the blight of poverty from the lives of elderly Americans. This program, popularly referred to as "Social Security," is the largest and most important income maintenance program in the United States.

The technical name for the Social Security program is *Old-Age, Survivors and Disability Insurance* (OASDI). It provides monthly benefits to retired and disabled workers, as well as their survivors and dependents.

The original purpose of the OASDI program was to partially replace income lost due either to retirement in old age or disability that prevented gainful employment. This remains the primary purpose of the program, although for some beneficiaries it is their sole source of income.

Social Security benefits are considered an entitlement earned by individuals based on taxes they paid during their working years. Others may be entitled to benefits because of a relationship to a worker who made contributions on their behalf.

Taxes collected for OASDI are put into trust funds created to receive income and disburse benefits. There are separate funds for OASI (Old-Age and Survivors Insurance) and DI (Disability Insurance). According to the law, funds in these trusts can be used only for the following purposes:

- monthly benefits when a worker retires, dies, or becomes disabled
- lump-sum death benefits to survivors
- vocational rehabilitation services for disabled beneficiaries
- administrative expenses

The trust funds are allowed to invest their assets in securities issued or guaranteed by the federal government and retain any additional income from these investments. According to the Social Security Administration (SSA), less than 1 percent of every Social Security tax dollar is spent on administrative costs.

Many people think that the Social Security taxes they pay are held in interest-bearing accounts earmarked for their own future retirement needs. The fact is that Social Security is a pay-as-you-go retirement system—the Social Security taxes paid by today's workers and their employers are used to pay the benefits for today's retirees and other beneficiaries.

The main reason for Social Security's long-range financing problem is demographics. We are living longer and healthier lives than ever before. When the Social Security program was created in 1935, a 65-year-old American had an average life expectancy of about $12\frac{1}{2}$ more years; today, it is 18 years and rising.

In addition, more than 80 million "baby boomers" started retiring in 2008 and in about 30 years, there will be twice as many older Americans as there are today. At the same time, the number of workers paying into Social Security per beneficiary will drop from 3.3 today to about 2.1 in 2034 (Figure 21.1). These demographic changes will severely strain Social Security financing.

Social Security is now taking in more money than it pays out in benefits, and the remaining money goes to the program's trust funds. There are now large "reserves" in the trust funds, but even this money is small compared to future scheduled benefit payments. In 2017 benefits owed will be more than taxes collected, and Social Security will need to begin tapping the trust funds to pay benefits. The trust funds will be exhausted in 2041. At that time, Social Security will not be able to meet all of its benefit obligations if no changes are made. (See Figure 21.2.)

Figure 21.1 Workers per Beneficiary Declining

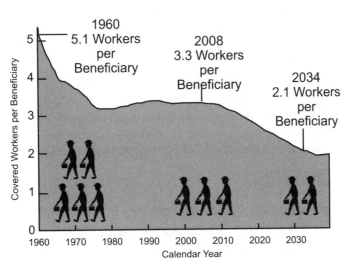

Source: Social Security Administration, The Future of Social Security, 2008.

Figure 21.2 Social Security Trust Fund Depletion

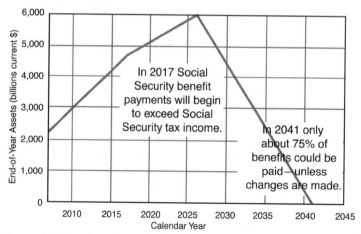

Source: Social Security Administration, The Future of Social Security, 2008.

Impact of Social Security on the Income of Seniors

Social Security is the major source of income for most seniors. According to the Social Security Administration:

- Nine out of ten seniors receive Social Security benefits.
- Social Security benefits represent an overall average of 37 percent of the income of seniors.
- About two-thirds of senior beneficiaries receive 50 percent or more of their income from Social Security.
- Social Security is 90 percent or more of total income for approximately one-third of seniors.

Social Security also raises more than one in every three elderly Americans out of poverty. Figure 21.4 paints a clear picture of the importance of Social Security to retirement income.

SOCIAL SECURITY AND POVERTY

After age 65 Social Security is particularly important to women and minorities, both of whom have high rates of poverty. For example, 27 percent of senior women who are not married are either poor or near poor. About a third of senior blacks and about 30 percent of Hispanics are either poor or near poor. Seniors who are married have the lowest poverty rates. (See Figure 21.5.)

Social Security Beneficiaries

PROFILE OF SOCIAL SECURITY BENEFICIARIES

In 2007 the majority (63 percent) of Social Security beneficiaries were retired workers, and 14 percent were disabled workers. The remaining 23 percent were spouses, children, survivors, or dependents of retired or disabled workers. (See Figure 21.3.)

Figure 21.3 Beneficiaries by Type

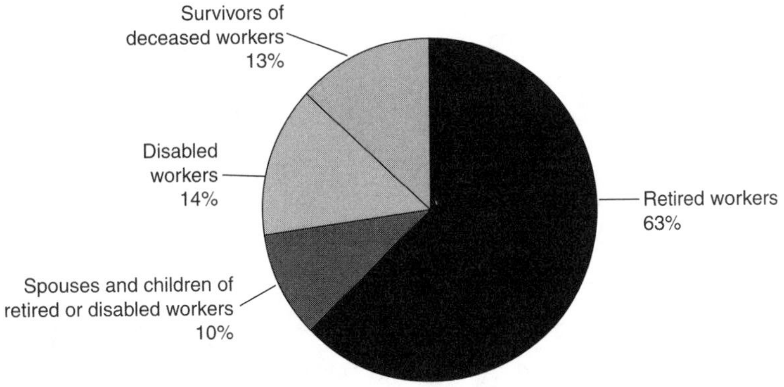

Source: Social Security Administration, Master Beneficiary Record, 100 percent data, Fast Facts & Figures About Social Security, 2008.

Age and sex distribution of beneficiaries

In 2007, 79 percent of all Social Security beneficiaries receiving benefits were age 62 or older.

Of all adults receiving monthly Social Security benefits, 44 percent were men and 56 percent were women. Seventy-nine percent of the men and 59

Figure 21.4 Percentage of the Aged Receiving Income, by Source

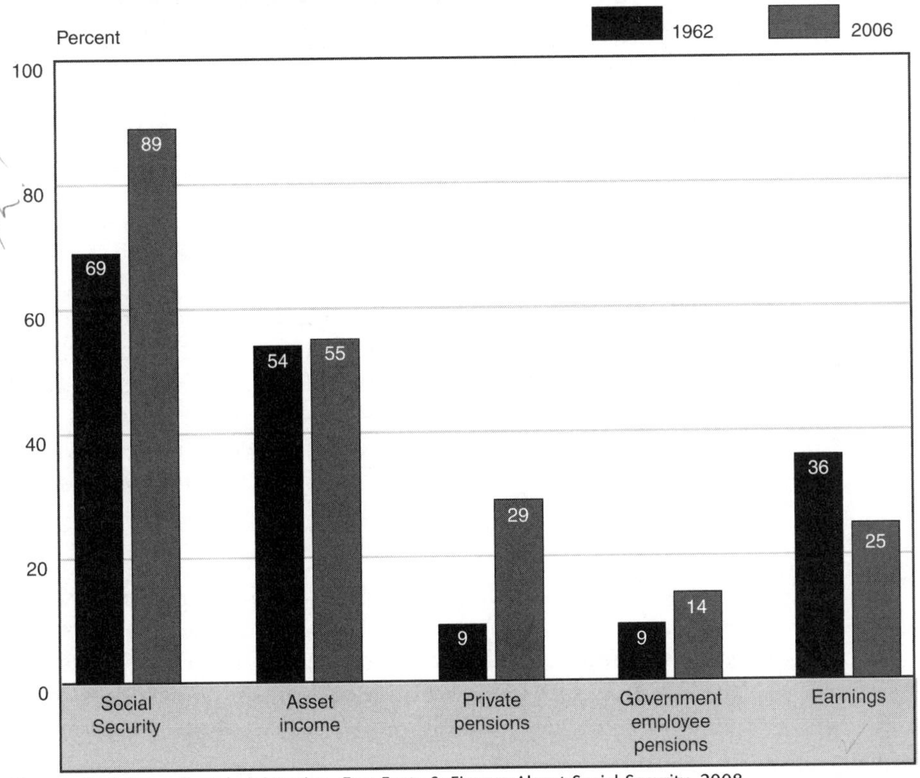

I don't understand this graph

Source: Social Security Administration, Fast Facts & Figures About Social Security, 2008

Figure 21.5 Poverty Status of Seniors, by Marital Status, Sex of Nonmarried Persons, Race, and Hispanic Origin: 2007

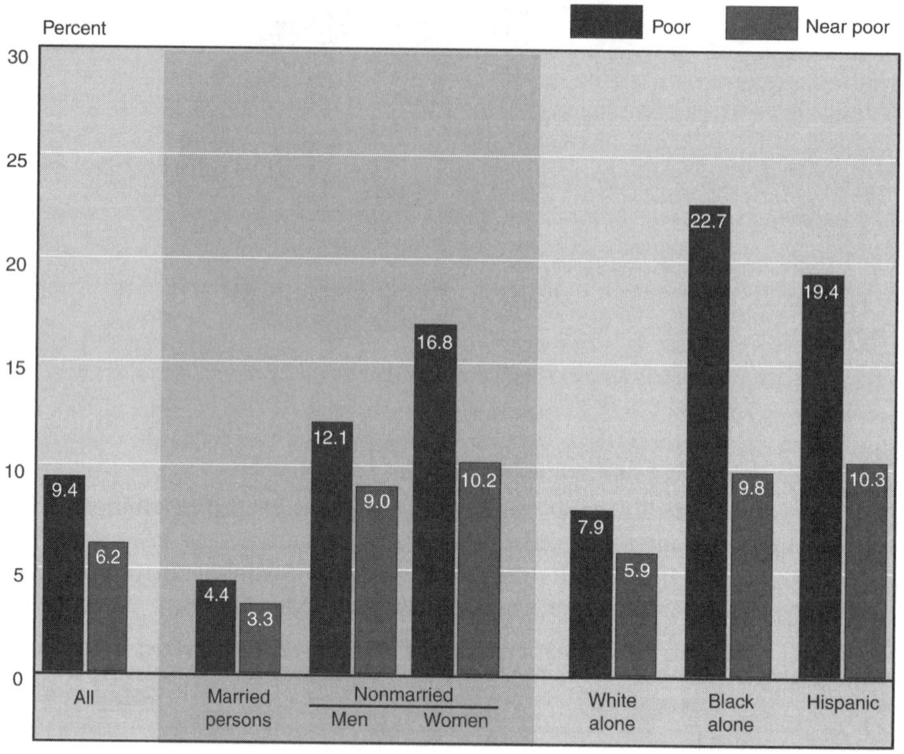

Source: Social Security Administration

Note: *Poor* is defined as having an income below the poverty line ($9,944 in 2007). The *near poor* have incomes between the poverty line and 125 percent of the poverty line.

percent of the women received retired-worker benefits. About one-fifth of the women received survivor benefits.

The proportion of women among retired-worker beneficiaries has quadrupled since 1960. The percentage climbed steadily from 12 percent in 1940 to 47 percent in 1980, 48 percent in 1990, and 49 percent in 2007. The proportion of women among disabled-worker beneficiaries has more than doubled since disability benefits first became payable in 1957. The percentage rose steadily from 19 percent in 1957 to 35 percent in 1990 and 47 percent in 2007.

ELIGIBILITY

As mentioned earlier, eligibility for Social Security benefits is based on employment and payment of taxes into the Social Security system. Social Security *credits* (formerly called *quarters of coverage*) are earned as workers pay taxes. Since 1978, credits have been based on annual earnings, with a maximum of four credits per year. In 2009, one credit is earned for each $1,090 in earnings, up to a maximum of four credits per year, $4,360. In the future, the amount of earnings needed for a credit will increase as the average wage level increases. According to current SSA guidelines, a worker needs 40 credits to qualify for retirement benefits.

Employment is a key concept in determining quarters of coverage. A business owner who receives only dividend income but no wages achieves no quarters of coverage during that period. Farm workers, domestic workers, and those in other unique working situations may take advantage of special earnings requirements for quarters of coverage.

Dependents of retired or disabled workers are eligible for Social Security benefits based on the worker's record. Dependents include spouses, divorced spouses, and eligible children.

Although most employees are covered by Social Security, there are some exceptions. Employees who are not covered include:

- most federal government employees hired before 1984
- about 20 percent of state and local government employees, including some teachers
- railroad workers

ENROLLMENT

Enrollment in Social Security is not automatic. Seniors must apply for benefits online at www.ssa.gov/onlineservices by going to a Social Security Office, by calling Social Security's toll-free number (1-800-772-1213) and scheduling a telephone appointment. Applications for retirement benefits should be made at least 90 days before retiring. Applications for disability or survivor benefits can be made as soon as seniors become eligible. Your senior clients may need assistance with the application process. Remember, they are not very adept at online registrations and some may not hear well or understand quetions by telephone.

Applicants for any type of Social Security benefit should be prepared to submit supportive documentation. This may include a Social Security card, certified birth certificate, proof of citizenship, marriage certificate, military records, or work records such as the most recent W-2 or tax return.

Social Security Retirement Benefits

Seniors can choose to collect full retirement benefits, reduced benefits at an early age, or delayed benefits for late retirement. This decision will affect the amount of the benefit, as well as the date when payments begin.

BENEFIT LEVELS

Full Retirement Benefits

Beneficiaries begin receiving full benefit payments once they reach the legally defined "full" retirement age. (See Table 21.1.) Historically, the full retirement age has been 65. However, beginning in 2000, the age at which full benefits could be collected started to gradually increase by increments of two months a year. This continued until 2005, when the full retirement became age 66. Then, in 2017, the age for full retirement gradually increases again in two months increments for each year until year 2022, at which point, full retirement will be defined as age 67.

Given these ongoing changes, individuals approaching retirement should confirm the exact age at which they qualify for full benefits. It is important that you understand that eligibility for Medicare remains at age 65.

Table 21.1 Social Security Full Retirement and Reductions by Age

Note: Persons born on January 1 of any year should refer to the previous year. If an applicant's birthday is on the first of the month, Social Security figures the benefit as if the birthday was the previous month.

YEAR OF BIRTH	FULL RETIREMENT AGE	AGE 62 REDUCTION MONTHS	MONTHLY % REDUCTION*	TOTAL % REDUCTION*	MONTHLY % REDUCTION* (SPOUSE**)	TOTAL % REDUCTION* (SPOUSE)
1937 or earlier	65	36	.555	20.00	.694	62.50
1938	65 and 2 months	38	.548	20.83	.679	62.92
1939	65 and 4 months	40	.541	21.67	.667	63.34
1940	65 and 6 months	42	.535	22.50	.655	63.75
1941	65 and 8 months	44	.530	23.33	.644	64.17
1942	65 and 10 months	46	.525	24.17	.634	64.58
1943-1954	66	48	.520	25.00	.625	65.00
1955	66 and 2 months	50	.516	25.84	.617	65.42
1956	66 and 4 months	52	.512	26.66	.609	65.84
1957	66 and 6 months	54	.509	27.50	.602	66.25
1958	66 and 8 months	56	.505	28.33	.595	66.67
1959	66 and 10 months	58	.502	29.17	.589	67.08
1960 and later	67	60	.500	30.00	.583	67.50

*Percentage monthly and total reductions are approximate due to rounding. The actual reductions are .555 (5/9 of 1%) per month for the first 36 months and .416 (5/12 of 1%) for subsequent months.

**The maximum spouses' benefit is 50 percent of the benefit the worker would receive at full retirement age. The monthly percent reduction for the spouse does not include that automatic 50 percent reduction.

Source: Social Security Administration.

Reduced Retirement Benefits

Beneficiaries can elect to receive reduced payments as early as age 62. (See Table 21.2.) Benefits are decreased by five-ninths of a percent for each month before the full retirement age. For example, if someone who would have received their full retirement benefits at age 65 decided to start those benefits early at age 62, the payment would be 80 percent of what it would have been at 65. As Social Security's full retirement age is now increasing toward 67, the percentage of benefits received for selecting early retirement will gradually decrease from 80 percent to 70 percent.

The trade-off in electing early benefits is that payments are permanently reduced. However, the beneficiary receives checks for a longer period of time. According to SSA, as a general rule, early retirement gives beneficiaries about the same total Social Security benefits over their lifetimes. However, each person's situation is different, so as people make decisions about their income level in retirement they should choose carefully before deciding to receive early benefits.

For people leaving the workforce before attaining full retirement age it may be sensible to take early Social Security benefits—especially if those benefits are necessary for current living expenses. Payments will be partially tax-free, and taking early retirement may enable a beneficiary to delay withdrawals from individual retirement accounts (IRAs) and employer-provided retirement programs that accumulate on a tax-deferred basis.

Table 21.2 shows a hypothetical situation in which waiting until age 65 to take Social Security benefits means the beneficiary will pass up $40,032 in payments, which will take 12 years to recoup. If the benefit is not needed at age 62, one option is to take early retirement and invest the payments to make up for the $278 per month difference between early and full retirement benefits.

Table 21.2 The Cost of Waiting

monthly benefit at age 62: $1,112

monthly benefit at age 65: $1,390

monthly difference: $278

annual difference: $3,336

cost of waiting till age 65: $40,032 ($1,112 × 12 × 3)

DELAYED RETIREMENT BENEFITS

For healthy seniors not needing Social Security payments for current living expenses, an argument can be made for delaying benefits to receive larger payments. Seniors who delay their Social Security benefits past full retirement age receive increased payments. (See Table 21.3.) The increase stops at age 70, even if seniors continue to delay taking benefits.

The decision to delay Social Security retirement benefits may be influenced by a number of factors. For example, employment income may be adequate and the payment will be higher when it is needed most. Further, delaying benefits can lower federal income taxes. Delaying benefits will also increase payments to widows or widowers.

Table 21.3 Increase for Delayed Retirement

YEAR OF BIRTH	YEARLY RATE OF INCREASE	MONTHLY RATE OF INCREASE
1930	4.5%	$3/8$ of 1%
1931–1932	5.0%	$5/12$ of 1%
1933–1934	5.5%	$11/24$ of 1%
1935–1936	6.0%	$1/2$ of 1%
1937–1938	6.5%	$13/24$ of 1%
1939–1940	7.0%	$7/12$ of 1%
1941–1942	7.5%	$5/8$ of 1%
1943 and later	8.0%	$2/3$ of 1%

ESTIMATING BENEFITS

Beginning in October 2000, the Social Security Administration began sending out yearly Social Security statements. The agency mails statements to workers ages 25 and older three months before their birthday. The statements allows workers to review their actual earnings record, see estimates of future benefits, and see a breakout of the benefits they might receive under various components of the Social Security program (Retirement, Disability, Family, Survivors, and Medicare). It also shows the difference in benefit amounts received at age 62, at full retirement age, and at age 70.

You can help your clients estimate Social Security benefits through SSA's internet page www.socialsecurity.gov/OACT/quickcalc. Beneficiaries can request a statement by calling Social Security and asking for a form SSA-7004, *Request for Earnings and Benefit Estimate Statement*, or by downloading the form from http://www.ssa.gov/online/ssa-7004.html.

CALCULATING BENEFITS

Social Security benefits are based on such factors as the recipient's date of birth, earnings, and type of benefit. The calculation is based on the highest 35 years of earnings in a person's entire working career. If the worker has less than 35 years of wages, zeroes are added for missing years. These earnings are adjusted to allow for changes in wage levels over the years.

Social Security applies a formula to these earnings and arrives at a basic benefit, called the *primary insurance amount* (PIA). This is the amount the beneficiary would receive at the full retirement age.

Social Security's benefit formula is designed to give a higher percentage of earnings to lower wage earners. For example, in 2009 Social Security will pay 90 percent of the first $744 in average monthly earnings, PLUS 32 percent between $744 and $4,483 in average monthly earnings PLUS 15 percent of any amount above that (these amounts are expected to change in 2010 and beyond). Thus, a retiree with an average monthly earning of $744 receives a Social Security benefit equal to 90 percent of that amount, or $699.60. Conversely, a retiree with an average monthly income of $5,000 receives $1,600, which is 32 percent of the average monthly earnings. While the percentages in this formula (90 percent, 32 percent, and 15 percent) do not change, the higher average monthly earnings produce a smaller replacement percentage due to the tiered formula.

SSA establishes minimum and maximum benefits for individuals and families. Everyone who qualifies for Social Security receives a minimum benefit. Individuals with very low Social Security benefits may also qualify for Supplemental Security Income (SSI). (SSI is covered later in this chapter.)

Benefit Adjustments

Cost of Living Adjustment (COLA)

Seniors receive an automatic *cost-of-living adjustment* (COLA) on January 1 every year. COLAs help prevent inflation from eroding Social Security benefits. For example, Social Security benefits increased by 5.8 percent in 2009.

The Social Security Act specifies a formula for determining the COLA. In general, the COLA is equal to the percentage increase in the Consumer Price Index for Urban Wage Earners and Clerical Workers (CPI-W) from the third quarter of one year to the third quarter of the next.

Reduction of Benefits Due to Earnings

Seniors who continue working while drawing Social Security benefits before their full retirement age may experience a reduction in their benefits due to a limitation on earnings for employment.

- The earnings limitation is adjusted annually. For 2009, the limit is $14,160 (check the Social Security web site for annual adjustments in the limit).

- For beneficiaries under their full retirement age, $1 dollar in benefits is deducted for every $2 in earnings above $14,160.

- For the year in which the beneficiary reaches full retirement age, $1 in benefits is deducted for each $3 in earnings above $37,680 (2009 limit) but only counting earnings before the month they reach the full retirement age.

- Starting with the month the beneficiary reaches full retirement age, there is no limit on earnings.

These rules became effective in January 2000.

If a senior earns more than the earnings limitation, Social Security reduces payments to the retired worker and family members receiving benefits on his or her work record. If a family member earns more than this limit, only that individual's benefits are affected.

RETIREMENT BENEFITS FOR FAMILIES

Family members of a retired worker eligible for Social Security may also qualify for monthly benefits. Eligible family members may include a spouse, dependent children, dependent parents, or a divorced spouse. The benefit level for a family member can be as much as 50 percent of the retired worker's rate. The maximum family benefit varies from approximately 150 to 180 percent of the retiree's benefit rate. If benefits of eligible family members exceed the family maximum, all family members will receive proportionally reduced rates; however, the retiree's benefits will not be reduced. Benefits paid to a surviving divorced spouse do not affect the benefit rates for other survivors.

Retirees may be eligible for benefits on their own work record or that of a current spouse or, if divorced, a previous spouse. Beneficiaries will receive the *higher* of 100 percent of the benefit calculated under their own record or 50 percent of the benefit calculated on a spouse's record. Here are some examples:

Example 1:

If a wife has a $1,000 benefit and a husband has an $800 benefit, the household benefit will be $1,800 per month. The rationale is that the husband's benefit on his own record is greater than 50 percent of his spouse's benefit so that both receive 100 percent of their own benefits. Whenever a death occurs, the surviving spouse receives the higher of the two benefits. In our example, the household benefit would be $1,000 regardless of whether the husband or wife died. If the surviving spouse is over age 60 and remarries, the spouse retains this survivor benefit.

Example 2:

If a wife has a $1,000 benefit and a husband has a $450 benefit, the household benefit will be $1,500 per month. The rationale is that the husband's benefit on his own record is less than 50 percent of his spouse's benefit so that he is entitled to receive $500 per month based upon his spouse's record. If his spouse dies, he will receive $1,000 as the higher of her benefit or his, making the household income $1,000.

RETIREMENT BENEFITS FOR SURVIVORS

Monthly survivor benefits can be paid to relatives of a retired worker eligible for Social Security benefits after the worker's death. As with family benefits, eligible family members may include a spouse, dependent children, dependent parents, or a divorced spouse. The benefit level for survivors varies from 75 to 100 percent of the deceased's basic Social Security benefit. The maximum family benefit varies between 150 to 180 percent of the deceased's benefit rate.

Benefits paid to a surviving divorced spouse age 60 or older (or age 50 to 60 if disabled) do not affect the benefit rates for other survivors. In addition to the monthly benefits, there is also a one-time death benefit that can be made to a spouse or minor children meeting qualifying criteria. Currently, this payment is $255.

WORKER'S DEATH AFTER RETIREMENT

At the time of a retired worker's death, the spouse's retirement benefit (typically 50 percent of the PIA) is automatically converted to a widow's or widower's benefit, which operates at 100 percent of PIA, presuming he or she is at least age 65. Benefits will be reduced for younger spouses or offsets are made to the widow's or widower's own retirement benefits.

THE WINDFALL ELIMINATION PROVISION

For Social Security recipients who work for an employer who doesn't withhold Social Security taxes, such as a government agency or an employer in another country, the pension they get based on that work may reduce their Social Security benefits.

The benefit can be reduced in one of two ways. One is the *government pension offset* and applies to those who receive a government pension and are eligible for Social Security benefits as a spouse, widow, or widower.

The other way—the *windfall elimination provision*—affects how retirement or disability benefits are figured if a recipient receives a pension from work not covered by Social Security. The formula used to figure the benefit is modified, resulting in a lower amount.

SOCIAL SECURITY DISABILITY INCOME BENEFITS (SSDI)

Disability benefits provide partial replacement income for beneficiaries who become severely disabled and are unable to perform substantial work. The disability benefit is based on the beneficiary's work record only. There is no option to receive disability benefits under a spouse's work record. The disability may be either physical or mental, but it must be expected to last at least one year or result in an early death.

Determination of disability is based on medical evidence. If the beneficiary's earnings average more than $980 a month (2009), he or she generally cannot be considered disabled.

To be eligible for SSDI (Social Security Disability Income), beneficiaries must be "fully insured" (i.e., have 40 credits) and "currently insured." Applicants may obtain a copy of *Disability Benefits* (SSA Publication No. 05-10029), which contains the medical criteria that SSA uses to determine disability. It is intended primarily for physicians and other health professionals.

To be currently insured, a beneficiary must have at least 20 work credits within the last 40 calendar quarters.

When reviewing disability claims Social Security representatives ask applicants the following questions in order to determine eligibility:

1. Are you working? If you are and your earnings average more than $980 (2009) a month, you generally cannot be considered disabled.

2. Is your condition severe? Your impairments must interfere with basic work-related activities for your claim to be considered.

3. Is your condition found in the list of disabling impairments? We maintain a list of impairments for each of the major body systems that are so severe they automatically mean you are disabled. If your condition is not on the list, we have to decide if it is of equal severity to an impairment on the list. If it is, your claim is approved. If it is not, we go to the next step.

4. Can you do the work you did previously? If your condition is severe, but not at the same or equal severity as an impairment on the list, then we must determine if it prevents you from doing the work you did in the last 15 years. If it does not, your claim will be denied. If it does, your claim will be considered further.

5. Can you do any other type of work? If you cannot do the work you did in the last 15 years, we then look to see if you can do any other type of work. We consider your age, education, past work experience, and transferable skills, and we review the job demands of occupations as determined by the Department of Labor. If you cannot do any other kind of work, your claim will be approved. If you can, your claim will be denied.

Beginning January 1, 2009, Social Security Disability beneficiaries could earn $980 a month and remain eligible for benefits. The Social Security Administration uses the term *substantial gainful activity* (SGA) to determine if work is substantial enough to make a person ineligible for benefits. Under this

new rule, monthly SGA earnings limits will be automatically adjusted annually based on increases in the national average wage index.

The SGA amount applies to people with disabilities other than blindness. For people who are blind, the SGA amount was increased to $1,640, effective January 2009.

Waiting Period

There is a five-month waiting period for Social Security disability benefits. The philosophy behind the requirement is that this period is long enough to permit most temporary disabilities to be corrected or for the person to show signs of probable recovery within less than 12 months after the onset of disability.

Disability benefits continue until the beneficiary is able to return to work or until retirement age if the individual cannot return to work. Benefit levels are adjusted if the beneficiary receives other government benefits or pension payments. The total combined payments for recipients generally cannot exceed 80 percent of their average current earnings before becoming disabled.

Retirement benefits begin automatically when disabled individuals reach their full retirement age. Family assistance is also available under the same rules that apply for retirement benefits. The maximum family benefit is generally limited to 150 percent of the disabled individual's benefit, including the payment to the disabled beneficiary.

TAXATION OF SOCIAL SECURITY BENEFITS

A portion of Social Security benefits are taxable for individuals whose income exceeds established limits. Taxation occurs in two tiers of 50 and 85 percent. Chapter 16 contains specific information about income thresholds and determining the amount of Social Security benefits that are taxable.

REPRESENTATIVE PAYEES

A *representative payee* is an individual or organization that receives Social Security or SSI payments for an individual who cannot manage or direct someone else to manage his or her money. The representative payee is responsible for using the funds to pay for the current and foreseeable needs of the beneficiary. With certain exceptions, a representative payee is *not* paid for services. There are two kinds of representative payees:

- An *individual representative payee* could be someone that a beneficiary lives with or a family member or friend who does not live with the beneficiary. It could also be a lawyer, a legal guardian, or a volunteer for a government or nonprofit agency.
- *Organizational representative payees* would include social service agencies, institutions, or an official of a state or local government agency or a financial organization. Some organizational payees, called *fee-for-service payees*,

are permitted to charge the beneficiary a fee for their services. The payee must file a request and be approved before they can collect a fee.

Supplemental Security Income (SSI)

"Since its inception, SSI has been viewed as the "program of last resort"."

Comment on the Website of the Office of
the Assistant Secretary for Planning and Evaluation,
U.S. Department of Health and Human Services

You should be aware of safety-net options for your senior clients with low incomes. The federal Supplemental Security Income (SSI) program provides monthly income to people who are age 65 or older, or are blind or disabled, and have limited income and financial resources. SSA runs the program. Nationally, in 2007 there were about 10 million people between 18 and 64 who were disabled and received either SSDI and/or SSI.

The amount of the SSI benefit depends on the state where recipients live. The basic SSI check is the same nationwide. In 2009, the SSI payment for an eligible individual is $674 per month and $1,011 per month for an eligible couple. The following is a list of the states that supplement the basic SSI amount:

- California
- Hawaii
- Massachusetts
- Nevada
- New Jersey
- New York
- Pennsylvania
- Rhode Island
- Vermont
- Washington, D.C.

Seniors who get SSI may also be able to get other low-income assistance from their state or county, such as Medicaid and food stamps. For information about all the services available in your community, call your local social services department or public welfare office.

HOW TO APPLY

SSI applicants can apply at their local Social Security offices or call 1-800-772-1213 for an appointment with a Social Security representative. Parents or guardians can apply for blind or disabled children under age 18. Applicants for SSI will have to show Social Security officials a number of documents such as

Social Security cards or a record of their Social Security number, birth certificate or other proof of age, information about the home where they live, payroll slips and other information about their income, and proof of U.S. citizenship or eligible noncitizen status.

The Future of Social Security

Many seniors worry that there will not be sufficient funding to pay their Social Security benefits in the future. At the same time, younger workers, whose taxes are paying the benefits of current recipients, worry that the program will go bankrupt before they retire.

Concern about the future of Social Security is warranted. The problem can be traced back to the origins of the program. Social Security is a pay-as-you-go system. Taxes received from workers today are used to pay benefits to retired and disabled workers currently receiving Social Security. Under this scenario Social Security is fully funded until about the year 2041. At that point, taxes received will be sufficient to pay only about 75 percent of the benefits promised under current law.

The 25 percent gap between income and benefits comes primarily from two factors. The first is a shift in the ratio of workers to beneficiaries. The ratio of workers paying Social Security taxes to people collecting benefits will fall from 3 to 1 today to 2 to 1 by 2032. The second factor is the demographic force that affects the first factor—the burgeoning wave of baby boomers who will begin to turn 65 in 2011.

already read

Creating a solution for the funding gap is one of the major public policy challenges facing the United States. How can we provide the promised benefits to all retirees without greatly increasing taxes on future workers?

Recent polls indicate the majority of Americans believe the Social Security system is broken and needs fixing. Naturally, proposed solutions vary widely. Among those being considered by Congress are increasing taxes; reducing benefits; raising eligibility ages; or a combination of these and other potential solutions. Virtually every idea has one thing in common: Each presents the idea of investing some portion of Social Security dollars in financial markets.

Approaches on how to do this vary. Some people advocate empowering Social Security trustees to serve as money managers, thereby extending the range of investments available to Social Security beyond the current limited choice of government bonds. Others would allow enrollees to invest a portion of their current payroll taxes in private accounts similar to IRAs or 401(k) plans. Still others would go even further and replace the current program with a substantially privatized system.

It is likely that due to the complexity of the economic, social, and political issues surrounding Social Security reform, public debate on this topic will continue for some time.

Social Security: Summary

Because Social Security is the major source of income for most seniors it is important that you understand the program and how it works. In addition, some of your clients may need to apply for SSI benefits to supplement their Social Security. SSI is also important if you have clients who "spend down" to receive Medicaid. You should be familiar with your state's SSI program, and if needed, know how to aid seniors in applying for benefits.

You should also be familiar with the options and consequences of decisions that many seniors face as they near and reach retirement, such as whether to continue working and whether to take early, full, or delayed retirement.

References

Unless otherwise noted, facts and figures in this chapter come from the Social Security Administration, available at http://www.ssa.gov

Resources

Access America for Seniors Newsletter, http://www.ssa.gov/enews. You can register to receive the free Access America for Seniors Newsletter, which covers a broad range of issues and legislative actions relative to Social Security, disability and health care.

Services

Social Security Administration, Office of Public Inquiries, http://www.ssa.gov, 1-800-325-1213, TTY 1-800-325-0778, Windsor Park Building, 6401 Security Blvd., Baltimore, MD 21235. The toll-free number operates from 7 a.m. to 7 p.m., Monday to Friday. Recorded information and services are available 24 hours a day, including weekends and holidays.

Estimate Social Security Benefits, http://www.socialsecurity.gov/OACT/quickcalc. Part of the SSA's Web site, this page provides a calculator for estimating Social Security benefits.

Part 6

THE COMMUNITY OF CERTIFIED SENIOR ADVISORS

The price of success is hard work, dedication to the job at hand,
and the determination that whether we win or lose,
we have applied the best of ourselves to the task at hand.

Vince Lombardi

Education is not the filling of a pail, but the lighting of a fire.

William Butler Yeats

Part 6 covers the key areas of knowledge you need to become a practicing Certified Senior Advisor (CSA)®. With your CSA designation firmly in hand, you join a body of professionals from a wide variety of fields who are making a positive difference in the lives of seniors and their families.

This section discusses ethics in general and the *CSA Code of Professional Responsibility* in particular. It also addresses special ethical concerns when serving the senior market and provides examples of ethical behavior to guide you in your interactions with seniors.

Remember that earning your CSA designation is an end and a beginning: an end to this initial exploration of what it means to age, and the beginning of learning even more about seniors as you serve them with your increased knowledge and the integrity and professionalism they deserve.

Chapter 22

Ethics in Doing Business with Seniors

I think one of my wealthiest clients is showing signs of dementia. Should I inform his children, who live out of state?

. . .

I received a brochure from a CSA I'm considering doing some comarketing with, and I noticed that she's making some deceptive claims about her services. Should I confront her?

. . .

My brother-in-law said he'd give me $500 if I persuade my senior clients to use his roofing company—would this be a conflict of interest?

Introduction

Ethics is a code of values which guide our choices and actions and determine the purpose and course of our lives.

Ayn Rand

How does one decide what is ethical business behavior? When James Cash Penney opened his first Golden Rule store in 1902, he and his partners adopted a company motto built on four words: *honor, confidence, service,* and *cooperation.* These words formed the "Penney Idea"—and all business policies, methods, and acts in the company were judged against one simple question: Does it square with what is right and just? (J. C. Penney, n.d.)

A hundred years later, it seems that the test of ethical business behavior rests on whether or not someone is caught—the notion that if you can get away with it, it's good business. In recent years, we've seen several once-respected business leaders doing the "perp walk" in handcuffs on their way to the courtroom. High-flying companies such as Enron and WorldCom that had been praised as American success stories have collapsed under the unethical business dealings of their top executives.

Accordingly, the American public has become increasingly cynical about the intentions of its business leaders. In June 2002, a Time/CNN poll revealed that 72 percent of Americans believed that business executives were engaging in an intentional pattern of deception (Gibbs, 2002). *Right* and *just* are not

651

terms you hear from corporate America in the 21st century. The challenge for you and other Certified Senior Advisors is to rise above the muddled mess of unethical activity that plagues business today, and to demonstrate consistently right and just behavior.

But who is to gauge what is ethical or unethical behavior today? How do you decide if you've made the right decision? According to some people, it's all relative. Absolute right and absolute wrong in business have gradually given way to a vast gray area of moral relativism, where the ends most often justify the means. Indeed, a July 2002 poll conducted by Zogby International for the National Association of Scholars showed that three-fourths of all college seniors reported being taught that right and wrong depend "on differences in individual values and cultural diversity" (National Association of Scholars, 2002). Only about a quarter of the students surveyed reported their professors as adhering to the traditional view that "there are clear and uniform standards of right and wrong by which every one should be judged."

The notion that there are (or ought to be) "clear and uniform standards of right and wrong" is at the heart of business ethics for a CSA. To become a CSA, you must agree to comply with the fundamental principles of ethical conduct as outlined in the CSA Code of Professional Responsibility. Many of the job-related decisions you will make as a CSA will involve moral or ethical judgments, like the questions that opened this chapter—and your reputation will be built by each judgment you make.

This chapter covers the basics of business ethics and examines the specific ethical considerations of serving the senior population, which can be more vulnerable to exploitation than other adults. It outlines the benefits of conducting your business in a consistently ethical manner, both for your business and also for the seniors you serve. In addition, it provides a seven-step process for ethical decision-making that you can use in your business.

These tools can help you avoid the creeping grayness of moral relativism, ensure that you are consistently meeting the standards of responsibility dictated by the SCSA, and enable you to be confident that you are acting in an ethical way.

Development of Ethics and Values

How do we wind up with the kinds of ethics, values, and morals we perceive as adults? For that matter, how do we define those terms? As used in this chapter, we can define these terms as follows.

- *Ethics:* The study of how we define right and wrong. Also, how we live based on our morals and virtues.
- *Morals:* Society's definition of what is right and wrong.
- *Values:* Our individual beliefs about what we consider worthwhile.

The term *ethics* is derived from the Greek word *ethos*, which means character. Philosophers have pondered the nature of ethics for thousands of years. The term also is frequently used to describe the specific principles and standards of conduct by which we live based on our morals and values. Often, expectations of ethical behavior are codified into law—when a society demands that its citizens adhere to common principles of behavior, there are consequences for defying those standards. For example, business and contract law addresses unfair and deceptive practices. These laws apply to all businesses, including those working with seniors.

Morals and values, however, tend to be more personal and subjective. Our experiences as children have an impact on the adults we will become. Generally, we learn our morals and values from our families, teachers, religious education, professions, and peers. Your values shape your attitudes and policies. Your attitudes toward seniors and how you treat your senior clients are based on your values. Whether consciously or not, your most deeply ingrained values guide and frequently affect your perspectives, choices, and actions.

Four Major Influences on Ethical Standards

Ethical standards are influenced by four major factors: family background, religion, education, and the filters through which we view the world.

Family background includes the home environment and extended family situations. Did your parents lie easily? Did they respect your privacy? Were their actions and words in harmony, or did they say one thing and do another? Did you witness racism, sexism, or ageism at home? These types of familial behaviors affect ethical development.

Religious leaders and traditions are powerful forces in ethical development. Faith traditions influence honesty, politics, and worldviews. Religion has a particularly strong influence on seniors. About three-quarters of persons over age 60 say that religion is very important to them (Koenig, 1995).

Education influences ethics through what is taught in the classroom as well as through the principles and values upheld by school administrators. Was there any exposure in your school system to ethical standards? Did students cheat? (Did they get away with it?) Was bigotry tolerated? Did your teachers ignore bullying? How were you treated? These are the types of values that greatly affect our attitudes and beliefs.

Reference filters are the glasses through which we look at the world. In his book *Principle Centered Leadership*, Stephen Covey writes, "We evaluate, we assign priorities, judge, and behave based on how we see life through these glasses (Covey, 1991).

Reference filters include our:

- perceptions
- ideas and thoughts
- beliefs and expectations
- decision-making capabilities
- critical-thinking processes—i.e., can we really think things through and make decisions for ourselves?

653

Reference filters are formed and shaped by our backgrounds. They are influenced by:

- race
- gender
- culture
- place of birth
- development
- parents
- friends
- associates

Business Ethics Defined

The measure of a man's character is what he would do if he knew he never would be found out.

Baron Thomas Babington Macaule,
early 19th-century English historian

Business ethics refers to a set of principles that should govern the conduct of business, whether at the individual or collective level—the way that people *should* act in business. Although the study of ethics in the philosophical sense has engaged academics for centuries, business professionals have less use for theoretical debate than a need to understand the practical aspects of what they should do versus what they should *not* do in a typical business day. However, there is a great deal of confusion and misunderstanding among business professionals about business ethics. When someone in an office brings up the topic of business ethics, ". . . it tends to bring up cynicism, righteousness, paranoia, and laughter" (McDonald & Zepp, 1990) Many leaders and managers believe business ethics is tantamount to religion because it seems to contain a great deal of preaching. Or, they believe it to be superfluous because it seems to merely assert the obvious: Do *good*!

"Do good" is not bad advice—but it's not enough. Many professional associations police themselves through the use of codes of standards for ethical business, although not all groups include published consequences for violating those standards. The Society of Certified Senior Advisors (SCSA) provides its official Code of Professional Responsibilty (the Code), which establishes minimum standards of acceptable professional behavior for CSAs by which all CSAs must abide. The CSA Board of Standards, Inc., is a nonprofit corporation charged with investigating, reviewing, and taking appropriate action with respect to alleged violations of the Code by CSAs. The Society takes its guidelines very seriously, and the Board of Standards is authorized to take actions ranging from censure or suspension to permanent revocation of a CSA's right to use the designation.

About the CSA Code of Professional Responsibility

The best way to establish, maintain, or enhance your ethical standards is to live by a code of ethics. A code is an open disclosure of the way an organization operates. It provides visible guidelines for behavior. A well-written and thoughtful code also serves as an important communication vehicle that sets clear standards and concrete consequences for violating those standards.

Practicing high ethics, or responsibility, is the task of everyone engaged in working with seniors—from home offices or independent producers to nursing-home owners and health care providers, from managers of brokerage firms to the salesmen and service representatives working with clients.

You are the representative of your company in dealing with seniors. Your high ethical standards are the key to establishing trust and building long-term relationships with your senior clients. As a CSA, you are called on to ask prospects and clients very personal questions about their lifestyles, their family situations, and their financial resources and goals. Your senior prospects and clients will answer those questions completely and honestly only if they believe that you are ethical (which includes keeping the answers in confidence), forthright, and well-intentioned.

SCSA requires that all prospective CSAs agree to comply with the letter and spirit of the *CSA Code of Professional Responsibility*, and that all practicing CSAs adhere to it.

Why? Because the bedrock foundation of the CSA designation is the trust it represents and the respect it conveys. Trust cannot merely be declared; respect cannot merely be asked. Instead, how much trust we engender and how much respect we legitimately deserve grow from every individual action of every CSA. Trust and respect define the reputation of the CSA designation.

This reputation, built over years by the hard work and high principles of CSAs, flows to everyone who adds the designation to their name. Conversely, any CSA who acts unethically diminishes the value of the designation to *all* CSAs.

CSAs must make an absolute commitment to their clients—seniors and others—that they hold themselves to the highest standards of behavior. To become a CSA, a candidate must answer at least 70% of the exam questions correctly. To remain a CSA, a person must adhere to the CSA Code 100%. Adhering to the CSA Code is a promise we make to ourselves and our clients.

As a CSA working with senior adults, you operate in a market that is closely scrutinized and regulated. Public demand, marketplace complexities, and a firm regulatory environment require strict adherence to market conduct and compliance regulations. You must combine high ethical conduct with diligent compliance. But simple compliance with the minimum standards doesn't necessarily mean that you are truly acting in an ethical manner: a particular act or deed may be deemed acceptable under the letter of the law, but it may not be truly ethical.

655

The *CSA Code of Professional Responsibility* consists of three parts: the Standards, the Rules, and the Disciplinary Procedures. The Standards and Rules focus on the areas of:

- competence
- honesty
- trustworthiness
- fairness
- professionalism

The Standards define the ethical and professional conduct to which CSAs must adhere while carrying out their business activities. The Rules are derived from the Standards and are meant to demonstrate specific applications of the underlying Standard. Appendix A to the Code adds the "Advertising Guidelines" CSAs are to follow. Appendix B includes the "Usage Standards for the CSA Logo & Marks."

CSAs are required to comply with the Standards and Rules in the *Code of Professional Responsibility*. CSAs must also follow all rules and regulations of their professions that are set by state and federal law, licensing boards, state agencies, companies, and industry organizations of which the CSA is a member.

Ethical Concerns in Serving the Senior Market

As a CSA, *you* need to be ethical when working with seniors, because many others will not be. Nobody likes to discuss it, but financial abuse is unfortunately and rapidly becoming one of the most prevalent problems facing our nation's elderly.

Seniors are common prey to financial abuse scams that include sweepstakes and telemarketing, predatory lending, fraudulent living trusts and annuities, cemetery and burial fund abuses, Internet fraud, and various types of identity theft. There are bad people who think seniors are easy pickings because they have significant assets from a lifetime of hard work, and because they are easy to push around. There are people out there ready and waiting to take advantage of a frail or lonely senior and steal their life savings—and some of these cons purport to sell the very same types of products and services as you. By your ethical actions and the reputation you build, you will *never* be confused with one of these odious scam artists.

Simply put, as a CSA you *must* act in a responsible and ethical manner when you are working with seniors. You must, because seniors as a group tend to be more vulnerable to being taken advantage of or abused—therefore, they are favored targets of unscrupulous characters that prey upon the weak. You have a responsibility to help and not to harm, because ethical standards are the bedrock foundation of your certification as a CSA. The CSA designation means that you agree to act in an ethical manner.

Following are some of the reasons why ethical behavior is so important when serving seniors.

SENIORS CAN BE MORE VULNERABLE TO EXPLOITATION THAN YOUNGER ADULTS

According to Edward C. King, executive director of the National Senior Citizens Law Center in Washington, D.C., "Older people—particularly those who no longer have any basic source of income, other than from their existing assets or government sources—are concerned about making sure that their assets will last them through their lives. Because this is such an issue for them, they are more likely to fall for a scheme that promises to increase their assets and the income from those assets. And because many seniors are isolated, they are prime targets for dishonest people who create schemes that directly address their biggest fears" (King, 2004).

Seniors can be exploited financially just as they can be abused physically or mentally. Although people of all ages can be victims of financial abuse, seniors are the most frequent targets (Otto, Stanis, & Marlatt, 2003), and many seniors lose their savings as a result of falling victim to unscrupulous sharks. Also, there are caregivers of shady background who strive to isolate and control their elderly charges.

Seniors may have cognitive problems that make it more difficult for them to understand the consequences of their decisions. They may be lonely or isolated. Senior women who live alone are particularly vulnerable to financial abuse—they may have less experience with handling financial issues and may be more readily manipulated than someone with more background in money management. Unethical tradesmen may take advantage of a senior who is in a jam—stories abound about door-to-door concrete driveway or roof repair services that overcharge seniors and then disappear with the money after doing a slipshod job. Seniors in crisis may turn to anyone who shows concern for them—to their detriment. As Edward C. King noted above, many predators specifically target seniors who appear to be in trouble.

As a CSA, you will of course avoid any such activity. But you should also watch out for signs that one of your clients is being abused by someone else. When it comes to abusive caregivers, for example, you may notice things that are of concern. "The signs can be very subtle," writes Ed Carnot, author of *Is Your Parent in Good Hands? Protecting Your Aging Parent from Financial Abuse and Neglect* (2003). "When you visit your client, you really have to use your eyes and see what is going on. Do you see any warning signs that might lead you to believe that there's a problem? For example, does the senior seem nervous or upset? Is the caregiver always present, not allowing the senior any privacy to meet with you?"

Carnot recommends the following broad guidelines for using in-home caregivers, to help to avoid physical or financial abuse of a senior.

- Require that the caregiver not accept *any* gift from the senior, or else they will be fired. Be sure that the caregiver *and* the senior are aware of this stipulation, so that the senior cannot be in any way pressured financially.

- Require that the caregiver maintain a detailed chart of the daily activities of the senior that is regularly sent to the senior's family members so they can see the senior's daily activities.

CSAs NEED TO BE ETHICAL AND PROFESSIONAL IN ALL THEIR DEALINGS

The National Center on Elder Abuse tracks reports of financial and material exploitation of the elderly. The trends they detect are disturbing. Their 1994 study of 39 states reported 29,643 incidents of financial exploitation; nearly a decade later in a similar study, 28 states reported receiving a total of 38,015 reports (Otto, Stanis, & Marlatt, 2003).

The number of reports of financial exploitation has led to increased attention to the problem at the state and federal levels. Some examples of state initiatives include those in Massachusetts and Oregon, whose attorneys general developed training for financial institutions in an effort to gain their cooperation in reporting and preventing financial exploitation of older persons. In Colorado, Attorney General Ken Salazar initiated a program called AARP Senior Watch to combat the financial exploitation of the elderly. According to elder law attorney Marco Chayet of Chayet, Young & Dawson, LLP, many states have severe penalties for anyone who injures a senior adult physically *or* financially.

As a CSA, you agree to consistently operate in an ethical manner as you work with seniors.

Benefits of Ethical Business Behavior

All my growth and development led me to believe that if
you really do the right thing, and if you play by the rules, and if you've got
enough solid judgment and common sense, that you're going
to be able to do whatever you want with your life.

Barbara Jordan

BENEFITS TO THE SENIOR CLIENT

To protect those who are not able to protect
themselves is a duty which every one owes to society.

Edward Macnaghten

There are many benefits to senior clients who are working with CSA professionals. The Society receives about 20 inquiries every day from seniors who are checking on the credentials of a CSA designee. Seniors *do* care about the designation—it gives them confidence that they are working with a legitimate, educated professional who has worked to understand the physical, financial, and social aspects of aging.

As a CSA, you can make it very clear to your senior prospects that you are subject to the directives of the CSA Code of Professional Responsibility—that you take ethical business practices very seriously and that you have committed yourself to continuing education as an expert on senior issues. This elevates their trust in you as a professional. The peace of mind this affords your clients is a benefit indeed.

BENEFITS TO THE CSA

Eighty percent of people say they decide to buy a
firm's goods or services partly on their perception of its ethics.

2003 survey, Wirthlin Worldwide

You can make your style of doing business a competitive advantage by serving prospects and clients in a highly ethical fashion, with full compliance to the CSA Code of Professional Responsibility. In Old West parlance, you're the cowboy in the white hat, the good guy, the hero. Consistently ethical business dealings will inevitably lead to more business, as your reputation as a straight shooter grows.

Never underestimate the power of your reputation. A growing trend on the Internet is the increasing number of consumer-generated media (CGM) Web sites that exist as repositories of individual stories of personal experience with a particular product or company. Sites such as http://www.complaint. com, http://www.planetfeedback.com, and the popular http://www.screwed byinsurance.com allow disgruntled consumers to vent and to rate their experiences. Don't assume that nobody will find out if you engage in questionable business practices with a client—with every passing day, it becomes easier and easier to uncover wrongdoing with a simple Web search.

Attention to ethics has powerful appeal in the marketplace—admittedly, managing ethics should not be done primarily for reasons of public relations. But, frankly, the fact that an organization regularly gives attention to its ethics can portray a strong positive to the public. People see those organizations as valuing people more than profit, as striving to operate with the utmost of integrity and honor. Aligning behavior with values is critical to effective marketing and public relations programs.

This is why the CSA Code of Professional Responsibility sets you apart as an ethical businessperson. Many seniors are very leery of people selling things, and many seniors have younger family members that want to protect them from wolves in business clothing and are happy to check out a professional for them. By demonstrating (providing proof, references, or examples) that you are an ethical businessperson and are allied with an ethical company, you'll close more business and be able to help more people.

Ethical Behavior in Action

Do all the good you can, by all the means you can, in all the ways you can, in all the places you can, at all the times you can, to all the people you can, as long as ever you can.

John Wesley

Always do right—this will gratify some and astonish the rest.

Mark Twain

As a CSA, you have pledged to conduct your business in an ethical manner. This section provides some tools to help you make ethical decisions. One important note—when working with seniors, be careful about the terminology you use when explaining your products and services. It is unethical to use industry jargon that is unfamiliar to the senior. You need to speak "senior language"— language that seniors can understand. Take pains to break apart complex issues, and use images and stories to help seniors follow what you are saying.

THE SEVEN-STEP PATH TO MAKING ETHICAL DECISIONS

The following recommendations for making ethical decisions are provided by the Josephson Institute of Ethics (2002).

1. Stop and Think

One of the most important steps to better decisions is the oldest advice in the world: Think ahead. To do so, it's necessary to first stop the momentum of events long enough to permit calm analysis. This may require discipline, but it is a powerful tonic against poor choices.

The well-worn formula of counting to 10 when angry and to 100 when very angry is a simple technique designed to prevent foolish and impulsive behavior. But we are just as apt to make foolish decisions when we are under the strain of powerful desires or fatigue, when we are in a hurry or under pressure, or when we are ignorant of important facts.

Just as we teach our children to look both ways before they cross the street, we can and should instill the habit of looking ahead before making any decision.

Stopping to think provides several benefits. It prevents rash decisions. It prepares us for more thoughtful discernment. And it can allow us to mobilize our discipline.

2. Clarify Goals

Before you choose, clarify your short- and long-term aims. Determine which of your many wants and don't-wants affected by the decision are the most important. The big danger is that decisions that fulfill immediate wants and needs can prevent the achievement of our more important life goals.

3. Determine Facts

Be sure you have adequate information to support an intelligent choice. You can't make good decisions if you don't know the facts.

To determine the facts, first resolve what you know and, then, what you need to know. Be prepared to get additional information and to verify assumptions and other uncertain information.

Once we begin to be more careful about facts, we often find that there are different versions of them and disagreements about their meaning. In these situations part of making sound decisions involves making good judgments as to who and what to believe.

Here are some guidelines:

- Consider the reliability and credibility of the people providing the facts.
- Consider the basis of the supposed facts. If the person giving you the information says he or she personally heard or saw something, evaluate that person in terms of honesty, accuracy, and memory.
- Remember that assumptions, gossip, and hearsay are not the same as facts.
- Consider all perspectives, but be careful to consider whether the source of the information has values different than yours or has a personal interest that could affect perception of the facts.
- Where possible, seek out the opinions of people whose judgment and character you respect, but be careful to distinguish the well-grounded opinions of well-informed people from casual speculation, conjecture, and guesswork.
- Finally, evaluate the information you have in terms of completeness and reliability, so you have a sense of the certainty and fallibility of your decisions.

4. Develop Options

Now that you know what you want to achieve and have made your best judgment as to the relevant facts, make a list of options—a set of actions you can take to accomplish your goals. If it's an especially important decision, talk to someone you trust so you can broaden your perspective and think of new choices. If you can think of only one or two choices, you're probably not thinking hard enough.

5. Consider Consequences

Two techniques help reveal potential consequences:

- *"Pillar-ize" your options:* Filter your choices through each of the Six Pillars of Character: trustworthiness, respect, responsibility, fairness, caring, and citizenship. Will the action violate any of the core ethical principles? For instance, does it involve lying or breaking a promise; is it disrespectful to anyone; is it irresponsible, unfair or uncaring; does it involve breaking laws or rules? Eliminate unethical options.

- *Identify the stakeholders and how the decision is likely to affect them.* Consider your choices from the point of view of the major stakeholders. Identify whom the decision will help and hurt.

6. Choose

It's time to make your decision. If the choice is not immediately clear, see if any of the following strategies help:

- *Talk to people whose judgment you respect.* Seek out friends and mentors—but remember, once you've gathered opinions and advice, the ultimate responsibility is still yours.

- *What would the most ethical person you know do?* Think of the person you know or know of (in real life or fiction) who has the strongest character and best ethical judgment. Then ask yourself what that person would do in your situation. Think of that person as your decision-making role model, and try to behave the way he or she would. Many Christians wear a small bracelet with the letters WWJD, which stand for the question "What would Jesus do?" Whether you are Christian or not, the idea of referencing a role model can be a useful one. You could translate the question into: "What would God want me to do?" "What would Buddha or Mother Teresa do?" "What would Gandhi do?" "What would the most virtuous person in the world do?"

- *What would you do if you were sure everyone would know?* If everyone found out about your decision, would you be proud and comfortable? Choices that look good only if no one knows are always bad choices. Good choices make us worthy of admiration and build good reputations. It's been said that character is *revealed* by how we behave when we think no one is looking and *strengthened* when we act as if everyone is looking.

- *Golden Rule: Do unto to others as you would have them do unto you.* The Golden Rule is one of the oldest and best guides to ethical decision-making. If we treat people the way we want to be treated we are likely to live up to the Six Pillars of Character. We don't want to be lied to or have promises broken, so we should be honest and keep our promises to others. We want others to treat us with respect, so we should treat others respectfully.

7. Monitor and Modify

Since most hard decisions still use imperfect information and best-effort predictions, some of them will inevitably be wrong. Ethical decision-makers monitor the effects of their choices. If they are not producing the intended results or are causing additional unintended and undesirable results, they reassess the situation and make new decisions.

INFORMED CONSENT

Informed consent is a legal condition whereby a person can be said to have agreed, or given consent, to allow something to happen, based on a full appreciation and understanding of the facts and implications of the action. It implies that the person has been informed of all the risks involved as well as the potential alternatives. For example, in a hospital, informed consent must be obtained from a prospective patient before a surgeon can schedule an elective operation. As a Certified Senior Advisor, it's extremely unlikely that you will be using a scalpel on your clients (unless you are also a surgeon)—but the actions you take on behalf of your clients can sometimes have just as much impact on a senior's life. So it's important for you to clearly communicate the risk and potential impact of a senior's decision when you complete a transaction with a senior.

An example of the elements of informed consent from the medical field is found in the guidelines offered by the American College of Obstetrics and Gynecology (ACOG). ACOG's position is that, separate and apart from any legal requirements, a patient has an *ethical right to informed consent*. It defines informed consent as having two main elements (ACOG, 1992):

- disclosure of information by the physician such that the patient is able to understand his situation and options;
- freedom of the patient to choose from the options or to refuse options.

In general, for informed consent to be legitimate three factors must be present (Beauchamp & Bowie, 1993):

1. Consenters must be able to understand the consequences of their actions.
2. All facts about the product or service must be adequately disclosed. The language used must be clear and understandable to consenters. Consenters must be given the opportunity to ask questions and to have questions answered.
3. The process must be voluntary. Consenters must have the right to accept, refuse, or change their minds within a mutually reasonable time frame. There must not be coercion or misrepresentation. Whether an action is voluntary can also be determined by physical or psychological conditions.

When working with seniors, there is sometimes a concern about an individual's ability to make informed decisions, due to cognitive decline or physical ailments. However, don't assume that all seniors are the same—never make assumptions about abilities or needs based on age alone.

Informed consent also assumes that the person making the decision is competent to do so. *Competence* and *incapacity* are legal designations—adults are generally presumed to be competent to make their own decisions, unless they are ruled to be incapacitated by a court or other legal body. A competent adult has the right to sign binding contracts and make legally binding decisions about their lives. A person is deemed competent to make their own decisions if they are in full possession of their faculties and their judgment is not impaired at the time of consenting (by sleepiness, intoxication, health problems, etc.). An incapacitated adult no longer has the ability to make decisions or care for himself or herself and has been adjudicated incapacitated after a review of medical or psychological evidence by a court. In such an instance, a guardian is appointed to assume responsibility for all legally binding decisions made on behalf of the incompetent adult.

Rules about competence and incapacity vary from state to state, but in general adults are presumed to be competent to make their own decisions unless some other person can legally prove they are not.

Attorneys speak of a *continuum of incapacity* that may affect a senior's ability to make an informed decision. Health care practitioners can determine seniors' capacity to make decisions with the aid of cognitive testing and related techniques. When working on behalf of clients who lack the capacity to make informed decisions, you should take reasonable steps to safeguard the interests and rights of those clients. Edward C. King of the National Senior Citizens Law Center says, "It is a very complex area—there are no clear-cut standards. It puts the professional in the position of having to monitor and try to make an evaluation that someone is competent" (King, 2004).

Sally Hurme, an attorney with Consumer Protection (AARP National Office), states, "There is fluctuating capacity with many seniors—it's not an on-or-off switch, it's not all or nothing. Professionals need to be aware of the signs and guard against taking advantage of a senior. To a degree, it is sort of a delicate balance: of the professional treating the elder with respect, assuming that the elder is fully capable of understanding the transaction—while on the other hand, the professional must be alert and not take advantage of the individual, if it looks like they're having some problems" (Hurme, 2004). Hurme also mentioned the concept of *sundowning*: "Older persons are much more likely to be sharp and alert earlier in the day. As the day ends, as the sun goes down, they're tired . . . it's a common perception that their acuity declines toward the end of the day." She suggests that professionals try to conduct serious business (signing contracts and the like) in the morning rather than the evening to make it more likely that the senior will be at his or her best.

Ethical CSA Behavior: Some Questions

Values are like fingerprints. Nobody's are the same, but you leave 'em all over everything you do.

Elvis Presley, American rock 'n' roll icon (1935-1977)

Watch your thoughts, for they become words.
Watch your words, for they become actions.
Watch your actions, for they become habits.
Watch your habits, for they become character.
Watch your character, for it becomes your destiny."

Unknown

Melody Kollath, a partner in Women Helping Women, a group of allied professionals who specialize in working with senior women, prides herself on "making friends for life" with her clients. In order to build such friendships, a sterling reputation is essential (Kollath, 2004).

The foreword to the *CSA Code of Professional Responsibility* emphasizes how CSAs must at all times practice ethical business conduct to maintain the integrity of the designation. How does this commitment manifest itself in the business arena? You should be able to answer yes to these questions:

- Do you apply the Golden Rule to your business dealings, holding yourself to a high standard of honesty and fairness? In practice, you might decline to sell someone a product that you know doesn't meet their particular needs.

665

- Do you focus on keeping yourself well informed and abreast of new developments in your industry, so that your sales counsel is as accurate and timely as possible? Do you make sure that you are continually learning and contributing to your profession?
- Do you avoid disparaging your competitor's products or services—do you speak well of all credible companies that serve your market, without trying to damage another's reputation?
- Are you prompt, courteous, and professional when you respond to client requests? Do you rapidly address any complaints or disputes that might arise with a client?
- Do you offer your clients informational materials that clearly and honestly outline your products and services, without obfuscation or vagueness?

Ethical CSAs also train their support staff in ethical decision-making. Here are a few ways you can get your staff to understand what is expected of them:

- Include a discussion of ethical practices in your new employee orientations.
- Share the seven-step method for ethical decision-making with your staff.
- Create a document that lists your company's code of ethics, and distribute a copy to each employee. (If you work for a large firm that already has such documents, be certain that you prominently display them in the office—and be sure that your staff is aware of them.)
- Review the CSA Code of Conduct with your staff—let them know that you have agreed to abide by the principles in the CSA Code.
- Teach your staff how to interact one-on-one with seniors on the phone or in an office meeting. Make sure your staff understands that they need to speak slowly and clearly and pitch their voices low when they are on the phone with a senior.

When working with seniors, your staff must understand that they need to *slow down, communicate carefully,* and make certain that the information they are imparting has been received correctly by the senior. Your people should get in the habit of asking the senior to *repeat information* to be sure they understand what they're being told. This is particularly important when they are transferring assets or transferring funds in an annuity. Train your staff to be very careful and clear when they explain major transactions to the senior.

DEVIOUS BUSINESS TACTICS TO AVOID AT ALL COSTS

How many times do you get to lie before you are a liar?

Michael Josephson, 20th/21st-century American ethicist

Once integrity goes, the rest is a piece of cake.

J. R. Ewing, lead character in the 20th-century American television show "Dallas"

According to attorney Sally Hurme, there are three spices in the witches' brew of taking advantage of a senior:

- the dollars a senior has
- the potential for declining mental acuity
- a senior's predominant concern of making sure his or her money is going to last

"When you stir these together," Hurme says, "the situation is ripe for an unethical business person to make a killing."

Hurme says, "A key goal of unscrupulous people is to isolate the senior, shut them off from other advice. They'll say things like, 'Don't tell your kids, don't tell your friends and neighbors.' The bad guy doesn't want the senior to take the time to really research the offer. The bad guy wants to get the senior so wrapped up in the excitement of the conquest that they won't take the time to read the fine print. In my view, the best thing an ethical professional can do is to go overboard in making sure that there are third parties involved. Your product is so good—it's so fair—that you want close scrutiny. An ethical professional will tell the senior, 'Bring in the kids, get all your questions answered before we go any further.'

"Compare and contrast the way the bad guys do it: They want to rush the sale. The warning sign that AARP cautions against is someone using a time-pressuring pitch line such as, 'One day only, the offer will not be here tomorrow,' pushing the senior to make a fast decision. This is again related to an effort to cut the person off from additional advice and make a hasty decision. To me, the sign of an ethical professional is someone who says to their senior prospect, 'I'm not going to *let* you sign this until you take it home and read it and talk to your family. Sleep on it, because I want you to feel comfortable with whatever it is you're about to do.' That's what ethical professionals should do."

ETHICAL CSAs DON'T

In abiding by the Code of Professional Responsibility as well as your own interests in maintaining a positive business reputation, your role as a CSA means you:

- Don't use fear, guilt, or other negative emotions to motivate a senior to buy or not buy products or services.

- Don't breach client confidentiality by sneaking to speak with a senior client's family members or other interested parties; unless legally required to disclose information, you should protect every senior's privacy.

- Don't misrepresent your professional credentials, skills, and capabilities or products and services (in speech or by omission).

- Don't withhold information that negatively affects a senior's ability to make an informed decision in the senior's best interests—or fail to disclose any information about possible risks or hidden costs associated with a decision.

- Don't fail to obtain full and complete information about the senior's needs and objectives, financial and tax situation, risk tolerance, objectives, health, and dependent status.

- Don't recommend or sell any product or service that you know is not appropriate for a senior based on your understanding of the senior's needs and objectives.
- Don't take advantage of a senior's positive feelings toward you in order to make a sale.
- Don't take advantage of a senior's diminished physical or mental capacities in order to make a sale.

When it comes to financial products, life and health insurance, LTCI and investment products, your role as an ethical CSA means you will avoid:

- churning—excessive trading (overtrading) of a client's assets to earn commissions rather than improve the client's situation;
- rebating—giving or promising a valuable gift if a senior purchases an insurance policy or other investment;
- not fully explaining a senior's rights as a policy owner—particularly the "free look" provision;
- twisting—using misleading terms, jargon, or language that is confusing.

According to Sally Hurme, "There are so many options on a variable annuity: Is it going to be deferred? Is it going to be fixed? How confusing can you make it? And you're going to sell this to an 80-year-old with a 10-year payout . . . that's probably not appropriate."

Your responsibility as a CSA also means restricting your advice to your sphere of expertise. That's why cultivating a community of experts for referral is such a benefit to your business. For example, if you lack proper professional knowledge or certification in tax counsel and financing, you must avoid recommending on your own that, for example, a senior spend down financial resources to qualify for Medicaid benefits.

If your business deals with health care services, your ethical responsibility requires that you never misrepresent one or more of the following:

- the type, number, features, or benefits of the health care services you provide
- your professional credentials or experience
- all costs—immediate or future, including money that might be spent on questionable treatments or medications, such as an "anti-aging vitamin complex" or similar products
- selling financial products that a senior does not need
- selling a product that has a higher commission when another product with a lower commission is more appropriate

Remember, CSAs who engage in any sort of devious business practices risk serious consequences from the SCSA, including censure, suspension, or even revocation of the CSA designation. It's not worth it—so don't do it.

Ethics in Doing Business with Seniors: Summary

Although there's no way to eliminate unethical practitioners from the marketplace (until they are caught, one by one) it *is* possible to build a strong, solid business on the foundation of your reputation as an ethical, responsible, caring professional. Keep in mind that you are a champion of good business practices and that you have a responsibility to treat your senior clients with dignity, respect, and fairness. If you focus on making ethical decisions in your business, you will build a reputation as the kind of person seniors *want* to do business with.

References

ACOG (American College of Obstetrics and Gynecology). (1992, May). ACOG Committee opinion on ethical dimensions of informed consent, No. 108. Washington, D.C.

Beauchamp, T. L., & Bowie, N. E. (Eds.). (1993). *Ethical theory and business* (4th ed.). Englewood Cliffs, NJ: Prentice Hall.

Bradley, K.S. Personal communication. July 21, 2004.

Carnot, E. J. (2003). *Is your parent in good hands? Protecting your aging parent from financial abuse and neglect.* Sterling, VA: Capital Books.

Covey, S. (1991). *Principle centered leadership.* New York: Simon and Schuster.

Gibbs, N. (2002, July 14). Summer of mistrust. *Time* [electronic edition]. Retrieved August 3, 2004, from http://www.time.com/time/nation/article/0,8599,320734-1,00.html

Hurme, S. Personal communication. July 28, 2004.

J. C. Penney. (n.d.). History of J. C. Penney. Available from http://www.jcpenney inc.com/company/history/history.htm

Josephson Institute of Ethics. (2002, November) The seven-step path to better decisions. *Making ethical decisions.* Retrieved August 3, 2004, from http://www.josephsonin stitute.org/MED/MED-4sevensteppath.htm

King, E.C., Personal communication. July 28, 2004.

Koenig, H. G. (1995). Religion and health in later life. *Aging, spirituality and religion.* Minneapolis, MN: Fortress.

Kollath, M. Personal communication. July 16, 2004.

McDonald, G. M., & Zepp, R. A. (1990). What should be done? A practical approach to business ethics, *Management Decision, 28*(1), 9–13.

National Association of Scholars. (2002, June). Ethics, Enron, and American higher education: An NAS/Zogby poll of college seniors. Retrieved August 3, 2004, from http://www.nas.org/reports/zogethics_poll/zogby_ethics_report.htm

Otto, J., Stanis, P., & Marlatt, K. (2003). Report on state adult protective services responses to financial exploitation of vulnerable adults. Washington, DC: National Association of Adult Protective Services Administrators.

Resources

Suggested Reading

The Blackwell Guide to Business Ethics, Norman E. Bowie (Ed.) (2002, Blackwell Publishers).

Business Ethics, Third Edition, Milton Snoeyenbos, Robert Almeder, & James Humber (Eds.) (2001, Prometheus Books).

Doing the Right Thing: Cultivating your Moral Intelligence, by Aaron Hass, PhD (1998, Pocket Books).

E2: Using the Power of Ethics and Etiquette in American Business, by Phyllis Davis (2003, Entrepreneur Press).

Ethics at Work: Basic Readings in Business Ethics, by William H. Shaw (2003, Oxford University Press).

Everyday Ethics: Inspired Solutions to Real-Life Dilemmas, by Joshua Halberstam (1993, Penguin Books).

Health Fraud and the Elderly: A Continuing Health Epidemic, Prepared Statement of the Federal Trade Commission before the United States Senate Special Committee on Aging. http://www.ftc.gov/os/2001/09/healthfraud.htm

On My Honor, I Will . . . How One Simple Oath Can Lead You to Success in Business, by Randy Pennington & Marc Bockmon (1992, Warner Books).

What Should I Do? 4 Simple Steps in Making Better Decisions in Everyday Life, by Bruce Weinstein (2000, Perigee Books).

Services

National Fraud Information Center/Internet Fraud Watch. http://www.fraud.org

Elderly Fraud, Consumer's Notebook, Office of the Attorney General, State of Louisiana. http://www.ag.state.la.us/publications/elderlyfraud.htm

EthicsWeb, Applied Ethics Resources on WWW, Business Ethics Resources. http://www.ethicsweb.ca/resources/business

Glossary

Absolute assignment Irrevocable transfer of complete ownership of a life insurance policy from one party to another. See also *assignment*.

Accessory apartment Conversion of surplus area in an existing single-family home into a separate living unit with its own kitchen, bathroom, and often its own entrance.

Accelerated death benefit life provision (also called **living benefit**) Provision sometimes contained in life insurance policies that dictates under what conditions the policy owner is able to receive a reduced policy benefit while alive. Typical conditions include the onset of serious or terminal illness or permanent confinement to a nursing home.

Accepting assignment Claim filing system in Medicare Part B that helps control seniors' out-of-pocket costs and expedites payments to physicians and other providers.

Accidental death and dismemberment (AD&D) rider Supplementary benefit rider or endorsement that provides for an amount of money in addition to the basic death benefit of a life insurance policy. This additional amount is payable only if the insured dies or loses any two limbs or the sight of both eyes as the result of an accident.

Active adult (retirement) communities Residential developments that offer living in a planned facility or development with organized leisure and recreation activities, plus no maintenance duties for residents. They are designed for seniors, but younger guests are welcome.

Activity of daily living (ADL) Six basic personal care activities: eating, toileting, dressing, bathing, transferring, and continence. The ability of someone to perform ADLs can help a professional assess their personal self-maintenance. Many long-term care policies use a person's ability to perform ADLs unaided as a gauge for deciding when to pay benefits.

Acute illness Severe illness with a rapid onset and a generally short duration.

Acute myocardial infarction Also known as a heart attack. Occurs when an area of heart muscle dies or is permanently damaged because of an inadequate supply of oxygen to that area.

Adjusted basis The owner's original basis in an asset, plus improvements or minus depreciation.

Adjusted gross estate Accumulated assets of a decedent, minus administrative expenses to settle the estate, funeral expenses, debts of the decedent, uninsured theft and casualty losses to estate property, and claims against the estate.

Adjusted gross income (AGI) Total amount of a person's wages, dividends, and other financial receipts, minus adjustments to income, such as alimony paid and deductible contributions to individual retirement accounts (IRAs).

Adjusted taxable gifts A decedent's post-1976 taxable gifts, reduced by taxable gifts included in the gross estate, which are added to a decedent's taxable estate to form the estate's tax base.

Adjustment disorders Distress leading to impairment in daily functioning, and which occurs within three months of a specific event and does not last longer than six months after the end of the stressful event.

Adjustments to income When calculating income tax, the deductions used to arrive at adjusted gross income. Adjustments to income include: deductible contributions to IRAs, one-half of the self-employment tax, self-employed health insurance deduction, qualified job-related moving expenses, alimony paid, and penalty on early withdrawal of savings.

Administrator (administratrix) Person who settles the estate when an individual dies intestate.

Adult day care Care provided at a community-based center for adults who need assistance or supervision during the day (including help with personal care) but who do not need round-the-clock care.

Advanced directive Statement made by an individual, usually in a written document, concerning the medical treatments to be provided and decision-maker to be appointed if the patient becomes terminally ill or incapacitated.

After-tax return Amount of income realized on investments after applicable income taxes are subtracted.

Ageism Prejudices and stereotypes that are applied to persons based solely on their age.

Age-period-cohort Method of understanding the psychology of growing older by analyzing three areas: aging effects, related to the process of growing older; period effects, related to events of a specific time in history; and cohort effects, related to common characteristics of a specific generation of people born in the same interval of time.

Aging Regular changes that occur in mature organisms as they live for chronologically longer periods.

Aging in place Concept describing a senior remaining in the same residence and coping successfully with associated vulnerabilities by themselves or with assistance.

Agnosia Inability to recognize familiar objects in the absence of sensory deficits.

Agoraphobia Extreme fear of being in places from which it is not easy to escape.

Alternative container A container, used in lieu of a casket, usually used for immediate burial. Alternative containers are constructed of simple pine boards, particleboard, or hard cardboard.

Alternative minimum tax (AMT) Payment that may be required of taxpayers who would otherwise have significantly reduced taxation through high use of tax preference items or adjustments. If the calculated alternative minimum tax is higher than the regular tax as calculated, the taxpayer is required to make the AMT payment.

Alzheimer's disease Progressive, degenerative form of dementia that causes severe deterioration of mental functioning, including loss of memory, impairment of judgment, abstract thinking, and deterioration of personality.

Aneurysm Localized enlargement of an artery. This can cause enough pressure to rupture and spill blood into the space surrounding brain cells.

Angina Localized pain related to the demands made on the heart, most commonly for the performance of physical exercise, but also to cope with emotional reactions.

Antipsychotic medications Used to treat symptoms associated with dementia.

Angioplasty Procedure used to widen vessels narrowed by stenoses or occlusions. Various types of these procedures and their names are associated with the type of vessel entry and equipment used.

Annual exclusion Maximum amount a person may give each year as a gift without having to pay a gift tax.

Annuitant Recipient of annuity distributions.

Annuity Income from capital investment paid in a series of regular payments.

Aphasia Partial or total loss of the ability to speak or understand speech due to a disorder in the cerebellum of the brain.

Apoptosis Cellular suicide to prevent a genetic error (as found in cancerous cells) from being passed on.

Applicable exclusion Amount of an individual's assets that can be held not subject to federal estate tax.

Apraxia Difficulty with physical movement despite otherwise normal physical functioning. Change in gait (walking) is one common example.

Arthritis Inflammation of the joints.

Artificial nutrition and hydration Provision of food or water to a patient using a tube inserted into the esophagus or surgically implanted into the stomach.

Asset allocation strategy Method of diversification aimed at reducing variability of return from a portfolio of investments. The point of asset allocation is to invest in different types of assets that have low correlation with others in the portfolio.

Asset What a person owns. Assets include cash and cash equivalents, invested assets, and use assets.

Assignment Act of a person transferring ownership of a life insurance policy to another person.

Assisted living facility Residential housing meant for seniors with physical or cognitive impairments that make it difficult for them to perform an average of two ADLs (see definition above) without assistance.

Assisted suicide Deliberate hastening of death by a terminally ill patient with assistance from a doctor, family member, or other individual.

Assistive technology Device used to improve the capabilities of an individual with disabilities. Assistive technology is an umbrella term that also includes durable medical equipment.

Atherosclerosis Blockage within blood vessels that contributes to the development of heart disease and other circulatory disorders.

At-need Funeral or burial at the time of death.

Authentic plans Intentions for the future that are genuine, real, and a truthful reflection of a person's beliefs.

Balance sheet (also called **statement of financial position**) Financial statement listing a client's assets, liabilities, and net worth as of a specific date.

Basal Rate of the body's metabolic processes at baseline or at rest.

Basal metabolic rate (BMR) Rate of the body's chemistry at baseline or at rest.

Basis Amount a person has invested in an asset, or the tax cost of an asset.

Bathing Washing oneself in either a tub or shower. This activity includes the task of getting into or out of the tub or shower.

Belonging Sense of community that fulfills our need to be part of a group that shares and validates our values and beliefs, and in which we feel safe, secure, and free to be ourselves.

Beneficiary In the context of insurance, the person or entity who has a remainder interest in policy proceeds. In the context of trusts, the person who benefits from the trust and who has beneficial ownership of trust assets.

Benefit period Defined length of time used to measure a patient's use of services for inpatient hospital and skilled nursing facility care, and separately for hospice care. In the hospital and skilled nursing facility context, a benefit period begins on the day a beneficiary enters an inpatient hospital and ends when he or she has not received inpatient hospital or skilled nursing facility care for 60 days in a row.

Benefit trigger Term used by insurance companies to describe the criteria and methods they use to determine when a person is eligible to receive benefits.

Benzodiazapines Any of a group of chemical compounds with a common molecular structure and similar pharmacological effects. Used as anti-anxiety agents, muscle relaxants, sedatives, hypnotics, and sometimes as anticonvulsants.

Bereavement Experience of the death of a loved one.

Bequest Act of transferring personal property by a will.

Biointerventions Actions designed to retard or reverse the aging process.

Biological nuclear family Kinship unit that consists of a husband and wife living together with children by birth or adoption only (i.e., does not include blended families).

Biomarkers Key physiological factors associated with aging.

Biomarkers of functional age Physiological factors used to estimate the rate at which the very fundamental processes of aging occur within individuals.

Bipolar disorder Mental process in which mood cycles back and forth between periods of mania, normal functioning, and depression.

Blended families Husband and wife living together with children brought to the family by one or both partners from previous marriages or relationships; may also include children from their union.

Board and care Residential setting—often a large, conventional, single-family house—consisting of multiple bedrooms, each occupied by one person, or alternatively by two to four residents. Residents may have to share the toilet and bathroom facilities, and most activities will occur in the building's common living areas.

Body donation Means of final disposition in which the deceased's remains are given for research to a medical school or dental school.

Bond Debt that represents a legal obligation of the issuer to pay principal and interest when due.

Boundaries Psychological fences that define emotional limits and delineate what is acceptable and unacceptable behavior. In healthy caregiving relationships, boundaries act as operational parameters that outline how the caregiver/care recipient relationship works.

Budget Financial statement listing expected income and expenses for a future period of time.

Burnout State of mental or physical exhaustion caused by excessive and prolonged stress.

Business ethics Principles that should govern the conduct of business, whether at the individual or collective level; the way that people should act in business.

Cancer Various malignant neoplasms characterized by the proliferation of anaplastic cells that tend to invade surrounding tissue and metastasize to new body sites.

Capital gain (capital loss) Increase (or decrease) in value a seller realizes on the sale or exchange of a capital asset. A net short-term capital gain is treated as ordinary income. A net long-term capital gain is generally subject to a maximum 20 percent tax rate.

Cardiopulmonary resuscitation (CPR) Emergency treatment that compresses the heart and forces air into the patient's lungs. It is applied when a patient's heart or breathing stops.

Carefrontation Time of introspection to help potential caregivers determine if they can legitimately embrace the role. Introspection is an honest appraisal of capabilities when caregivers take a hard and truthful look at who they are and what they can handle physically, emotionally, and mentally.

Caregiver Person who provides unpaid care to someone who requires help with activities of daily living (ADLs) or instrumental activities of daily living (IADLs).

Care managers (also called **geriatric care managers**) Persons who help navigate seniors through the sometimes confusing long-term supportive services system.

Carriers (Medicare Part B) Private companies who contract with the Centers for Medicare and Medicaid Services to make coverage determinations and process Medicare claims.

Cash-flow statement Personal financial analysis that lists inflows and expenditures made by a person or family over a particular period.

Cash model Method of funds distribution in which the recipient decides how to spend money for the care, including purchasing services from vendors, hiring a friend to help with activities of daily living, purchasing assistive technology, or modifying their home to make it more accessible.

Cash surrender value option Insurance policy provision allowing a policyholder to surrender the contract in exchange for an amount of money equal to an insurance policy's accumulated value, less any loans on the policy. Upon payout of the cash surrender value, the insurer no longer provides coverage.

Casket Metal, wood, or plastic container in which a deceased's remains are interred.

Categorically needy Definition of financial deficiency required of individuals who receive federally assisted income maintenance payments such as Aid to Families with Dependent Children (AFDC) or Supplemental Security Income (SSI).

Cell Basic living unit of the body.

Cemeterian Owner or staff of a cemetery.

Certificate of deposit (CD) Fixed-income investment vehicle available through financial institutions such as banks, savings and loan associations, and credit unions.Interest rates and maturities of CDs are fixed at the time of purchase. Maturities vary from a few months to a few years, and early redemption may result in the payment of penalties.

Charitable gift annuity Agreement by a charity to provide a lifetime annual payout in exchange for assets received from a donor.

Charitable lead trust (CLT) Institution that accepts assets from a donor and in return pays income to one or more charities while the remainder is distributed to family members at the termination of the trust. Charitable lead trusts generally do not reduce a donor's taxable estate for federal estate tax purposes.

Charitable remainder trust (CRT) Irrevocable agreement between an institution and donor designed to pay income to living beneficiaries. A donor transfers assets into a CRT, reserves an annuity income interest in the property (generally for life), and contributes the remainder interest in the property to the charity or charities at the donor's death.

Chemotherapy Treatment of cancer using specific chemical agents or drugs that are selectively destructive to malignant cells and tissues.

Chronic illness Medical condition with one or more of the following characteristics: permanency, residual disability, requiring rehabilitation training, or requiring a long period of supervision, observation, or care.

Chronically ill Term used in a tax-qualified long-term care contract to describe a person who needs long-term care either because of an inability to do everyday activities of daily living (ADLs) without help or because of a severe cognitive impairment.

Chronological age Calculation of age in terms of number of years a person has lived; calendar age.

Churning Excessive trading (overtrading) by an investor of a client's assets to earn commissions rather than improve the client's situation.

Code of ethics Open disclosure of the way an organization operates, providing members or employees visible guidelines for behavior.

Cognitive impairment Deficiency in a person's: short- or long-term memory; orientation as to person, place, and time; deductive or abstract reasoning; or judgment as it relates to safety awareness.

Columbarium Building with niches or spaces for urns containing the cremated remains of the deceased.

Commercial annuity Agreement by an insurance company (or similar entity) to pay a sum of money to an individual in exchange for receipt of money or property from the individual.

Common-law state A state that deems property originally purchased in that state may not be held as community property.

Community property Assets acquired by either or both spouses during a marriage, if the couple lives in a community property state. In general, each spouse is considered to own half of the property, regardless of who provided the means to purchase or acquire the property and regardless of how title is held.

Community property state A state that deems spouses can own property as community property. These include Alaska, Arizona, California, Idaho, Louisiana, Nevada, New Mexico, Texas, Washington, and Wisconsin.

Community spouse (CS) A spouse who continues to live at home in the community while his or her spouse lives in a nursing home.

Community spouse resource allowance (CSRA) Amount that Medicaid regulations permit a community spouse to retain.

Competence In the context of health care, ability of a patient to make independent decisions about medical treatments.

Compound rate Percentage of interest earned on an investment, expressed either as an annual rate or a rate per compounding period.

Compounding Process of interest accumulating on both a principal balance and previously earned interest.

Comprehensive financial plan A financial plan that covers just about all of a person's financial objectives, including consideration of risk management, investment planning, tax planning, retirement planning, and estate planning.

Compulsions Repeated behaviors (e.g., hand washing, reciting a word to prevent someone from getting hurt, checking locks, cleaning) intended to reduce a person's anxiety, often about an obsession.

Conductive hearing loss Inability of sound waves to pass satisfactorily to the inner ear. Common causes of this are wax buildup in the ear canal, perforated eardrum, fluid in the middle ear, or damage to the ossicles.

Conduit IRA Unofficial term for an IRA used to park a distribution from one qualified plan until it can be rolled over to another qualified plan. With a conduit IRA, the forward-averaging potential of the distribution can be preserved.

Confusion (disorientation) Loss of sense of position in relation to time, space, or other aspects of the environment. Confusion may be the first sign of an illness, such as a urinary tract infection.

Congruent plans Intentions for the future that are consistent, corresponding, and harmonious with each other.

Conservator (guardian of the assets) Person appointed by the court to manage the financial and legal affairs of an incapacitated individual.

Continence Ability to maintain control of bowel and bladder function or, when unable to maintain control of these functions, to perform associated personal hygiene (including caring for catheter or colostomy bag).

Contingent beneficiary Person who stands next in line to receive an asset if the primary beneficiary predeceases the owner or disclaims the asset.

Continuing care retirement community (CCRC, also known as **life care)** Communities that provide a type of combined health, housing, and social care insurance for older persons. A person signs a contract and agrees to pay an entrance fee and a monthly service fee in exchange for a living unit, health care, and lifetime nursing care if needed.

Continuity theory Concept that as people get older they usually seek to pursue the same activities they engaged in earlier in life.

Continuum of incapacity Fluctuation of ability to perform tasks. Many seniors vacillate between being capable and incapable to do many tasks, never being fully able, but also never being completely unable.

Coronary arteries Vessels that supply nutrients and oxygen to the heart muscle.

Coronary artery bypass graft (CABG) Surgical procedure in which one or more blocked coronary arteries are circumvented by a blood vessel graft to restore normal blood flow to the heart. These grafts usually come from the patient's own leg, arm, or chest arteries and veins.

Cost basis Amount paid (i.e., its cost) to purchase a capital asset.

Cost of living adjustment (COLA) Annual fluctuation in wages used to offset a change (usually a loss) in purchasing power, as measured by the

Credits (previously called **quarters of coverage**) Units of work history that determine a worker's eligibility for future Social Security benefits. Workers can earn a maximum of four credits each year, and most people need 40 credits to qualify for benefits. Younger people need fewer credits to qualify for disability or survivor benefits.

Cremation Means of final disposition in which the body is incinerated.

Crematorium (crematory) Facility where a body is cremated.

Crossover claims Statements of claim and payment information from a Medicare fiscal intermediary or carrier used to inform a Medigap insurer of deductibles or coinsurance charges required of the beneficiary. The Medigap insurer uses the crossover claims to pay the provider for deductibles or coinsurance charges the beneficiary would otherwise owe.

Crypt Space in a mausoleum that encloses a casket with the remains of the deceased.

Custodial care (personal care) Care, often provided by someone without professional training, to help individuals meet personal needs such as bathing, dressing, and eating.

Daily benefit Amount of insurance benefit (in dollars) paid to a beneficiary for long-term care expenses.

Decoupling Act of levying a state tax that is not dependent on the rules of the federal system.

Default surrogate Person, in the absence of an advance directive, who has decision-making authority to advise the physician.

Deferred annuity Investment product in which payments do not begin immediately upon funding; rather, they are deferred until a future date.

Delirium Reversible organic mental disorder characterized by disturbances of attention, memory, and orientation, with altered levels of consciousness ranging from mild confusion to stupor. Delusions, illusions, or hallucinations may be present.

Delusion False belief that persists despite logical argument and contradictory evidence.

Delusional disorder Persistent delusions in the absence of other symptoms.

Demand bill Statement of cost submitted by medical care providers to Medicare, even if they think that Medicare will not pay for a service. After a Medicare fiscal intermediary or carrier issues a denial, the senior can request reconsideration or review of the adverse decision.

Demand response (also called **dial-a-ride**) Service that provides transportation from one specific location to another.

Dementia Pervasive cognitive decline that includes: sleep disturbance; loss of interest in pleasurable activities; poor attention or concentration; loss of appetite; agitation or retardation of movement; irritability; memory impairment; difficulty organizing; language deficits; and, in later stages, incontinence.

Demographic transition Change in population structure identified with developing countries and associated improvements in public health and medicine. According to the demographic theory, as countries become developed, they experience a shift in growth rate from rapid population growth to slow growth, from slow growth to zero growth, and finally to a reduction in population.

Diabetes Metabolic disorder in which the body is unable to properly utilize glucose. May be Type 1 IDDM (insulin-dependent diabetes mellitus) or Type 2 NIDDM (non-insulin dependent diabetes mellitus).

Diabetic ketoacidosis Emergency condition in which extremely high blood glucose levels, along with a severe lack of insulin, result in the breakdown of body fat for energy and an accumulation of ketones in the blood and urine.

Diastolic pressure Measurement (the bottom number of a blood pressure reading) of the pressure remaining in the arteries between heartbeats.

Direct cremation Disposition where the deceased is cremated without embalming or funeral service with the body present.

Direct rollover Tax-free transfer of cash or other property between two taxdeferred retirement plans (i.e., qualified plans, IRAs, 403(b) plans, governmental Section 457 plans, etc.) where the transferred cash or property never passes through the hands of the owner.

Disability Reduction in functional capacity that results from physiological, psychological, or social impairments. Short- and long-term disability are a result of acute and chronic conditions, respectively.

Disclaim Act of waiving the right to an inheritance, resulting in the inheritance passing to the next in line, in accordance with the terms of the will, trust, or laws of intestacy.

Discrimination Behaviors, specifically those that restrict, impair, exploit, humiliate, or otherwise hurt seniors.

Disease Interruption in the process of health, manifested by abnormalities or disturbances of functioning.

Disinhibition Personal loss of normal behavioral limits or self-restraint, as through the influence of external stimuli such as drugs or alcohol, or as a result of brain damage.

Distribution Outflow from a retirement plan. For mutual funds, a payment by a mutual fund to shareholders, either in cash or shares, for dividends received from securities in the fund or capital gains generated from the sale of securities in the fund.

Diversification The process or strategy of investing in different types of assets to reduce risk.

Domestic elder abuse Mistreatment of an older person by someone who has a special relationship with the elder (spouse, sibling, child, friend, or caregiver) in either the older person's home or in the home of the caregiver.

Do not resuscitate (DNR) order Physician's order, inserted into a patient's medical chart, stating that CPR shall not be used as a lifesaving procedure.

Dressing Putting on and taking off all items of clothing and any necessary braces, fasteners, or artificial limbs.

Durable power of attorney for health care (proxy statement) Legal document prepared by an individual authorizing a family member or friend to make health care decisions on their behalf in case of incompetence.

Dual enrollees Individuals covered by both Medicare and Medicaid.

Dysphagia Condition in which some stroke patients have trouble eating and swallowing.

Dysthymia Chronic, less severe form of depression including depressed mood most of the day, most days, for at least two years that causes significant distress or impairment in daily functioning.

Earned income credit (EIC) Refundable tax credit created to assist low-income working families.

Eating Feeding of oneself by getting food into the body from a receptacle (such as a plate, cup, or table) or through feeding tube or intravenous delivery.

Elder cottage housing opportunity (ECHO) Small, freestanding, removable housing units, typically in the side or backyard of a single-family home to provide housing for elderly parents so that they can be near their adult children for mutual aid and support but still live independently.

Electroconvulsive therapy Treatment that involves inducing a brain seizure by passing an electrical current through the brain for a few seconds via small electrodes attached to the head.

Elimination period (waiting period) Length of time an individual must pay for covered services before the insurance company will begin to make payments. It serves as a kind of deductible: The longer the elimination period in a policy, the lower the premium.

Embalming Process in which the body fluid of a decedent are drained and chemicals inserted to retard decay.

Emergency fund Reserve of cash or cash equivalents (i.e., assets that could be quickly converted to cash without loss of principal) available to handle emergencies. Financial planners typically recommend an amount equal to three to six months of fixed and variable expenses.

Empathy Process of identifying with and understanding another's circumstances, feelings, and motives.

Employee Retirement Income Security Act of 1974 (ERISA) Federal law governing the operation of most private tax-deferred retirement plans. Qualified employer-sponsored retirement plans must comply with ERISA.

Endurance activity Activity that lasts at least 30 minutes, conducted to increase breathing and build stamina, which supports independence and enjoyment of activities.

Equity Ownership, in particular pertaining to having the right to share in future profits or appreciation in value (e.g., of property or stock).

Error theory Hypothesis that aging is caused by environmental attacks to our body systems, resulting in damage over time.

Escort service Transportation business or agency that picks up clients at home, guides them through appointments, and then returns them home.

Estate All property interests a person owns, including property over which the person exercises decisive control.

Estate plan Documents that detail the instructions to be followed during disability or after death. People without an estate plan in effect choose to let the laws of the state provide the instructions to be followed during disability or after death.

Estate planning Process of directing one's affairs to provide income, investments, and appropriation of assets for oneself or others during life and upon disability or death.

Estate tax Tariff levied upon a decedent's estate by the federal government and some states, based on the value of the decedent's assets at death.

Estrogen Sex hormone found primarily in women, but also in small amounts in men. This hormone has many roles, one of which is to slow thinning of bone as one ages, but it also may help prevent frailty and disability.

Ethical wills Systematic writing down or communicating one's intangible legacy of values to children and family members.

Euthanasia Act or practice of terminating (which can take a variety of forms) the life of a person.

Excess charge Fifteen percent markup on Medicare's approved amount allowed to physicians who do not accept assignment.

Exclusion In the context of income tax, amount not considered when calculating gross income. Includes amounts that otherwise would be included in a taxpayer's gross income, except that a particular code section specifically provides for their noninclusion. Common exclusions include those for municipal bond income, gifts and inheritances, death proceeds from a life insurance policy, and the gain (limited by IRS code) from selling a principal residence.

Executive functioning Group of mental processes that includes problem solving, abstract thinking (recognizing, for example, that an apple and an orange are both fruit), organization, and judgment.

Executor (executrix or personal representative [PR]) Representative responsible for distributing property when an individual dies with a valid will.

Extraordinary medical measures Medical treatment that would not provide a distinct benefit, would not serve a patient's best interest, or would be considered unreasonable in improving or saving a patient's life.

Family household Group of two or more people related by birth, marriage, or adoption and residing together, along with other unrelated people who may be living in the housing unit.

Family limited partnership (FLP) Agreement among family members about how to manage and own family wealth. In this agreement, it is common for the business owner to maintain control of the business while transferring title.

Family partnership Business agreement limited to only family members. Used by senior family members to transfer interests in the business to junior family members at a reduced gift tax cost by means of valuation discounts.

Fiber Portions of plants that mammals cannot digest and, therefore, cannot be absorbed through human intestines.

Filing status Categorization of taxpayers used to determine deduction amounts and tax assessments. Each filer declares a filing status in their tax return: married filing jointly (or separately), single, head of household, estates, and trusts.

Financial planning Development and implementation of total, coordinated plans designed to achieve an individual's financial objectives.

Fiscal intermediaries (Medicare Part A) Private companies contracted by the government to make coverage determinations and process Medicare claims.

Fixed-amount annuity Retirement product in which the dollar amount of the payout must be at least the amount of the premium paid. If the annuitant dies before full receipt of this amount, the remainder is payable to a beneficiary. The annuitant receives payments until death, even after the guaranteed amount is paid.

Fixed-amount settlement option Provides the beneficiary a stated amount of income each month until life insurance proceeds are exhausted. Each payment consists partly of interest and partly of principal. The insurer guarantees a minimum rate, but usually pays the rate actually earned on investments.

Fixed-income security Investment that promises a stated amount of income, either in the form of periodic payments (such as interest) or a stated ending payout (such as with zero coupon bonds). Because payouts are fixed, these securities tend to be subject to interest rate risk and purchasing power risk.

Fixed-period annuity Retirement product in which the number of payments that a recipient will receive is guaranteed. If the recipient dies before the guaranteed number of payments has been distributed, the balance is payable to the beneficiary. If the annuitant outlives the guaranteed period, he or she will continue to receive payments until death; however, no benefits would be payable to a beneficiary in such a case.

Fixed-period settlement option Retirement product stipulation that establishes a fixed period of time over which payments of life insurance policies are made to a beneficiary. Payment amounts vary based on the payout term chosen.

Fixed-route and scheduled services Services that transport seniors along an established travel circuit with designated stops where riders can board and be dropped off.

Freedom-of-choice law State statute that designates the next of kin to make funeral arrangements.

Free look Period of time during which an investor may review contract and agreement papers while reserving the option to cancel or not commit to an investment or plan.

Fully insured Having earned enough credits (previously called quarters of coverage) under Social Security. A fully insured person is eligible for survivors' benefits for a qualified spouse, child, or dependent parent; a death benefit payment; and retirement benefits for himself or herself, a qualified spouse, and a qualified child. Most people need 40 credits to qualify for benefits.

Functional age Age as determined by what activities or actions a person is capable of.

Funeral Ritual conducted to honor a decedent whose body is present.

Funeral director Individual licensed by the states to arrange or prearrange funeral services.

Funeral rule Trade rule issued by the Federal Trade Commission requiring funeral homes to disclose prices and prohibiting certain deceptive and unfair practices.

Garden plot Cemetery gravesite that has no above-ground marker.

Gasketed Term that describes a burial casket that has seals and other features that retard the entrance of water and protect against rust.

Gatekeeper In the context of home observation programs, a service person who visits a home regularly and is trained to notice anything unusual or any indication of need and report it to the local Area Agency on Aging.

General enrollment period Time span (January 1 through March 31 of each year) during which eligible seniors may sign up for Medicare. The effective date of coverage is the following July 1.

Generalized anxiety disorder Medical condition that impairs daily functioning, in which the sufferer experiences excessive worry or anxiety about multiple things.

Generativity Act of attention to one's legacy for future generations.

Geriatric nurse practitioner (GNP) Nurses who have completed advanced clinical education (often master's degree level) that focuses on the health and disease issues faced by seniors.

Geriatricians Medical doctors (MD) or osteopaths (DO) who have completed a fellowship-training program in geriatrics.

Geriatrics Medical study of aging.

Gerontology Scientific study of the biological, psychological, and social aspects of aging.

Gerostranscendence Distinctive path toward age-connected spirituality that theorizes that seniors are predisposed to consider the spiritual dimension, which includes a preoccupation with the interconnection among generations, the relation between life and death, and the mystery of life.

Gift splitting Act of doubling tax exclusion amounts of $11,000 per person per year by each exercising the exclusion, effectively allowing a couple to gift a total of $22,000.

Glaucoma Elevated pressure within the eye that can result in damage to the retina.

Glucose tolerance Ability of the body to control blood sugar (glucose).

Grave liner Product used to limit ground settlement with in-ground burials. Liners are usually made of concrete.

Grief Psychological response to the loss of a loved person or object.

Gross income Amount used as the starting point for calculating income taxes. It includes all income from all sources (except excludible income, such as municipal bond interest). Items such as wages, commissions, tips, honoraria, interest, dividends, net business income, rents, royalties, gambling income, and partnership income all must be recognized and included in gross income for tax purposes.

Growth hormone Human hormone that promotes physical growth through the complex interaction of several hormones and growth factors.

Guaranteed renewable Condition of an insurance policy that, unless its benefits have been exhausted, it cannot be cancelled by an insurance company and must be renewed when it expires. Under this condition, the company cannot change the coverage or refuse to renew the coverage for any reason, including health condition and marital or employment status, other than nonpayment of premiums.

Guardian Court-appointed fiduciary responsible for a minor or incompetent person.

Hallucination False perception believed to be real that occurs in the absence of adequate sensory experience.

Hands-on assistance Physical help (minimal, moderate, or maximal) without which an individual would not be able to perform one or more activities of daily living.

Health care Treatment or procedure to diagnose or attempt to relieve or cure a physical condition.

Health care proxy Individual in an advance directive named to make health care decisions when the patient is incapacitated.

Health Insurance Portability and Accountability Act (HIPAA) Federal health insurance legislation passed in 1996 that allows, under specified conditions, long-term care insurance policies to be qualified for certain tax benefits.

Health maintenance organization (HMO) Institution that provides comprehensive service benefits, with emphasis on preventive care. Care is typically provided through physicians and facilities that contract with, or are managed by, the organization.

Heir Person entitled to inherit property under state intestacy statutes.

Hemiparesis One-sided weakness, though less debilitating than paralysis.

Hemiplegia Paralysis on one side of the body, a common disability that results from stroke.

Hemorrhagic stroke Bursting of a brain artery that spreads blood into the surrounding tissue.

High-density lipoprotein (HDL) "Good cholesterol" that appears to act as a kind of scouring agent, cleansing the arteries of plaque.

Home and community-based service (HCBS) Service that allows people of all ages who have physical limitations to remain independent in the least restrictive setting possible and to be connected with their community.

Home and community-based services waiver Also called 1915(c) waiver, stipulation that gives states the flexibility to develop and implement creative alternatives to institutionalization.

Home health care In-home services for nursing care or occupational, physical, respiratory, or speech therapy. Also included are medical, social worker, home health aide, and homemaker services. Home health care services may be temporary, intermittent, or long-term.

Homebound Condition in which a patient has a normal inability to leave home and leaving home requires a considerable and taxing effort.

Homemaker services Companies who assume duties required in a normal household when a homeowner or resident is unable to complete such duties themselves.

Homesharing Living arrangement in which a homeowner rents out a room or rooms in exchange for either rent or a combination of companionship, housework, yard work, grocery shopping, or rent.

Hospice Medical institution focused on meeting the physical, emotional, and spiritual needs of those dying and their grieving families.

Household The people who occupy a single housing unit. A household includes related family members and all the unrelated people, if any, such as boarders, foster children, etc., who live together. A person living alone or a group of unrelated people living together, such as partners or roommates, is also counted as a household.

Housing unit Apartment, house, trailer, or any other structure designed for people to live in.

Hyperosmolarity Condition in which the blood is concentrated with sodium, glucose, and other molecules that normally attract water into the bloodstream. When the kidneys are conserving water, however, this creates a vicious cycle of increasing blood-glucose levels and increasing dehydration.

Hypertension Abnormally high blood pressure.

Immediate burial Final disposition in which the deceased is buried without embalming or a funeral service with the body present.

Impoverishment Outliving one's income or assets.

Incapacity (loss of capacity) Patient's inability, as determined by a physician, to make their own health care decisions, caused by pain, medications, brain damage, or an unconscious state.

Income cap states States that set an income threshold for Medicaid disability and deny applications based upon the existence of income that exceeds the threshold.

Incontinence Inability to control the release of urine and feces.

Indemnity method Process of paying insurance benefits in which the benefit is a set dollar amount and is not based on a specific service received or on expenses incurred. The insurance company needs to decide only if you are eligible for benefits.

Indirect rollover Transfer of cash or other property between tax-deferred retirement plans, including but not limited to qualified plans or IRAs, in which the owner takes temporary receipt of the funds. The amount rolled over is tax-free and without penalty if completed by the 60th day after the distribution from an IRA or employer plan. Indirect rollovers from qualified plans and 403(b) plans are subject to mandatory withholding by the employer.

Individual annuity Investment product that provides annual payments over the life of one individual.

Individual retirement account (IRA) Investment plan that any individual with earned income can establish and fund. An individual may contribute no more than $3,000 in one year to an IRA, and the contribution may be fully deductible, partially deductible, or not deductible.

Infantilize To treat or condescend a person as if they were still a young child.

Infarction Death of brain cells.

Inflation General increase in the level of prices within the economy due to the devaluation of the dollar (i.e., more dollars are required to buy a particular item).

Inflation protection Insurance policy option that provides for increases in benefit levels to help pay for expected increases in the costs of long-term care services.

Inflow Pertaining to the cash flow statement, the dollars, such as from salary, dividends, interest, rental income, alimony, child support, or investment redemptions, received by an individual during a particular period.

Informal support network Group of people, composed of family members, friends, and neighbors, who collectively care for someone who faces chronic illness or disability.

Information return Tax return that provides information to the tax collector but does not compute the tax liability.

Information triage Narrowing of information by the brain to a level or amount the conscious mind can handle.

Informed consent Legal condition whereby a person can be said to have agreed or given consent to allow something to happen based on a full appreciation and understanding of the facts and implications of the action.

Initial enrollment period Span of time during which seniors who did not elect to take early retirement benefits may enroll in Medicare. They have seven months to enroll, starting three months before the month of their 65th birthday.

Institutional abuse Mistreatment of an older person living in a residential facility (e.g., nursing home, foster home, group home, or board and care facility) by people who have a legal or contractual obligation (e.g., as paid caregivers, staff, or professionals) to provide the elder victim with care and protection.

Institutionalized spouse (IS) Spouse who lives in a nursing facility while the partner continues living at home.

Instrumental activity of daily living (IADL) Activities needed for independent living, including using the telephone, preparing food, shopping, and handling finances.

Insurance Device by which an individual can contract with another party to exchange a large, uncertain risk for a relatively small, certain premium.

Insidious onset Development of a disease in which the disease's presence is not apparent at the beginning.

Interest settlement option Beneficiary's choice to leave life insurance proceeds with the insurer to accumulate interest at a guaranteed rate. Many insurers pay interest above the guaranteed rate, consistent with investment earnings.

Interment In-ground burial.

Interdependence Mutual, reciprocal relationship between two or more people, whereby people get their needs met better together than they would alone and can also increase the resources available to a person.

Intestate Condition in which a person dies without a valid will in place. Property in such cases is distributed in accordance with state law.

Intimacy Mutual exchange of affection, trust, and confidence.

Intubation Threading a tube to a patient's lungs to provide ventilation or mechanical respiration.

Inurnment Placing cremated remains in an urn.

Invasive cancer Cancer that progresses to invade surrounding tissues.

Irrevocable beneficiary designation Assignment of a beneficiary to a life insurance policy in which the policy owner does not retain the right to change the named beneficiary.

Irrevocable life insurance trust (ILIT) Institution that owns the life insurance policies of a person. It pays the premiums to keep the insurance in force, collects the death benefits when the insured dies, and distributes the money according to the terms of the trust.

Ischemic stroke Sudden block of an artery supplying the brain with blood that decreases or stops blood flow to the brain.

Itemized deduction Specialized expenses (such as home mortgage interest paid, state and local income taxes, real and personal property taxes, and charitable contributions) that are totaled and then subtracted from adjusted gross income in the tax calculation process. Total itemized deductions are used in place of the standard deduction if the total itemized deduction amount exceeds the standard deduction amount for the taxpayer.

Joint and last survivor annuity Annuity product option in which the annuity is paid over the lifetimes of more than one person. When the first annuitant dies, the annuity payments for the survivor continue, but are sometimes reduced by a quarter or half.

Joint survivorship life insurance Life insurance that covers more than one life. First-to-die life insurance pays benefits upon the death of the first of the two parties to die.

Joint tenants Property that is owned simultaneously by more than one person.

Lawn crypt Below-ground mausoleum.

Lean body mass Total of all parts of the body that are not body fat and are biologically active tissues (e.g., bones, vital organ tissue, central nervous system).

Level of burden index Scale that measures the challenges caregivers face. The index combines the number of ADLs and IADLs that require help, as well as the amount of time devoted to care giving.

Life expectancy Length of time that estimates the number of years a person will live.

Life income annuity Annuity product in which payments are distributed only until the annuitant dies. No benefits are payable to a beneficiary.

Life income with period certain settlement option Life insurance option in which payments are guaranteed for a stated amount of time, such as 10 or 20 years, after which, if the annuitant is still alive, he or she continues to receive payments until death, but there is no benefit for a beneficiary. If the annuitant dies before the guaranteed period is over, payments continue to a beneficiary until the end of the guaranteed period.

Life span Maximum length of time biologically possible for a given species.

Life stage Combination of physical and social attributes that define periods of a person's life, such as adolescence, young adulthood, adulthood, middle age, later maturity, and old age.

Lifelines (life review) Activity in which participants recall key events and life altering or meaningful experiences that powerfully affected their lives.

Life-sustaining procedure Medical treatment used to prolong life without reversing underlying medical conditions. This could include mechanical ventilation, renal dialysis, chemotherapy, artificial nutrition and hydration, and other treatments.

Lifetime reserve days Sixty days of coverage guaranteed to each Medicare beneficiary who has exhausted a standard benefit period's 90 inpatient days and remains hospitalized.

Lipoprotein Combination of cholesterol and protein that circulates in the bloodstream.

Living trust (inter vivos trust) Trust that is established during the life of the grantor. A revocable trust is a trust that can be changed or revoked at any time by the individual who established it.

Living will Document signed by a competent person stating what health care measures should or should not be taken in terminal situations if the person is incompetent to make such decisions at that time.

Look-back period Span of time beginning on the date of a Medicaid application going back thirty-six (36) months for transfers of money to an individual and sixty (60) months for transfers to trusts. Transfers within the look-back period create a period of Medicaid ineligibility.

Long-term care insurance (LTCI) Coverage for various custodial care expenses in the event the insured becomes incapacitated as defined in the policy.

Long-term care rider Sometimes included as an attachment to life insurance policies, provides coverage for various custodial care expenses in the event that the insured person becomes incapacitated as defined in the policy.

Low-density lipoprotein (LDL) "Bad cholesterol" that contributes to the development of heart disease by causing waxy, obstructive plaque buildup within the coronary arteries of the heart.

Lump-sum distribution Retirement plan distribution that meets the following four requirements: made in one taxable year; representative of the full balance to the participant's credit from all qualified plans of a single type; payable due to the participant's death, attainment of age $59^{1/2}$ or (for common-law employees only) separation from service; and made from a qualified pension, profit sharing, or stock bonus plan.

Macular degeneration Deterioration of the tissue in the center of the retina (the macula) resulting in decreased central vision and reduced ability to see fine detail.

Magnetic resonance imaging (MRI) Procedure using a nuclear magnetic resonance spectrometer to produce electronic images of specific atoms and molecular structures in solids, especially human cells, tissues, and organs.

Major depressive episode Period of more than two weeks in which a person feels sad or has a loss of interest or enjoyment in life; and changes in appetite and sleep, agitation or retardation of movement, fatigue, feelings of worthlessness or guilt, attention and concentration problems, or thoughts of suicide.

Major medical insurance Insurance that covers medical expenses incurred inside and outside of a hospital. It features cost sharing devices (such as deductibles and coinsurance) and a relatively high maximum limit for covered expenses.

Mania Period of elevated or irritable mood, inflated self esteem, decreased need for sleep, extreme talkativeness, racing thoughts or shifting ideas, high distractibility, increased activity, or dangerous behavior that impairs daily functioning.

Marginal tax bracket Tax rate at which the last dollar of income is taxed.

Married couple household with own children Husband and wife living together with children by birth, adoption, or marriage who are under the age of 18 and never married.

Marital deduction Tax deduction that allows for unlimited gifts to a spouse who is an American citizen.

Marital trust Trust that mandates that the income of the trust be paid to the surviving spouse.

Mausoleum Building containing crypts for the burial of the dead.

Means-tested Description of a program that is available to those who meet financial requirements, such as Medicaid.

Medicaid Program that provides medical assistance for certain individuals and families who have low incomes and resources. It is a jointly funded cooperative program between the federal and state governments.

Medical model Delivery of health care under the supervision of physicians and nurses.

Medically needy Definition of Medicaid applicants whose income levels are higher than others receiving assistance but who have medical bills in excess of their income.

Medicare Federal program providing hospital and medical insurance to people ages 65 or older and to certain ill or disabled persons. Benefits for nursing home and home health services are limited.

Medigap Insurance sold by private companies that is intended to supplement Medicare coverage.

Melatonin Hormone that appears to play a part in regulating seasonal changes in the body and assists with sleep.

Member of a protected class Individuals residing in a family home who qualify it as a non-countable resource in the Medicaid application. The members include the applicant's spouse, a child under 21, a child of any age who is blind or permanently and totally disabled, a brother or sister with an equity interest in the home and who resided in the home for at least one year preceding the Medicaid application, or any child who was residing in the home for two years prior to admission to the nursing home and providing care that permitted the applicant to stay in the home.

Memorial park Cemetery restricting burials to garden plots or sites with no above-ground markers.

Memorial service Ritual to honor the dead without the body being present.

Memorialization Installation of a grave marker or memorial to honor the dead.

Mercy killing Intentional act of a health care provider or individual to take the life of a patient. This is a criminal offense, regardless of the motivation.

Metabolism Body's chemical processes that build and destroy tissue and release energy, thereby generating heat.

Metastatic cancer Cancer that migrates to distant locations.

Mild cognitive impairment (MCI) Subtle but measurable memory disorder. A person with MCI experiences memory problems greater than normally expected with aging, but they do not show other symptoms of dementia, such as impaired judgment or reasoning.

Miller Trust Certain trust that may be set up to create an exemption to help an applicant qualify for Medicaid.

Minimum monthly maintenance needs allowance (MMMNA) Certain portion of an institutionalized spouse's income permitted to a community spouse to bring the community spouse's income up the minimum monthly maintenance needs allowance.

Minimum required distribution Amount that must be withdrawn from a retirement account once a certain age is reached.

Molecule Smallest unit into which a substance can be divided.

Money market deposit account Investment vehicle available through savings and loan associations and banks. Earnings rates are determined by the institution and tend to be lower than rates for money market funds.

Mourning Social and cultural response to loss.

Mutual fund Open-end investment tool that pools the money of many investors and hires an investment adviser to invest that money in order to achieve one or more financial objectives.

Net worth Residual value after liabilities are subtracted from assets. Net worth represents the amount that is owned by an individual or family if unencumbered by debt.

Neuroplasticity Ability to learn new things even into advanced age.

Nondeductible IRA Individual retirement account in which contributions are taxable as part of current income.

Nonforfeiture option Limited to permanent life insurance policies, the three standard non-forfeiture options are: lump-sum distribution of cash value, reduced paid-up insurance, and extended term insurance.

Nonparticipating life policy Insurance agreement in which excess premium payments (dividends) are not distributed to the policy owner.

Noncancelable policy Insurance contract that cannot be cancelled nor have its rates changed by the insurance company.

Nonfamily household Person living alone, or two or more people who live together but who are not related, such as roommates or boarders.

Normal retirement age Age at which full Social Security old-age benefits are available or otherwise specified in documents.

Nursing home (nursing facility, skilled nursing home) Specifically qualified facility that has the staff and equipment to provide round-the-clock skilled nursing care or rehabilitation services as well as other related health services. On average, its occupants need at least some assistance with an average of 3.8 activities of daily living.

Old-Age, Survivors, Disability, and Health Insurance (OASDHI) program Protection for qualified participants and their beneficiaries against losses associated with retirement, death, disability, and illness.

Old-Age, Survivors, and Disability Insurance (OASDI) Technical name for the Social Security program

Obsession Persistent thought, idea, or image that is anxiety provoking and, at least initially, believed by an individual to be absurd.

Obsessive-compulsive disorder (OCD) Mental condition defined by recurrent obsessions or compulsions that are severe enough to impair the individual's daily functioning.

Occupational therapist Health professional who works with patients to improve their ability to perform activities of daily living and tasks in their work environment.

Organ Aggregate of many different cells, held together by a supporting structure, that performs a specific function in the body.

Organizational determination Date from which a person has 60 days to request review of coverage denial under a Medicare Advantage plan.

Osteoarthritis Noninflammatory disorder of movable joints characterized by an imbalance between the synthesis and degradation of the articular cartilage, leading to the classic pathologic changes of wearing away and destruction of cartilage.

Osteoporosis Weakening of bone structure as bone cell breakdown outpaces new bone cell formation.

Outflow Expenditure or use of cash.

Outer burial container Generic term used to describe grave liners and vaults.

Out-of-hospital do not resuscitate (DNR) order Doctor's order authorizing emergency medical services technicians to honor a DNR order. Patients may wear some form of identification, such as a bracelet to inform technicians of the DNR.

Palliative care (comfort care) End-of-life care focused not on curing a disease or condition, but on treating pain and physical symptoms, along with providing emotional and spiritual support.

Panic attack Limited period (usually several minutes) of intense fear that comes on unexpectedly, accompanied by multiple physical symptoms.

Parkinson's disease Progressive nervous disease, occurring most often after the age of 50, associated with the destruction of brain cells that produce dopamine. Parkinson's disease is characterized by muscular tremor, slowing of movement, partial facial paralysis, peculiarity of gait and posture, and weakness.

Participating policy Life insurance policy in which dividends (actually a return of premiums that were excessive, given the insurer's actual claims experience or level of expenses) may be paid to the policy owner.

Partnership policy Type of policy that allows the insured to protect (keep) some assets if they apply for Medicaid after using policy benefits.

Patient's best interest Guideline for use by proxy, physician, or hospital ethics committees for determining health care decisions when a senior's treatment wishes are unknown.

Patient Self Determination Act (42 U.S.C. 1985cc(f) and 1396a(w) Federal legislation requiring institutional health care providers participating in the Medicare or Medicaid programs to inform patients of their right to complete advance directives.

Payable-on-death (POD) account Savings account opened with a funeral director or cemeterian used to fund services, burial, or cremation upon death of the accountholder.

Pension plan Qualified, employee retirement plan. A defined benefit plan provides a specified retirement benefit to participants. A defined contribution pension plan usually provides for periodic contributions from the employee, specified in a written formula, and an unspecified retirement benefit equal to the value of a participant's account balance at retirement.

Permanent life insurance Policy that has cash value and is designed to be kept until death. Permanent life insurance contracts include: adjustable life, endowments, interest sensitive whole life, limited pay policies, universal life, variable life, variable universal life, and whole life.

Perpetual care Service and fund to maintain a grave site forever.

Persistent vegetative state Condition that limits cognitive function, caused by injury to the cerebral cortex.

Personal emergency response system (PERS) Electronic device designed to let a user summon help in an emergency.

Personal exemption Dollar amount that a taxpayer generally may deduct for each person supported by the income reported on the tax form. Exemptions are subject to phase-out (elimination) based on an excess of the adjusted gross income over a specified threshold amount.

Personal financial planning Process of determining whether and how an individual can meet life goals through the proper management of financial income and assets.

Personal model (consumer-directed personal assistance services) Method of individual health care delivery in which a senior receives in-home services from personal assistants who are not supervised by medical professionals.

Phobia Extreme fear of a specific situation or object.

Physical therapist Health professional who provides services to help patients restore function, improve mobility, relieve pain, and prevent physical disabilities.

Polypharmacy Management of multiple prescription medications for seniors dealing with several chronic illnesses simultaneously.

Power of attorney Written document executed by one person who authorizes another person to act on his or her behalf.

Planned giving Method of distributing assets that provides donors with additional economic benefits for themselves or other beneficiaries. Planned giving includes the use of charitable gift annuities, pooled income trusts, charitable trusts split interest gifts, and charitable family limited partnerships.

Planned senior apartment (also known as **independent living, congregate living facility**) Housing designated for and designed with specific features for older people. Services offered can range from basic maintenance to housekeeping, meal plans, social activities, transportation, and exercise rooms.

Plasticity (brain plasticity) Ability of the brain to learn and change.

Posttraumatic stress disorder (PTSD) Mental condition stemming from a traumatic event. It may involve recurrent thoughts, nightmares, or feelings of reliving the event, great distress, avoidance of thoughts of people who were involved in the event, feeling distant from others, having difficulty experiencing emotions, irritability, trouble sleeping or concentrating, and hyperawareness of surroundings.

Pour-over will Provision of a will that instructs a court to transfer, or pour over, a dead person's probate assets into a trust, used if a senior has a trust and dies owning property that was not transferred to it.

Prearrangement Advance planning for a funeral or burial, sometimes structured with an agreement to deliver specific goods and services.

Prejudice Negative attitude toward a category or group of people based not on current experience but on preconceived beliefs; favorable or unfavorable belief about the characteristics of a category or a group.

Preneed Funeral or cemetery purchase made before a death.

Preneed plan Arrangement for a funeral or burial in advance of need.

Presbycusis The most commmon age-related hearing loss; a sensorineural disturbance caused by death of the hair cells in the inner ear.

Primary insurance amount (PIA) Monthly payment to retired workers who begin receiving benefits at full retirement age or if they are disabled and have never received a retirement benefit reduced for age.

Private annuity Transfer of property to an individual not regularly engaged in the issuance of annuities, in exchange for an unsecured promise of periodic lifetime payments.

Private contract Agreement for medical services between a patient and a provider who does not give services through Medicare. Assignment does not apply to private contracts.

Probate Legal process of administering and distributing an estate after death.

Productive aging Concept of the older population with greater capacity for employment, volunteering, and caregiving. As the older population has become healthier, more active, and more economically secure, productive aging has emerged to contradict the mostly negative view of older adults as frail, immobile, vulnerable, or unable to contribute to society.

Professionally managed service Care arrangement in which someone other than the senior makes the decisions about care and services.

Program of All-Inclusive Care for the Elderly (PACE) Health insurance benefit that features a comprehensive medical and social service delivery system and integrated Medicare and Medicaid funding.

Programmed theory Hypothesis that aging follows a biological timetable.

Psychotic Condition in which an individual exhibits symptoms of not being in touch with reality, primarily through hallucinations and delusions.

Pure life income option Life insurance stipulation that pays proceeds over the lifetime of the beneficiary, with no residual benefits available to a second beneficiary if the first one dies.

Qualitative Relating to or expressed in terms of quality. Qualitative research is based on individual, often subjective, analysis.

Quantitative Relating to or involving the measurement of quantity or amount. Quantitative research is often considered objective and repeatable by separate researchers under similar conditions.

Quarter of coverage Measurement used to determine a worker's insured status (fully or currently) and, therefore, the amount and type of benefits available under Social Security. A worker is credited with one quarter of coverage, up to a maximum of four annually, for each $500 of earnings through covered employment.

Radiation therapy Use of x-rays or gamma rays to kill tumor cells in difficult to reach locations. Radiation is also used to eliminate a tumor without destroying large amounts of good tissue.

Reasonable and necessary care Medicare rule used to categorize individual health care decisions.

Rebating Giving or promising a valuable gift if in exchange for the purchases of an insurance policy or other investment.

Reduced paid-up insurance option Life insurance stipulation allowing a policyholder to take the cash value of a policy as paid-up but for a reduced face amount.

Refund life income settlement option Life insurance option that provides the beneficiary with lifetime income with the guarantee that if the beneficiary dies before receiving the full amount of the original life insurance proceeds, the shortfall will be paid to an alternate beneficiary.

Religiosity Devoutness or excessive devotion to religion.

Remains Body of the deceased. (Cremains are remains of a cremated body.)

Representative payee Individual or organization that receives Social Security or SSI payments on behalf of an individual who cannot manage or direct someone else to manage his or her money.

Required beginning date (RBD) For individual retirement accounts (IRAs), qualified plans, and section 403(b) arrangements, the date by which distributions must begin.

Required minimum distribution (minimum distribution) Lowest annual required distribution amount for an IRA holder who reaches age 70½.

Respite care Occasional care provided by a third party for the purpose of relieving family caregivers for a period of a few hours to several days.

Revocable beneficiary designation Naming of a life insurance beneficiary in which the policy owner retains the right to change the beneficiary.

Rheumatoid arthritis Chronic disease marked by stiffness and inflammation of the joints, weakness, loss of mobility, and deformity.

Rider Addition to an insurance policy that changes the provisions of the policy.

Ridesharing program Service that arranges for seniors to be driven by volunteer drivers to specific destinations.

Right of survivorship Right inherent in some forms of property ownership that entitles surviving owners to succeed to a deceased owner's interest in the property outside of probate.

Role Pattern of individual activity that occurs within a specific type of social situation.

Rollover Movement of funds from one retirement plan to another.

Roth IRA Nondeductible IRA with several unique features: Withdrawals are not taxable if left in the account for five years; the owner may continue to make contributions to the account after he or she is age 70½; and there is no required beginning date for withdrawals.

Sarcopenia Combination muscle loss and increased body fat that results in overall weakening of the body.

Schizophrenia Chronic and severely disabling disorder with symptoms of hallucinations and delusions, disorganized speech and behavior, and deficiency of motivation, emotional expression, or speech.

Section 1115 demonstration waiver Medicaid rule that offers flexibility to states in delivering Medicaid long-term care services.

Self-employment tax Social Security tax imposed on income earned by self-employed individuals.

Self-neglect Behavior of some older adults, such as refusing or failing to acquire adequate food, water, clothing, shelter, personal hygiene, medication, or safety precautions, which threatens their health or safety.

Senescence Progressive deterioration of many bodily functions over a period of time.

Separate property Property that was acquired by either spouse before marriage or individually inherited, individually received as a gift, or purchased with individual funds. Ownership of this property belongs exclusively to the spouse that held it prior to marriage, inherited or received it, or purchased it with individual funds.

Sepsis Infection in the blood or other tissues.

Serial caregiving Care giving in which each successive caregiver burns out and is replaced by another person.

Serotonin reuptake inhibitor Medicine that relieves symptoms of depression.

Skilled care Daily nursing and rehabilitative care that can be performed only by or under the supervision of skilled medical personnel. This care is usually needed 24 hours a day, must be ordered by a physician, and must follow a plan of care. Individuals usually get skilled care in a nursing home but may also receive it in other places.

Social gerontology Study of the social lives of older people.

Social phobia Extreme fear of public or performance situations in which an individual may feel threatened or embarrassed.

Social policy Actions of governments in making decisions and allocations for social programs such as Social Security, Medicare, and Older Americans Act programs.

Social Security Government program in which covered workers meeting certain past-service requirements and their qualified dependents are eligible for limited retirement, medical, disability, and death benefits. The program is funded through a special income tax on covered workers.

Social Security Disability Income (SSDI) Benefit for disabled people under full retirement age who have enough Social Security credits and a severe medical impairment (physical or mental) that is expected to prevent them from doing substantial work for a year or more, or have a condition that is expected to result in death.

Social support Network that provides people with a sense of being loved, cared for, esteemed, and valued.

Society Extended group of relationships that has a distinctive cultural and economic organization.

Special enrollment period Time after an employer's health plan coverage ceases to be a person's primary insurance (usually at retirement), during which a senior may enroll in Medicare without penalty.

Spending down Expending assets in order to qualify for Medicaid.

Spirituality Basic value around which all other values are focused; central philosophy of life that guides a person's conduct; supernatural and nonmaterial dimensions of human nature.

Stage model of grief Theory of emotional progression through distinct stages in response to a traumatic event or loss.

Standard deduction Deduction from adjusted gross income that any taxpayer may take, with the amount available being determined by the taxpayer's filing status. The standard deduction is used in place of itemized deductions if the standard deduction exceeds the itemized deduction amount available.

Standby assistance Arrangement in which a caregiver stays close to an individual to watch over and provide physical assistance if necessary.

State Health Insurance Counseling and Assistance Program (SHIP) Program with trained volunteers who offer unbiased, one-on-one counseling to help Medicare beneficiaries understand their health insurance benefits and options.

Statement of financial position (also called **balance sheet**) Declaration that identifies the assets, liabilities, and net worth of an individual or family.

Stock insurance company For-profit insurer owned by stockholders.

Stop loss (upper limit) Maximum out-of-pocket amount.

Stretch-out IRA Retirement account with a beneficiary named who will keep money in a retirement account as long as possible after the death of the original account holder.

STUG (Sudden, Temporary Upsurge of Grief) reaction Behavior seen in response to a specific emotional event.

Subdural hemotoma Collection of blood and blood breakdown products between the surface of the brain and its outermost covering (the dura) that remains even several weeks after an injury.

Subjective age Individualized concept of one's age based on personal feeling.

Substance dependence Mental disorder surrounding abuse of a specific medication or drug. Includes development of a tolerance for the substance; withdrawal symptoms; considerable time spent obtaining, consuming, and recovering from using the substance; desire or unsuccessful efforts to reduce the amount of the substance or stop taking it; use of larger amounts of the substance over a longer period of time than was intended; giving up or decreasing involvement in important social, occupational, or recreational activities because of the substance use; or continuation of substance use despite problems it may be causing.

Substantial assistance Hands-on or standby help required for a person to accomplish activities of daily living.

Substantial gainful activity (SGA) Income-producing work that provides enough money to make a person ineligible for benefits.

Substituted judgment An interpretive decision based on a patient's advance directive.

Subtrust (bypass trust, family trust, credit shelter trust) Investment vehicle used to avoid the marital deduction and apply the estate tax coupon of the first spouse to die. A subtrust provides that the surviving spouse is the primary beneficiary, and may even provide that the surviving spouse is the trustee of the subtrust.

Sundowning Behavioral disorder associated with an increase in confusion and agitation during evening hours.

Supplemental Security Income (SSI) Federal program funded by general tax revenues designed to help aged, blind, and disabled people who have little or no income and require help meeting basic needs for food, clothing, and shelter.

Systolic pressure Measurement (the upper number of a blood pressure reading) of the pressure blood exerts on the arterial walls during heartbeats.

Task model of grief Concept of dealing with grief in which an individual has a number of tasks to complete. The effort given to each task may increase or decrease in importance over the course of the grief.

Tax credit Dollar-for-dollar deduction that offsets calculated tax. Credits are allowed for the elderly and permanently and totally disabled, child and dependent care expenses, foreign taxes paid, expenses for the construction and rehabilitation of qualified low-income housing, and certain education expenses through the Hope or Lifetime learning credit.

Tax elimination (or reduction) Technique that uses deductions, exemptions, and credits to reduce otherwise taxable income or the tax itself, or a technique that results in nontaxable income or economic benefit that is not taxable.

Taxable income Amount upon which the appropriate income tax is calculated. It consists of income after subtracting adjustments, deductions, and personal exemptions.

Tax-deductible Term that describes expenses that may be excluded from current taxable income.

Tax-deferred Term that describes earnings or income not subject to federal income taxes until a later date. Regarding earnings produced within an IRA, taxdeferred earnings are taxed only upon distribution to the account owner.

Tax-qualified long-term care insurance policy Policy that conforms to standards in federal law and offers certain federal tax advantages.

Tenant-based assisted housing Program that makes it possible for eligible lowincome applicants to afford rental housing available in the private market.

Termlife insurance (pure protection) Life insurance that provides protection for a stated time period and pays benefits only if the insured dies within that period.

Testosterone Hormone primarily found in men, but also in women in small amounts. Although production of testosterone peaks in early adulthood, most men in older age still produce amounts within normal limits.

Thermogenesis Body's way of generating heat through shivering.

Tinnitus Hearing condition accompanied by some hearing loss, frequently referred to as ringing in the ears but often sounding more like buzzing, chirping crickets, blowing, roaring, or popping.

Tissue Group of cells that makes up a part of the body.

Toileting Getting to and from the toilet, getting on and off the toilet, and performing the associated personal hygiene.

Totten Trust Simple trust agreement that makes a funeral director or cemeterian the beneficiary. The consumer is the owner and, during life, controls the account and pays taxes on any earnings. At the time of death, the principal and earnings are paid to the funeral home and/or the cemetery.

Traditional funeral End-of-life ceremony with a series of rituals and customs to honor the dead, including embalming of the body, an open casket arrangement, services at a house of worship, and an interment.

Traditional giving Method of distributing assets in which a donor enjoys the satisfaction of supporting worthwhile causes while receiving a tax deduction. In addition to outright lifetime gifts, traditional giving may include leaving items to charity at death or gifting life insurance to charity.

Traditional nuclear family Living arrangement consisting of a husband and wife living together with children by birth or adoption only, with the father as the sole breadwinner and the mother as a full-time homemaker.

Transferring Act of moving into and out of a bed, chair, or wheelchair.

Transient ischemic attack (TIA) Mini-stroke caused by temporary disturbance of blood supply to an area of the brain, resulting in a sudden, brief decrease in brain function. It lasts less than 24 hours, most often less than one hour.

Traumatic grief Syndrome with two clusters of symptoms: separation distress symptoms including searching and yearning for the deceased, having intrusive thoughts about the deceased, and experiencing excessive loneliness since the death; and trauma symptoms similar to those in posttraumatic stress disorder.

Treasury bill Short-term obligation of the United States government that is issued at a discount and redeemed at face value upon maturity. Income received upon maturity is not taxed at a state or local level.

Treasury bond Long-term obligation of the United States government. Interest is paid semiannually and is not taxed at a state or local level.

Treasury note Intermediate-term obligation of the United States government. Interest is paid semiannually and is not taxed at a state or local level.

Trust Fiduciary arrangement set up by a grantor whereby property is held and managed for a named beneficiary by a third party, known as a trustee.

Trustee Person or organization that holds legal title to property held in a trust. The trustee holds and manages the property for the benefit of the trust beneficiary or beneficiaries.

Twisting Use of misleading terms, jargon, language that is confusing.

Underwriting Process of examining, accepting, or rejecting insurance risks, then classifying those selected, in order to charge the proper premium for each.

Urn Container used to hold cremated remains.

Values audit Review used to understand what is important when setting personal goals.

Valued social role Position in society deemed worthy of value.

Values questionnaire Inquiry that can help prioritize what matters most to a person.

Variable annuity Investment product in which the benefits paid out vary according to changes in the value of the portfolio supporting the annuity.

Vascular dementia Step-like deterioration in intellectual functions that results from multiple infarctions of the cerebral hemispheres.

Vascular depression Syndrome often experienced by people with vascular illness in which they experience relatively little guilt or sadness, but have poor motivation or initiative, move very slowly, and do not recognize that what they are experiencing is related to a mental disorder.

Vault Structure used in lining a grave to limit settlement with in-ground burials. Vaults are normally made of steel-reinforced concrete and lined with metal or asphalt.

Ventilation Mechanical respiration.

Viewing Funeral practice in which the deceased lies in a casket and family and friends are allowed to view the embalmed remains.

Vital capacity (VC) Amount of air that can be taken in and breathed out rapidly in one very deep breath as a measurement of lung function.

VO2 max (maximum oxygen consumption) Measure of the ability of the heart and cardiovascular system to respond to stress.

Waiver of liability Rule that applies when a senior did not know or could not be expected to know that Medicare would deny payment for lack of medical necessity.

Waiver of premium Provision in an insurance policy that relieves the insured of paying the premiums while receiving benefits.

Whole life insurance Insurance coverage that furnishes life insurance protection at a level premium amount for the insured's whole life and includes a savings element on which a minimum rate of return is guaranteed.

Will Legal document that specifies how a person wishes to distribute probate property and provides other instructions in the event of death.

Windfall elimination provision Method of figuring retirement or disability benefits when a recipient receives a pension from work not covered by Social Security. The formula used to figure the benefit is modified, resulting in a lower amount.

Zero hour Time for family members to consider how much each will contribute to the caregiving of the senior.

Index